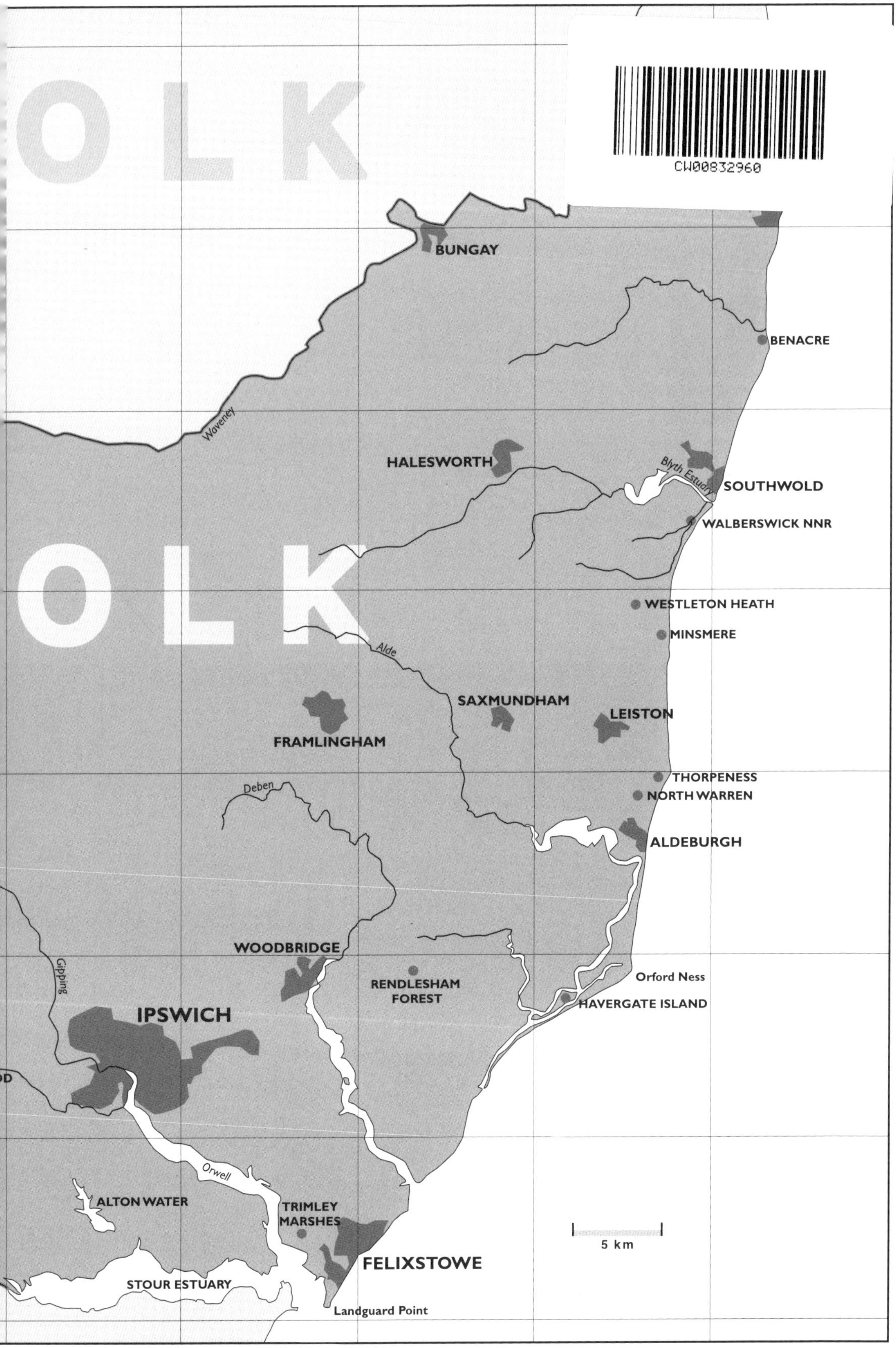
OLK
BUNGAY
BENACRE
Waveney
HALESWORTH
Blyth Estuary
SOUTHWOLD
WALBERSWICK NNR
OLK
WESTLETON HEATH
MINSMERE
Alde
SAXMUNDHAM
LEISTON
FRAMLINGHAM
THORPENESS
Deben
NORTH WARREN
ALDEBURGH
WOODBRIDGE
Gipping
RENDLESHAM
FOREST
Orford Ness
HAVERGATE ISLAND
IPSWICH
Orwell
ALTON WATER
TRIMLEY
MARSHES
5 km
FELIXSTOWE
STOUR ESTUARY
Landguard Point

The Birds of
SUFFOLK

The Birds of SUFFOLK

Steve Piotrowski

CHRISTOPHER HELM
LONDON

Published by Christopher Helm, an imprint of A & C Black Publishers Ltd., 37 Soho Square, London W1D 3QZ

ISBN 1-7136-6354-5

A CIP catalogue record for this book is available from the British Library

A & C Black uses paper produced with elemental chlorine-free pulp, harvested from managed sustainable forests.

Printed in Slovenia on behalf of Compass Press Ltd.

Produced and designed by Fluke Art, Cornwall

10 9 8 7 6 5 4 3 2 1

www.acblack.com

Publication of this book
has been aided by financial assistance from
The Suffolk Naturalists' Society

CONTENTS

This book is dedicated to all Suffolk ornithologists, past and present, who have contributed records to further our knowledge of the birds that pass through or reside in Suffolk.

FOREWORD

by

the Earl of Cranbrook MA PhD DSc (Hon.) DL
Patron of the Suffolk Naturalists' Society &
President of the Suffolk Wildlife Trust

The county is England's most ancient territorial unit. With natural boundaries, distinctive landscapes and a local voice, Suffolk has a biogeographic and cultural identity. Steven Piotrowski has done a service to our county by compiling this new ornithology, fourth in succession from Babington (1884-86), through Ticehurst (1932) and Payn (1962, 2nd edition 1978).

Suffolk is gloriously rich in birds. Landing point after the North Sea crossing, in season its 80km coastline swarms with migrants. Ten principal river systems emerge through six bird-rich estuaries. Behind lie expanses of wetland habitat. Where embankments collapsed, decades ago, amazing mudflats provide superb feeding grounds for waders. Inland, although sadly depleted by forestry plantation and agricultural extension, the Sandling heaths still support Woodlarks and Nightjars. The unique Breckland hosts the nucleus of Britain's Stone Curlew population. Crucial reserves are managed for public benefit by statutory and voluntary organisations. New habitats are becoming important. Expired sand and gravel works have created chains of small lakes, where water birds flock. But Suffolk is above all a farming county. About 85% of the land is managed for agriculture and 65% is arable. Intensification of the 1970-1980s permanently altered the landscape and bird habitats. On the threshold of the new millennium, huge imponderables are posed by collapsing prices for farm produce and the impact of livestock diseases. Future land-use must meet the challenge to provide livelihoods for farmers and enhanced habitats for birds.

Writing the foreword for William Payn, my father remarked that thirty years – a generation – is "probably just about the right interval between such reviews of the status of all the birds now found or once found in the county". This newest *Birds of Suffolk* is a manual for the present generation of birders. They are more numerous than ever: in the mid-1990s, 300 observers provided data for the Suffolk Biological Records Centre. They take advantage of the latest technology. They achieve new successes, and share a respect for birdlife. The Suffolk Ornithologists Group (SOG), founded in 1973, and the Suffolk Naturalists Society (SNS) have provided a focus for combined effort and effective reporting. Steve Piotrowski was editor of the Suffolk Bird Report from 1986-1992, has served as Chairman of both the SNS and SOG and is now President of the latter organisation. He generously acknowledges the massive contribution made by his colleagues. They will join me in welcoming this fine addition to Suffolk's heritage of county bird books.

Lord Cranbrook
2nd February 2001

ACKNOWLEDGEMENTS

Mick Wright and Ray Waters organised the fieldwork in Suffolk for the *New Atlas* and, in conjunction with the national survey, data were also gathered to produce distribution maps of all the county's breeding birds. The Suffolk Atlas Working Group, consisting of Derek Moore (Chairman), Mick Wright, Ray Waters, Howard Mendel and the author, was formed in 1987 to monitor the progress of both surveys and to provide guidance in the early stages of production. This committee was superceded by the Suffolk Atlas/ Avifauna Working Group: Martin Sanford (Chairman), Peter Lack; Howard Mendel; Reg Clarke and the author, to oversee the work to publication.

The author is extremely grateful to Dr Peter Lack, the late Brian Brown, Nick Green, Mike Marsh and Dr Susan Piotrowski, who not only meticulously examined the text, but also provided the necessary encouragement to ensure that this work was brought to its conclusion. Valuable comment was also received from Philip Murphy, Bob Warren and Mike Crewe and, as joint author of *The Birds of Buckinghamshire*, the advice of Dr Peter Lack was invaluable throughout the many stages of this book.

Bob Warren, Philip Murphy and David Walsh helped with the literature search by extracting notes, papers and observations, relating to Suffolk, from *British Birds* magazine. Brian Brown and Derek Moore supplied extracts of relevant papers from their libraries, Bob Walthew kindly loaned various journals and papers, and numerous others were borrowed courtesy of the Ipswich Museum.

In conjunction with their work at the Suffolk Biological Records Centre, Martin Sanford and Reg Clarke were responsible for the collection of records and preparation of the maps from data obtained during the *New Atlas* fieldwork. Reg Clarke also collated the gazetteer and index for the book and has assisted greatly with the distribution of the later drafts to the referees.

A number of records were reassessed by the Suffolk Ornithological Records Committee who also provided its interpretation on the status of each species. The hard work of this committee throughout the production of this book and during previous years is very much appreciated.

Brian Small has co-ordinated the commissioning of line drawings which complement the text. The author is grateful to Brian Small, Adam Kennedy and Stuart Ling for the highly artistic vignettes. Stan Dumican helped enormously in selecting a range of photographs from the many submitted for publication.

Ringing data were kindly supplied by the British Trust for Ornithology (BTO) Ringing Scheme which is supported by the BTO, the Joint Nature Conservation Committee (on behalf of the Countryside Council for Wales, the Department of the Environment (Northern Ireland), English Nature and Scottish Natural Heritage), the Heritage Service – National Parks and Wildlife (Ireland), and the ringers themselves.

Finally, thanks are due to Suffolk's County Recorders: Brian Thompson (SE Suffolk), Dick Walden (NE Suffolk) and Colin Jakes (W Suffolk) for collating the records and to the many fieldworkers who have faithfully submitted details of their observations for inclusion in the Suffolk Bird Report. These records have now been used within this book to help provide the wider picture.

INTRODUCTION

Birdwatching is one of the most popular leisure pursuits in Britain. Interest in birds has blossomed to such an extent during the latter half of the 20th century that the Royal Society for the Protection of Birds (RSPB) can now boast a membership in excess of one million. Love of the open countryside and the sheer unpredictability of the occurrence of migrant birds have persuaded many to pursue the study of birds.

Birdwatching comes in a variety of forms, from simply taking delight in the birds visiting a garden birdtable, to visiting every corner of the country for the sight of a rarity, popularly known as twitching. Some enthusiasts go on to study birds and bird conservation as a profession. Suffolk is one of England's premier counties for birdwatching. Like other east coast counties, it lies on the migration path of birds passing between Scandinavia and Africa and, given the right weather conditions, can be blessed with a diversity of migrant species.

Amateur ornithologists brave the harshest of winter weather to complete monthly counts of waders and wildfowl on the estuaries, inland lakes and ponds, and many sites are surveyed as part of the Common Birds Census and Breeding Bird Survey which monitor changes in breeding populations. Ringers work at migration sites and Constant Effort Sites where year-to-year changes and breeding success can be established. Such work requires great dedication and self-discipline. Seawatching can be extremely hard work, but is rewarding. The number of seabird records has greatly increased since the 1980s.

Access to bird 'news' became easier during the 1960s and birdwatchers became willing to trek further from their local patch to view other people's 'finds'. The presence of a MacQueen's Bustard at Hinton in 1962 caused a fever of excitement amongst local and national birdwatchers, resulting in Suffolk's first 'twitch'. However, only 10-12 people saw this great rarity following news of its whereabouts (B. J. Brown pers. comm.), whereas today one would expect more than 3,000 to be present within a few hours. Twitching became more fashionable during the 1970s as the emphasis switched from behavioural studies of birds to their plumage characteristics. Optical aids and text books improved enormously and many papers concentrated on identification.

For many years, the news of rarities was gleaned from local contacts and through an elaborate 'grapevine' system, but, in 1986-1987, information technology caught up with the twitching scene and commercial bird information services were introduced. Initially, these were restricted to crude answer-phone systems, but soon information-specific pagers were developed, followed by mobile telephone answering services and internet websites. Nowadays, no self-respecting twitcher would be without this means of contact, wherever he or she may be.

Prior to 1958, all records were published at the discretion of the County Recorder, largely based on his ornithological expertise and knowledge of the observer's reliability. Ticehurst was particularly ruthless over suspect records, but other recorders were less so. Acceptance sometimes depended as much on an observer's local standing rather than the details of the sighting.

Since 1958, national rarities have been considered by an independent national body – the *British Birds'* Rarities Committee (BBRC) and, as a result, the vetting of records has become more stringent. A written description is mandatory, together with other collaboratory evidence such as photographs. It has long been the policy of the Suffolk Ornithological Records Committee to accept the decisions of the BBRC and a consensus reached on any disagreements.

Planning the fieldwork for the *New Atlas* in 1987 stimulated interest in a new Suffolk avifauna. The data were collected in such a form as to enable distribution maps to be prepared for Suffolk as well as contributing to the national effort. A new Suffolk avifauna is long overdue, as William Payn's *Birds of Suffolk* (2nd edition) was published in 1978.

Ornithologically, we are in the midst of change. Some formerly common species are now extinct, on the verge of extinction or are occurring in much reduced numbers, whilst others are increasing or making an attempt at colonisation. Many such changes can be attributed to changes in farming practices or to global warming, a subject which will be dealt with later in this book.

ABBREVIATIONS

The following abbreviations are used throughout the book:

Journals/Organisations/Committees

BBRC	*British Birds* Rarities Committee
BTO	British Trust for Ornithology
BOURC	British Ornithologists' Union Records Committee
EBR	Essex Bird Report
LBO	Landguard Bird Observatory
LFC	Lowestoft Field Club
NB&MR	Norfolk Bird and Mammal Report
RSPB	Royal Society for the Protection of Birds
SNS	Suffolk Naturalists' Society
SBR	Suffolk Bird Report
SBRC	Suffolk Biological Records Centre
SOG	Suffolk Ornithologists' Group
SWT	Suffolk Wildlife Trust
SORC	Suffolk Ornithological Records Committee
WWT	Wildfowl and Wetlands Trust

Surveys

BoEE	Birds of Estuaries Enquiry	BBS	Breeding Bird Survey
CBC	Common Birds Census	CES	Constant Effort Site
WeBS	Wetland Bird Survey		

Nature reserves/conservation areas

ESA	Enviromentally Sensitive Area	NNR	National Nature Reserve
LNR	Local Nature Reserve	WR	Wildfowl Reserve

Others

ad.	adult	B.F.	Beet Factory
Com.	Common	Eu.	Eurasian
ecl.	duck/drake of indiscernible age and/or sex due to being in eclipse plumage		
Fm	farm	f.s.p.	full summer plumage
GP	Gravel Pit	Gt	Great
ha.	hectare	HQ	headquarters
imm.	immature	incl.	including
Ind. Est.	Industrial Estate.	juv.	juvenile
km	kilometre	Lt	Little
nr	near	n.d.	date unknown
n.y.	year unknown	N	north, S – south, E – east, W – west, etc.
P. Stn	Power Station	Pk	park
pr(s)	pair(s)	Pt	Point
R.	River	RAF	Royal Air Force
Res.	Reservoir	RG	Ringing Group
S. Fm	Sewage Farm	St	Street

THE COUNTY OF SUFFOLK

BOUNDARIES

The Watsonian Vice-County boundaries were established for biological recording and the limits are dealt with in detail by Mendel (1984) and Piotrowski (1986). The SBRC recognises the Watsonian boundaries as the geographical limits of all biological recording within the county. Administrative boundary changes since 1974 have resulted in areas now administered by the County Councils of Norfolk, Cambridgeshire and Essex being covered by Suffolk for biological recording, and vice versa. On most occasions the administrative boundary was redefined principally to allow the urban sprawl from major towns, such as Great Yarmouth, Thetford, Newmarket, Haverhill and Sudbury, to extend into neighbouring counties. The fixed Watsonian boundaries are used in this book.

In the past, records from Lothingland have been claimed for both Norfolk and Suffolk. Ticehurst stated that many of these really belong to Suffolk, but others from border villages, towns and rivers, not precisely defined to a locality, could have been in either county. He stressed that nearly all observers visiting Breydon Water approach from the southern bank, due to its greater accessibility, but, although the boundary line lies in mid-channel, the mudflats are more extensive on the Norfolk side. Some historic records listed as either 'Yarmouth', or 'near Yarmouth', may also have occurred in Suffolk, as collectors would have operated on the marshes both to the north and south of the estuary. Nevertheless, the origins of many specimens, previously claimed jointly for Norfolk and Suffolk, are dubious and, in consequence, 'Yarmouth' records have been omitted, unless it has been possible pin-point a locality within 'Watsonian' Suffolk. For example, records have been included if listed as: *"in mouth of River Yare"*, *"Cobholm Island"*, *"south wall"* or *"south of river"* and notable inclusions are: Cirl Bunting (1888); Glossy Ibis (1906); Greater Sand Plover (1981); Whiskered Tern (1987) and Franklin's Gull (1991). Birds that occur on the ebb and flow of the tide on the Breydon estuary itself, such as waders, wildfowl, gulls and terns, have also been included.

The North Sea forms the eastern boundary and the coastline is about 80km long stretching from the mouth of the Yare in the north to the Orwell Haven in the south. The Rivers Waveney and Little Ouse determine the northern boundary with Norfolk. The administrative boundary differs with the Watsonian around Thetford as the town boundary stretches to south of the Little Ouse – an area now administered by Norfolk County Council. The boundary with Cambridgeshire to the west is not so well defined. To the south lies the River Stour which forms the boundary with Essex and there are minor discrepancies around Newmarket, Haverhill and Sudbury.

TOPOGRAPHY

The Suffolk landscape has been described by many authors as gently undulating. The highest point is at Depden, in west Suffolk, which is 125m above sea level.

GEOLOGY AND SOILS

Stiff boulder clay over a foundation of chalk exists over much of Suffolk. The chalk lies close to the surface in river valleys around Needham Market, Sudbury and Haverhill. The glacial sands of the breck and coastal sandlings were laid down during the Anglian Ice Age that occurred about 500,000 years ago. For a full account of geology and soils refer to Killeen (1992).

SUFFOLK HABITATS

THE COAST AND ESTUARIES

The sea

The area of the North Sea immediately off the Suffolk coast has a long history as one of the richest fishing grounds in British waters. Lowestoft and Great Yarmouth were formerly two of the country's most prolific fishing ports where thousands of tons of fish were landed annually. The herring and the sprat were the principal species caught and the massive shoals that wintered in the North Sea were thought to be an infinite supply of food. Smoke-houses for kipper production were prominent along the Suffolk coast and an extensive area of the Lowestoft Denes was set aside for net repairing and drying. There are many relicts of this era still surviving today. Unfortunately, these golden years were short-lived and over-fishing by the herring-boat fleet led to the herring's near-extinction in the North Sea and belated restrictions in catches. There are signs that the sprat population has now recovered to some extent, but it is doubtful whether herring numbers will ever return to former levels.

The number of birds that winter offshore depend entirely on the availability of food and the presence of fish shoals and other marine life. For example, during the heyday of the herring fishery, Storm Petrels were regularly seen trailing the boats as they entered port, but this species is now very much a rarity. Common Scoters were attracted to the extensive mollusc beds between Great Yarmouth and Dunwich in the 1950s and a build up in Gorleston Bay peaked at 5,000 in January 1955 (Taylor *et al.* 1999). Wintering numbers of Common Scoter have failed to reach four figures since 1982. Ticehurst commented that the arrival of the Red-throated Diver, Fulmar and Pomarine Skua closely followed the herring and sprat shoals.

Since the early 1990s, there has been a gradual build up in offshore flocks of some species which could confirm the recovery of the smaller fish. Record counts for the Red-throated Diver, Great Crested Grebe, Cormorant, Common Gull, Kittiwake and Guillemot are broken almost annually and wintering Pomarine Skuas are attracted by huge numbers of gulls offshore. The diver and grebe flocks are not always apparent as they no doubt follow the sprat shoals as they venture southwards. Although there has been a southerly shift in the sprat's wintering range (Camphuysen 1989), Suffolk's offshore waters are at the southern limit (Darby in prep.), so it is likely that the birds are often further north and out-of-sight from land. Peak numbers of both species most often occur in late January and February. Another explanation for the record number of birds is the demise of predatory fish such as cod and haddock resulting in larger concentrations of smaller fish and their fry. There is currently much criticism of our fishery policy and it will remain to be seen whether restrictions currently in place have any significant effect on the numbers of fish and on marine birds.

The shore

The beaches are generally a mixture of sand and pebbles. The shingle banks are more predominant to the south of Aldeburgh. This type of seashore is a harsh habitat for invertebrates and, in consequence, feeding opportunities for shorebirds are limited. Exceptions are the sandy beaches of Lowestoft which regularly host a wintering flock of Sanderlings.

Granite boulders imported from Norway and strategically placed to protect Ness Point at Lowestoft from the sea have given Suffolk a small length of 'rocky shore', offering a rich feeding site for wintering Purple Sandpipers. The seaweed-clad jetty at Landguard is the county's only other regular wintering site for this species.

Little Terns, Ringed Plovers and Oystercatchers nesting on open beaches are disturbed by day-visitors and only those in remote areas or receiving special protection show any real sign of breeding success. Grassland behind the beach often hosts other ground nesters such as Skylarks and Meadow Pipits.

Cliffs

Sandstone cliffs are a feature from Gorleston to Lowestoft, Pakefield to Kessingland, Covehithe to Easton Bavents, and Dunwich and Thorpeness. Many play host to Sand Martin colonies, but otherwise they are of limited ornithological value, except perhaps for providing vantage points for seawatching. Fulmars have nested in cavities in the more robust shell crag at Bawdsey, although most of these cliffs have become overgrown with tamarisk and other shrubs.

Coastal erosion, a natural feature of coastal Suffolk for centuries, has become increasingly apparent at Covehithe and Dunwich. Several hundred metres have been lost at Covehithe since the 1960s.

Estuaries

The water from ten rivers enter the North Sea through six estuaries which are rich feeding areas for wintering and passage wildfowl and waders. The tidal flats of the southern estuaries are particularly rich in marine vegetation such as common and dwarf eel grass (*Zostera marina* and *Z. noltii*) and green algae (predominantly *Enteromorpha* and *Ulva spp.*), which form the principal food for wildfowl such as the Wigeon and Brent Goose. A survey by the Institute of Terrestrial Ecology in 1973 revealed that eel grass beds occupied some 99ha. of mudflats on the Orwell and 244 on the Stour. *Enteromorpha* covered 142 and 219ha. on the Orwell and Stour respectively (Beardall *et al.* 1988). Although no surveys have mapped vegetation on mudflats of other estuaries, the aforementioned plants are known to be prevalent in some areas of the Deben, Ore and Blyth.

The River Waveney enters the River Yare at Breydon Water, an estuary which has seen significant changes since the early 1800s. It was then reed-fringed along both shores, but the deepening of Great Yarmouth harbour allowed more salt water onto the flats, causing silting and building of mudflats. The only remaining reedy areas are at Berney, on the Norfolk side of the estuary, and at Burgh Castle. The Glebe marshes at the latter, once a mixture of pasture and arable, were flooded during exceptionally high tides in January 1976 (Allard 1990). Breydon Water has played host to many rarities, including many first records for Suffolk but, by the 1930s, it was considered "too disturbed, too polluted and too silted to be of any great attraction" (Ticehurst 1932).

The Blyth meets the sea at Southwold Harbour, and the extensive mudflats adjacent to the A12 were formed when the river breached its banks in 1921 and 1926, resulting in the flooding of adjoining marshes. The Alde-Ore estuary forms Suffolk's longest stretch of tidal water and there is a difference of three hours between high tide at Snape and the river mouth. The tidal stretch of the Deben runs from Bromeswell to Felixstowe Ferry. The Orwell and Stour combine to meet the sea at Landguard Point. The latter estuary is the county's broadest being 2km across at its widest. Both the Orwell and Stour have suffered greatly from erosion losing 32.6% and 44% of saltmarsh habitat respectively between 1973 and 1988 (Norris & Buisson 1994).

Marshes and lagoons

The land behind the shingle ridges and sea-walls is relatively flat and along many stretches the sea level at high tide is higher than adjoining marshland – e.g. Minsmere and Walberswick. Salt water flowing into these areas, either natural or artificial, can result in lagoon systems which attract thousands of birds. The Walberswick-Dunwich shore pools were once a haven for passage and breeding waders, but, nowadays, the area is overrun by visitors and the habitat is regularly disturbed by bulldozers as breached shingle walls are repaired following winter storms.

Man-made lagoons and shingle-topped island systems have become a regular feature at coastal nature reserves and have proved attractive to breeding terns and waders. This habitat type is created by scraping and manoeuvring soils with bulldozers and there can be no finer examples than those at Minsmere and Trimley Marshes. There are few significant areas of natural grassland remaining at coastal localities, although the areas that remain can be attractive to wildfowl and waders, especially where pools are created by manual control of water levels.

The broads and meres

Suffolk has four freshwater broads situated close to the River Waveney in north Suffolk: Fritton Decoy, Barnby Broad, Blundeston Lake and Flixton Lake. All are relicts of flooded peat diggings of the Middle Ages and have a similar history to the Norfolk Broads. Barnby, Blundeston and Flixton are rarely-watched private waters. However, all four are set in some of Suffolk's most picturesque countryside and the woodland surrounding Fritton Decoy regularly attracts good numbers of raptors.

Oulton Broad was once part of a large estuary incorporating Lake Lothing and much of the flora-rich meadows at Castle Marshes. The brackish open waters of Benacre, Covehithe and Easton Broads are fast diminishing in parallel with cliff erosion and are likely to disappear altogether within the next few decades. Ticehurst described Easton as the largest of the three broads which was still navigable by ships in 1529. The site is now dominated by reed with only small areas of open water.

A small mere situated on the Minsmere Levels, known as Dunwich Broad, was finally drained in 1890 (Axell 1977). The area has since been developed into one of Europe's finest nature reserves and a series of brackish and freshwater pools attract a diversity of waterfowl.

Thorpe Mere was once a mixture of semi-tidal mud-flats and saltings with a creek running to the sea blocked by a shingle ridge at its eastern end. It was a haven for waders and wildfowl which was aptly illustrated by Hele (1870 and 1890). Following draining in 1911-1912, much of its ornithological value was lost and a small lake at the northern end, known as The Meare, has since been used for recreation.

Coastal scrub and gardens

Coastal scrub and gardens form an important feeding habitat for drift migrants and there are times when bushes are alive with birds. The vegetated earth banks at Landguard Point have seen huge concentrations in recent years, although the parks and gardens at Lowestoft and Southwold, and scrub at Minsmere, Sizewell and Thorpeness also host many migrants during the passage periods.

The Denes to the north of Lowestoft were formerly prolific for passage migrants, although these were largely destroyed during the 1930s – a loss which was lamented by Ticehurst who said: "Even within my time the Lowestoft denes was an excellent place for birds, especially for those arriving or halting on passage, but on the one side the incursion of the sea has destroyed all the marram-covered sand-hills, while on the other the Town Council have done their best to destroy all cover by grubbing up every bush". F. C. Cook reported that Nightingales, Garden Warblers, Lesser Redpolls and Turtle Doves once nested there (Payn 1978).

The smallest patch of bushes can play host to migrant birds, especially if the surrounding area is relatively free of cover. For example, the patch of tamarisk and holm oak, once part of the garden of the old cottage that stood at the mouth of Stony Ditch on Orfordness, is sometimes teeming with migrants. The gardens and allotments at Shingle Street and the hawthorn hedge at the back of the sea wall at East Lane, Bawdsey, are at times similarly productive and regular ringing sessions at Bawdsey Manor have shown the importance of the site for passage migrants. Suffolk's best known migration observation station is Landguard Point, Felixstowe, where the daily presence of observers has ensured a comprehensive picture of migration through the site. Most of the action occurs overhead and thousands of birds are logged. The vegetated banks act as an oasis for the small proportion of migrants that are grounded.

LOWLAND HEATH

The Sandlings

Up to the 1920s, the sandlings stretched unbroken from Ipswich to Lowestoft but, since then, all but a few areas have been destroyed, most lost to agriculture, afforestation and urban development.

Vast tracts were lost in the 1920s when the forests of Dunwich, Rendlesham and Tunstall were planted by the Forestry Commission. The Cold War resulted in more areas of prime heathland being lost to development due to a need for fast-response airfields (Woodbridge and Bentwaters) on Britain's east coast. The largest of the remaining heather-dominated heaths are found around Westleton and Dunwich.

From the 1960s, Ipswich began to expand rapidly eastwards swallowing up huge tracts of Suffolk's most beautiful countryside, including some of the best examples of Sandlings heath, for example Bixley, Warren, Foxes, Black, Rushmere and Martlesham.

Breckland

Breckland is a unique area of lowland heath which formerly encompassed some 400 square miles of north-west Suffolk and south-west Norfolk. Prior to the Enclosures Acts of 1760 and 1843, the Breckland landscape consisted of vast open plains with huge areas of dunes created by wind-blown sand. Enormous flocks of sheep grazed on the open heaths and there was an abundance of rabbit warrens. The region derived its name from the agricultural practice of short-term tillage, where small areas were sown, usually with rye, and allowed to revert back to heath once the poor soils became exhausted. These fields were known as 'brakes' or 'brecks'.

Pine belts, planted from about 1812 to protect crops from sand storms, broke up these great plains. This practice proved detrimental to species such as the Great Bustard which became extinct during the 1830s. Babington stated: "This great district was once much more open than it is at present now that fir plantations have been largely introduced... the increasing inroads of civilisation upon the Breck district have been disastrous indeed to its ornithology."

Vast tracts have since been lost to arable farming and huge conifer forests were planted leaving few remaining areas of true breck. The best known of the remaining Suffolk brecks are the nature reserves at Tuddenham and Cavenham Heaths, Lakenheath and Wangford Warrens, and Barnhamcross Common.

The brecks host the nucleus of Britain's Stone Curlew population and there are also good concentrations of Wheatear. Crossbills and Siskins breed in the conifer forests and Woodlarks and Nightjars occupy the open heaths and woodland glades.

FENS AND MARSHES

The flat, featureless, arable land in the north-west corner of Suffolk was formerly part of a vast area of watery fenland which stretched through Cambridgeshire to Lincolnshire. In Suffolk, there is little remaining evidence of this once great wilderness except for place names such as Burnt and Sedge Fens, Botany Bay and Stallode Wash. Bitterns once abounded here and wildfowl occurred in large numbers. Cranes, Greylag Geese and Marsh Harriers almost certainly bred there and one or two pairs of the latter still occur from time to time. The RSPB has recently purchased several hectares of mostly arable land near Lakenheath and are attempting to recreate the ornithologically-rich fenland habitats.

INLAND WATERS

There has been a significant increase in freshwater in the past three decades resulting from the greater demand for drinking water and the exploitation of sands and gravels for the construction industry.

Rivers

The Gipping, Stour, Waveney, Little Ouse and Lark are Suffolk's main catchments and the rivers and their many tributaries flow through some of the county's most picturesque countryside. The abundance of marginal vegetation is a characteristic of Suffolk rivers and the edges and banks have long been favoured by breeding Whitethroats, and Reed and Sedge Warblers. The rivers in north-west Suffolk appear to be more suitable for breeding wildfowl with the Lark Valley hosting Britain's largest concentration of Gadwall along with good numbers of Tufted Duck.

Barges were once an important means of transportation and most rivers were canalised to allow access to inland towns and villages. Even the smallest rivers were navigable and the barge trade continued until the late 1920s. Although the many tow-paths allowed easy access to the river, the disturbance rendered many stretches unsuitable for breeding birds. In recent years, the decaying locks and weirs have been home to Grey Wagtails, which have nested in cavities amongst the ivy-clad brickwork. However, the straightening of the banks has been largely detrimental to aquatic birds, with most waters now hosting only a few pairs of Moorhens, Coots and Mallards and, more exceptionally, a nesting pair of Little Grebes. Although Kingfishers still exist on most rivers, pollution of small streams has resulted in a marked decline in numbers.

Lakes and reservoirs

Alton Water reservoir is the largest area of standing freshwater in Suffolk. It was constructed in the early 1970s and its attraction for birds became apparent immediately after flooding. Throughout the 1980s and early 1990s, the reservoir was the county's greatest freshwater fishery and the principal breeding site for Great Crested Grebes. However, low water levels caused by a succession of droughts in the 1990s inhibited nesting attempts and a dramatic decline in fish numbers may be a significant factor in the grebe's lower breeding success. Anglers blame Cormorants for the decline in fish numbers, but there is also some concern with regard to the quality of the source waters. The reservoir has acted as a refuge for wintering wildfowl and numbers increase significantly during periods of harsh weather.

Over-abstraction for the irrigation of crops during summer has resulted in an increase in the number of storage reservoirs. These have some conservation value, attracting insects which provide food for Swifts, Swallows, Sand and House Martins, and providing feeding and nesting areas for wildfowl.

Most of the inland lakes were once gravel pits and are dealt with in the next section. Livermere is one of the Breckland meres and is partly controlled by the rise and fall of the water levels in the chalk. The lake is of considerable ornithological importance, attracting wildfowl and waders as well as passage gulls and terns. Barton Mere is of similar origin, but has dried up completely as a result of the droughts of the 1990s. The Micklemere is an area of shallow water and is part of Pakenham Fen. Redgrave Lake is man-made, being dammed at its western end. Framlingham Mere and Cornard Mere were once much larger and now have limited ornithological value. The history of the county's lakes is dealt with in greater detail by Simpson (1982).

Gravel Pits

The river valleys hold the majority of flooded gravel workings and, although working pits are quickly colonised by Little Ringed Plovers and Sand Martins, they soon become overgrown with fringe vegetation and willow scrub. The plethora of pits has resulted in vast increases in the populations of Great Crested Grebe, Tufted Duck, Canada Goose and other wildfowl species. The Waveney, Gipping and Lark Valleys host the bulk of the pits and although many have been taken over for recreation pursuits, such as angling and sailing, a series of workings at Lackford have been dedicated to nature conservation. Now superbly managed by volunteers from the SWT, Lackford Wildfowl Reserve has been transformed into one of West Suffolk's premier birdwatching sites.

Ponds

Many Suffolk ponds are polluted and have been left to become overgrown with a tangle of vegetation and, in consequence, have little or no ornithological value. Moorhens appear to be more able to tolerate such conditions, but the waters are avoided by species that prefer open water. Village ponds usually have their resident flock of feral Mallards and perhaps a few geese, but otherwise they are largely 'sterile'.

WOODLAND AND PARKLAND

Ancient oaks at Staverton, Sudbourne and Butley and along several valley slopes are the few remaining relics of our native forests. Suffolk is a well-wooded county and evidence of afforestation dates back to Norman times. The Doomsday Survey of 1086 detailed huge areas of forest which were broken only by pastures for grazing by livestock and deer. For example, woodland, belonging to the Liberty of St Edmund, stretched from Cosford to Bury St Edmunds and there were some 2,000 acres (800ha.) at Menham Manor and about 500 (200ha.) at Melford Manor (Simpson 1982). A high demand for timber by ship builders resulted in the felling of many ancient oaks and, by the end of the Napoleonic wars, England and Wales were among the least wooded countries in Europe (Holloway 1996).

Medieval woods are distributed throughout the county and studies carried out by English Nature indicate that 440 woods, of over two hectares in size, date back to at least 1600 (Beardall & Casey 1995). Most were managed by a coppicing regime providing a valuable source of firewood, poles and fencing. This type of thicket-like under-storey is favoured by a number of bird species, particularly Willow and Garden Warblers, Nightingales and Long-tailed Tits.

The industrial revolution saw a general switch from firewood to fossil fuels, although Suffolk was a significant distance from coal-fields and, in consequence, the collecting of wood continued here throughout the 1800s.

Woodland clearance continued through the Middle Ages to around 1830, with many woods being lost to agriculture and, since 1920, 90 ancient woods, covering some 576ha., have been grubbed out (Beardall & Casey 1995).

The Forestry Commission was established under the 1919 Forestry Act and, soon after, the huge blocks of non-native conifers became a feature on the coastal heaths at Dunwich, Tunstall and Rendlesham and inland at Thetford and North Stow in Breckland. Landowners were encouraged to plant smaller areas of land in return for grant aid. These actions resulted in considerable losses of heathland species such as the Stone Curlew, Ringed Plover and Wheatear, although there were gains for Long-eared Owl, Crossbill and

Coal Tit. Generally, dense stands of conifers allow little light penetration and, in consequence, the forest floors become bare of vegetation. In the early days, the forests were managed solely for timber production and nature conservation came well down the order of priorities. A change of policy in recent years, however, has resulted in more mixed woodland blocks and a management regime which is more sympathetic to the needs of wildlife.

An estimated 80% of planted conifers was razed during the 'great storm' of 16th October 1987. Tragic as this may have appeared at the time, it did provide a great opportunity for reshaping these habitats, and the subsequent replanted woodland has resulted in a phenomenal increase in nesting Woodlarks. There are plans afoot to ensure that a large reservoir population of this bird is maintained by carefully leaving glades and clearings, and managing the timing of clearing regimes. The Nightjar has also exploited the relatively young plantations.

FARMLAND

Agriculture has dominated the countryside for centuries and our wild birds have been forced to adapt to changing farming practices. It is doubtful whether Grey Partridges, Lapwings and Skylarks existed in lowland Britain when it was dominated by forest, but such species would have benefited as Neolithic farmers carved out fields to grow their crops. The open glades allowed colonisation by ground nesters and areas of poor soil evolved into the heathland habitats that we know today.

Many grazing pastures were lost when horses replaced oxen between 1500 and 1800, and there became a greater demand for cereal crops (mainly oats) for animal feed (Holloway 1996). Livestock grazed on open fields during the day and were penned on tilled land during the night to provide manure. However, the Enclosure Acts saw the end to open pastures and common grazing, and crop rotation, which began in the 1870s, resulted in higher yields.

Due to a abundance of low-cost labour, mechanisation was slow to catch on. The first threshing machine was introduced during the late 1820s, although it was not until the 1950s that the tractor finally replaced the horse. It has been widely reported that Corncrakes have long been sufferers from agricultural mechanisation. However, this species was never plentiful in Suffolk and it is more likely that the draining of marshlands and, in particular, wet meadows were the principal factors in its decline.

About 85% of Suffolk is currently managed for agriculture compared with about 75% in the rest of England and Wales. Large cultivated fields dominate most of the Suffolk landscape with 65% of all farmland under crops (Beardall & Casey 1995). The once great livestock industry has now all but collapsed with most grazing marshes and meadows falling to the plough. Efficient, modern-day farming has resulted in precious little marginal land, with fields being ploughed to the very limits of woodlands, roads, rivers and dykes. Agricultural changes have been the root cause of the decline of around 20 of Suffolk's most common species and some now appear on the list of the Birds of Conservation Concern (Gregory *et al.* 1996). This would have been unthinkable two decades ago. This list was compiled by the leading conservation bodies. Massive contractions in the range of Stone Curlew, Turtle Dove and Corn Bunting were depicted in the BTO atlases and CBC data has shown alarming declines during the past 25 years. For example, Tree Sparrow populations have fallen by 92%, Grey Partridge by 80%, Corn Bunting by 77%, Spotted Flycatcher by 68%, Reed Bunting by 61%, Song Thrush by 60%, Skylark by 58%, Linnet by 53%, Bullfinch by 51% and Turtle Dove by 50%. There have also been declines in the populations of the Kestrel by 40%, Swallow by 38%, Starling by 35%, Blackbird by 33%, Marsh Tit by 37%, Willow Tit by 32%, Dunnock by 29% and Goldfinch by 28% (Gregory *et al.* 1996).

There have been some positive opportunities for redressing the balance on Suffolk farms. The Ministry of Agriculture took advantage of European funding to introduce Environmentally Sensitive Areas and there are currently three in Suffolk: the Broads; Breckland and Suffolk river valleys. The scheme seeks to pay farmers to manage by agreed prescriptions in ways which will benefit wildlife. Another government initiative is Countryside Stewardship which encourages sensitive management of important wildlife features in return for financial reward. Although much has been achieved, both schemes are voluntary and need to be more specifically managed and more widely available if they are to be at all effective (D. R. Moore *in litt.*).

Significant overproduction of food crops in Europe led to the introduction of 'set-aside' in 1989. This was never meant as an environmental improvement scheme, but because of efforts initially by the Suffolk Farming and Wildlife Advisory Group, farmers were encouraged to seek benefits. The introduction of permanent features like woodlands, hedgerows and headlands encouraged many to do more. Even 'rotational set-aside' has revealed great benefits for birds and, in particular, the Skylark. There is now a mood that subsidies to farmers must be linked to environmental improvement in the future. This view is widespread not only in Britain, but in many parts of Europe. If this is achieved then it may not be too late to save the once common birds of our farms.

HEDGEROWS

Hedgerows have been a feature of the Suffolk countryside for centuries, sometimes defining parish boundaries or following the lines of tracks which date back to Anglo-Saxon times. They acted as stock-proof barriers and, from a wildlife point of view, linked areas of woodland.

The number of native trees found in a typical stretch of a hedgerow often indicates its age, with each additional species representing about 100 years of history. Most Suffolk hedges are primarily of blackthorn or hawthorn. Since 1945 one-fifth of Britain's hedgerows have been destroyed (Holloway 1996) mainly because it is uneconomic to use modern farm machinery in small fields, but legislation introduced in 1996 aims to protect the hedges which remain and recognises that they are a valuable habitat for wildlife.

URBAN AND SUBURBAN AREAS

Suburban areas have become extremely important for many resident species of birds, providing nesting habitat during the summer and feeding stations during winter. The Rock Dove (Feral Pigeon), Collared Dove, Blackbird, House Sparrow and Starling are the most common birds in town centres. The Blackbird has only recently made the transition from a dweller of the countryside to the town and this may well be the reason why it has become so much more numerous than the Song Thrush. The domestic cat has largely replaced natural predators, although many suburban gardens now receive visits from both Magpies and Sparrowhawks, often to the annoyance of those who offer harbourage to nesting song-birds.

Summer visitors also frequent urban areas. Swifts nest in and hunt over towns and buildings, and Hobbies are becoming increasingly frequent. House Martins have long been known to nest under the eaves of houses in suburban areas and Black Redstarts have filled the vacant niche left by Robins in a few industrial areas.

Ipswich has some of the most picturesque parks and even Christchurch and Holywells Parks, which are situated in the heart of the town, offer refuge to woodland species which are sometimes difficult to observe in the countryside. These include Tawny Owl, Green, Great and Lesser Spotted Woodpeckers, Marsh Tit, Nuthatch, Siskin and Lesser Redpoll.

HABITAT CHANGES

Changes in the countryside as a result of intensification of agriculture, road-building, urbanisation and the development of leisure activities, particularly on the estuaries, have taken place at an alarming rate during the latter half of the 20th century. Much of Suffolk's prime wildlife habitat has been degraded or completely destroyed. For example, 86% of Sandling heaths has been lost since the 1930s, 85% of Breckland since the 1940s, 70% of ancient woodlands since 1870, 12.5% of species-rich grassland since 1980 and 70% of intertidal habitats since reclamation began (Beardall & Casey 1995).

Emergency measures during the Second World War resulted in some of the greatest losses as many neglected pastures, heathland and other marginal lands, e.g. Levington Heath, were ploughed to increase food production. This ended the agricultural recession. The destruction of prime wildlife habitats (e.g. Waldringfield Heath) continued unabated throughout the 1950s and 1960s.

THE CLIMATE OF SUFFOLK

Suffolk is one of Britain's driest counties with between 500mm and 600mm of rainfall each year. The south-east corner is particularly dry and often remains so whilst the rest of the county is receiving a deluge of rain. Trimley St Mary and Dovercourt in Essex, which bound the Orwell Haven, boast of being the driest parishes in Britain. Ground frosts are very frequent in Breckland and near Ipswich – a consequence of the sandy soils in those areas (Lamb 1987). Attempts to establish the Red Grouse and Black Grouse in Breckland during the 1930s probably failed because of the low rainfall in that region.

CLIMATE CHANGE OVER THE LAST 500 YEARS

Climatic conditions have fluctuated greatly over the past 500 years. Lamb (1987) speculated that climatic change may well have been responsible for "the main abandonment of tillage in favour of sheep and rabbits in the Breckland" during the mid-1400s and it may well have been the overgrazing of animals that further loosened the underlying light soils and exposed them to wind and erosion. A tremendous storm in 1668 moved masses of Breckland sand from Lakenheath to Santon Downham, blocking the river and partly burying the village. A long cold period known as the Little Ice Age began around 1550 and lasted for about three centuries. Half the winters in the period 1680-1700 were cold and, although the following 40 years were warmer, they culminated in the most severe winter on record, when harsh NNE winds continued to blow through April and May. Thrushes and Blackbirds suffered greatly during harsh winter weather in 1776 and, during 'the Siberian Days' of 1784, nearly all ivy and holly was killed by frost (Norman 1994). It is generally accepted that the Little Ice Age ended around 1850, although any marked amelioration was not noticeable until the 1890s. This warming continued through to 1940, but thereafter winter temperatures deteriorated and, around 1950, summers became cooler. This downward trend continued into the 1970s, with the winter of 1962/3 considered as the coldest in central England since 1740 (Elkins 1983). During that winter, standing freshwater remained frozen for some ten weeks (Axell 1977), which resulted in the populations of the Grey Heron, Bittern, Kingfisher and Bearded Tit declining greatly.

A strengthening Gulf Stream and more equatorial air being fed via warm sectors of depressions to the northern polar region between 1900 and 1940 resulted in temperature gains in the Arctic. Arctic breeding birds benefited from the ameliorating climate during the early part of the 20th century. The large growth in the Icelandic population of Black-tailed Godwits from 1913 (Cramp *et al.* 1974-1994) is reflected in increased wintering numbers. Although more numerous in Ireland than Great Britain (Prater 1975), the winter population on the Stour has grown considerably from an average monthly count of 685 in 1969-1975 to 1,859 in 1989-1994. This increase has resulted in the Stour becoming the most important estuary for the species in Britain.

Insects are also sensitive to climatic change. Between 1800 and 1985, 21 species of butterfly (Mendel and Piotrowski 1986) and four species of dragonfly (Mendel 1992) were lost to Suffolk. The demise of some butterfly species can be attributed to habitat losses and changes in land management, most notably the lack of grazing, but others (most of the fritillaries for example) may well have been affected by climate. Less livestock and the loss of rabbits through myxomatosis resulted in a decline in dung-beetles – an important food source of the Stone Curlew and Red-backed Shrike. The availability of smaller insects also would have been reduced by wind and rain and it is more likely that climatic change was ultimately responsible for the decline of Stone Curlew and Spotted Flycatcher, and the loss of the Red-backed Shrike and Wryneck as breeding species.

GLOBAL WARMING

The Polar ice-cap expanded and contracted throughout the last millennium. The climate was much warmer around 1300-1400 and, as a result of melting glaciers, the sea was about a half a metre higher than it is today (Lamb 1987). Coastal erosion took place at an alarming rate and, following a series of floods, several coastal hamlets and towns were lost to the waves. These included the prosperous ports of Dunwich in Suffolk and Ravenspur at the mouth of the Humber estuary.

A severe drought in 1975-1976 was followed by another in 1990 and the years 1995-1997 were reported to have been the driest period for 200 years. This succession of droughts has contributed to a period of climate warming in north-west Europe and the emission of 'greenhouse' gases into the atmosphere is almost certain to accelerate this change. Much of Suffolk's coastal strip and the area of fenland in the north-west corner are below the 15 metre contour and, in consequence, the predicted rise in sea levels may well result in low-lying areas in these districts being submerged. Some of the county's prime nature reserves are now under threat: Walberswick, Minsmere, North Warren, Havergate Island, Hazelwood and Boyton Marshes, Orfordness and Landguard Point. The ornithologically-rich coastal broads of Benacre, Covehithe and Easton have been shrinking dramatically since the 1960s and Covehithe cliffs are eroding faster than any other stretch of coast in Britain. Increasingly arid conditions should provide more sparsely vegetated land which will be to the benefit of Stone Curlew and Woodlark. Warmer summers and milder winters should aid further range expansion of Cetti's and Dartford Warblers.

WEATHER EVENTS AND THEIR EFFECTS ON THE COUNTY'S AVIFUANA

Birds are greatly affected by weather, and birdwatchers ponder over weather maps hoping to recognise patterns that can result in a spectacular 'fall' of passerines or a seabird movement. North-easterly winds in autumn often bring many passage migrants, and gales during this season are ideal for seabird movements. Populations of resident species may crash in severe winters as shown by CBC records. A southerly airflow in spring assists the migration of summer visitors and scarce migrants often overshoot their expected destinations. Early summer visitors are occasionally caught out by sudden cold spells, and summer storms wreak havoc amongst the breeding population. Lack of rainfall can be disastrous with drought conditions hampering the efforts of Swallows and House Martins to collect mud for nest-building and creating difficulties for thrushes as they search the hard ground for earthworms and grubs to feed their brood.

HARSH WINTERS

Severe weather with snow causes considerable hardship amongst wintering populations and invariably causes cold-weather movements of birds. When onshore winds persist, a check along the shore for dead birds shows the level of mortality caused by severe weather. Towards the end of the 1928/9 winter, over 320 corpses of 35 species were found on the tideline between Hopton and Southwold (Ticehurst 1932). Between 24th January and 12th March 1940, 259 individuals of 37 species were counted between Gorleston pier and Benacre Sluice (Ticehurst & Witherby 1940; Cook 1944). During the harsh winter of 1946/7, 355 corpses of 41 species were found along the same stretch of shoreline and, in early 1963, 1,036 individuals of 50 species were counted between Gorleston and Minsmere. Wildfowl tend to move to more southerly climes when such conditions persist and offshore movements are occasionally spectacular. An icy blast on 10th January 1987 resulted in a coastal movement with Shelduck (2,700) and Wigeon (27,900) being the principal species involved. The same conditions were also responsible for the arrival of up to nine Great Bustards.

Sedentary species may choose to brazen out such conditions and garden feeding stations sometimes receive hundreds of extra visitors. Deep snow cover and severe frosts can be disastrous for ground feeders – thrushes in particular. Blackbirds appear more able to withstand harsh-weather periods than Song Thrushes, perhaps because they are more able to survive in suburban environments where there is an abundance of berry-bearing shrubs and trees and food is put out by householders. A prolonged frost, which lasted 59 days during the winter of 1890/1, caused high mortality amongst thrushes and, although Redwings and Fieldfares vacated the country altogether (Norman 1994), the more sedentary Mistle Thrush suffered greatly. Although extensive snow falls cause feeding difficulties, ice glaze, which occurs when rain falls at sub-zero temperatures and freezes onto vegetation, is far more damaging, sometimes resulting in large-scale starvation of many small passerines. Arboreal species such as Treecreepers and Long-tailed Tits are particularly vulnerable when such conditions prevail and heathland residents also suffer greatly. Severe winters in 1860/1, 1880/1, 1886/7, 1916/7 and 1939/40 affected many residents, but the Dartford Warbler was particularly vulnerable and the latter winter proved to be its last stand in Suffolk. After this it was lost as a breeding species for over half a century. Small passerines find various ways of surviving and, during cold winter nights, will seek shelter to minimise heat loss. Wrens enter cavities such as nest boxes in large numbers, whereas Long-tailed Tits and Treecreepers huddle together.

Wetland birds suffer when lakes and rivers are frozen. Populations of Grey Heron and Kingfisher diminish drastically under these conditions although many individuals move to the warmer estuarine waters. Bitterns disperse from their reedbeds and become more widespread. Predators initially benefit from severe weather and Short-eared Owls and Hen Harriers roost close to their feeding areas in harsh weather in an attempt to save energy. A most remarkable severe-weather casualty concerned a flock of Snow Buntings which regularly wintered at Newmarket Heath in the late 19th century. The species is not normally susceptible to harsh weather, but, following a snow-storm in January 1881, many were found starved to death (Ticehurst 1932).

During bad weather an exodus of open country feeders, such as Golden Plovers, Lapwings, thrushes, Skylarks and finches, is often witnessed and movements can occur on a grand scale. With the onset of hard weather on 1st January 1962, birds were moving south before sunrise, with the peak movement occurring between 9 am and 10.30 am. Around 14,000 birds passed through Minsmere. Those identified included 2,000 Lapwings, 700 Skylarks, 1,000 Fieldfares, 1,000 Chaffinches, 200 Bullfinches and 850 Yellowhammers.

Starvation will force birds to exploit unfamiliar sources of food. For example, prolonged frosts result in Reed Buntings venturing into gardens to take scraps from birdtables and Blackcaps have been observed on peanut holders. The severe frosts and blizzards, which occurred in February and March 1947, resulted in the ground remaining snow-covered for many weeks. In desperation, Green Woodpeckers attempted to feed on estuarine mud-flats and, soon after the thaw, nine emaciated bodies were found between the groynes at Shotley (Robertson 1954). Other species rely heavily on the activities of humans for their winter survival. For example, Robins will patiently wait whilst gardeners turn over the soil and will follow the tracks of other mammals and even machinery. Industrial premises can also attract wintering species. For example, Black Redstarts are noted in most winters around the ports of Lowestoft and Felixstowe and Starlings and Pied Wagtails take advantage of urban warmth by forming communal roosts on buildings or in shrubberies in the centre of towns. The micro-climate created by warm waters at sewage works attracts sufficient invertebrates to ensure the survival of a number of Chiffchaffs and Pied Wagtails, and a few Grey Wagtails visit the filter beds.

Some species store food for the winter months. Jays collect and bury vast quantities of acorns, and Marsh and Coal Tits store food under bark. Shorebirds normally continue feeding through the severest of harsh-weather periods but plummeting temperatures and biting winds can cause a build-up of estuarine ice – a hazard which can spell disaster for the hardiest of species. The full effects of habitat losses are soon realised when such conditions prevail. In the wake of the loss of a considerable area of mudflats to the Port of Felixstowe, waders on the southern estuaries suffered greatly during an icy blast in February 1991. Estuarine tidelines were littered with corpses, mainly between the Alde and the Stour, the principal species being Shelduck, Grey Plover, Dunlin and Redshank. Mortality was extremely high and the 448 Redshank carcasses found on the Deben alone constituted a loss of nearly half of the estuary's average wintering population.

Wet winters or late winter thaws often enhance wetland habitats, providing a good supply of invertebrates to the benefit of passage and breeding waders. The massive thaw that followed the severe winter of 1947 caused widespread flooding, particularly in the Fens and Breckland. Curlews formed a breeding colony on Breckland heaths which has been present ever since. Wet meadows, especially those with standing water, encourage waders such as Snipe, Black-tailed Godwit and Redshank to breed.

EARLY BREEDING AND SPRING IMMIGRATION

Mild winters followed by warm springs induce early breeding. Species such as the Great Crested Grebe, Grey Heron, Mallard, Lapwing, Snipe, Moorhen, Coot, Stock Dove, Collared Dove, Tawny and Short-eared Owls, Robin, Blackbird, Song and Mistle Thrushes, Long-tailed Tit, Magpie, Rook and Crossbill are traditional early breeders and new nests are regularly found before the end of March. Recently fledged Crossbills have been found in mid-January, giving an egg-laying date in early December, and a pair of Mistle Thrushes was seen nest building on 20th January 1949. Other early breeders include a Moorhen incubating on 2nd February 1946 and a Robin with a full clutch on 20th March of the same year.

A good southerly airflow aids spring migration and the first Stone Curlews, Sand Martins and Wheatears of the year normally occur in mid-March. There was a remarkable spring passage in 1859 – the highlights being 22 Hoopoes, many Ring Ouzels, a Woodchat Shrike and an Ortolan Bunting.

SUMMER EXTREMES

The effects of sudden cold snaps during summer months could not have been more aptly illustrated than on the mornings of 5th and 6th June 1816, when gardeners employed by the Rev. Fonnereau, then the resident of Christchurch Mansion, Ipswich, found hundreds of Swallows sitting on the grass, in groups of 30-40, suffering from the effects of cold and hunger (Sheppard & Whitear 1824-1825). House Martins also suffered in this period and many were collected elsewhere in Ipswich. Bitterly cold, north-easterly winds, combined with severe weather during 24th-29th May 1869, proved disastrous for hirundines, when thousands were collected in Ipswich alone. Similar events occurred during Whitsun 1891 and in May 1902. A reduction in aerial-borne insects occurs during cold weather periods, but warm and dry summers can also be detrimental to the birds' breeding success. Dry conditions in southern Europe often result in marshland breeders venturing further north in search of wetter areas. Black-winged Stilts have bred in Britain during such conditions and, during a heat-wave in the summer of 1906, 12 Glossy Ibises, a White Pelican, a Greater Flamingo and 13 Red-crested Pochards were reported in Suffolk.

AUTUMN MIGRATION

Autumn is the most exciting season for birdwatchers studying migration as summer visitors depart for their wintering grounds *en masse*. It is during passage that birds are most vulnerable to weather conditions, with wind, rain and poor visibility inhibiting migration. Low cloud is also hazardous.

Failure of food supplies elsewhere in Europe can often result in invasions of Waxwings, Crossbills and Jays into Britain, although passage is often assisted by wind direction. An extremely cold prevailing wind from the east of Europe resulted in an unprecedented influx of Jays in October 1880 (John & Roskell 1985).

THE 'GREAT FALL'

One of the most amazing ornithological events of recent times was the 'Great Fall' of 3rd -5th September 1965. A low pressure system to the south-east of Britain produced an overnight, light, NNE wind and an approaching depression brought an early-morning thunderstorm. Freshening, southeasterly winds were soon followed by continuous heavy rain and as the depression tracked northwards, the onshore winds brought an "avalanche" of passerines (Axell & Pearson 1966), with an estimated 100,000 Wheatears, 4,000 Whinchats, 250,000 Redstarts, c.3,000 Garden Warblers, 1,200 Willow Warblers and "tens of thousands" of Pied Flycatchers. The migrants were considered to have been of Scandinavian origin and during the week following the 3rd, some 3,000 passerines were ringed, of which four were recovered in Iberia.

OTHER NOTABLE FALLS AND WEATHER EVENTS

Weather systems similar to those of the 1965 'Great Fall' had disorientated migrants on the Suffolk coast ten years earlier (Axell & Pearson 1966). Similar species were involved, although few counts were made. A ferocious storm on 16th October 1987 caused widespread damage on the Suffolk coast. Vast tracts of woodland were destroyed and thousands of parkland and hedgerow trees uprooted. Conifer plantations proved to be the most vulnerable and 2.8 million trees were destroyed in Suffolk alone (Heathcote 1988). Woodland birds were severely affected by the gale and populations plummeted during subsequent years, the most notable being Hawfinch and Lesser and Great Spotted Woodpeckers. Only the latter species has recovered to anywhere near its former levels. A few Sabine's Gulls were forced close inshore and a Little Bunting and a Desert Wheatear were found at Landguard Point. The following October was much calmer, although an easterly airflow during mid-month, along with low cloud and light rain, grounded passing migrants and around 10,000 Robins were noted in the Felixstowe area alone.

Very occasionally, raptors pass through Suffolk in exceptional numbers. Ticehurst refers to September 1881, when Honey Buzzards and other birds of prey were unusually numerous, and there was a similar event in September 2000 when strong SSE winds forced Ospreys and Honey Buzzards off their normal migration path to be recorded in record numbers at both inland and coastal localities (Piotrowski 2002).

Marsh Harrier and Bittern. This led to the acquisition of some of Britain's finest nature reserves such as Walberswick, Minsmere and Havergate Island. The importance of monitoring was not lost on early wardens and meticulous records were collected for most major sites. However, recording was not carried out as scientifically as it is today. Counts on estuaries were not co-ordinated and were largely carried out on an *ad hoc* basis and the optical aids were inadequate for the task. In consequence, many sites relied heavily on the skill of the observer in identifying birds and it is obvious from the consistent round-figure totals that large gatherings were often the observer's 'best guess'. Seabird sightings were extremely rare.

The SOG initially published papers, field notes and sightings in a bi-monthly bulletin and, as standards in the quality of production improved, the journal moved to quarterly, being published as *The Harrier*, which is considered to be one of the best regional newsletters in Britain today.

One of the great landmarks of British ornithology came in 1968 when fieldwork started on a most ambitious project to plot the distribution of British and Irish breeding birds. This was the biggest co-operative effort ever undertaken anywhere in the world and culminated in the publication of *The Atlas of Breeding Birds in Britain and Ireland* (Sharrock 1976). Fieldwork for a similar project, concentrating on wintering birds, took place between 1981 and 1984. The results of this project were detailed in the *Atlas of Wintering Birds in Britain and Ireland* (Lack 1986) and, in 1988, work for *The New Atlas of Breeding Birds in Britain and Ireland 1988-1991* (Gibbons *et al.* 1993) was underway. The county's ornithologists were actively involved in all three surveys which were published by T. and A. D. Poyser for the BTO and the Irish Wildbird Conservancy. The three projects are dealt with in greater detail in the chapter on surveys.

As a result of the continuing upsurge in interest and the demand by birding members of the SNS, the annual Bird Report was again issued as a separate publication, but now completely independently of the *Transactions.* Vignettes, drawn by accomplished Suffolk artists, were introduced and became a feature of the reports, but, otherwise, there were few major changes in format during these embryonic years. Standards improved rapidly throughout the 1980s and colour photographs were added for first time in 1985. *British Birds* introduced a prestigious annual prize for the best county bird report in 1990. This was won by Suffolk at its first attempt. Around 300 observers forwarded bird records to the SBRC in the mid-1990s – a six-fold increase on that of the early 1950s.

RINGING AND MIGRATION

Man's fascination with the migrations of birds goes back centuries. Early philosophers failed to understand why some species disappeared during the winter months only to reappear the following spring and, in consequence, suggested explanations which relied on logic rather than fact. For example, Aristotle watching Redstarts in Greece believed that they moulted into Robins as the seasons changed (Mead 1983). Theories concerning the disappearance of the Swallow, ranged from spending the winter months buried in mud on the bed of lakes to migration to and from the moon. Kites were thought to have hidden in a torpid state in crevices amongst rocks during winter.

A number of experiments and observations carried out in the early 1800s discounted the hibernation theory and supported that of migration and, by the 1820s, East Anglian naturalists were firmly entrenched in the latter ideas. Messrs Sheppard and Whitear stated "...the proximity of the counties of Norfolk and Suffolk to the northern part of the Continent, affords an opportunity to many migrative species of birds to visit these parts of the kingdom, in their passage to and from their breeding haunts" (Sheppard & Whitear 1824-1825). Hele (1890) studied migration from his Aldeburgh home and regularly logged the "Royston crows, rooks, jackdaw, owls, woodcocks, starlings, larks or the enormous 'mobs' or 'rushes' of small birds that reach our shore". As an example, he cited movements, between 11am and 1pm, on 21st October 1877 involving Roystons (Hooded Crows), Starlings, Bramblings, a single Woodcock, larks and other small birds.

A variety of marking techniques to determine ownership rather than movements was employed as early as 1708-1709 (Thompson 1926). The first proven inter-county movement featuring Suffolk dates back to 1850, when a Grey Heron shot at Nacton was found to be wearing an inscribed brass plate showing that it had originated in Lincolnshire. Knowledge of migration grew considerably through the 19th century and was greatly enhanced by a national ringing scheme which commenced in 1909. Proposals for a network of coastal observatories around Britain, to monitor the movements of seabirds, were forwarded as early as 1834. National schemes did get underway, elsewhere in Europe, and reports from Belgium, Sweden, Russia and Germany were published in 1880 (Mead 1983). The marking of birds proved to be a most valuable tool in our knowledge of migration, determining not only site fidelity, but also migration routes, stopping-off points, wintering quarters, longevity and breeding success. There was much excitement during the early years of the ringing scheme with numerous letters regarding recoveries being published in national journals. Rings were originally inscribed with the ringer's name and address, with the ring number on the reverse and there were also appeals for rings, together with the birds' legs, to be returned to the ringer. Ticehurst featured highly amongst these early pioneers and his rings were inscribed 'Ticehurst, Tenterden,' (he was then still living in Kent). Suffolk's first foreign recovery involved a Little Tern ringed at Sizewell Thorpe on 27th June 1912 and recovered in France exactly two months later.

Ticehurst enthused about the potential of Lowestoft as a migration watch-point. It had many of the ingredients of other well-known migration sites in Britain, including a lighthouse attraction and lots of cover holding an abundance of food for tired and hungry migrants. It was also situated on the most easterly point of the British mainland. Between 1910 and 1927, Ticehurst and his friend Fred Cook monitored migration in the area, keeping a detailed log of weather conditions including wind speed and direction, numbers and species involved and direction of travel. Their enthusiasm is aptly depicted in Ticehurst's account of the Rook which included detailed diagrams of their incoming approach. Records from light-vessels were also valuable indicators of passage movements at that time.

The *Transactions* of the SNS detailed an amazing wartime account of immigration witnessed at a searchlight station at Lowestoft towards the end of October 1944 (Cook 1944). It described how a horde of Starlings gathered around the station during the night of 21st October in such vast numbers that many branches were torn from adjacent oaks by the birds' combined weight. As Starlings are diurnal migrants, it is likely that birds were disturbed from an overnight roost, although other searchlight stations in the district were also 'swamped' by Starlings that night. Cook visited the station a few days later and was fascinated by what he saw. He stated "...in the slowly revolving and almost vertical beam there wavered in bewilderment and panic migrating birds, that it was almost impossible to identify by sight, as all were rendered intensely silvery by the brilliant light". He recognised the calls of Fieldfares, Redwings, Blackbirds, thrushes and Skylarks, and noted the occasional bird that "...came fluttering down the beam on to the lantern, apparently with complete immunity". A few nights later "...when the moon shone serenely out of the sky" no birds (or moths) could be located in the beam. Previously, there were a few records of bird being drawn to Suffolk lighthouses and lightships, but this must surely have been the first evidence of birds being attracted *en masse*.

Ticehurst also predicted that the coastal towns of Southwold and Aldeburgh, as well as Orfordness, Shingle Street and Landguard Point, would be well-favoured by passage migrants, although the sites needed to be "worked regularly" for this to be proved.

The Dingle Bird Club established a ringing station at Walberswick in 1953. The two Dingle hills were in prime position for the study of migration and two Heligoland traps were constructed to increase the number of birds caught. From 1953–1962, 12,000 birds of 110 species were ringed and all but 600 were passerines. The county's first Western Bonelli's Warbler was trapped by the group in April 1961, and was followed by Suffolk's first Pallas's and Radde's Warblers within the next three years. Early morning coastal movements of larks, pipits, Starlings, Tree Sparrows, finches and buntings were noted annually between late September and mid-November. Northward movements of Linnets were considered to be "a curious feature of Suffolk" (Pearson 1963), although, as this phenomenon was not subsequently witnessed at migration sites further south, it is likely that these birds were coasting locally. Extensive studies were carried out on the resident Bearded Tit population which stimulated a number of papers. Although work at the Dingles is less intense today than in those early years, there are still valuable studies being carried out on Bearded Tits and the migration periods are still covered.

Ringing took place at Benacre in the 1950s and again in the 1970s and the Sluice Bushes at Minsmere were well worked during the 1960s. Suffolk's first Common Rosefinch was trapped at Benacre Pits on 2nd September 1959.

Perhaps the most significant development of migration studies in Suffolk coincided with the growth of the Port of Felixstowe. The towering floodlights illuminated a huge area of land and sea, and the number of migrants present was at times beyond belief. This effect was soon to be realised at nearby Landguard Point. Access to the former military area had been restricted for many years and, when the army moved out, the land was divided – the majority going for dock development, some to tourism and a small section as a nature reserve. There was scant reference to Landguard Point by previous authors and the few ancient records for the site (e.g. Snowy Owl and Storm Petrel) revolved around the old wooden lighthouse which was destroyed by fire in 1925. Observers who visited the site in the 1960s, saw little in the way of migrants. However, all was to change in 1975 when public access to the peninsula was reinstated and a LNR was established. Increased observer coverage no doubt contributed to a string of rarities found at the site and interest blossomed to such an extent that in 1982 a bird observatory was founded in the old wartime bunkers which overlook the reserve. Ringing and migration studies are carried out on a day-to-day basis and much has been learnt about passage birds that migrate through Suffolk. From 1981-2002, no fewer than 14 species recorded at Landguard Point were new to the county list – namely Crested Lark, Blyth's Pipit, Thrush Nightingale, Red-flanked Bluetail, Desert Wheatear, Lanceolated, Paddyfield, Subalpine, Spectacled, Sardinian and Dusky Warblers, Southern Grey Shrike, Lark Sparrow and Yellow-breasted Bunting.

The port was extended further up the Orwell estuary in the late 1980s, swallowing the old oysterbeds and mudflats in front of Fagbury Cliff. However, the trees on the cliff itself were preserved and thousands more were planted as part of the compensation measures. It was soon realised that the illuminated plantations were attracting many passage migrants and the site then became the focus of attention for birdwatchers. For a short period Fagbury rivalled Landguard Point as the county's premier migration ringing site. Ringing coverage was maintained throughout passage periods and yielded some amazing results. The annual total ranged between 5,000-8,000 during the period 1992-1994 and no less than 70% of these were warblers. Pied Wheatear and Blyth's Reed and Arctic Warblers were new species for Suffolk. However, all was to change in 1995. In spring of that year, the brilliant white lamps on one of the floodlight towers were replaced by less intense, peachy-orange ones and gradually throughout the summer and autumn all were changed. This had an immediate effect on the birds that were grounded at the site with numbers plummeting alarmingly. The most dramatic declines involved *Sylvia* and *Acrocephalus* warblers.

Since 1983, Landguard Bird Observatory has carried out intensive studies on the mixed Herring and Lesser Black-backed Gull colony on Orfordness. In 1996, this study was enhanced by the use of colour rings. Early returns are encouraging, with the recovery rate increased from around 7% to 20% in the first two years.

The Wildfowl and Wetlands Trust (WWT) took over Nacton Decoy and commenced migration studies there using traditional trapping techniques to catch ducks for ringing. In the period 1967-1981, a total of 15,569 ducks was ringed from which over 2,500 recoveries, averaging one in six, were received. The creation of Abberton and Alton Water Reservoirs proved more attractive than the small ponds at Nacton and, faced with dwindling numbers, the WWT ceased its operations in 1982. There was once much scepticism about the origins of Nearctic ducks appearing in British waters, but a Blue-winged Teal shot on the Deben and bearing a Canadian ring proved conclusively that Atlantic crossings are more than just a possibility

Many waders are long-distance travellers, some flying from Arctic breeding grounds to winter in the tropics or even further. Patterns of migration are complex and ringing has shown that different populations have discrete wintering grounds with some races travelling much further than others. For example, Dunlin wintering in Suffolk are mostly of the race *arctica* which breeds in north-eastern Greenland. Those breeding in northern Britain and Iceland are of the race *schinzii*, which winters largely in Morocco and Mauritania and occur in Suffolk as a passage migrant. The race *alpina* breeds in Scandinavia and Arctic Russia.

Lapwings passing south at the end of May are known to be the first autumn migrants and, by the middle of June, returning Curlew, Spotted Redshank and Green Sandpipers also appear. Some wader species use Suffolk purely as a staging post on their long journeys and neither winter nor summer here. Coastal lagoons form the main attraction for these transients and in May, July and August good numbers of Common, Wood and Curlew Sandpipers, Little Stints, Greenshanks, Bar-tailed Godwits and Whimbrels appear. The tundra race of the Ringed Plover is purely a passage migrant rarely occurring before the last week of May during the spring. Onshore gales often force migrating wader flocks close inshore and large movements are occasionally noted at migration watch-points.

Britain is hardly renowned for its raptor movements as most breeding species remain here in winter and summer visitors are quite rare. Honey Buzzards, Montagu's Harriers, Ospreys and Hobbies all move north from their African wintering grounds and a few pairs nest in Britain annually. Only the Hobby breeds in Suffolk, the other species occurring principally as passage migrants. All four species are noted at migration watchpoints, although both the Honey Buzzard and the Montagu's Harrier are noted less than annually. Occasionally, freak weather conditions force the birds to British shores as seen in the autumns of 1876, 1881, 1993 and 2001 when there were exceptional numbers of Honey Buzzards in Suffolk (Piotrowski 2002). At least 100 individuals were noted during the influx of September 2001 together with around 40 Ospreys.

The only substantial influx of Rough-legged Buzzards between 1915 and 2001 occurred in 1974 which compares with nine such events between 1839 and 1915.

Spring influxes of any raptor species are rare, although records show a significant increase in the number of Buzzards in mid-March and early April. Red Kites are also more common during this period. Red-footed Falcons are regularly overshooting migrants and have been noted in Suffolk almost annually. In 1992, ten visited the county, part of an invasion of unprecedented proportions (Rogers *et al.* 1995).

Up to the mid-1970s, the vast majority of seabird records related to birds being recovered on fishing boats or lightships, tideline corpses or found wrecked in harbours or inland. However, improvements to optical aids and a better understanding of the migration patterns and the conditions when movements are likely to occur have resulted in an increase in the number of observers willing to face biting onshore winds to record seabird movements. Identification skills are largely based on shape, 'jizz' and habits, rather than plumage characteristics, so now mere dots on the horizon can be identified with certainty by a trained eye. A small band of observers has spent countless hours gazing out to sea and their results have improved our knowledge of movements off the Suffolk coast. For example, up to 1975 there were only eight records of Sooty Shearwater, but it is now known that the species is a regular passage migrant recorded from late August to October. Similarly, the Long-tailed Skua was once considered an extreme rarity, but it has now been found to occur annually in small numbers. The scarcity of some seabirds demonstrates changes in man's activities. For example, Storm Petrels were once plentiful but overfishing led to the collapse of the herring fishery and, in consequence, the species is very much a rarity.

CONSERVATION AND PRESERVATION

FOOD FOR FREE

In days gone by, birds were largely regarded as a sustainable food source and very few species escaped the pot. Robert Reyce, in his *Breviary of Suffolk* (1618), gave an indication of the culinary desires as well as the quarry species of that time: "Of our wilde fowles the parttidge, phesaunt, woodcock, ring dove, quails, larks, lapwings, plover, bitterns, bustard, snite, dotterel, sheldrake, shoveler, peewit and such like ...afford the good housewife a dainty supply" and "... of ravens, rooks, jacdawes, kites, bussards, ringtayles, pyes, etc., are not commonly eaten but are ravenous and hurtfull in their prey". The eggs of many birds were collected for food and even those of the Rook and Jackdaw were considered good to eat (Sheppard & Whitear 1824-1825).

A series of Tudor Acts designed to increase food production resulted in the persecution of birds considered to be a threat to crops, livestock or game. Raptors were the principal target, but also crows, sparrows and some finches. Evidence of the targeting of Bullfinches is detailed in the Bedingfield parish accounts of 1568 and Buzzards in the accounts of Bredfield and Cratfield for 1580. Sparrows were slaughtered in their thousands with bounties paid for the destruction of both birds and eggs from the 1770s to the 1830s (Ticehurst 1932).

The vast watery fens that formerly encompassed north-west Suffolk, much of Cambridgeshire, south-west Norfolk and south Lincolnshire were once a haven for breeding and wintering wildfowl. This proved to be an important food source to local communities and a variety of catching techniques were employed to gather in the harvest. Flightless adults and unfledged young were rounded up and driven into netted traps, but, as the fens shrunk in size, this practice reduced the breeding stock to such an extent that legislation was introduced to limit the trapping. The banning of the taking of wildfowl during the moulting season in England in 1710 (Kear 1990) was an early conservation measure.

Dutch engineers started drainage work in the fens in 1606 (Bircham 1989), but with them they brought fresh ideas on duck catching by use of decoy ponds with large-diameter, tapering funnels. In the late 18th century, 200 decoys were sited in Britain but, by 1886, only 47 were operational, reducing to 28 by 1918 (*Wildfowl Word*, winter 1982: Slimbridge). Early fowlers soon realised that a dramatic increase in duck numbers occurred during the autumn and winter, and decoy ponds situated in regions with a good migratory passage proved to be the most productive. Most of Suffolk's decoys were in the vicinity of the coast and estuaries and, in consequence, were in prime positions to attract passing migrants. For example, decoys were built at Fritton, Flixton, Herringfleet, Benacre, Worlingham, Friston, Iken, Campsea Ash, Chillesford, Purdis Hall Farm (two ponds sometimes listed as Bixley or Nacton), Nacton Wood/Orwell Park and Brantham. There were only two decoys in West Suffolk: at Euston Park and Lakenheath. Fritton and Orwell Park were still being managed commercially during the 1920s and the latter until its closure in 1966, the last fully-operational decoy in Britain. This decoy was built in 1835 and catches there were well documented (Matthews 1969). From 1919-1968, no less than 195,000 ducks were caught (Ogilvie 1975) although, during the last two years, the birds were ringed rather than killed. The site reached its peak in the 1920s, when catches of 7,783, 9,303 and 8,351 were logged in 1920/1, 1925/6 and 1928/9, respectively.

THE SPORTING SCENE

Although game was once killed by sling-shot and bows and arrows, falconry was regarded as the only means of taking birds in a sporting way and, in mediaeval times, was a favourite pursuit of kings and the landed gentry. Falcons achieved a high monetary value and, in 1199, Gyr Falcons and Peregrines were used by the townsmen of Dunwich as part settlement of a debt which brought a charter from King John. It was believed that the Gyr Falcons were imported from Iceland whereas the Peregrines were gathered locally (Ticehurst 1932). Corton Church still played host to a Peregrine eyrie until around 1800 and the nestlings were collected annually for hawking. The first instance of nest protection, albeit for the wrong reasons, involved the Corton Parish Clerk who received a retaining fee for the preservation of the young falcons. The nobility regularly met on Suffolk's open heaths and warrens, where falcons were flown to bring down crows and Red Kites. As these birds became scarce, the sportsmen turned their attention to herons and even Stone Curlews, although the latter provided poor sport (Ticehurst 1932). Hawking was an expensive sport with the employment of a falconer being an essential part of its upkeep. A tombstone in the churchyard of Fakenham Magna is a testimony to the lost art in Suffolk. It states: "William Sakings died March 16, 1689, he was Forkner [falconer] to Charles I. and II. and James II." (Ticehurst 1932).

The introduction of the breech-loading shotgun in 1853 marked the advent of the wholesale rearing of Pheasants. Suffolk hosted a wealth of sporting estates and habitats were managed exclusively for this species. Many creatures were persecuted in the interests of the preservation of game, and birds with hooked bills were the main targets. Shrikes and occasionally Nightjars also ended up on gamekeepers' gibbets. Introduction attempts to enhance sporting interests including Red and Black Grouse, Capercaillie, Barbary Partridge and Bobwhite Quail. The number of gamekeepers increased considerably between 1870 and 1910, and few sporting estates would have been without its team. Persecution resulted in the Raven being finally lost to Suffolk as a breeding species in 1870 and the Buzzard four years later; the female from Suffolk's last breeding pair being wounded on her nest. Raptors and crows were shot, pole-trapped and poisoned, and their nests located and destroyed. As a consequence, both the Carrion Crow and Magpie were on the brink of extinction by the start of the First World War.

It is clear from the sentiments expressed in his book that Ticehurst was one of the county's early conservationists or 'sentimentalists' as they then would have been labelled by the shooting fraternity. In 1912, Ticehurst was so concerned about the fate of two pairs of Montagu's Harriers, that he pleaded with three owners of coastal heaths to preserve nesting harriers on their land. Two were sympathetic to his cause, but the third said that he would not blame his keepers if they killed every hawk and certainly would not give instructions to the contrary. This typifies the attitudes of that day and Ticehurst believed that the harriers were killed "... lest an odd game chick or two were taken". In his frustration, he summarised his feelings as follows: "... such greed is deplorable... how any landowner, who ought to be proud to give a pair of these birds harbourage, can care so little for the wildlife on his property that he should acquiesce in the illegal destruction of almost our rarest breeding bird passes my comprehension".

A Buzzard caught in a trap at Wrentham in 1947 (Collings 1948) and a Honey Buzzard found hanging from a scarecrow near Bury St Edmunds the following year shows that protection laws were viewed with contempt and there was little fear of prosecution. The wanton slaughter of raptors continued through to the early 1970s, when trophies were still openly displayed on gamekeepers' gibbets. Obviously, old habits died hard! Even today it is strongly suspected that the re-colonisation of the Buzzard is being checked by illegal shooting and poisoning on well-keepered estates. There are currently moves amongst the shooting fraternity to add Sparrowhawk to the quarry list under the guise of the raptor's persecution of songbirds. Having spent much time and effort on the recovery of the raptor populations, the conservation bodies are understandably concerned about such a move and would be very much against any additions to the quarry list. It is inconsistent to allow Sparrowhawks to be shot in Britain whilst at the same time making moves to stop the wholesale slaughter of Honey Buzzards in southern Europe.

Man has been hunting wildfowl for centuries, but it is comparatively recently that wildfowling has developed into a sport. The development of the breach-loading shotgun, rubber (Wellington) boots and specially-trained dogs to retrieve quarry, in the 19th century, resulted in an upsurge of interest in coastal duck hunting. Wildfowlers were attracted to remote areas of Suffolk estuaries where the thrill of the storm and the sight and sound of incoming flights of Wigeon proved an irresistible attraction. Although it has been generally accepted that wildfowling has little effect on populations, few wildfowlers contribute towards the preservation of habitat or take an active part in the fight against the development that threatens estuarine environments leading to a loss in sporting opportunities.

THE TROPHY HUNTERS

The early 1800s were certainly the era of 'what's hit is history and what's missed is mystery' and, macabre as this may seem today, the collection of specimens was then a respectable pursuit and the first step to a scientific approach to ornithology. Many first county records of unusual species were proved by the presence of well-documented specimens. The following 'firsts' for Suffolk were either killed or trapped:-

1807:	Roller
1816:	Dipper
1818:	*Red-crested Pochard
	Eider
	*Parrot Crossbill

1820:	Little Bustard
1824:	Glossy Ibis
	Golden Oriole
pre-1825:	Gyr Falcon.
1825:	*Caspian Tern
	Bee-eater
1827:	Collared Pratincole
1828:	Cream-coloured Courser
1829:	Woodchat Shrike
1830:	Little Crake
	*Pectoral Sandpiper
1831:	Squacco Heron
1832:	Black Stork
c.1835:	Alpine Swift
1836:	*Broad-billed Sandpiper
pre-1846:	Tengmalm's Owl
	Scops Owl
1847:	Snowy Owl
1852:	White-billed Diver
	Ruddy Shelduck
	*Eskimo Curlew
1853:	Buff-breasted Sandpiper
1859:	Ortolan Bunting
1862:	Red-footed Flacon
	Shore Lark
1863:	Black Guillemot
	Pallas's Sandgrouse
	Serin
1875:	Spotted Eagle
1886:	Mediterranean Gull
1888:	Cirl Bunting
1889:	Short-toed Lark
1892:	Sharp-tailed Sandpiper
1910:	Willow Tit
1938:	Lesser Yellowlegs
1971:	Blue-winged Teal

Those marked with an asterisk indicate a first record for Britain. In addition, two of three Spotted Eagles noted during the winter of 1891/2 were also shot.

THE FASHION GURUS

During the mid-1800s, there was a high demand for plumes for the fashion trade. Grebes, egrets, Kingfishers and some seabirds were slaughtered in their thousands on the sea cliffs of northern and western Britain. The skins of Great Crested Grebes adorned the hats and muffs of Victorian ladies and, as a result, the East Anglian grebe population was brought to the verge of extinction. Elsewhere in Britain, seabirds' wings were collected for millinery decoration and it was the passing of the Seabirds Protection Act in 1869 that provided the grebe and other species with a respite to recolonise their former haunts. It was concern about the exploitation of birds that saw the birth of the RSPB in 1889, an organisation which has had an enormous impact on the protection of birds and their habitats.

CAGE AND AVIARY

In the late 1800s and early 1900s, it was fashionable to have a singing bird caged in the parlour. Canaries were bred specifically for that purpose, but more often local songbirds were caught and sold to dealers on the open market. Linnets, Goldfinches, Greenfinches and Bullfinches were the most popular songsters and local populations, especially those close to towns, declined rapidly. Goldfinches were almost wiped out around Ipswich and Bury St Edmunds and other finches became scarce. Legislation was introduced to prohibit the use of birdlime in 1925 and the Protection of Wild Birds Act of 1933 restricted the trade in songbirds. Any loopholes were finally sealed in 1953 when the Act was substantially revised (Holloway 1996).

HABITAT LOSSES

Habitat loss has had the most marked effect on bird populations and this is particularly apparent in Suffolk. The cereal-dominated central areas are now more reminiscent of the North American prairies with hardly a hedge or tree in sight. This has had a devastating effect on bird populations which can be clearly demonstrated by the blank patches on the distribution maps.

Almost all wildlife habitats have suffered in one way or another and are dealt with in detail under the habitat section.

Most coastal heaths or the sandlings have been lost to agriculture, afforestation or housing. Breckland has also changed greatly. During the Cold War years, huge tracts of prime wildlife habitat were swallowed up by the construction of American airbases.

The loss of estuarine habitats has been devastating for wintering waders. Port development and marinas have been responsible for the main losses and the areas that remain have come under increasing pressure from sports enthusiasts (e.g. jet-skiers and power boats) and bait diggers.

There was a huge effort amongst conservationists to save Fagbury Flats, at the mouth of the Orwell estuary, from being swallowed up by the Port of Felixstowe. Many conservation groups joined forces to launch *Operation Redshank*, and this culminated in a long parliamentary debate. Although the mudflats were lost to development, Trimley Marshes Nature Reserve was provided as compensation.

HABITAT CREATION

Habitat creation has been widely practised since the Second World War. This was initially by accident, as can be seen by the expansive reedbeds at Minsmere, Walberswick and formerly Kessingland, the initial purpose of which was to make life difficult for invading Germans. It was soon realised that a number of rare species had colonised these new habitats and as a result were proclaimed as nature reserves. Negotiations for lease of the new marshes at Minsmere opened in 1947 when Avocets were found breeding there – the first time in Britain for 100 years. Wardening of the area also began in 1947. A number of wetland habitats has been enhanced by raising water levels and digging scrapes, thereby creating a series of lagoons and islands. This method was pioneered by H. E. Axell at Minsmere in 1962 and its success has been repeated on nature reserves throughout the world. The affects of this technique can be almost immediate, although controlling of water levels form an essential part of management if both passage and breeding waders are to be continually attracted to the area. Reedbed control can be particularly time-consuming, but it is essential that open areas of water are maintained and that the reedbed is kept wet. This has been achieved most effectively at Walberswick where the reeds are cut commercially. Floating rafts have been proved to be beneficial to nesting Common Terns on larger areas of standing water such as at Weybread Pits and smaller platforms have also been effective for Great Crested Grebes.

Heathland restoration has been carried out on a grand scale, both with regard to management improvements and to reclamation from arable land. The Sandlings project has made great headway in the management of heathland after years of neglect. Nightjars and Woodlarks have benefited greatly from this work and there has been a welcome return of the Dartford Warbler.

Perhaps the most remarkable example of nest-site creation involves the Kittiwakes at Lowestoft, which have nested on buildings in the harbour area since 1958. The colony went from strength to strength reaching 87 nests by 1983 (Brown 1986). Local wildlife enthusiasts and, in particular, members of the Lowestoft Field Club, developed an affinity to their colony. However, the proprietors of the buildings that hosted nests were sometimes not so enthusiastic due to the mess left by the birds. In consequence, there were a number of measures employed to discourage the birds. When the birds' one remaining site, the South Pier Pavilion, was due to be demolished, the Association of British Ports agreed to construct a purpose-built wall as an alternative site. Brian Brown, who had meticulously recorded the colony's history, designed and championed this exciting new venture (Brown 1990). The colony then increased rapidly and in 1995 a record 259 pairs raised 303 young.

The planting and felling of woodland and the growing of hedgerows are a simple but long-term solution to the creation of habitat, although with hardwoods the planters are unlikely to see the true rewards for their labour. Conifer plantations have little wildlife value, although a planting regime which gives differing age structures is more beneficial to species such as Nightjar and Woodlark. Poplars are one of the fastest-growing deciduous trees and the large plantations in north-west Suffolk were particularly valuable for breeding passerines. Golden Orioles colonised the woods in 1967. This attracted the attention of hundreds of birdwatchers, many of whom made an annual pilgrimage to the woods to admire the splendour of these beautiful birds. Sadly, most of the woods were felled as the timber is no longer in demand by the manufacturers of matches. Fortunately the RSPB has now purchased the area and is planning to recreate the fenland habitats where Bitterns once abounded, as well as preserving the poplar woods.

NATURE RESERVES

Suffolk is reasonably well-off for nature reserves, although in many parts of the county they act almost as an oasis in an arable desert. The larger coastal areas of heath and marsh are now protected by a number of conservation bodies. Benacre Estate and Walberswick and Blythburgh NNR are managed by English Nature. The latter area includes Westleton Heath. Dunwich Heath and much of Orfordness is owned and managed by the National Trust. The RSPB manages Minsmere, one of Europe's best-known bird reserves, along with Havergate Island and is currently enhancing valuable habitats at North Warren and Boyton Marshes. The SWT owns or manages 50 reserves and, although most are relatively small, they are of extreme wildlife importance. Hazelwood Marshes is one of the few relics of the once expansive area of coastal grazing marsh and has recently been acquired by the SWT as a nature reserve. Landguard Point is managed primarily for its rare coastal flora, although it is also Suffolk's principal watch-point for migrant birds and the birth of LBO in 1982 ensured that the site was to become one of the best monitored in the county.

Most nature reserves in central and west Suffolk are ancient woodlands, although the SWT have developed the former gravel workings at Lackford principally as an attraction for wildfowl. Although not highly regarded for their birdlife, the internationally important fenland reserves of Redgrave and Lopham, near the sources of the Little Ouse and Waveney, and the nearby Market Weston Fen are botanically rich, and the former is nationally known for its populations of the Great Raft Spider. The Breckland reserve of Thetford Heath is a typical example of open grassland habitat and although the heaths of Berner's Heath, Deadman's Grave, Weather Heath and Horn Heath are not official nature reserves, they are, nevertheless, immensely important for wildlife. The Suffolk County Council administers a Country Park at Kettleshall Heath, but most of the heathland is suffering from conifer encroachment and is of little conservation value. The RSPB are currently involved in an exciting project which involves the restoration of fenland at Lakenheath.

SPECIES PROTECTION

Many Acts of Parliament have been introduced in the interests of wildlife preservation, although the earlier ones were designed solely to protect gaming interests. In 1209, King John issued an edict forbidding the taking of wildfowl by any method to allow him to hunt them with falcons (Kear 1990) and Henry VIII and Edward VI enacted that "none to destroy or take away the eggs of any wildfowl on pain of one year's imprisonment and to forfeit for every egg of a Crane or Bustard so taken 20d, of a Bittern Heron or Shoveller [sic. Spoonbill] 8d, of Mallard Teal or other fowl 1d, to be divided between the King and the prosecutor" (Ticehurst 1932).

Although the laws had been strengthened to protect vulnerable species from egg-collecting, poisoning, trapping and shooting, enforcement was formerly down to the local authorities and each county differed in its approach. The rogue element of society, which included game preservationists, egg-collectors, cage-bird enthusiasts and taxidermists, flouted the law and, as a consequence, 'watchers' were employed to protect the nests of vulnerable species. The RSPB employed its first watcher in 1901, and the return of Avocets to Suffolk in 1947 prompted the appointment of Dick Wolfendale – a summer warden at Minsmere. He was the county's first full-time paid ornithologist, but his living conditions were hardly luxurious. Dick was provided with a tent for his first season at Minsmere, but in the next few years a mess hut and sleeping hut were erected. H. E. Axell became Minsmere's first full-time warden in 1959 and his creative thinking led to the development of The Scrape which has since been the home of some of Britain's rarest breeding birds and enjoyed by millions of visitors.

Nowadays, the RSPB employs over 30 staff to warden and administer nature reserves at Minsmere, North Warren, Havergate Island, Wolves Wood and Lakenheath. In addition, a Species Protection Unit is employed to watch over vulnerable species during the breeding season. English Nature has a local office at Bury St Edmunds and employs wardens to manage NNRs on the coast and in Breckland. The SWT relies heavily on its volunteer workforce, although 40 people are employed through its Ashbocking HQ.

POLLUTION

Spillages of oil on the open sea have had a devastating effect on fisheries and seabird populations and the effects of these are immediate as tidelines become littered with corpses. The pollution of rivers and estuaries is far less obvious, with agricultural chemical residues running into streams, and sewage and industrial effluents dramatically affecting water quality. This results in the loss of invertebrates and fish and subsequently causes starvation of aquatic birds such as Kingfishers.

INTRODUCTIONS AND REINTRODUCTIONS

There have been many attempts to enhance the county's avifauna by introducing new species or by reintroducing those that have become extinct. Non-native species were released into the Suffolk countryside mostly to provide additional sporting opportunities for shooters, but others escaped from ornamental collections, and some were deliberately released.

Sporting releases

The Pheasant has been a feature of the Suffolk countryside since at least 1419 and was introduced by the Normans. Attempts to establish the Red-legged Partridge in Britain from 1673 finally succeeded in Suffolk during the early 1800s. Red and Black Grouse were introduced to coastal and Breckland heaths in an attempt to recreate moorland grouse shoots. The population of Red Grouse was estimated at 350 in 1908, but both species were extinct by the 1930s. Attempts to establish Capercaillie, Barbary Partridge, Bobwhite Quail and Chukar were unsuccessful. Golden Pheasants were liberated on sporting estates in the late 1890s and a small population still thrives in young conifer plantations in Breckland.

Breckland landowners lamented the loss of the Great Bustard and, between 1876 and 1906, there was a series of attempts to re-establish the birds, with the release of imports from Spain. Unfortunately, these experiments failed.

Several thousand ducks, mostly Mallard, are reared and released annually for shooting purposes. The Gadwall is a non-native species that has been liberated on waters in north-west Suffolk to provide diversity for shooters and it is considered by some that the Breckland Shelduck population originated by the same method.

Ornamental releases

Ornamental wildfowl collectors have imported species from all over the world and, although there have been many escapes, few of these have become established. The Canada Goose was introduced to stately homes during the 17th century and from these it has colonised most of Britain. The Ruddy Duck's spread from Slimbridge has been spectacular albeit controversial due to its effect on native White-headed Ducks elsewhere in Europe. There are moves to exterminate the North American impostors. The Greylag and Egyptian Geese have both been established from feral stock.

Other species were introduced purely as ornamental additions to our avifauna. The Little Owl was one of the few species to fill a valuable niche being a crepuscular hunter of open agricultural areas. Perhaps the most bizarre introduction attempt concerned Black Woodpeckers which were brought from Sweden and released in the Brandon area in 1897. Ring-necked Parakeets have probably colonised south-east England by similar or accidental releases, although they have failed to become established in Suffolk.

Releases for conservation reasons

A coordinated experiment between The Joint Nature Conservation Committee and the RSPB has seen the successful re-introduction of the Red Kite in the Home Counties and the Scottish Highlands and wandering

WINTERING SPECIES

1. Species that formerly regularly wintered in good numbers, but are now scarce: Bean and Pink-footed Goose.

2. Species reported annually in winter, but prior to 1900 were rare or absent: Shag, Little Egret, Bewick's Swan, Red-crested Pochard, Eider, Marsh Harrier, Peregrine Falcon, Avocet, Common Sandpiper, Pomarine Skua, Mediterranean Gull, Lesser Black-backed Gull, Ring-necked Parakeet, Blackcap and Chiffchaff.

PASSAGE MIGRANTS

1. Passage migrants recorded regularly prior to 1900, but now scarce: Storm Petrel, Corncrake, Little Bustard, Dotterel and Roller.

2. Passage migrants rarely reported prior to 1900, but now annual: Fulmar, Sooty Shearwater, Pectoral Sandpiper, Long-tailed Skua, Sabine's Gull, Marsh, Icterine, Pallas's and Yellow-browed Warblers, Serin and Common Rosefinch.

SUMMER VISITORS

1. Summer visitors recorded regularly prior to 1900, but now scarce: Montagu's Harrier, Corncrake, Wryneck and Red-backed Shrike.

2. Summer visitors rarely reported prior to 1900, but now annual: Little Egret, Marsh Harrier, Red-footed Falcon, Hobby, Little Ringed Plover, Mediterranean Gull, Sandwich and Roseate Terns.

SURVEYS, PROJECTS AND ENQUIRIES

by

Mick Wright

The urge to learn more about birds is as great now as it has ever been and the driving force behind many successful surveys. In Britain and Ireland there exists a major collaboration between the amateurs, professionals, voluntary bodies and industry in studying birds. This is assisted by an army of volunteers who are the envy of the rest of the world. When he launched the magazine *British Birds* in 1907, it was H. F. Witherby's aim to systematically investigate many aspects of British birds, such as their breeding ranges, status and distribution. However, it was not until 1928 that E. M. Nicholson, with Witherby's backing, organised the first ever national census of a bird species, the Grey Heron. The survey is still carried out annually and, since 1934 it has been under the auspices of the BTO.

The number of surveys carried out over the years is vast, covering a wide spectrum of bird biology and ecology. Some have been based locally and others over the whole county or nationally, and range from research into bird migration e.g. the Bird Ringing Scheme and the Bird Observatory network, to long-term studies monitoring bird populations. These latter surveys help monitor changes in the environment and habitats generally. The surveys have ranged from single-species surveys, such as those of Woodlark, Shelduck, Nightingale and Great Crested Grebe, to multi-species schemes such as the Birds of Estuaries Enquiry (now the Wetland Bird Survey), Common Birds Census and *Bird Atlas* projects.

Many surveys provide baseline data on status at a particular point in time. These can be repeated to show any changes in the birds' status, not only for scientific purposes but to aid conservation planning and management should steps need to be taken to halt and reverse the decline of a population. The results from many surveys are documented centrally by the BTO as part of its Integrated Population Monitoring Programme, bringing together the data on bird numbers, breeding success and survival. This chapter catalogues and briefly discusses the surveys and projects undertaken in Suffolk.

NATIONAL AND LOCAL MULTI-SPECIES SURVEYS

Ringing Scheme

The Ringing Scheme was started in 1909 and taken over by the BTO in 1937. Birds are marked with uniquely-numbered metal rings, and information on movements and survival is obtained when these marked birds are subsequently recaught by ringers or found dead by members of the public. At present approximately 40,000 birds of about 135 species are ringed each year in Suffolk. Results are reported annually in *Suffolk Birds.*

Nest Record Scheme

The Nest Record Scheme, started by the BTO in 1939, is an ongoing project gathering information on breeding biology. Data such as laying date, clutch size, brood size and fledging success are collected nationally and one can compare annual and regional variations. Several observers in Suffolk contribute records to the national scheme which currently receives about 40,000 cards each year.

The Common Birds Census (CBC)

The Common Birds Census was started by the BTO in 1962, and was discontinued in 2000 (it was replaced by the BTO/JNCC/RSPB Breeding Bird Survey [BBS] which began in 1994). The CBS collected information on the numbers of breeding birds on a series of plots, each of which was ideally censused over several years. The main habitats covered were farmland and woodland although there have been several 'special' plots censused over the years covering a variety of other habitats. Every year a national index of the population level of the most common bird species was produced.

One of the first plots (89ha.) for which detailed results were published was for Reydon Grove Farm, near Southwold by Benson and Williamson (1972). In eight survey years, they found that a total of 66 species had held territories at an average density of 700 pairs per km^2. The habitat at Grove Farm had changed little up to 1997 and a survey using the same methodology was repeated by David Pearson in 1997 (Pearson 1998) and 1998. There are a number of references to the Reydon Grove Farm study in the main body of this book.

CBC Plots in Suffolk 1962-2000
(Grid reference, name of observer and start and end years are given)

Farmland Plots

TL688727	Jackson P.	1979-1980
TL754656	Thornhill W.A.	1973-1974
TM069378	Hawes L.W.	1989-2000
TM074341	Fitch M.	1975-1981
TM181348	Goyder H.P.G.	1975-2000
TM126555	Garstang J.	1987-2000
TM166713	Grindrod C.	1989
TM368504	Royale-Bantoft	1966-1973
TM370790	Meek M.	1963-1963
TM405675	Grindrod C.	1989
TM466635	Brenchley A.	1987
TM488791	Benson G.B.G.	1962-1973
TM420874	Muddeman N.	1974-2000
TM435922	Beccles BC	1970-1986
TM475916	Carter Dr N.	1993-2000

Woodland Plots

TL868547	Kerridge T.P. & Clarke G.	1981-1984
TL828604	Devlin T.	1994-2000
TL8080	Larcombe P. & Raynor A.	1995-2000
TM055440	Walter M.	1973
TM050565	Proctor R.	1973
TM268437	Thompson B.G.	1981-2000
TM349466	Miller A.R.	1972-2000

Special Habitat Plots

TL857708	May R.H.	1967-1969
TM296503	Hubbard A.C.	1979-2000
TM46	Nature Conservancy	1965-1982

Waterways Bird Survey (WBS)

This survey grew out of the Common Birds Census over concern for the well-being of wildlife along river and stream corridors. It began as a national survey in 1974, with similar aims as the CBC but for a restricted set of species which occur along waterways, and many of which were not adequately covered by the CBC.

Waterways Bird Survey Plots in Suffolk 1974-1995
(Observer, waterway, and start and end years are given)

Parker B.	Lark	1976 1982
Hayward F.P. & D.E	Gipping	1992 1993
Garstang J. & A.	Gipping	1991 1995
Elliott M. C.	Waveney	1995
Cryer R. & Macklin R.	New Cut	1990 1993

Breeding Bird Survey (BBS)

The Breeding Bird Survey was launched by the BTO in the spring of 1994 with the aim of monitoring the numbers of breeding birds in a wider range of habitats than that covered by the CBC. Results are based on visits to randomly selected 1-km squares of the National Grid and, like the CBC, using those squares censused in consecutive years an index of population levels can be obtained. The number of squares censused in Suffolk was 29 in 1994 and 36 in 1995. Although a few squares have ceased to be covered, the number of squares surveyed overall has continued to increase to 47 in 1999. Results of the 1994, 1995, 1997 and 1998 seasons appeared in *Suffolk Birds* and it is intended to publish the results annually.

Constant Effort Sites Scheme (CES)

This scheme, launched by the BTO in 1981, gathers information on numbers and productivity of breeding birds using a standard catching regime of mist-nets.

CES sites in Suffolk

(Grid reference, ringer or ringing group operating the site, location and start and end years are given)

TM204478	Brian Thompson	Playford Bog	1985	1988
TM483731	Tony Thompson	Dingle Hill	1986	1989
TM162402	Landguard RG	Bourne Park	1987	1989
TM264425	Brian Thompson	Newbourne Springs	1992	1997
TM2338	Newton & Wright	Levington	1997	2000
TL8070	Lackford RG	Lackford Pits	1992	2000
TL974784	Market Weston RG	Market Weston	1992	2000
TL884477	Lackford RG	Lineage Woods	1992	2000
TM1436	John Glazebrook	Alton Water	1999	2000

The Wetland Bird Survey (WeBS)
(including Birds of Estuaries Enquiry [BoEE] and National Wildfowl Counts [NWC])

In October 1993, WeBS was started from an amalgamation of two long-running schemes. The BoEE started in the winter of 1969/70, described by Wright (1989), and the NWC began in 1954, organised in the early years by G.B.G. Benson and R.M. Blindell. There are now monthly counts of waders and wildfowl at all major waterfowl sites, both inland and coastal, the latter coinciding with the high spring tides.

The national importance of Suffolk's estuaries was demonstrated by Wright (1989) who showed that for the five winter periods between 1984/5 and 1988/9 the average peak winter count for waders was 65,227 (maximum 70,176) and for wildfowl 34,700 (maximum 39,749). These wintering populations included an impressive list of 16 species in nationally, and nine in internationally, significant numbers.

There is increasing concern about the fate of wetlands and these counts provide vital information for their conservation. Perhaps the most important development locally has been the continuing increase in the size of the Port of Felixstowe and their encroachment onto the mudflats of the Orwell estuary.

The First National Breeding Atlas

This survey was organised by the BTO and the Irish Wildbird Conservancy (now BirdLife Ireland) and, at the time, was the largest survey to be undertaken by naturalists anywhere in the world. The fieldwork, during the breeding seasons of 1968-1972 inclusive involved over 10,000 observers, which is more than had ever taken part in organised birdwatching previously. The resulting publication (Sharrock 1976) gave maps of the distribution of all breeding species by 10-km squares of the National Grid. Overall the project was a resounding success but in Suffolk the coverage for one or two 10-km squares was rather poor due to a shortage of recorders. Most notable among these was TL97 (Ixworth) where Starling and other common species were recorded only as 'possibly breeding' in the entire 10-km square.

The New Atlas of Breeding Birds in Britain and Ireland

Twenty years on from the start of the 1968-72 Atlas, an even larger survey of breeding birds in Britain and Ireland was launched, with fieldwork occupying the breeding seasons of 1988 to 1991 inclusive. This project was also organised by the BTO, this time in collaboration with both the Irish Wildbird Conservancy and the Scottish Ornithologists' Club. The resulting publication (Gibbons *et al.* 1993) was a landmark in bird book publishing. Overall coverage nationally was comparable between the two atlas projects although in Suffolk it had improved partly as a result of the Suffolk Breeding Bird Survey being undertaken at the same time (see below).

The Winter Atlas

The second atlas project undertaken by the BTO in collaboration with the IWC was *The Atlas of Wintering Birds in Britain and Ireland*, with fieldwork undertaken during the winters of 1981/2 to 1983/4. Counts of birds were made in each 10-km square and the resulting maps (Lack 1986) showed for the first time where many birds were located through the winter period. Previously only the winter distributions of waterfowl and waders were well-known and even for some of these the Atlas showed much new information. The maps of many species, especially some of the waterfowl, show the importance of Suffolk compared with the rest of Britain and Ireland, for example, for Bean and Brent Goose, Avocet, and Black-tailed Godwit.

Ornithological Sites Register

Following the completion and resounding success of the first breeding season atlas, the next large-scale national project has often been thought of as the ornithological 'Domesday Book'. Fieldwork for the survey was carried out over the three years 1974-1976, but information pertaining to the Atlas years (1968-72) was included in some cases.

The project aimed to document the ornithological importance of individual sites, for subsequent use by the various conservation agencies, planners and others. It also allowed for a detailed review of the status of various habitats from an ornithological point of view, which formed the subject of a book by Fuller (1982).

Review of Site Changes

In the ten years after the compilation of the Ornithological Sites Register, it was clear that some major changes had occurred. The main aim of this survey (fieldwork 1985-1986) was to record these changes, although the whole was done on a sample of previously registered sites.

In Suffolk it was found, for example, that changes to Blythburgh, Walberswick, Dunwich, Minsmere, Havergate and Cavenham were for the better, probably entirely due to these areas all being well-managed for conservation, although Red-backed Shrikes had been lost from one of them. Breckland sites had suffered through heathland loss (two-thirds of Eriswell Heath had gone, for example), coniferous plantations and rabbit control, which, in turn, had had an adverse effect on the breeding populations of Stone Curlew and Wheatear. At Livermere the heronry had been wiped out by gamekeepers during the 1970s. Despite all Suffolk estuaries being extremely important wetland sites, the changes here were markedly different to elsewhere. Floodplain grazing marshes were still being drained and reverted to arable, there was an intensification of recreational pursuits and loss of intertidal areas due to dockland development and new marinas. Finally a new site was added to the register, Lackford Pits, a wetland of importance especially during the winter months.

Operation Seafarer

The seabird colonies of Britain and Ireland are of outstanding international importance, although very few species breed in any numbers along the Suffolk coast. The national results, from fieldwork done in 1969-1970, were published as a book (Cramp *et al.* 1974). In Suffolk the following breeding populations were found, with the percentage of the national total in each case:-

Species	Suffolk (pairs)	Percentage of national total
Black-headed Gull	3,330	4.5%
Lesser Black-backed Gull	150	0.3%
Herring Gull	151	<0.1%
Kittiwake	30	<0.1%
Sandwich Tern	160	1.3%
Common Tern	310	2.1%
Little Tern	70	3.9%

Seabird Colony Register

Carried out from 1985-1987, this amounted to a repeat of the 1969-70 survey (see above) although the methods were slightly different. The results were published as a book (Lloyd *et al.* 1991) and the Suffolk results were as follows:

Species	Colonies	Suffolk (pairs)	Britain & Ireland
Fulmar	2	11	
Black-headed Gull	11	2,574	3.1%
Common Gull	1	23	0.2%
Lesser Black-backed Gull	1	5,043	5.7%
Herring Gull	1	3,390	1.8%
Kittiwake	1	90	
Sandwich Tern	1	200	1.1%
Common Tern	4	122	0.8%
Little Tern	12	328	11.7%

It is clear that there have been some substantial changes. Most notable among these are the arrival of the large gull colony on Orfordness and the considerable increase, both in terms of numbers and the proportion of the national total, of the Little Tern. Clearly the beaches of Suffolk are being well-maintained for this bird.

European Atlas of Breeding Birds

This survey was carried out mainly by the BTO regional representatives in the county. They thoroughly searched for records for 1985-1987 inclusive to compile breeding species lists for the three squares in Suffolk: TL (NE), TM (NW) and TM (NE). In 1988 fieldworkers were asked to try to fill some of the gaps and to check their own records for the whole fieldwork period. The results, showing breeding distribution maps on a European scale of 50-km squares were published in a book (Hagemeier & Blair 1997).

Suffolk River Valley ESA Winter Bird Survey

The designation of the Suffolk river valleys as an 'Environmentally Sensitive Area' by the Ministry of Agriculture, Fisheries and Food in 1988 was recognition of the aesthetic and wildlife value of this landscape. In response to this initiative the Nature Conservancy Council, in cooperation with the Suffolk Wildlife Trust's Estuaries Project, undertook a survey principally to establish the relative importance of selected areas of coastal grasslands for wintering birds. Grasslands totalling 1,759ha. and involving 21 sites were surveyed in 1989-1990.

In order to compare the relative ornithological importance of the 21 sites, a scoring system was devised taking into account species' rarity as well as diversity. Minsmere Levels scored the highest, followed by Kessingland Levels and Southwold Town Marsh where Gadwall was present in nationally important numbers. See Holtzer (1991) for a full assessment of the results.

Suffolk River Valleys and Coast Breeding Waders and Wildfowl Survey 1997

This survey was jointly funded by English Nature, The Environment Agency, RSPB and Suffolk Wildlife Trust. The survey area consisted of the Suffolk River valleys ESA, adjoining habitats, plus the Stour Estuary and the upper Orwell. Over 1% of the estimated national breeding population of the following species was recorded: Mute Swan (1.4%), Shelduck (2.1%), Gadwall (9.0%), Shoveler (1.9%), Tufted Duck (1.2%), Oystercatcher (1.2%), Avocet (1.2%), Ringed Plover (1.1%) and Redshank (2%). See Babbs (1998) for a full assessment of the results.

SURVEYS OF INDIVIDUAL SPECIES OR SMALL GROUPS OF SPECIES

Great Crested Grebe

This species was first surveyed in 1931 (Harrison & Hollom 1932) and a second national census was undertaken in 1965 (Prestt & Mills 1966) following a report of high levels of organochlorine insecticide residues in Great Crested Grebes (Moore & Walker 1964). This was followed by a further national census in 1975. Nationally the population was found to have risen by about 55% from 1965 to 1975 and also that the species was spreading into marginal habitats, such as lowland rivers (Hughes *et al.* 1979).

The county's estimated total population was 38 in 1965, on six of the eight waters visited, compared with 45, on 13 of 17 waters visited in 1975.

Grey Heron

The Heronries Census has the distinction of being the longest-running single-species survey of any European bird, the survey having started in 1928. Every year nests in a sample of heronries are counted for monitoring purposes (with results published in SBRs), and in addition full national censuses have been carried out in 1928, 1954, 1964 and 1985. Finally, the SNS and SOG conducted a survey of all known Suffolk heronries in 1977.

The aim of the annual sample census is to count occupied nests at as many sites as possible each year. The national censuses also asked for information on nest-sites.

The annual monitoring has shown that the Grey Heron is subject to short term fluctuations in response to severe winters and Suffolk ornithologists were able to show the effects of the October 1987 'Great Storm' on the county's heronries (Wright 1990). Many traditional nesting sites were completely destroyed in this storm and it resulted in 77 out of 126 nests having to be rebuilt in new trees for the 1988 breeding season.

Cormorant

A national survey of wintering Cormorants was carried out between September 1985 and April 1986 involving monthly counts at all inland and coastal sites. In addition, three counts were made at all known roosts on pre-selected dates throughout the winter period.

The national total counted at coastal and inland sites during the midwinter period (November to February) was between 12,710 and 15,279 birds (Porter 1987). In Suffolk, the numbers were found to vary between 300 and 500 birds and of these around 80% were concentrated on the estuaries. Overnight roosts were located at Melton, at Sizewell and on the River Stour, holding a combined total of 300 birds (Waters 1987).

Mute Swan

National surveys were carried out in 1955-1956, 1961, 1978, 1983 and 1990. Coverage in Suffolk in 1955-1956 was patchy especially in the north of the county (*Suffolk Birds* for 1955 reported 66 pairs and 466 non-breeding birds); in 1961 the census was not carried out in the county; in 1978 the county was not properly surveyed, and in 1983 only 56% coverage was achieved (Ogilvie 1986).

In 1977, the SOG organized a census of the species breeding in Suffolk and achieved 98% coverage. The breeding population was found to be in the region of 125 pairs (Marsh 1978) and the 1990 census with a similar coverage revealed 131 breeding pairs (Wright 1991), indicating that the breeding population was stable despite changes in the numbers locally (see Wright 1991).

Canada Goose

During the spring of 1972 the SNS organized a survey of breeding and non-breeding birds at all known localities. It was thought that the entire county was effectively covered, although a few isolated pairs may have been overlooked. The survey found a total of 105 breeding pairs and 229 non-breeding birds with the highest breeding concentration at Euston Lake and the largest gathering of non-breeding birds at Sotterley Hall (Payn 1973).

Naturalised Goose Survey 2000

The aims of this survey were to assess the population size and distribution of naturalised geese and to assess productivity in these populations. Two complimentary survey methods were adopted: (1) Counts were made of birds in randomly selected tetrads during visits in mid-April to mid-May and again in mid-June to mid-July, (2) a site-based approach surveyed all known moult sites in late June/early July.

Shelduck

Since the 1960s there has been a gradual increase in numbers (National Waterfowl Counts index), but the breeding numbers were unknown. The 1992 national breeding census, organized by the WWT, aimed to obtain estimates of the breeding and non-breeding populations and information on breeding success.

The manpower input to the survey and the coverage attained were excellent. The results of the spring counts gave a total of 3,781 birds and indicated that there were 1,129 pairs and 140 territorial males in Suffolk. The summer counts revealed 1,277 adults and 1,284 juveniles (Wright 1994).

Tufted Duck

Since the formation of the SOG in 1973, members consistently recorded increases in the breeding population of the Tufted Duck in Suffolk. To determine the breeding population and provide a baseline for any future surveys, the SOG organized a county-wide census in 1980. Observers were asked to visit their chosen or allocated area at least once in July and again in August. The information required for each visit included the exact locality of the site, type of habitat, number of broods and the size of each brood. The results show that a total of 257 pairs and 1,129 ducklings were counted with the Lark river valley supporting most birds (Murphy & Piotrowski 1981).

Birds of Prey in Suffolk

The SOG organized this ambitious project to record the winter and summer distributions of both nocturnal and diurnal birds of prey. Information on location of observations, breeding, unusual numbers, migration and behavior was required. For Kestrel, the commonest raptor, it was suggested that a summary of sightings would be sufficient. The survey produced a huge volume of records which involved 20 species of birds of prey, including the owls. All records submitted appear in a special publication written by Paine (1980).

Although still being persecuted, birds of prey are now making a comeback. For this reason and because this group of birds is well-loved by birders, the SOG was stimulated to organize and fund a new survey from 1995-1998. The main aim was to search comprehensively for breeding raptors and owls over a three-year period, in order to obtain a measure of their abundance and distribution in Suffolk. The methodology was kept simple and straightforward with no limitations or restrictions on the amount of time spent in the field. The fieldwork was organized, wherever possible, through 10-km square coordinators. All suitable breeding habitat in each 10-km square were to be surveyed both in the daytime and at night (preferably in the two hours following sunset) to establish the presence of territories and to confirm breeding. The following information was collected: six-figure grid reference, tetrad letter, nearest place name, S (to indicate 'seen' in suitable breeding habitat), B (to indicate breeding); date and any remarks. In addition fieldworkers were asked to indicate observations/territories on maps that were provided.

Apart from being very successful, the survey provided a sound base-line database against which repeat surveys can be measured. In all, 722 tetrads were visited which included 509 surveyed tetrads. See Wright (2000) for a full assessment of the results, trends and population estimates.

Lapwing

There have been four national surveys of breeding Lapwings. The 1937 and 1960-1961 surveys were mainly to provide information on habitat use. For the latter in Suffolk, the Rev. P. H. T. Hartley surveyed approximately 365 acres (about 145ha.) of agricultural land at Badingham over a seven-year period up to 1961 and he reported no changes, but there were few or no breeding birds in the area.

The survey of 1987 was also designed to estimate numbers. Fieldwork was done in April and, in Suffolk, involved counting birds in 45 tetrads (one in each 10-km square of the National Grid). The 28 fieldworkers achieved 100% coverage with 75 pairs observed. This equates to just over 1,800 pairs of Lapwings in the county, and there was a strong preference, as elsewhere, for crops such as spring-sown cereals, tilled land and grazed grassland (Wright 1988). A repeat of this survey in 1998 set out to re-survey all the squares initially selected in 1987. The results were alarming, in just 12 years the estimate of breeding numbers showed a decline of 53% (Wright 2000).

Ringed Plover

Fieldwork for the first national census was carried out between May and July 1973 with some additional data collected in 1974. The results revealed a total of 95 breeding pairs around the Suffolk coast and none inland (cf. over 5,700 pairs in Britain) (Prater 1976). The Norfolk total of 465 pairs and Essex with 211 showed that East Anglia was a major stronghold for the species.

In 1979, the SOG surveyed all relevant habitat (coastal, heathland and gravel pits) to reassess the breeding population. A total of 223 pairs was found breeding including 14 pairs located away from the coast (Piotrowski 1980). Although the results indicate a massive increase on the 1974 results, Piotrowski (1980) suggested that the apparent expansion of the Ringed Plovers population may have been due to better coverage by observers, especially at Orfordness and the estuaries.

In 1984 a repeat national survey showed a marked increase in the breeding population when compared to the 1973 figures, but a decline of 20% when compared to the more recent SOG survey of 1979. Waters (1985) found that the decline at Suffolk's three largest colonies (Orfordness, Walberswick and Benacre) was about 30% and that this accounted for almost all of the decline in the county total. He went on to say that these changes strongly suggested the detrimental effect of increased public pressure on our beaches.

BTO Nightjar Survey 1981

The survey showed that the Breckland area of Suffolk was one of the most important breeding areas for this species in Britain. The situation on the coast was one of decline, thought to be due to habitat destruction. The survey found 89 and 34 churring males in Breckland and the coastal belt respectively (Brown 1982).

From 1981 this species has been monitored by regular surveys organised by the Forestry Commission, SWT and the SOG.

Waders Breeding on Wet Lowland Grasslands

The BTO, in cooperation with the RSPB and the NCC, organised a survey over England and Wales to assess the extent of the remaining damp grasslands and their importance for breeding waders. Five species were surveyed: Lapwing, Snipe, Curlew, Redshank and Oystercatcher. The results demonstrated the very low numbers of waders which breed on lowland grasslands in England and Wales. In Suffolk, 15 lowland grassland sites were surveyed and produced totals of 60 pairs of Lapwing, 11 drumming Snipe and 43 pairs of Redshank. No Curlew or Oystercatcher were found on the sites although it must be noted that it was only wet grassland which was surveyed.

The Breeding Wader Monitoring Scheme was initiated in 1984 by the BTO and the Wader Study Group following on from the survey of 1982 to provide annual information on the trends in the breeding populations of waders.

A repeat on a random sample of about 300 sites was undertaken in 1989. National results indicated that the breeding population of Lapwings had declined by 30% since 1982 and that of Snipe by 10%, while those of Redshank and Curlew had remained more or less stable and that of Oystercatcher had gone up by 60%.

Winter Shorebird Count

The Winter Shorebird Count was undertaken in the winter of 1984-85. The aims were to assess the population size of waders wintering on all non-estuarine coasts around Britain and Northern Ireland and to identify those stretches of open coast which are of special conservation value for wintering shorebirds.

Nationally, almost 300,000 waders of 19 species were recorded (Moser & Summers 1987). These results were then integrated with the counts from estuaries in a re-appraisal of the size of the populations of waders wintering in Britain (Moser 1987). In Suffolk, the survey was carried out on 16th December 1984 in a cold, force 4-5 easterly wind with continual rain throughout the day. Almost 85km of coastline was walked and 207ha. of shoreline between high and low water was surveyed. The Lowestoft shoreline supported the most birds which numbered 27 Purple Sandpipers, 10 Turnstones and 12 Sanderlings (Wright 1986). This survey was repeated over the 1997/8 winter period.

Wintering Gulls

Roosts of wintering gulls have been censused in January of 1953, 1963, 1973, 1983 and 1993. Only inland sites in England and Wales were counted during the first three censuses so comparisons over five decades are only possible for these regions. Figures show that over the last 40 years there has been an almost regular increase of wintering gulls which reached almost 1.5 million in January 1993 (Waters 1994). In Suffolk during the 1993 census a total of 18 inland, estuary or coastal sites was surveyed. When comparing the 1983 results with the 1993 figures (37,160 and 73,124 respectively) it would appear that the wintering population has doubled in the space of a decade (Bimpson 1994).

Cuckoo

'Cuckoo Day' was planned for Sunday, 27th May 1973. Observations of either heard or seen birds were requested and, through the media, the survey was extended to involve as many people as possible. The response was tremendous with over 500 letters, from most parts of the county, being received. Many observers felt that 1973 was a better than average year for the species (Jeanes 1974). Due to the fact that the survey was an unqualified success, it was repeated again on Saturday, 27th May 1978, employing exactly the same methods as before. Although the response was very good a number of fieldworkers stated that they had heard the Cuckoo either before or after the survey date and that the birds were quiet on the survey day itself! The majority of observers felt that the weather was responsible for this and also that the Cuckoo was less common that year than in 1977 (Paine 1978).

Kingfisher

The Kingfisher was surveyed in Suffolk in 1974. Kingfishers were found at 84 sites during the winter and 52 sites in the summer, with 11 definite and 15 probable breeding sites located (Cage 1975).

Woodlark

The information available, for the period 1968 to 1983, on the status, distribution and movements of the British Woodlark population was summarised by Sitters (1986). In coastal Suffolk in 1972 there were 12 pairs (SBR). In 1986 the BTO set out to find out how many Woodlarks breed in Britain and their habitat requirements. The results indicated that for coastal Suffolk there were 25 pairs (in 1984 John Grant had estimated the coastal Suffolk population to be at around 25 pairs also) and in Breckland Suffolk there were 28 pairs. Also, important habitat data were gathered for analysis (Waters 1987). The second national survey in 1987 revealed that Suffolk held between 403 and 457 breeding pairs, more than any other county and around 30% of the total UK population (Wotton 1998).

A RSPB and Forest Enterprise research project has monitored the Breckland population for 23 consecutive years 1973 to 1996. In the latter year a record total of 311 (the Suffolk part held 144) singing males and/or pairs were recorded (Hoblyn 1997). The Sandlings of coastal Suffolk, through cooperation between the RSPB, SWT and Forestry Commission have been surveyed annually for 7 years 1990-96, and in 1996 there was also a record total of 192 pairs/territories (Wright 1996). It appears that within the forest areas of Tunstall and Rendlesham that breeding numbers may have levelled off, as predicted by Bowden & Hoblyn (1990). Therefore overall between 1986 and 1993, the Breckland population of Woodlarks increased by 267% and the Suffolk coastal one by 372-424%. In both areas, there was a particularly large population increase between 1991 and 1992 (Sitters *et al.* 1995).

Black Redstart

In a BTO national survey of 1977, a total of 20 territories was found in Suffolk out of a national figure of 104 territories holding males in 16 counties. All the Suffolk birds (the largest total in any county) were in coastal sites (Morgan & Glue 1981).

The breeding population at Felixstowe in 1985 was substantially higher than had previously been recorded, and this triggered the instigation of an even more detailed survey the following year to see if these birds were breeding in areas not usually visited by birdwatchers and, if so, in what numbers. All major towns and industrial areas in the county were searched and details on habitat, breeding activity and age of the males were recorded. The survey found 39 territories with at least 22 pairs breeding (Beecroft 1987).

Nightingale

The BTO conducted a national survey in 1976, following the success of earlier surveys in Kent. In Suffolk, 155 singing birds were reported (Hudson 1976) out of an estimated national population of around 4,000, although only 3,230 were counted.

Assessment of records: records prior to 1958 were published at the discretion of authors and editors. Since that time they have come under the scrutiny of the Suffolk Ornithological Records Committee (SORC) and those designated 'nationally rare' have been assessed by the British Birds Rarities Committee (BBRC). The decisions of the BBRC have been accepted by SORC with few exceptions. The committee has also provided a judgement on the status of each species. Discussion on the status of national rarities is largely based on the comprehensive reports of the BBRC which are published annually in *British Birds.* The figure given for the number of occurrences is based on the most recent entry in the report at the time of going to print. Frequency of occurrences and the species' origins are analysed with reference to Dymond *et al.* (1989).

Species account layout: the first line under the species heading is a brief statement on status using the following definitions:

Abundant: occurs in large numbers in suitable habitat and season

Common: occurs regularly or is widely distributed in suitable habitat

Fairly common: occurs in small numbers in suitable habitat and season

Locally common: occurs in small numbers but restricted to specific habitats

Uncommon: occurs annually in small numbers

Scarce: one or two records each year or restricted to specific habitats

Rare: occurs less than annually

Very rare: 6-25 records in past 30 years

Accidental: less than six records in past 30 years

This is followed by a summary of the species' abundance and the types of habitat most often favoured. For residents and summer visitors, there is a paragraph detailing abundance and distribution, which, in most instances, is complemented by a map showing the breeding range. The habits of species, which occur primarily as winter visitors or passage migrants, are described. This is followed by passage numbers and/or movements, together with any returns of ringed or marked birds. Birds found in unusual circumstances are described last. All records of rarities are listed if the species has occurred 15 times or less.

Ringing definitions: the term 're-trap' is a bird captured and released by the original ringer or his associates, at or near (within 5km) the locality where it was originally ringed or was last 'controlled'. A 'control' is a ringed bird caught again (whether by the original or an other ringer) at a point more than 5km from the locality where it was first ringed. A 'recovery' is a bird found dead or found at another locality and not subsequently released, or caught accidentally (e.g. in fruit netting) or intentionally by non-ringers.

Distribution Maps: The distribution maps have been produced by the SBRC using 'DMAP' software written by Dr Alan Morton (Department of Pure and Applied Biology, Imperial College, Silwood Park, Ascot, Berks. SL5 7PY). The unit of measure is the tetrad, a 2km x 2km square.

The symbols used are: ● = breeding, ● = seen and ■ = almost certainly breeding.

The base data were abstracted from the *'Provisional Atlas of Breeding Birds of Suffolk'* compiled by Martin Sanford of the SBRC. Over 150 people took part in *The Suffolk Breeding Birds Survey 1987-1992* from where the source data were obtained. Casual breeding records for the period 1992-1995 have been added to the maps and records up to and including 1997 have been added to selected species. No historical records have been plotted..

The maps show the general distribution of most of Suffolk's commoner breeding species, but do not show their status or density, nor any increases or declines over the recording period.

For some of the common species (e.g. Wren, Robin, Blackbird, House Sparrow, etc.), the records of birds seen within the tetrad during the breeding season have been plotted as almost certainly breeding.

Red-throated Diver *Gavia stellata*

A common winter visitor and passage migrant

Red-throated Diver (*Stuart Ling*)

The shallow, inshore waters of Sole Bay, north to Benacre, provide the Red-throated Diver with food-rich wintering grounds. Small flocks are regularly reported between October and March but, on occasion, huge congregations occur and the wintering population was estimated to be around 1,500-3,000 during the 1990s. Ones and twos in August and September are now quite regular and numbers increase in October, with the main arrival taking place in late November and December.

The diver flocks are best viewed on calm seas and are often impossible to locate in choppy conditions. It is likely that birds disperse to calmer waters elsewhere when stormy weather prevails, although regular high counts suggest that they are resident off Suffolk throughout most of the winter. The species is common in both passage periods.

The importance of the herring and sprat shoals to this species was recognised by Ticehurst, who considered that the diver's return towards the end of September was linked closely to the migration of fish. Despite a marked decline in the herring fishery, flock sizes still appear to be regulated by sprat shoals.

The habit of feeding in loosely packed groups, scattered over a large area of sea, makes assessing numbers difficult, as birds constantly dive and drift with the tide. The best estimates have been obtained when flocks suddenly take flight, perhaps ahead of a passing ship or when moving to new feeding areas.

There were few reports of large gatherings up until 1960, and a flock of about 300 off Dunwich in December of that year was considered exceptional. However, since the late 1970s, three-figure totals have become commonplace and flocks of 1,500-2,000 were present during eight consecutive winters from 1993/4 to 2000/1. An unprecedented 2,724 lifted from the sea off Covehithe on 23rd January 1994, giving some indication of the wintering population. The Sole Bay concentrations are believed to be the largest ever recorded in the Western Palearctic.

Significant gatherings normally remain until early March and a light spring passage continues until May. Ticehurst referred to an offshore passage of 40 flying north in groups of 3-4 on 2nd May 1892, followed by 20 three days later. Oversummering has yet to be proved, although there have been 18 single-day records for June or July at coastal localities up to the end of 2002.

Birds seek refuge in harbours, estuaries and freshwater localities near the coast, particularly during periods of harsh weather. Most records refer to singles although up to six were present together on gravel pits near Ipswich on 11th-26th March 1956. Occurrences well inland are rare and normally involve dead or moribund individuals, often showing traces of oil.

One found long dead at Havergate Island in 1990 had been ringed as a pullus in Renko, Finland, in July 1987. It is likely that the origins of East Anglia's wintering population lie both to the east and west of the Norwegian Sea as a bird ringed in Greenland was found dead in Essex in 1959 (Cox 1984).

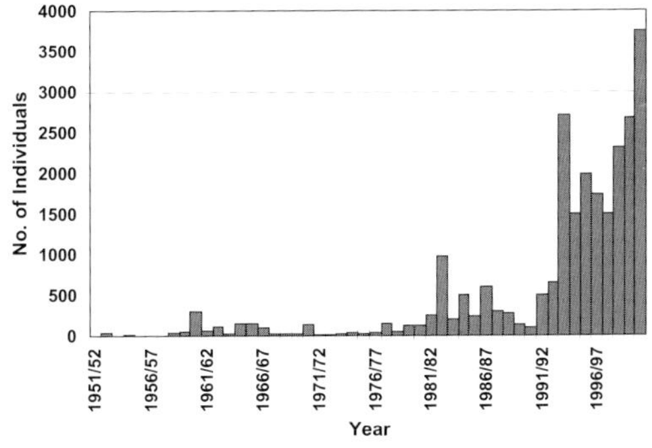

The largest single-day winter counts of the Red-throated Diver per annum (1951/52-2000/2001)

Black-throated Diver *Gavia arctica*

An uncommon winter visitor and passage migrant

Small numbers of Black-throated Divers are occasionally noted amongst the flocks of wintering Red-throated Divers in Sole Bay. They are less gregarious than Red-throated Divers and are usually seen as ones and twos frequenting coastal and estuarine waters. The species is more obvious when on enclosed waters such as Lowestoft Harbour, Oulton Broad, Benacre Pits, Ipswich Docks and Alton Water, and individuals may linger at such sites for several weeks. The records for the 1990s suggest an average wintering population in the region of 5-15.

Ticehurst stated that "hardly a severe spell of weather passes, but that one or more turn up in our tidal waters" and there has been little change over the 20th century. However, the upsurge in seawatching since the late 1980s has resulted in an increase in sightings, particularly during passage periods.

The county's largest gatherings of six and seven were recorded in Sole Bay on 6th April 1964 and 10th December 1982 respectively. The larger estuaries attract one or two each year and there are regular sightings on Alton Water, where groups of three were recorded on 7th-9th January 1984 and on 25th-31st December 1993. The deeper waters towards the dam end of the reservoir are normally favoured, with the divers oblivious to the sail-boarders who also use that area.

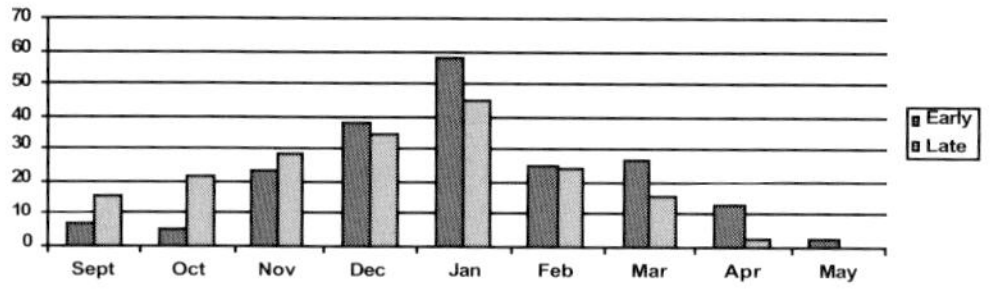

Above: The seasonal occurrences of Black-throated Diver 1947-1998 by half month

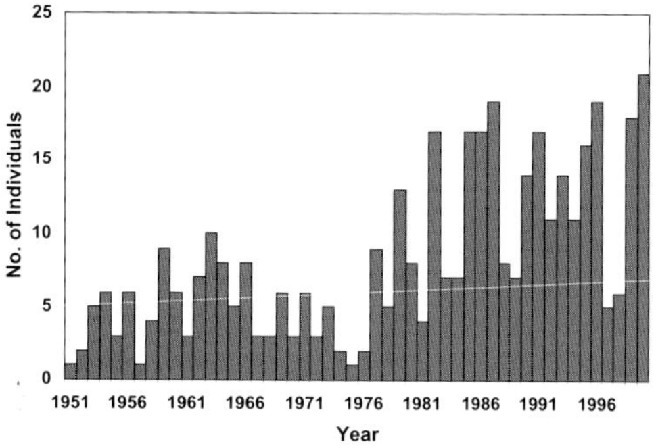

Right: The annual totals of the Black-throated Diver from 1951-2000

The earliest autumn record involved an adult in full summer plumage at Covehithe on 1st September 1990 that stayed in the area for several weeks. Passage continues through to the end of September, followed by an obvious lull in occurrences before the arrival of wintering birds in November. New arrivals increase at the onset of harsh-weather periods, with a significant proportion occurring in January.

Most birds leave in February and there is a distinct period of passage in early March. Birds occasionally linger into April and there have been six records for May. A pair in full breeding plumage was on the Stour on 7th May 1926, and the latest spring record involved one that frequented Minsmere from 5th April to 25th May 1956. There are no reports for the summer months of June, July and August.

The eight records of single birds noted at inland localities are: Stowmarket in February 1855, the Little Ouse in January 1863, "caught" during winter at Syleham on the River Waveney in 1947, Barnham on 14th November 1954, West Stow on 18th-30th November 1973, Lackford from 26th November to 26th December 1987, Bramford from 1st March to 6th May 1991 and Lackford on 8th January 1995.

Great Northern Diver *Gavia immer*

An uncommon winter visitor and passage migrant

Although noted almost annually at coastal and estuarine localities (only five blank years since 1950), this species is the rarest of the three regularly occurring divers. Preferring sheltered bays and enclosed waters, such as those at Ipswich Wet Dock and Alton Water, this diver is most often noted in ones and twos. Records of three on the sea with Red-throated Divers off Minsmere on 21st November 1964 and four in Ipswich Docks on 13th November 1977 are the highest counts.

The frequency of sightings of birds moving offshore in late October and early November suggests a light passage in this period, although the majority of winter visitors arrive in late December and early January. The earliest autumn record refers to a sighting off Felixstowe Ferry on 9th September 1984.

Unusually, one at Benacre on 9th November 1977 had retained its summer dress.

Most depart by the beginning of March and there are few April records. However, the species has been reported in May on seven occasions, with half of these records referring to birds moving off Felixstowe. The latest for the spring involved an overwintering bird that lingered at Alton Water until at least 23rd May 1995. It was a first-year bird that had not attained full breeding plumage.

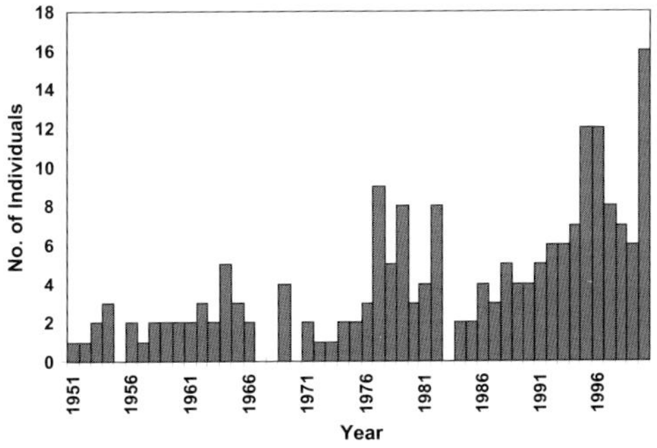

The annual totals of the Great Northern Diver from 1951-2000

There are only eight inland records: "obtained" at Culford, sometime prior to 1884, one "shot... just after floods" at Brandon in February 1897, "picked up by otter-hounds" at Long Melford in March 1937, "found alive in a beet field" at Ousden in November 1952 and released at Stoke-by-Nayland, in Cut-off Channel at Eriswell on 1st-5th April 1965, "injured under pylons – subsequently died" at Tunstall on 21st November 1973, at Beccles/Worlingham, flying SSE on 1st February 1977 and on the River Waveney, at St Olaves on 3rd February 1979.

White-billed Diver (Yellow-billed Diver) *Gavia adamsii*

Accidental: three records

1852	Pakefield: shot "early spring"
1978	Felixstowe: offshore, 5th January
1994	Southwold: offshore, ad. in f.s.p. flying south 6th November

The Pakefield specimen, which has been well-documented by both Ticehurst and Payn, was initially held at Keswick Hall, Norfolk, but is now displayed in the Norwich Castle Museum. The 1978 record is remarkable in that it was observed from a North Sea ferry and the 1994 individual was a real prize for local seawatchers. Burn and Mather (1974) examined all British records and some previously claimed for Suffolk were not accepted on the grounds that they were insufficiently substantiated. This diver had been reported in Britain and Ireland on 224 occasions up to the end of 2000 (BBRC), most frequently from Britain's east coast and the Scottish islands.

Little Grebe *Tachybaptus ruficollis*

A locally common resident, passage migrant and winter visitor

Although widely distributed in western and southern Suffolk and all along the coast, the breeding population of the Little Grebe is largely restricted to unpolluted freshwater lakes, reservoirs, larger ponds, dykes and rivers. A few attempt to overwinter at their nesting sites but, generally, birds will move to estuaries, harbours, coastal lakes and lagoons, especially during hard weather periods. Continental birds probably supplement numbers in winter.

There has never been a full, county-wide, breeding census and clues to population levels have been gleaned during studies of other species or groups that frequent aquatic environments, e.g. Tufted Duck and dragonflies. SBRs indicated a peak of 59 pairs at 33 sites in 1990, but birds nesting in relatively unchecked river systems and around more remote lakes and ponds are frequently overlooked and, therefore, 80-100 pairs is a more realistic figure. For example, the grebe was found in 41 10-km squares during fieldwork for the *68-72 Atlas*, whereas Payn suggested a breeding population of 4-18 pairs from 1974-1977. The *New Atlas* indicated little change in distribution.

Ticehurst speculated as to why no more than two pairs bred on Easton Broad. He listed the saline water and harassment by "tame swans" as possible reasons as well as the presence of otters, which he stated were "abundant and no doubt make havoc with the waterfowl".

Wintering birds can be found at both inland and coastal sites, but are very rare on the open sea.

Freezing conditions will force all birds to tidal waters, with the upper reaches of river estuaries becoming favoured refuges. Suffolk's largest reported assembly is 95 on the Deben at Waldringfield in December 1975, and the estuary has hosted the county's highest concentrations since 1987. Based on peak co-ordinated (WeBS) counts, the Deben is one of Britain's ten most important estuaries for the species (Pollitt *et al.* 2000). It is likely that the wintering population has shifted from the Orwell to the Deben since the mid-1970s, as there has been a marked decrease at the former estuary that has corresponded well with the increase on the latter. Inland concentrations are rare with "rafts" of 50 being noted on only two occasions: on the River Lark at Icklingham during the winter of 1954 and on the River Stour at Bures, sometime prior to 1962 (Payn 1978). Most of the latter were likely to have been the offspring of local breeders, which gives some indication of the breeding population at that time.

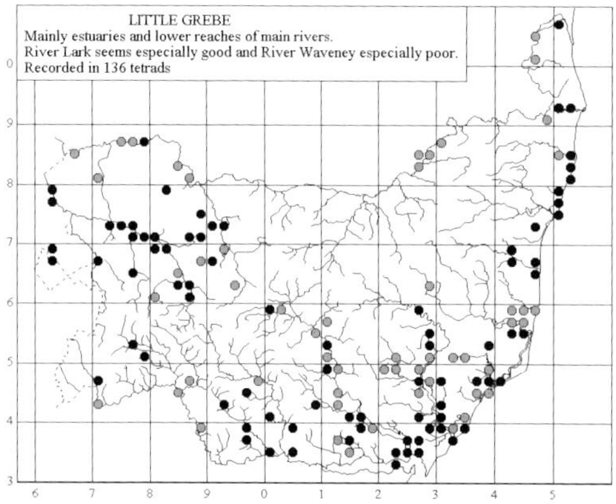

LITTLE GREBE
Mainly estuaries and lower reaches of main rivers.
River Lark seems especially good and River Waveney especially poor.
Recorded in 136 tetrads

Payn considered that the Little Grebe was "at times a very pronounced migrant", apparently based on Ticehurst's records of a bird striking a lighthouse at night and another taken on board a boat some 40miles (c.60km) off Lowestoft in October. Immigration from the continent has been proved, with individuals ringed in Latvia and Denmark being found in south-eastern counties and British-ringed birds recovered in Germany, Holland and France (Mead & Clark 1993). However, the regularity of such migration and the numbers involved is unclear. Little Grebes found in unusual circumstances include one removed whole from the belly of a pike at Thornham, another coming to feed with "barndoor fowls" at Fritton (Ticehurst 1932), one "accidentally" shot whilst flying into a hedge during a partridge drive at Hawkedon (Payn 1978), one found in a coal shed at Yoxford, and one rescued in Felixstowe town centre and fed on egg sandwiches prior to release at Landguard Point.

Great Crested Grebe *Podiceps cristatus*

A locally common resident, passage migrant and winter visitor

Great Crested Grebe and Black-necked Grebe
(*Adam Kennedy*)

Most lakes, broads, reservoirs, gravel pits and larger ponds host nesting pairs of Great Crested Grebes and breeding also takes place on slow-moving rivers such as the River Waveney, a locality avoided by the Little Grebe. Few species have a more protracted breeding season, with courtship and nest building often reported in late January and adults still tending chicks in November. During winter, substantial numbers are found on the river estuaries and feeding flocks are increasingly being noted at offshore localities.

In the mid-19th century, the Great Crested Grebe was brought to the verge of extinction in Britain by an insatiable demand for skins from the millinery trade. Suffolk held three pairs in 1860 out of only 45 in the whole of England (Harrison & Hollom 1932). Protection came via the Seabirds' Protection Act 1869 and the Great Crested Grebe's recovery was swift. Babington thought that it was "not uncommon" and Ticehurst considered that it occupied all available breeding habitat in the county. A national census in 1931 revealed 42 pairs at ten sites in Suffolk, a population which remained relatively stable for almost half a century, with 38 pairs at eight sites in 1960 (Payn 1978) and 33-34 at 19 in 1977. Fritton Lake was the county's most favoured site throughout this period holding 20-30 pairs.

The construction of Alton Water Reservoir in the 1970s was of enormous benefit to this species and this reservoir is currently Suffolk's principal breeding site, holding just over half of the county's total of nesting pairs (65 pairs out of a record total of 120 in 1983 and 57 pairs out of 93 in 1991). However, fledging success is limited at this site due to disturbance, fluctuating water levels and, possibly, predation. In the 1970s and 1980s there was a dramatic increase in the number of reservoirs and flooded gravel workings around the county, coinciding with the house-building boom of the same period. This provided a profusion of suitable breeding habitat that the species was quick to exploit. Data have not been received for all sites every year, but the county's breeding population currently exceeds 100 pairs.

Correlation between wintering and breeding numbers is evidenced by the recent massive increase in flock sizes on the larger river estuaries. The Orwell and the Stour both hold significant wintering populations and small groups of non-breeders remain on the estuaries throughout the summer. A count of 57 on the Stour for the whole of November 1973 was thought noteworthy, but nowadays the estuary regularly hosts four times that number, with monthly totals of 200+ occurring regularly since 1989. The highest total was 322 for November of that year. In mild winters, flocks of 100 or more remain on Alton Water and a site record of 200 was noted on 30th December 1995.

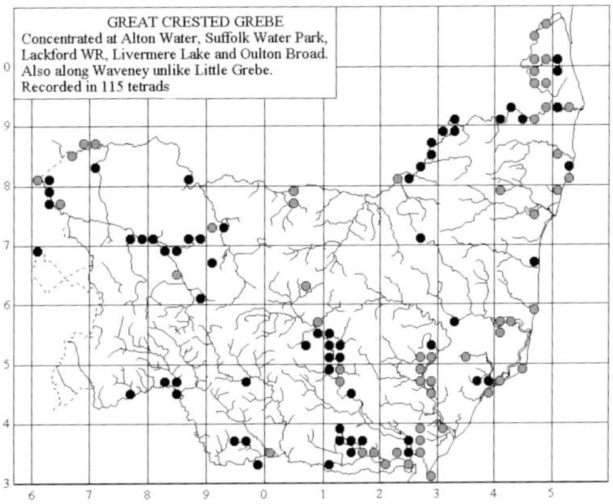
GREAT CRESTED GREBE
Concentrated at Alton Water, Suffolk Water Park, Lackford WR, Livermere Lake and Oulton Broad.
Also along Waveney unlike Little Grebe.
Recorded in 115 tetrads

Sizeable offshore gatherings are a comparatively recent phenomenon. Ticehurst made no mention of them and Payn considered two birds on the sea off Minsmere, 16th June 1956, worthy of note. However, the severe winter of 1962/3 forced many to seek refuge in marine environments as evidenced by the 23 tideline corpses found between Gorleston and Minsmere during the latter stages of that cold weatherperiod. In the 1980s, flocks of 30-100 were regularly reported on the sea in the Sole Bay area, with even higher counts between 1992 and 2001: 180 on 16th February 1992, 200 on 22nd February 1993, 475 on 23rd January 1994, 636 on 25th February 1995, 346 on 28th January, 469 on 21st February 1999, 1,439 on 20th April 2000 and 639 on 6th January 2001. It is interesting to note that most peak counts are in January and February, coinciding with the presence of sprat shoals. Red-throated Diver numbers also peak during this period. The spring gathering in April 2000 was exceptional.

A Dutch-ringed bird recovered at Oulton Broad on 16th February 1970 provides evidence of immigration from the continent but as with the Little Grebe, the frequency of immigration is unclear.

Red-necked Grebe *Podiceps grisegena*

An uncommon winter visitor and passage migrant

Small numbers of Red-necked Grebes are noted annually, principally at coastal and estuarine localities in autumn and winter, and less regularly in spring and summer. Records from the open sea are rare, although a few are reported moving offshore, particularly during autumn passage.

Ticehurst considered the species to be "an almost annual visitor" and Payn remarked that its status was unchanged. Influxes occur in severe weather and the most significant to have been recorded occurred in 1865, 1891, 1895, 1922, 1937 (Witherby *et al.* 1940) and, more recently, in 1979. The 1865 invasion, which occurred in February and March, was large with 29-30 being killed in the Great Yarmouth area alone (Babington 1884-1886). Red-necked Grebes suffered greatly during the 'arctic' winter of early 1963 when ten tideline corpses were found between Gorleston and Minsmere. The 1979 influx again occurred in February and followed a spate of cold, easterly winds produced by a series of anticyclones centred over Scandinavia. About 10% (55 birds) of the total for Britain and Ireland occurred in Suffolk (Chandler 1981), including up to seven at Benacre on 18th-25th February. Since the mid-1980s, Red-necked Grebes have been recorded more often with occurrences in double figures in most years. The upsurge in seawatching activities has produced a significant increase in offshore records.

A national increase in the late 20th century in the number of summering individuals has included Suffolk, with records from Covehithe on 17th July 1974, Alton Water from 29th May to 6th June 1977, Walberswick on 29th July 1977 and Livermere Lake on 22nd June 1996. However, the most interesting report came from Loompit Lake, Trimley St Martin, where a pair in superb breeding plumage was present from 22nd May to 7th June 1988, a year when breeding was confirmed elsewhere for the first time in Britain (Spencer 1990, Parslow-Outo & Elliott 1991). The male was seen to offer the female nesting material as part of a spectacular display ritual and, when one of the birds disappeared, there was some speculation that there was a nest. This, however, was not found and the remaining single bird was last recorded on 26th June.

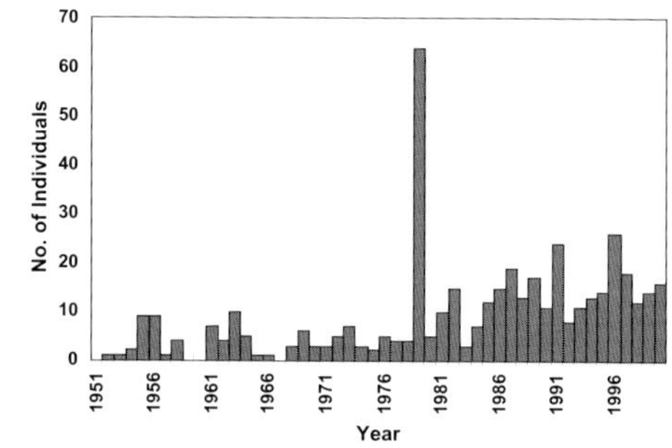

The annual totals of Red-necked Grebe from 1951-2000

There were only four reports from inland localities up to the 1979 influx: Stanningfield in 1903, Bradfield St George in 1908, Livermere Lake in 1957 and Bury St Edmunds B.F. ponds in 1976. Four more, part of the February 1979 influx, were noted at Coddenham, Culford, Hunston and Sudbury. However, since 1987, the larger, well-watched, inland gravel pits have contributed to an increase in records, with Lackford, Weybread and Bramford being the principal localities. Three together at the latter site, in October 1991, is the largest inland gathering.

Slavonian Grebe *Podiceps auritus*

An uncommon winter visitor and passage migrant

January and February are the best months to observe this predominantly winter visitor. It is recorded annually with numbers often increasing during harsh-weather periods, but is rarely noticed during offshore movements.

Slavonian Grebes are most often noted in ones and twos on the open sea and estuaries, coastal lakes and pools and, more rarely, on dykes and flooded meadows. Small groups occasionally occur amongst the mixed grebe and diver flocks in Sole Bay, with maxima of three on 26th February 1956 and 24th December 1980, four on 30th November 1985 and seven on 12th January 1961, the latter being the county's largest-ever gathering. Ticehurst reported a "fair sized flock" on the Deben during the winter of 1920/1, but the record is not quantified. Four Slavonian Grebes at Alton Water on 16th-26th March 1983 is the largest group so far recorded at a freshwater locality.

This species was involved in the 1979 grebe influx (although to a lesser extent than Red-necked Grebe), when about 25 were recorded at 11 coastal and two inland sites.

Slavonian Grebes nest at upland sites, unlike Red-necked and Black-necked Grebes which both frequent lowland lakes. Therefore, there is no nesting potential in Suffolk and individuals in full summer plumage clearly relate to late migrants. The presence of a Slavonian Grebe on Livermere Lake on 1st June 1969, constitutes the county's latest spring record.

Autumn passage birds are frequently reported, but they rarely occur before October. Since 1950, there have been only two records for August, namely singles at Benacre on 14th August 1968 and Bury St Edmunds B. F. ponds on 24th August 1971, and three for September. Wintering birds often linger into March and April, but individuals on spring passage are scarce. During the period 1950-1999, there were only 12 new arrivals in April and one in May.

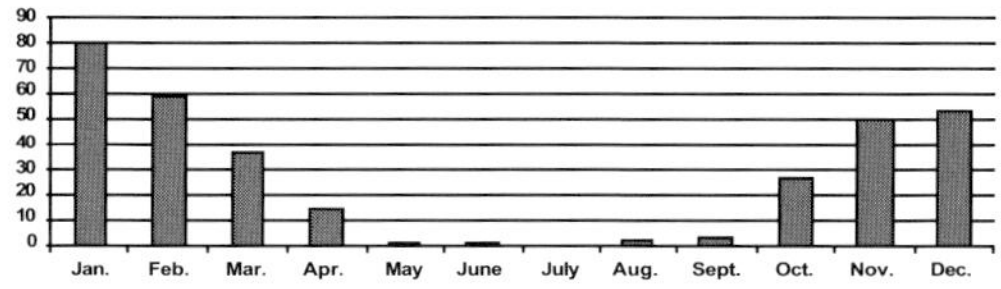

Above: The seasonal occurrence of the Slavonian Grebe from 1951-2000

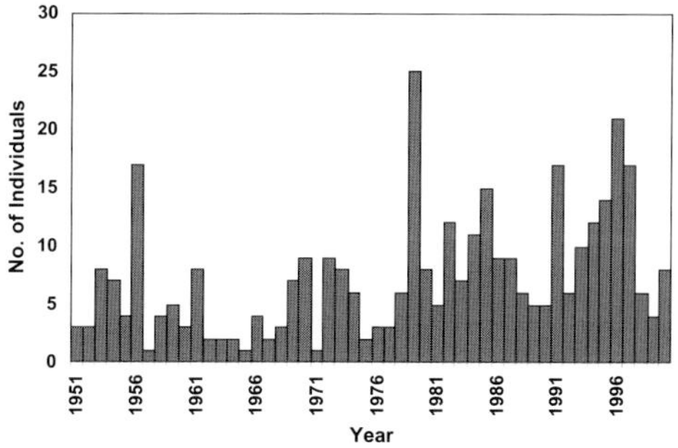

Right: The annual totals of the Slavonian Grebe from 1951-2000

Babington referred to Slavonian Grebes being shot at Bosmere (no date) and others at Ampton (1864) and Livermere (1867). There then followed a gap of 102 years before the next inland occurrence, again at Livermere, but between 1969 and 1998 there have been records involving 14 individuals. The bulk of these have occurred at flooded gravel workings such as those at Lackford and Weybread.

Black-necked Grebe — *Podiceps nigricollis*

An uncommon winter visitor and passage migrant

The Black-necked Grebe is the scarcest of the grebes in Suffolk. It is found annually in small numbers in all seasons, but particularly during winter from December-February. It is elusive and prefers larger estuaries, but is occasionally found on freshwater dykes and pools. However, outside the main winter period, the species is found almost exclusively at freshwater sites such as Alton Water, Minsmere and Livermere. Summer records of Black-necked Grebes are becoming increasingly frequent. A few pairs breed annually, often colonially, at lowland lakes elsewhere in Britain, with numbers ranging from 37-81 pairs between 1989 and 1999 (Ogilvie *et al.* 2001) but, as yet, there are no confirmed breeding records in Suffolk.

At the beginning of the 20th century, the species was noted less than annually on spring and autumn passage, but it was possibly overlooked during winter (Ticehurst 1932). It became particularly scarce in the 1950s to 1960s, when there were six years with no recorded sightings and only eight individuals were reported from 1962 to 1971. Occurrences have since become more frequent, probably due to better observer coverage. Records for the period 1980-1999 show an average of about six birds per annum. Nowadays, it is chiefly a winter visitor with January being the most favoured month, although there is a distinct spring passage in April/May.

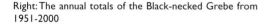

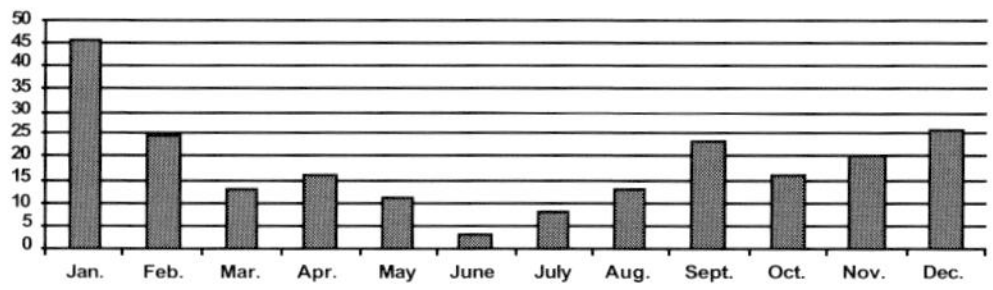

Above: The seasonal occurrence of the Black-necked Grebe from 1951-2000

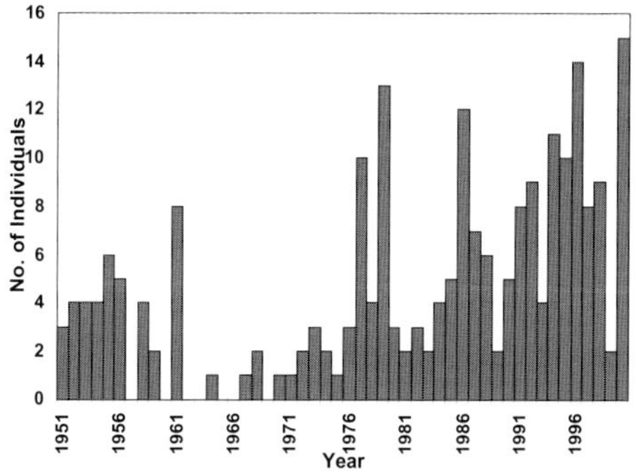

Right: The annual totals of the Black-necked Grebe from 1951-2000

Although groups of 2-3 occasionally occur, Black-necked Grebes are most often reported singly. A group of five on the Deben at Waldringfield on 3rd December 1977 was exceptional.

It is perhaps surprising that successful breeding has yet to be confirmed, as it did occur just over the county border at Burwell Fen, Cambridgeshire in 1937 (Bircham 1989). Ticehurst described the grebe as "one of the rarer species which, if given adequate protection, would probably establish itself as a breeding species in East Anglia", but early nesting attempts were thwarted by shooters who slaughtered potential breeding pairs. The recent increase in flooded gravel workings and reservoirs has created an abundance of suitable waters and there are numerous records of pairs in full summer plumage, sometimes displaying and even nest building. From 1979-2000, such birds were noted almost annually. In April 1983, a displaying pair visited Alton Water and in May 1986 three lingered at Thorington Street Reservoir, and a pair was recorded at Livermere Lake. In June 1988, one built a nest platform on the edge of Benacre Broad and showed much aggression to the resident Little Grebes. Disturbance and lack of marginal vegetation may be the most significant factors in the species' failure to colonise suitable waters in Suffolk.

Post-breeding birds are regularly recorded in August and September and there are four July records, with one on Havergate Island on 21st July 1955 being the earliest. The Black-necked Grebe is occasionally noted on seawatches, but a flock of eight, flying south close inshore at Landguard Point, on 30th September 1994, was unprecedented. Three birds, feeding in the Orwell Haven the following day, were presumably part of this flock.

A disorientated individual landed on the A12 trunk road at Martlesham on 14th February 1986 and was taken to the nearby Suffolk Police H.Q., before being released on the River Deben at Waldringfield. It seems likely that the grebe mistook the wet, illuminated, asphalt road for a stretch of water. This bizarre record occurred during the coldest February since 1947 (Grant 1987).

Fulmar (Northern Fulmar) *Fulmarus glacialis*

A fairly common summer visitor and passage migrant

Fulmars
(*Stuart Ling*)

The colonisation of the British Isles by the Fulmar is one of the great conservation success stories of the 20th century. The British breeding population was once restricted to the Scottish island of St Kilda, but from there it has spread rapidly to occupy all suitable coastal sites. It is now the most numerous seabird of the northern hemisphere and there has been a marked range extension in the western Atlantic (Lloyd *et al.* 1991). A small nesting colony became established at Bawdsey and prospecting adults have also been noted at suitable cliffs elsewhere in the county during the summer months. The Fulmar occurs in all seasons, although it is rare in winter and is most numerous during passage periods, when substantial movements are occasionally logged. Fulmars are seen regularly along the length of the coast, although the stretch between Covehithe and Minsmere has been the most productive in recent years.

Hele and Babington described the Fulmar as a very rare straggler to Suffolk and it was considered by Ticehurst to be a bird of autumn passage, with its late September arrival coinciding with herring shoals. He

Westleton Heath (*Derek Moore*). One of Suffolk's best examples of sandling heath, a unique habitat that once stretched from Ipswich to Lowestoft.

Nightjar (*Stan Dumican*). Nightjars churring over heath and breck are one of the delights of a summer evening.

Tree Pipit (*Stan Dumican*). The song-flight of the Tree Pipit is now restricted to heathland and young forestry plantations on the coast and in Breckland.

Dartford Warbler (*Alan Tate*). The recolonisation of the sandlings began in the mid-1990s and reached 61 pairs by 2002.

Dunwich Forest (*Derek Moore*). The planting of non-native conifer blocks during the 1920s resulted in the loss of huge areas of heath and breck.

Sparrowhawk (*Ray Upson*). The Sparrowhawk has recovered significantly since DDT poisoning depleted its numbers in the 1950s.

Long-eared Owl (*Stan Dumican*). Although a few pairs breed in conifer belts in the Breck and the coastal strip, the owl is more known as a winter immigrant, with most arriving in late October and early November and departing in March.

Hazelwood Marshes (*Derek Moore*). An area of prime grazing marsh on the north bank of the River Alde.

Little Egret (*Alan Tate*). Successful breeding took place at two sites in 2002 and further colonisation looks likely.

Stour Estuary (*Derek Moore*). The extensive mudflats host wader flocks of international importance.

Oystercatcher (*Stan Dumican*). Small groups explore exposed mudflats, and roosts of several hundred form on adjacent fields at high tide.

Red-necked Grebe (*Alan Tate*). A breeding pair held territory at Loompit Lake in 1988.

Sizewell Rig (*Derek Moore*). The bubbling warmer waters that flow from the nearby power station attract thousands of gulls in all seasons.

Mediterranean Gull (*Alan Tate*). Formerly an extreme rarity, this is now a regular visitor to coastal Suffolk, and breeding occurs annually at one site.

Walberswick NNR (*Derek Moore*). The reed-beds of Westleton Marsh host good populations of Bitterns, Marsh Harriers, Bearded Tits and other aquatic species.

Reed Warblers (*Stan Dumican*). Extensive reed-beds, *Phragmites*-fringed rivers, lakes, gravel workings, ponds, dykes and even small streams with a few reeds provide this species with a nesting and feeding habitat.

Green Woodpecker (*Stan Dumican*). The unmistakable, laughing 'yaffle' echoing across heathland, open deciduous woodlands, well-timbered parkland and large gardens is a familiar sound during spring and summer.

Castle Marshes (*Derek Moore*). Castle Marshes is part of an extensive area of meadows and dykes adjacent to the River Waveney.

Barn Owl (*Stan Dumican*). Following the national trend, the population in Suffolk has declined markedly and the owl is now virtually restricted to the eastern half of the county, with only a few reported elsewhere.

Lapwing (*Stan Dumican*). Nesting is mainly on heathland, meadows and tilled land, with marked concentrations along the coast, to about 15 miles inland, and in the Brecks.

Orfordness (*Derek Moore*). This shingle wilderness hosts the largest colony of Herring and Lesser Black-backed Gulls in lowland Britain.

Orfordness Gull Colony (*Steve Piotrowski*). A huge area of grassland has become established on the estuary side of the shingle ridge.

Ivory Gull (*Alan Tate*). This confiding individual spent most of its daylight hours scavenging along Aldeburgh beach, although it was also seen at Orfordness, Walberswick and Southwold.

Lesser Black-backed and Yellow-legged Gulls (*Steve Piotrowski*). Yellow-legged Gulls are recorded in increasing numbers and, in recent years, mixed pairs have nested at Orfordness.

Colour-ringing on Orfordness (*Steve Piotrowski*). Since this initiative began, there have been a number of recoveries of gulls ringed at Orfordness

The Scrape, Minsmere (*Derek Moore*). The creation of systems of islands and lagoons is a management technique that has been used to enhance wildlife areas all over the world.

Avocets (*Derek Moore*). Avocets returned to breed at Minsmere and Havergate Island after an absence of more than a century and from there colonised many other East Anglian sites.

Staverton (*Derek Moore*). A fine example of ancient oak woodland, dating back to the Domesday Book.

Redstart (*Stan Dumican*). There has been a significant decrease in the breeding population since the 1970s.

Firecrest (*Alan Tate*). Occurs principally as a passage migrant, with peak numbers noted in both spring and autumn during south-easterly winds.

Jay (*Stan Dumican*). Jays are generally secretive during the breeding season, but become more obvious in autumn when they gather acorns from more open ground.

Dingle Marshes (*Derek Moore*). An area of grazing marsh, reed-bed and coastal lagoons to the north of Dunwich village.

Pochard (*Stan Dumican*). The county's breeding population currently ranges between 4-5 pairs per annum.

Landguard Point (*Steve Piotrowski*). The vegetated banks provide refuge for thousands of tired and hungry migrants during passage periods.

Pallas's Warbler (*Alan Tate*). When late-autumn winds switch to the eastern quarter, appearances of this jewel from the Far East are almost inevitable.

Thrush Nightingale (*Steve Young*). Three of the four Suffolk records were logged at Landguard Point.

Crested Lark (*Rob Wilson*). This individual was very confiding, spending the afternoon feeding on rough ground and scampering across car parks, footpaths and on the Felixstowe promenade.

Yellow-billed Cuckoo (*Alan Tate*). One of the many national rarities that has been recorded at Landguard Point.

Red-backed Shrike (*Alan Tate*). It has long been known as the Butcherbird due to its curious habit of storing food items by impaling them on thorns or barbed wire.

Ness Point (*Derek Moore*). This most easterly point of the British mainland is Suffolk's only example of 'rocky' shore and is a good vantage point for observing seabird movements.

Black Redstart (*Alan Tate*). Industrial wasteland, warehouse complexes, construction sites, docklands, old maltings and other buildings provide this species with competition-free breeding areas.

Purple Sandpiper (*Alan Tate*). Seaweed-clad coastal defences and jetties offer this wader a rich feeding habitat during winter and passage periods.

Glaucous Gull (*Alan Tate*). An annual winter visitor to coastal sites.

Hen Marshes (*Derek Moore*). One of Suffolk's newest nature reserves that has been created specifically for the conservation of the Bittern.

Willow Warbler (*Stan Dumican*). Britain's commonest summer visitor, nesting along woodland edge and in rides and clearings.

Framlingham Mere (*Derek Moore*). An inland lake that provides a notable attraction for wildfowl.

Kingfisher (*Stan Dumican*). The species is almost exclusively found near water, preferring freshwater sites throughout the year, with some moving to estuarine localities during severe winter periods.

Song Thrush (*Ray Upson*). Nationally, a decline of 52% in the breeding population resulted in the species being added to the 'red list' of Birds of Conservation Concern.

River Stour (*Derek Moore*). A wildlife corridor that meanders through some of Suffolk's most picturesque countryside.

Little Owl (*Ray Upson*). This owl favours open countryside with an abundance of hedgerows containing old trees, and traditional farm buildings.

Waxwing (*Alan Tate*). Irruptions from remote taiga regions of Fennoscandia and western Siberia occur in most years.

Bradfield Woods (*Derek Moore*). One of Suffolk's finest examples of ancient woodland, where coppice rotation is practiced for the benefit of wildlife.

Great Spotted Woodpecker (*Stan Dumican*). Occurs in most wooded areas, old orchards and parks and regularly visits gardens, sometimes attracted to nut-feeders.

Long-tailed Tit (*Stan Dumican*). These delicate little birds wander far from their breeding areas and are regular visitors to migration watch-points.

Alton Water (*Derek Moore*). Suffolk's largest area of standing freshwater attracts huge wintering wildfowl flocks especially during periods of severe weather.

Great Crested Grebe (*Stan Dumican*). Around 100 pairs nest in Suffolk, half of which are at Alton Water.

Little Ringed Plover (*Stan Dumican*). An increase in the number and extent of working gravel pits has provided this diminutive plover with new breeding habitats.

Black-winged Stilt (*Stan Dumican*). The coastal nature reserves provide ideal feeding habitat for this elegant wader and their creation may be a reason for the increase in records since 1976.

Acid Grassland at Cavenham Heath (*Malcolm Wright*). The heather and birch mix is a favoured habitat of heathland and open-country species

Curlew (*Stan Dumican*). A small breeding population exists in the breck and non-breeding birds oversummer on estuaries.

Wheatear (*Stan Dumican*). The breeding population is now restricted to a few sites in the Breck and one on the coast.

Calcareous Grassland at Cavenham Heath (*Malcolm Wright*). This type of habitat hosts typical Breckland species such as the Stone Curlew and Wheatear.

Linnet (*Ray Upson*). The Linnet breeds widely throughout the county, with the greatest densities around the River Blyth, around Stowmarket and in much of south Suffolk.

Stone Curlew (*Stan Dumican*). In Breckland, there is a stable breeding population, but numbers have dwindled to just one or two pairs on the coast.

was aware of only one record for each of the months of December, January and February, so overwintering was thought unlikely. It was scarce up to the 1960s and offshore movements were unknown. Early SBRs (1950-1959) show a gradual increase in sightings, principally between 28th April and 2nd September, which was attributed to the expansion of the Fulmars' breeding range into Norfolk (Hervey 1954). Double-figure counts were considered noteworthy up to the early 1980s, but it was not until the late 1980s that large offshore movements were noticed. Nowadays, autumn passage is earlier with the main movements occurring between mid-August and mid-September.

Suffolk's first summer records occurred in June and July 1947, when there were three sightings of probably the same individual off Dunwich and Minsmere. A pair copulating on Hopton Cliffs in April and May 1950 was an early sign of the species' nesting potential and, from the mid-1960s, Fulmars began prospecting around the sandstone cliffs at Pakefield, Covehithe and Dunwich. The Bawdsey colony became established in the late 1970s and successful breeding was first confirmed there in 1983, the single chick reared was the first of 22 to fledge at this site up to 1988. There was an annual increase in the number occupying the ledges and a peak of 40 adults was reached in April 1993. However, since 1989, adults and chicks have suffered the effects of regular raids by foxes and, in consequence, breeding success has been limited. During the period 1990-1994, only two young fledged. Breeding has long been expected at Dunwich cliffs, but despite prospecting adults regularly occupying burrows (12 were present in 1985), this has yet to be proven. Regular cliff falls probably prevent the formation of suitable ledges or burrows. Breeding colonies are deserted soon after the nestlings fledge in September. Returning birds are noted from early January, although the Bawdsey ledges were reoccupied progressively earlier from 1985 to 1992, with birds present by 18th December in the latter year.

Prolonged arctic weather sometimes results in huge 'wrecks', the largest being noted in February and March 1962 (Pashby & Cudworth 1969), when 86 corpses were recovered from Suffolk's beaches. However, winter records are generally scarce, with normally less than ten sightings reported between December and March each year. Northerly movements involving 50 off Covehithe on 2nd December 1987 and c.400 off Aldeburgh on 25th January 1998 were exceptional records for those months.

Northerly passage is noted in spring, although this rarely gets underway until April and continues through to early June. All counts of 50 or more in a day have been since 1990 and three-figure counts include: 412 off Covehithe on 16th April 1994, 233 off Southwold on 21st May 1994, 185 and 295 off Minsmere on 15th and 16th April 1994 respectively, 103 off Covehithe on 11th May 1996, and 104 and 163 off Thorpeness on 7th and 31st May 1999 respectively.

Autumn dispersal begins in August and migration peaks from mid-month until mid-September. The species becomes scarce after the end of September. Movements are principally northerly and the largest autumn count involved 403 birds moving off Covehithe on 10th September 1989. Other three-figure day-counts were logged on two occasions in August 1995 and August 1996.

Although almost exclusively pelagic, individuals occasionally venture up river estuaries to be seen several miles from the coastline. However, there are only eight records from West Suffolk up to the end of 1998:

c.1878	Brockley: "caught... fed on small birds which it ate very voraciously"
1949	Ampton: 25th March
1980	Lakenheath: Little Ouse, long dead 14th May
1986	Eriswell: 5th June
1988	Long Melford: 29th August
1993	Cavenham: 4th March
1994	Lackford: W.R., 21st August
1998	Moulton: corpse 24th July

Despite the large number of Fulmars observed offshore, there are only five records of blue-phase morphs: one dead on Southwold beach on 25th January 1957, one flying north amongst a party of 18 pale-phase Fulmars off Landguard Point on 17th October 1981, a tideline corpse near Minsmere following storms on 14th February 1983, three off Covehithe on 5th May 1994 and one at Southwold on 20th November 1999.

The longevity of the species is demonstrated by one found at Bawdsey which had been ringed as a nestling on Orkney 30 years previously.

Cory's Shearwater *Calonectris diomedea*

A very rare (autumn) passage migrant: 28 records involving 37 individuals

Suffolk is hardly renowned for large seabird movements and it is therefore not surprising that the first Cory's Shearwater was not recorded until 1974, when one was identified independently by two observers, from Dunwich and then Lowestoft, within a 45-minute period.

The second and third records occurred in 1980, a remarkable year for the species, when no fewer than 17,246 were noted off the British and Irish coasts (Dymond *et al.* 1989). Cory's Shearwaters have since been recorded on 25 dates (34 individuals) with the bulk of the sightings from Covehithe and Southwold. The records range from 5th July to 19th October, with five off Southwold on 30th September 1991, the largest recorded movement to date.

The breeding population is confined to islands in the Mediterranean and the west Atlantic, and wanderers, particularly during early autumn, are regularly sighted off the British and Irish coasts. There were few records for the British Isles prior to 1958 (Dymond *et al.* 1989), but the species is now noted annually, principally off southern Ireland and Cornwall, and occasionally in substantial numbers.

Great Shearwater *Puffinus gravis*

Accidental: six records

1898	Lowestoft: "shot... brought in by boat" 10th November
1907	North Sea: Outer Gabbard light-vessel, 24th September
1929	Gorleston: Gorleston Beach, male "picked up" 7th January
1982	Minsmere: 5th September
1990	Landguard Point: flying north 22nd September
	Lowestoft: Ness Point, same individual north 22nd September
1992	Southwold: flying north 10th September

The first three records were listed by Ticehurst (1932) and repeated by Payn (1962), but then curiously omitted by the latter author in the second edition of his book. The Gorleston bird was found on the beach and kept in the collection of Dr Riviere, author of *A History of the Birds of Norfolk*; its omission by Payn was probably due to confusion over county recording boundaries. The Outer Gabbard light-vessel was stationed due east from Bawdsey and, although the authenticity of the 1898 Lowestoft record has never been doubted, the exact sea area where it was obtained is uncertain.

The Minsmere individual was a result of an early September storm and part of a significant seabird movement (Piotrowski 1983a). The Landguard Point bird was spotted amongst gulls that followed a fishing boat into the mouth of the Orwell. The shearwater was watched for almost 20 minutes as it flew up and down the estuary and rested on the sea, before it flew off north to be observed later the same day off Lowestoft.

Sooty Shearwater *Puffinus griseus*

An uncommon autumn migrant

Until comparatively recently, this oceanic wanderer was considered a very rare offshore visitor to Suffolk waters, noted irregularly during early autumn. However, following several years of intensive seawatching, which began in earnest in the mid-1980s, this species is now being recorded in significant numbers. Since 1987, annual totals have reached double figures. The highest annual total up to the end of 2001 was 106 in 1989.

Suffolk's first record was a single observed from a boat just south of Gorleston Harbour on 31st August 1947. There were no more reports until 1960 when one passed close inshore at Lowestoft on 29th August. The county's total had reached only eight by 1975, but a gradual increase in sightings followed and on 23rd August 1977 a party of five flew past Minsmere. A late, southerly movement off Minsmere on 10th October 1987 involving 28 birds was the largest for the 20th century, but all previous records were eclipsed in early September 2002 when a phenomenal passage was recorded. The compilation of reports for 1st September revealed that at least 340 birds had moved north, exclusively noted between Orfordness and Ness Point. During the next two days a further 224 were reported and smaller movements for the rest of the month contributed to a September total of over 700. Two flying north off Southwold on 6th February 1999 constitutes Suffolk's only winter record and there were other reports elsewhere in the North Sea on that day. There have been no spring records and the first birds of the year are often noted in late July or early August. The county's earliest for the autumn was off Covehithe on 2nd July 1989. Migration normally peaks in late August and early September, and the species becomes scarce from mid-October onwards. The latest date involved one off Landguard Point on 27th October 1990.

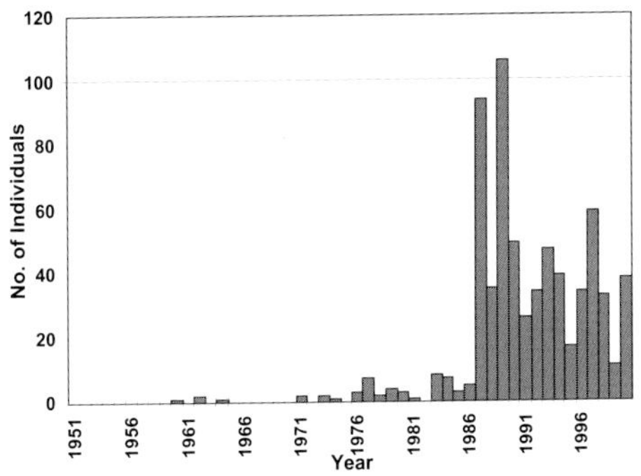

The annual totals of Sooty Shearwater from 1951-2000

Manx Shearwater *Puffinus puffinus*

An uncommon passage migrant, mainly autumn

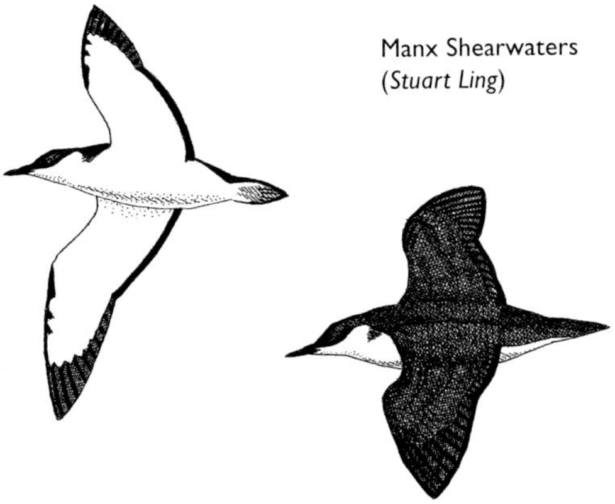

Manx Shearwaters (*Stuart Ling*)

Manx Shearwaters shearing gracefully into brisk northerly winds are a rare sight off Suffolk. Small numbers are reported from coastal sites, principally during autumn passage, although spring records have become increasingly frequent in recent years. Severe westerly gales in early September occasionally propel inexperienced youngsters from their west coast breeding grounds across the country to inland Suffolk. A tideline corpse on Minsmere's shore on 22nd February 1964 constitutes the county's only winter record.

The only 19th century records refer to individuals being picked up following westerly gales, the first being found on Newmarket Racecourse in 1869.

Apart from one, all of the 14 records of storm-driven birds found at inland localities have occurred between 1st and 24th September. The exception involved one 'wrecked' at Haverhill on 22nd June 1987. An exhausted bird picked up on a road at Aldeburgh on 6th September 1967, had been ringed as a nestling at Skokholm, Pembrokeshire only seven days earlier.

Ticehurst stated that "it only very occasionally comes near the shore" and his reference to three off Kessingland on 20th July 1917 appears to be the county's first reported offshore movement. The species remained scarce throughout the first half of the 20th century and there were just two sightings in the 1950s. Although reported almost annually in the 1960s, the maximum year total was only three. The 1970s showed little increase, except in 1979 when an unprecedented total of 14 was recorded. However, as with the Sooty Shearwater, the true status of this species was not realised until intensive seawatching activities began in the mid-1980s. Double-figure counts have since been consistently reported, with annual totals of 149 in 1999 and 246 in 2000. There have been few November records and the latest ever sighting involved two flying north off Covehithe on 2nd December 1987.

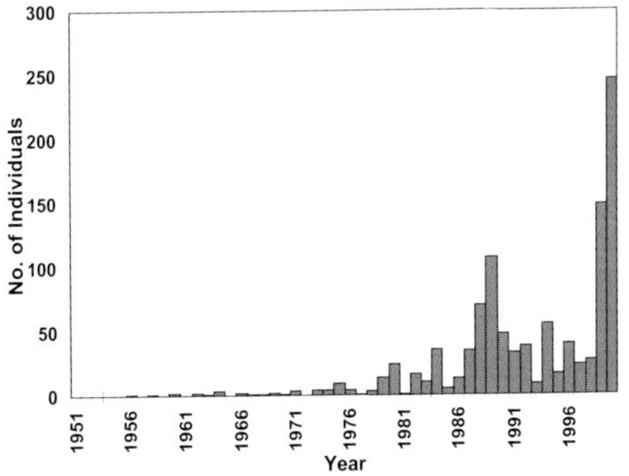

The annual totals of Manx Shearwater from 1951-2000

Balearic Shearwater *Puffinus mauretanicus*

Accidental: five records

1998	Leiston-cum-Sizewell: three S 23rd July
	Southwold: two N 8th August
2001	Leiston-cum-Sizewell: S 17th July
	Southwold: single N 18th August and S 19th August
	Dunwich/Orfordness: S 19th August

The above are the only acceptable records from the numerous claims for this shearwater off the Suffolk coast. The 1998 records occurred in a 12-day period when the species was plentiful in the North Sea and English Channel, and the August 2001 records, which conceivably could have involved just one individual, occurred with a seabird movement during strong SSE winds. There are a number of reports for 2002 that are being considered by the SORC.

The Balearic Shearwater was formerly classified as a race of Manx Shearwater, but attained its species status in 1991 under the name Mediterranean Shearwater *P. yelkouan*. In 2000, it was further divided into Balearic Shearwater *P. mauretanicus* and Yelkouan Shearwater *P. yelkouan* (Cramp *et al.* 1974-1994, BOURC). The latter species has yet to be recorded in Britain.

The breeding colonies are confined to offshore islets of the Balearics, and the species winters off north-west Africa and western Europe. It is a regular visitor to British waters, mainly between July and October, but is relatively rare in the North Sea.

Storm Petrel (European Storm-Petrel) *Hydrobates pelagicus*

A very rare passage migrant

This highly pelagic and largely nocturnal migrant now rarely ventures into inshore waters. It is noted irregularly, principally from September to November, and occasionally during the winter months. Exhausted birds will sometimes take refuge on passing ships during stormy conditions.

Authors in the 19th century suggested that the Storm Petrel was common, often attracted to refuse thrown overboard from fishing boats as catches were processed inshore or on the beach. Allard (1990) described how fishermen "amused themselves" by knocking down petrels "with osier wands as they followed herring trailed behind boats on pieces of string". The species was a regular visitor to Lowestoft Harbour, most abundant during harsh-weather periods, when many were killed. Following severe gales in November 1824, 200-300 were shot at Great Yarmouth and, in November 1872, "immense numbers" were resting on the sea off Lowestoft (Payn 1962). The demise of the region's herring fishery, along with the improvements to the industry's processing techniques, has undoubtedly contributed to the pronounced decline in the frequency of sightings.

Lightships and lighthouses were often an attraction and there were frequent sightings at other coastal localities. In October 1867, three from a party of six were shot whilst flying near the Orford lighthouse and, in September 1883, two were caught on the lantern glazing of the lighthouse at Landguard Point (Babington 1884-1886). One killed on the Stour in May 1820 is Suffolk's first record and this, together with one found freshly dead at Culford on 24th May 1966, are the only spring occurrences.

The numbers of 'wrecked' birds in inland Suffolk illustrates their abundance during the 19th century. At least a dozen such individuals were picked up during the late 19th century, compared with only three since 1932.

It is now a scarce visitor to coastal Suffolk. There were a mere 28 individuals between 1950 and 2000, with no more than four records in any one year and, unlike other seabird species, the upsurge in seawatching has failed to produce the anticipated increase in reports. The highest annual total of recent years occurred during the exceptional seabird year of 2002 when at least nine birds were noted.

Leach's Petrel (Leach's Storm-Petrel) *Oceanodroma leucorhoa*

A scarce passage migrant

Severe storms between late September and October often force small numbers of Leach's Petrels close inshore, especially when south-easterlies persist. It is extremely rare during all other months, although early winter storms can result in occurrences in November and, sometimes, in December. The only midwinter bird was found dead at Henham in January 1964.

Ticehurst described this petrel as occurring "at irregular intervals, sometimes several years passing by without one being noticed, and it always occurs under stress of weather" and Payn records it as "a rare and irregular visitor". However, in recent years, a better understanding of the conditions in which this petrel is likely to occur has resulted in an increase in the frequency of sightings. During the period 1950-2000 there were 105 records (nearly four times that of Storm Petrel) and, since 1977, there have been only seven blank years. The best year was 1997, when 21 were noted. Nine passing south, at the head of strong south-easterly gales with driving rain on 28th September 1991, is the best single-day count. Six of these were off Southwold and constitutes the county's largest recorded movement.

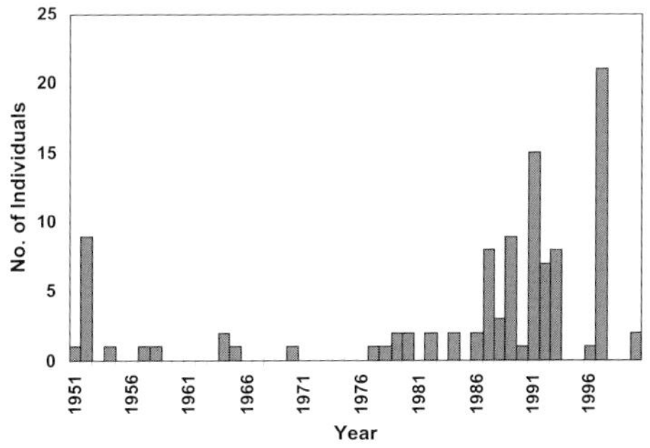

The annual totals of Leach's Storm Petrel from 1951-2000

There have been seven records in spring and summer involving singles at Breydon Water on 14th April 1875, Great Yarmouth (obtained) in April 1876 and June 1850, Dunwich on 8th May 1984 and Landguard Point on 21st April 2001. One at Breydon Water on 6th July 1867 probably relates to an early returning bird and another following a fishing boat off Dunwich on 11th August 1991 is the only record for that month.

Like most seabird species, it is occasionally subject to 'wrecks' when severe weather may drive birds inland. The most significant of these occurred from mid-October to early November 1952, when violent storms off the west coast of Britain scattered hundreds throughout the country (Boyd 1954) including at least nine birds in Suffolk.

Gannet (Northern Gannet) *Morus bassanus*

A common offshore passage migrant

Gannets (*Brian Small*)

Small numbers of Gannets frequent offshore localities throughout the year, although the species is much scarcer during winter. There is evidence of a regular spring passage and some of the county's largest movements have occurred in this season. Substantial numbers occur in autumn with peak migration noted in September and October.

Ticehurst described the species as "a common inhabitant of the North Sea off our coast", although his comments are largely based on fishermens' reports. He states "one does not sight them from land" except "when a heavy wind is blowing from an eastern quarter". Its status has changed little and there is no doubt that improvements in optical aids, together with the skill and numbers of observers, have accounted for the considerable increase in reports. Nowadays, the characteristic shape moving on the horizon can easily be recognised from shoreline vantage points, although weather conditions are crucial to the numbers visible. Ticehurst made no reference to offshore movements and early SBRs list every record. In 1950, a corpse washed up on Walberswick beach was the year's only report and a movement of 15 in 30 minutes in October 1956 was the largest for that decade. The first three-figure count was 131 off Lowestoft on 18th September 1960, a record which stood for 26 years until surpassed by a passage off Covehithe involving 142 in one hour on 12th October 1986. Three-figure day-totals are now reported annually, with 9,660 in 1995 being largest year total and it included 426 moving north off Covehithe on 30th March. All six movements involving more than 400 birds were northerly and five occurred in early spring. A total of 1,800 flying north off Ness Point, Lowestoft on 21st April 2001 is the largest recorded movement.

Prolonged gales may force birds to inland localities, to be found in circumstances often attracting media attention. Individuals have been noted at the following inland sites: Icklingham, Culford, Melton, Elmswell (twice), Nayland, Ipswich (twice), Great Welnetham, Redgrave, Barnham, Glemham, Weybread (three times), Kirton, Hadleigh, Ashbocking, Laxfield, Brightwell, Hessett, Hollesley Heath, Bury St Edmunds, Lakenheath, Cavenham and Risby.

Disorientated individuals can be aggressive if approached. For example, an injured bird at Icklingham, in November 1849, fiercely attacked a dog that ran up to it (Babington 1884-1886) and another was "arrested" by the police at Thorpeness, in February 1951, after pecking a local resident (Payn 1978). An intriguing record involved an adult found dead at Brightwell that had swallowed a brass rod 445mm long. Ringing recoveries have shown that the origins of visiting birds are varied. Gannets from colonies at Ailsa Craig off west Scotland, Bass Rock (2) and Andoy, Norway have been found in Suffolk.

Cormorant (Great Cormorant) *Phalacrocorax carbo*

A locally common passage migrant and winter visitor; a few oversummer

The Cormorant occurs at both inland and coastal localities throughout the year, but is far more numerous during the winter months. Few areas of standing freshwater escape the attention of the species.

A tree-nesting colony at Fritton Lake held many nests in 1825, but was deserted two years later, being "wiped out in a day by a single man's stupidity" (Ticehurst 1932). Breeding took place at Holbrook Marshes by the River Stour, during the 1920s, but other accounts from this river, which included a nest on a buoy off Wrabness and half-grown birds seen by Bures Mill are unreliable and should be dismissed (Piotrowski 1990a). Displaying groups became more regular at freshwater sites during the 1990s culminating in a breeding colony becoming established at Loompit Lake, Trimley St Martin from 1998 (one nest). Numbers here increased rapidly from 19 nests in 1999 to 63 nests, from which 95 birds fledged, in 2000. Tree-nesting birds have recently colonised sites in the neighbouring counties of Norfolk, Cambridgeshire and Essex, with Abberton Reservoir holding around 500 pairs during the mid-1990s (Essex Bird Reports). Small numbers oversummer annually at inland lakes and along river systems, but estimating the numbers involved is complicated by the arrival of colour-ringed immigrants from the continent as early as 7th June. An estimate of the non-breeding summering population is best determined by the numbers present from mid- to late May. Counts from the early 1990s showed that around 80 birds summered at that time.

The national survey of wintering birds, organised by the BTO in 1985-1986, estimated monthly, daytime totals between 300 and 500 respectively (Waters 1986a). Large numbers were found feeding in the river estuaries by day and roosting communally at night. The Sizewell rigs have long been favoured by roosting birds, as have a group of dead oaks near Wilford Bridge, Bromeswell (often loosely referred to as the 'Melton roost'). A willow tree roost at inland Bures has been used constantly for 85 years (Waters 1986b), and the Melton roost has regularly held over 100 since at least 1972. Cormorants arrive at their roosts just before dusk and leave soon after dawn, following distinct flight lines, many of them overland (Warren 1981).

In the late 1700s, the Cormorant was even more plentiful than it is today. Ticehurst, referring to a manuscript dated 11th September 1775, stated "a vast number of these birds, even to some thousands, roost every night upon trees at Belton (presumably Fritton) Decoy". The species has traditionally been subject to much persecution, due to its voracious appetite for fish, and it is therefore not surprising that it had apparently decreased by the late 19th century (Babington 1884-1886). There has been a steady increase throughout the 20th century, perhaps accelerated by protection offered under the Wildlife and Countryside Act 1981, which makes unlicensed killing illegal.

Three-figure flocks are regularly noted at coastal and estuarine sites with the Deben, Orwell and Stour hosting the largest numbers. A congregation of 358 attracted to Alton Water in December 1990, when water levels were exceptionally low following a long period of drought, is the largest count from a freshwater site. Fish struggling in shallow water must have made easy pickings. A feeding flock off Pakefield in late January/early February 2002 yielded the highest totals, peaking at 430 on 31st January which was a county record.

Ringing recoveries have shown that the origins of visiting birds vary enormously. Birds, either found dead or identified while alive by the presence of brightly coloured leg rings, have originated from colonies on the Farne Islands (3), Bass Rock (1), Solway Firth (1), St Margaret's Island, Pembrokeshire (5), Puffin Island, Anglesey (2), Abberton Reservoir, Essex (many), Denmark (2) and Holland (5). A movement from Switzerland to Aldeburgh in 1991-1992 constituted the first British recovery from that country.

Taxonomists split the species into two European races, the nominate *P. c. carbo*, which is confined to the coasts of the North Atlantic and *P. c. sinensis*, restricted to central and southern Europe (Cramp *et al.* 1974-1994). Ringing recoveries indicate that continental birds of the latter race regularly visit Suffolk (Piotrowski 1990a), but their identification is not as easy as some authors suggest. However, Ekins (1994) believes that 60% of the February nesting birds at Abberton Reservoir are of *sinensis* origin assuming that the shape of the gular patch is a reliable feature.

Shag (European Shag) *Phalacrocorax aristotelis*

A fairly common winter visitor and passage migrant

Lowestoft Harbour, nearby Lake Lothing and Ipswich Docks are the most favoured sites for Shags, and rarely does a winter go by without one or two being present. Elsewhere, wintering birds usually confine themselves to the saline reaches of estuaries, although very occasionally, freshwater habitats such as Oulton Broad and Alton Water are chosen. There is evidence of a small spring passage.

At the turn of the 19th/20th centuries, the Shag was thought to be an extreme rarity. Babington listed a mere five records and Ticehurst had difficulty judging its status, saying that "the majority of records relate to single birds taken at sea off our coasts, probably in herring nets, or individuals which, under stress of gales or snow, have sought refuge in our tidal estuaries". Throughout the 20th century, there has been a steady increase in the number visiting Suffolk. However, it is almost certain that Shags were overlooked in the early days and identification problems may well have persisted up to the 1960s. For example, there were no Shags reported in the 1950 SBR, but under the entry for Cormorant, there are details of a bird perched on the front stay of a herring drifter, the wire being at a 45-degree angle. Although we can now only speculate as to the true identity of the bird, this behaviour is more typical of Shag than Cormorant.

During the period 1985-1987, there were 47,000 breeding pairs in Britain and Ireland which represents an increase of about 25% since 1969-1970 (Lloyd *et al.* 1991). There has been a corresponding increase in the number of occurrences in Suffolk from an average of nine birds per annum for the period 1965-1974 to 49 for 1985-1994.

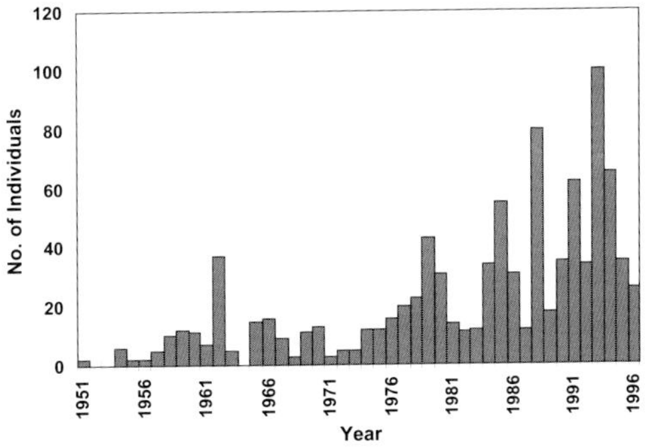

The annual totals of Shag from 1951-2000

When severe weather causes food shortages in their normal feeding areas, the species disperses, causing sudden and dramatic increases to the county's wintering population. Plunging temperatures (-10.8°C) on 28th January 1979, persuaded 32 to seek refuge in Lowestoft Harbour (Brown 1980), Suffolk's largest ever gathering. When storm-driven birds arrive in numbers, a few linger into the spring and even attempt to oversummer. Lowestoft Harbour hosted three until 3rd August 1960 and, in 1988, 20 were present on 6th-9th May, with six in June and one up to 26th July. Birds were recorded perched on ledges occupied by Kittiwakes on Lowestoft's South Pier Pavilion (since demolished) and on the purpose-built 'kittiwake wall'. Maybe the latter will provide the substitute rock face which one day will be colonised.

Immatures are sometimes blown inland where mortality is high. Records for the period 1884-1991 provide 35 inland records, some found in the strangest circumstances. At Lavenham, in 1911, one was caught at night after being attracted by a bicycle lamp, whilst two others were perched on the nearby church tower, and in 1943 one was shot from a farmhouse chimney at Hartest. At Darmsden, in 1936, a man was thrown from his bicycle as a result of colliding with a Shag and, in 1986, one was found dead in a chicken run in north Ipswich. The most notable 'wrecks' occurred in 1954, 1962, 1985, 1988 and 1991.

Inexperienced juveniles have on occasions provided much entertainment. One took battered fish from a hand-held fork at Southwold (Piotrowski 1990b) and another repeatedly stole bait from an angler as he prepared to cast his rod at Landguard Point. Birds have also been reported hitching rides on passing ships. Ringing recoveries have shown that the bulk of wintering birds originate from colonies in northern Britain. Of 71 found between 1909 and 1995, 40 were ringed in Scotland, 27 in northern England and only four in southern England. Interestingly, there have been no Suffolk recoveries of birds ringed at the Welsh or Irish colonies, although at least one has originated from Lundy Island, Devon.

Bittern (Great Bittern) *Botaurus stellaris*

A scarce and decreasing resident, passage migrant and winter visitor

Bittern (*Adam Kennedy*)

During the 17th century, the Bittern's range extended throughout England and Wales to southern Scotland, but nowadays it has become one of Britain's rarest breeding birds. A decline has been noted throughout Europe (Day 1981) with land drainage and shooting being the principal factors involved. A few pairs nest annually in Suffolk's coastal reedbeds, dispersing during the winter months. Immigrants from elsewhere in Europe are occasionally reported.

The fenlands of north-west Suffolk used to hold a substantial Bittern population. In the 17th century, Bitterns were hunted for food and are mentioned by Reyce (1618) in his "Breviary of Suffolk". In the 18th century, they were still common in the fenlands and shooting parties reportedly bagged between 20 and 30 in a morning, roast Bittern being an East Anglian speciality (Payn 1978). Ticehurst referred to breeding

Bitterns in the Mildenhall and Thetford districts during the early 19th century, although they were mercilessly slaughtered. Of the 78 records listed by Babington, 55 were killed, mostly during winter. Severe weather conditions in January 1848 resulted in several being killed near Ipswich and 14 in the Orford area. More unusual records include one captured after being knocked down with a stick at Bury St Edmunds jail (1862) and another found drowned in a Bildeston well (1881).

The drainage and reclamation of the fenlands had a disastrous effect on the Bittern and it ceased to breed in Suffolk sometime prior to 1868. As so many reedbeds had been destroyed, earlier authors were pessimistic regarding its chance of recolonisation. For example, Ticehurst remarked "there are very few spots left where there could be any reasonable hope of the Bittern re-establishing itself as a breeding bird". However, territorial birds were present intermittently on the coast from 1901 to 1929 and pairs raised broods at Lowestoft and Dunwich in 1934. Coastal grazing marshes were flooded as a Second World War anti-invasion measure and soon large tracts of reedbed became established providing an ideal breeding habitat. By the early 1950s, around 14 pairs were nesting at up to seven coastal sites, the bulk of the birds frequenting Minsmere, where 11 booming males were estimated to be present in 1953. The population consolidated in the 1960s and reached a peak of 20 pairs at five reedbeds during the following decade. However, there has since been a downward trend with about 9-12 boomers noted annually.

Censusing this secretive species is a difficult task. It had been generally believed that Bitterns remain reasonably static once holding territory and it was common practice to plot the location of each boomer to determine the number of territories. Berry (1978), assessing numbers at Minsmere, explored a method involving a combination of booming males and feeding flight lines, and recent sonogram studies have detected differences in the vocabulary of each booming male, which allows an accurate assessment of the numbers present (Tyler 1994). It has been found that individuals will boom from several areas in the reedbed and in consequence, numbers at the larger sites may have been overestimated in the past.

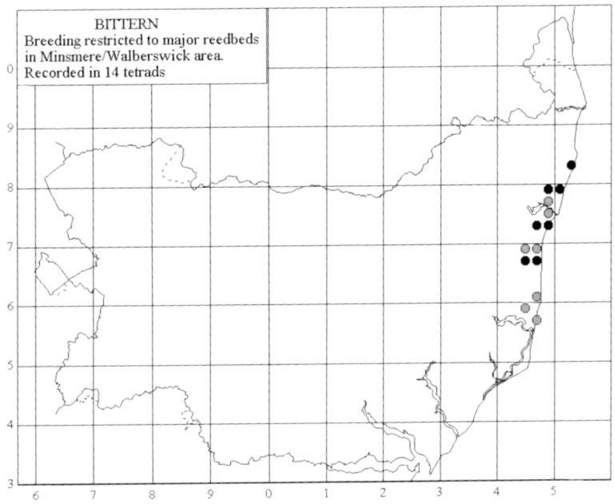

Its susceptibility to severe winter weather is well known and it was estimated that the effects of the 1962/3 winter reduced the East Anglian population by 41% (Bibby 1981). Bitterns will disperse during winter and are joined by immigrants from abroad. Ringing recoveries have shown that birds from Sweden, Germany, the Netherlands and Belgium reach Britain (Mead & Clark 1993), but no foreign-ringed birds have been found in Suffolk. There is no evidence to suggest an exodus of British-bred birds to warmer climes, when their feeding areas become frozen. The number of moribund individuals found, when such conditions persist, shows that birds often starve rather than emigrate. In 1963, all standing freshwater remained frozen for some ten weeks, which resulted in starving birds being found in unusual circumstances. This prompted the RSPB to launch 'Operation Bittern' which involved the collection of emaciated individuals and their transportation to Minsmere, where they were cared for in aviaries before being released on the marsh. The birds had been gathered from "far and wide" and included one "bemused with fatigue and hunger" which had stood with a queue of people at a bus stop in a London suburb (Axell 1977).

Five ringing recoveries relating to Suffolk demonstrate post-juvenile dispersal. Nestlings from Minsmere have been found in London, Derbyshire, Norfolk and County Longford, Ireland, and one from Norfolk was shot at Kessingland. Migrants, either arriving from the sea or moving offshore, have been noted at Bawdsey (winter 1880), Minsmere (April 1962), Benacre (November 1966), Southwold (October 1989) and Aldeburgh (2 in December 1993).

Although small numbers regularly occur at sites away from known breeding areas in winter, the Bittern is a rare visitor to west Suffolk. In 15 years from 1983-1997, the species has been reported from only three river valleys: at Lakenheath, Lackford (3 records) and on the short stretch of the Stour between Glemsford and Cornard (9 records).

Little Bittern *Ixobrychus minutus*

Accidental: 27 records referring to 32 individuals – has bred

1932	Breydon Water: shot 18th September
1937	Shingle Street: male 19th August
1961	Aldringham-cum-Thorpe: Thorpeness, male 13th May
1970	Minsmere: female 7th May
1977	Minsmere: male 22nd May & female 26th May
1980	Minsmere: pair, June-July

British records of this diminutive heron have declined significantly since the late 19th century. The Little Bittern is a summer visitor to western Europe, and is an extremely rare visitor to the county's reedbeds, with only eight recorded in the 20th century.

Breeding was occasionally noted at wetland sites on the Suffolk coast during the 19th century. Ticehurst referred to a female shot on Oulton Broad in June 1830, which was "found to contain a perfect egg" and to a young bird which was caught by a dog in a gorse bush at Mutford on 15th September 1885, "with down still on its head". In total, Babington lists 23 records and Ticehurst a further two, with almost all referring to birds that were shot.

Most 20th century records refer to brief sightings of birds flying low over the reeds, although the Thorpeness bird was almost trodden on. The 1977 and 1980 Minsmere records caused much speculation as to whether breeding had been attempted. The species can be extremely elusive and, although no juveniles were seen, the 1980 male did hold territory and was heard 'barking' on several occasions. The record was published in *British Birds* (Sharrock *et al.* 1982) but was never submitted for formal acceptance by BBRC. Dated records show that most birds have occurred during the summer months. The extreme dates are February (1842) and 11th November (1886), both referring to birds which were killed. Considering the county's proximity to the continent, Suffolk's total is rather meagre compared with national statistics that show a total of 354 occurrences up to the end of 2000, with 204 of them since 1958 (BBRC).

Night Heron (Black-crowned Night Heron) *Nycticorax nycticorax*

Very rare passage migrant and winter visitor: 27 records

Babington listed six or seven records for the Great Yarmouth area and others for Eye, Bildeston and Sudbourne (pair – probably the same as those detailed by Hele for Orford). Ticehurst added two more for the 19th century from Mendham and Felixstowe Ferry.

Of the 17 records between 1914 and 2001, 11 were for the spring period of 25th March to 14th June, and two for late summer – 20th July and 12th August. This bias towards spring occurrences conforms to the national trend (Dymond *et al.* 1989). The remaining four records were for the winter period between 24th November and 14th February. All involved immatures, and included one "captured alive after being shot and winged" at Flatford on 4th January 1919, and another found dead at Bawdsey during cold weather on 14th February 1986.

A flock of full-winged birds breeds with Grey Herons at Great Witchingham Wildlife Park, Norfolk (Taylor *et al.* 2000), and, as Night Herons are widely kept in captivity, there were suspicions that many were escapes. However, a nestling ringed near Belyayevka Black Sea region and recovered in Lincolnshire, together with the overall pattern of occurrences, suggests that the majority of records relate to wild birds. The crepuscular habits of the species may mean that some birds being overlooked.

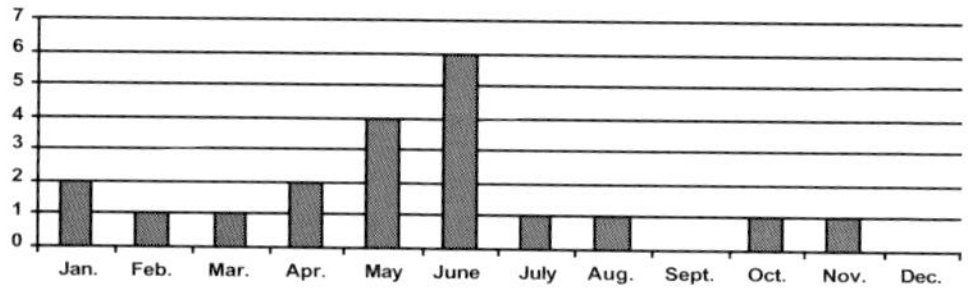

The seasonal occurrence of Night Heron 1883-2001 (dated records only)

The breeding range extends through southern Eurasia, Africa and the Americas, and it is an annual visitor to the British Isles, being noted on 613 occasions up to the end of 2000 (BBRC).

Squacco Heron *Ardeola ralloides*

Accidental: ten records

1831	Lowestoft: Oulton Broad, May
1833	Oulton: June and another September
1834	Lowestoft: Lake Lothing, June
pre-1836	Lowestoft/Pakefield: Lowestoft Beach, "caught in fisherman's net spread on beach"
c.1838	Suffolk: "fresh killed specimen"
1882	Aldringham-cum-Thorpe: Thorpe Meare, female "shot" June
pre-1884	Flixton: "killed"
pre-1884	Hacheston: Glevering Hall, "killed"
1912	Aldeburgh: "magnificent adult male...shot on a pond" 5th May

There has been a drastic decrease in the European breeding population of the Squacco Heron since early in the 20th century, initially (until c.1920) due to persecution by plumage hunters (Cramp *et al.* 1974-1994) and then as a result of habitat loss.

Up to the end of 2000, this diminutive heron had visited the British Isles on 147 occasions, 51 times since 1958 (BBRC). It is surprising that with such an abundance of reedbed habitat, Suffolk has failed to attract this heron in recent years. The Aldeburgh individual constitutes the only 20th century record for Suffolk.

Cattle Egret *Bubulcus ibis*

Accidental: three records involving five individuals

1988	Minsmere: The Scrape, in gull roost, 9th August
1992	Ousden: three photographed, 3rd May
2001	Blyth: estuary/shore pools, 26th August to 16th September

Only their finders saw the first four birds, so the long-staying 2001 individual came as a relief to local birdwatchers. It spent much of its time perched on trees or on posts in the middle of the estuary and, when feeding, often associated with Little Egrets. The Ousden trio were part of a national influx that involved at least 18 individuals (BBRC).

The Cattle Egret extended its range dramatically during the 20th century, most noticeably between 1950 and 1970, to become almost cosmopolitan in the tropics (Voisin 1991). The populations on all continents have increased, the nearest breeding birds to Britain being located in northern France. This range expansion has coincided with a significant increase in records in the British Isles – only two prior to 1958, but 112 since then to the end of 2000 (BBRC).

Little Egret *Egretta garzetta*

An uncommon but increasing visitor

The Little Egret has become a regular feature on river estuaries, coastal lagoons and broads in all seasons, with peak numbers normally noted in early autumn. Since the late 1960s, occurrences have been more or less annual and, following large influxes from 1989 onwards, numbers have increased significantly. In September 1999, Britain's non-breeding population was estimated to be more than 1,650 birds (Musgrove 2002) and over 60 were present in Suffolk during the summer of 2001. All south coast counties have seen a noticeable influx of birds in late summer with numbers tailing off in late autumn and winter.

There are few species whose status has changed more dramatically than the Little Egret. It was extremely rare during the 19th century and, up to 1965, Suffolk's tally amounted to a mere four records. From 1966-1992, Little Egrets occurred more or less annually but, thereafter, there was a staggering increase in line with the national trend. The saline coastal waters from Benacre to the Orwell were the most favoured feeding areas.

Grey Herons commonly raid goldfish ponds and birds flying over rooftops have become a familiar sight in some suburban areas. Fish are the species' favoured prey, although amphibians, small mammals, insects, reptiles, occasionally crustaceans, molluscs, worms, birds and plant material, also form part of the heron's diet. Little Grebes have been taken at Hopton and Lackford, although at the former locality the ambitious heron choked to death on its meal. An enterprising bird cornered a brood of Gadwall ducklings under a waterside bush at Lackford and ate all except one of them (SBR), and another snatched a Reed Bunting at Haverhill (SBR). Stoats, water voles, rats, moles (e.g. Bures on 21st November 1982) and rabbits have also been tackled. One was observed feeding on a starfish on the shoreline at Pakefield and pellets collected at Benacre consisted almost entirely of the remains of great diving beetles (SBR).

Purple Heron *Ardea purpurea*

A scarce passage migrant: 112 records

Since the first record in 1833 and up to the end of 2000, there have been over 100 records of this secretive heron in Suffolk. There were only nine 19th century records and, following a flourish of three between 1901 and 1907, the species was absent for over 50 years. Since 1966, the Purple Heron has almost become an annual visitor and Suffolk is now one of the best British counties for the species, with 95 out of a national total of 686 being noted during the period 1958-1999 (Fraser & Rogers 2001). Over one-third of the Suffolk occurrences were between 1968 and 1974.

All records are concentrated between mid-April and early November, with May being the best month. The earliest occurred at Church Farm Marshes, Aldeburgh on 11th April 2000, and the latest at Minsmere (two) on 3rd November 1968 and Shotley on 3rd November 1990.

The years 1968 and 1973 were exceptional, with ten and nine respectively at Minsmere, which raised speculation that the Purple Heron might one day breed in coastal reedbeds. The latter total included an unprecedented southerly movement of seven birds on 18th June.

The large reedbeds at Minsmere and Walberswick are the most favoured sites and a pair displaying at the former locality in 1966 led to speculation that breeding would soon take place. Purple Herons occasionally inhabit smaller reedbeds and are seen beside rivers and ponds. Even so, singles at Little Cornard on 2nd-6th September 1980, Glemsford on 2nd-7th September 1983 and Livermere Lake on 24th May 1994 and on 20th May 2000 are the only records for the western half of the county.

Single Purple Herons arriving from offshore have been seen at Pakefield on 22nd August 1969, Lowestoft on 8th August 1971 and Easton Bavents on 22nd August 1991.

Black Stork *Ciconia nigra*

A very rare passage migrant: 16 records

c.1911	Hollesley: spring
1969	Brandon: 26th May
1970	Cretingham: 27th April to 19th July
	Stanstead: River Glem, 29th-30th April
1977	Tuddenham-Mildenhall: 4th-6th June
1979	Breydon Water: S 31st July
1985	Walberswick: 6th September
1990	Ellough-Iken: juv. intermittently 28th July to 12th September
1991	Santon Downham: NE 3rd July
1996	Ipswich: NE 26th August
1998	Benacre-Walberswick area: 12th August to 12th September

Five Black Storks were shot in Suffolk during the 19th century and it has since been noted as above.

All Suffolk records fall between April and September, and many refer to birds soaring away. The 1990 bird was probably the same as one sighted in Northamptonshire the day before it was found in Suffolk. During its particularly long stay, it frequented many coastal sites, including the Blyth, Alde and Deben estuaries, and the Minsmere, Walberswick and Benacre areas. It also visited sites in Essex.

This very rare visitor to the British Isles, with 116 records from 1957 to the end of 2000 (BBRC), has a breeding range extending from Iberia and France, where it is increasing, eastwards to Manchuria (Cramp *et al.* 1974-1994). The European population winters in Africa.

White Stork *Ciconia ciconia*

A very rare passage migrant: 41 records

White Stork
(*Stuart Ling*)

Ticehurst, exploring reasons for the decline in visitations of the White Stork to Suffolk, said: "no bird receives more protection in Europe, and even in Asia, than does the Stork, either by law or sentiment or both, yet here we have over a large breeding area a very marked diminution due to natural causes unknown". Range retraction has continued throughout the 20th century and, although the cause is not fully established, *BWP* suggested climate change, habitat changes, loss of nest sites, insecticides, less favourable human attitudes and shooting, as possible factors.

Such large, conspicuous birds are easily recognised by non-birdwatchers, so it is possible that most occurrences are reported and well-documented. Long-stayers, however, will fly several miles to feeding areas, often across county boundaries and so may be lost for several weeks.

There are records of 13 individuals in the 19th century (most were shot), only four for the first half of the 20th century and 20 from 1950 to 1999. In September 1957, a White Stork roosted for two nights on chimneys of a house at Covehithe. A few days later, it was discovered after dark on the garden path of a cottage at Easton Bavents where it was caught and imprisoned in a shed for 24 hours, before being released on Southwold Golf Course.

The White Stork is highly migratory, moving from its European breeding grounds to winter in Africa. Most of the county's records have occurred during spring (February-June) or autumn (July-November) passage periods. However, in recent years, there have been some particularly long-staying individuals whose origins must be questionable. For example, one frequenting the Darsham/Yoxford area from 22nd October 1974, was noted at a number of localities until 7th May 1976 and another, found at Walberswick on 9th May 1982, was reported from many sites in Norfolk and Suffolk and was last seen at Breydon Water on 7th May 1983. Why these birds should choose to overwinter remains a mystery, but the possibility of escapes from free-flying groups at Whipsnade, Bedfordshire, or even Zwin, Belgium, cannot be ruled out. Consideration should also be given to the reintroduction programme in the Netherlands as the source of some of the birds that visit Britain (Dymond *et al.* 1989). In fact, Suffolk's only ringing recovery involved one ringed as a nestling at Groot-Ammers in the Netherlands on 7th June 1997 and found dead at Bawdsey on 23rd March 1999.

Glossy Ibis *Plegadis falcinellus*

A very rare passage migrant: 42 records

1979 Benacre: 9th May
1981 Minsmere: two 8th-9th May and one, presumed same, 18th and 29th May
1982 Minsmere: 12th August
1992 Minsmere: 6th May
Walberswick: Tinker's Marshes, 6th May
Carlton Colville: 6th-8th May

There were four records involving nine individuals during the 19th century. A flock of six (two of which were shot) at the mouth of the River Yare on 24th September 1824 constituted the first Suffolk record. During the first quarter of the 20th century, the Glossy Ibis was still plentiful as a breeding species in eastern Europe and this is reflected in the records. There were 19 birds recorded in the period 1903-1935, including three flocks of four during the heatwave of 1906. Four specimens, taken from groups visiting the Alde and Butley Creek in 1903 and 1906 respectively, remain on display at Ipswich Museum and the two shot on the Yare are exhibited at the Castle Museum, Norwich.

There had been only 79 occurrences in Britain and Ireland from 1957 to the end of 2000 (BBRC) of which five have occurred in Suffolk. The 1981 birds are presumed to be those that took up residence in north Kent between December 1975 and February 1985. After visiting Minsmere, the pair spent a day in the Norfolk Broads before one returned to the Kent site.

Spoonbill (European Spoonbill) *Platalea leucorodia*

An uncommon summer visitor and passage migrant – formerly bred

Small numbers of Spoonbill are noted annually, principally during the summer months, but double-figure counts are rare. Although a few arrive in May, sometimes as early as March, numbers normally increase in summer. Most leave by October, but there have been 11 instances of overwintering up to the end of 2000. Spoonbills tend to frequent lagoon-type habitats such as Minsmere, Orfordness and Havergate Island.

The Spoonbill became extinct as a British breeding species during the 17th century, with the last nests being noted at Trimley in Suffolk. Their presence was confirmed by Sir Thomas Browne (Stevenson 1866, Keynes 1931) who, writing in 1688, said: "The Platalea or shouelard wch build upon the tops of high trees, they have formerly built in the Hernerie at Claxton and Reedham now at Trimley in Suffolk they come in March and are shot by fowlers not for their meat butt for their handsomeness of the same remarkable in their white colour a copped crowne and spoone or spatule like bill". It is difficult to imagine just how the Trimley landscape looked at that time, but it was prior to the 'walling' of the Orwell Estuary and the draining of associated marshes. A fairly substantial, reed-fringed estuary mouth must have existed at that time.

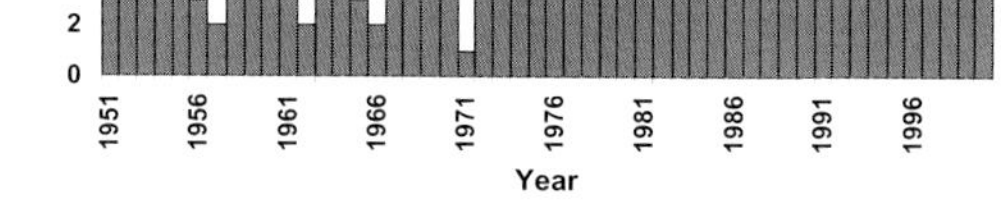

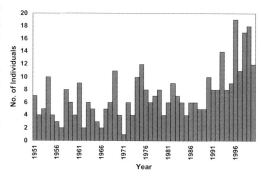

The annual totals of Spoonbill from 1951-2000

The Spoonbill's status has changed little in the last 100 years. Ticehurst described it as "an annual visitant in small numbers chiefly on spring passage". The species is normally noted singly or in groups of up to ten. However, gatherings of 16-19 have been noted at Breydon Water on 13th May 1884, 27th-28th April 1901 and 5th June 1929, Walberswick on 16th May 1946 and Minsmere from 1st July to early August 1996. The last flock consisted of 19 and usually remained hidden in Minsmere's reedbed to be seen only occasionally when they took flight.

Pairs frequently show breeding behaviour, including display, mutual preening, bill crossing and nest-building. For example, at Minsmere in 1970, two distinct pairs engaged in much courtship, which included the carrying of straw and sticks. One stole nesting material from under a brooding Herring Gull. In 1997, seven birds took up residence at a local nature reserve and three nests were built. An egg was laid in one of these but this was soon predated and, although the birds remained in the area throughout that summer, there were no further breeding attempts that year. Up to five pairs returned the following summer and at least three nests were built. Apparent incubation took place from early June to mid-August, but although it was suspected that hatching had taken place, there was no conclusive evidence to show that any chicks fledged. The colony was again occupied in the summer of 2002 when up to 19 birds tended ten nests, but again no fledging was recorded. Failed breeders from the latter site contributed to the county's largest ever gathering of 28 birds on 21st-22nd August 2002.

There are eight ringing recoveries in Suffolk up to the end of 2001 and all birds involved were from colonies in the Netherlands. Most were colour-ringed and demonstrated the mobility of visiting birds. It had long been suspected that individuals regularly commuted between different estuaries and coastal wetlands, and this was confirmed in 1991, 1993, 1999 and 2001 when three colour-ringed juveniles ringed as nestlings at Dutch colonies were tracked in Suffolk and then at a number of sites in Britain and France. One ringed in 1991 was noted on Trimley Marshes, then in Norfolk, Kent and Sussex, then in France and two years later again in Suffolk (Marsh 1993, 1994). Another, seen at Minsmere in 1999, visited Scotland, Cleveland, Norfolk and Leicestershire and one, again at Minsmere, in 2001, frequented Norfolk, Berkshire, Surrey and Cambridgeshire before being killed when it hit power cables in Hertfordshire.

Spoonbills have been noted in West Suffolk on five occasions, but only three times during the 20th century. One visited Livermere Lake on 28th-29th April 1990, followed by four more on 6th May of the same spring and one was at Lackford Wildfowl Reserve on 8th April 1993.

Mute Swan *Cygnus olor*

A common resident and winter visitor

There are few larger rivers, lakes, meres and coastal marshes that do not host a breeding pair of Mute Swans. The species is feared as well as admired by the general public, as breeding pairs will fiercely defend their nests and young, although stories of swans breaking a man's leg with a single swipe of a wing are now considered to be old wives' tales (probably designed to dissuade young boys from robbing nests when birds were individually owned). Non-breeding herds of up to 50 graze on open fields during the summer and feeding concentrations of several hundred are not uncommon during winter.

Many authors have suggested that the Mute Swan's ancestral origins lie in eastern Europe, although there is evidence to suggest that it is an indigenous bird in East Anglia. It has certainly been around since Roman times, and in medieval Britain swans were highly valued as food and jealously guarded in swanneries. Ticehurst's statement "numbers are kept on various lakes and rivers throughout the county and presumably all have owners" shows that they remained in this semi-domesticated state up to at least the 1930s. Payn (1962) reported "a great increase" from 1930 to 1960 and, because of damage to arable crops and grassland and the swan's habit of driving away other wildfowl, it was considered a pest in some areas.

In 1977, SOG organised a census that revealed a breeding population of 125 pairs (Marsh 1979). This was repeated in 1990 when 131 pairs were found, a rise of about 5% (Wright 1991). This is despite concerns that, in the late 1970s and early 1980s, between 3,000-4,000 birds were dying each year in Britain of lead poisoning (Goode 1981). Non-breeding herds totalling 600 were found oversummering during the 1990 survey.

Mute Swans build large nests beside fresh or brackish waters, on saltings, on shallow water in reedbeds and on small islands in lakes and ponds. The distribution map clearly shows concentrations along rivers, although the upper reaches in central Suffolk are avoided, presumably due to a lack of suitable bank space. During the period of peak wintering numbers on the Stour (see below), around 500 remained throughout the summer (Payn 1978), although this figure fell to 175 by 1977. Communal nesting was noted on the northern bank of the Stour during 1977 with 11 out of 14 nests found in the upper reaches of the estuary in a colony at Cattawade (Marsh 1979).

Large concentrations have occurred at estuarine localities during winter, notably on the Alde, Deben, Orwell and Stour. The bulk of the Stour population was centred around the granaries at Mistley Quay where numbers rose steadily during the 1950s and peaked at 950 in 1959. Although the swans still favour this stretch of the river, their numbers have dwindled and, nowadays, herds rarely exceed 150. Large wintering herds have also been noted at Ipswich docks – a maximum of 400 in 1971, Lake Lothing – c.450 during the winters of 1979/80 and 1980/1, and the Alde – regularly 300-350 during the 1960s. Wintering herds are fairly transient, their movements depending on the availability of food. Ringing has proved interchange between sites and a build-up at Ipswich Docks usually involves those displaced from Mistley. Modern unloading techniques employed at ports result in far less spillage and in consequence the sites noted above are no longer a great attraction. Wintering herds are now much smaller and more dispersed, and tend to concentrate on grazing marshes and even arable fields.

There was much speculation as to the origins of birds that visited tidal waters in the late 19th and early 20th centuries. Babington thought them "stragglers ... from some swannery", although Tuck (1891) considered such birds to be continental migrants. Ticehurst noted that occurrences were more regular during hard weather periods and thought it possible that birds "from the East" occasionally reached the Suffolk shores. In more recent times, observations of colour-ringed birds have helped in the understanding of the species' habits, and birds marked at their winter quarters in Ipswich Docks during the 1970s were found nesting as far afield as Minsmere, Snape and Orfordness. Local ringing has shown that Mute Swans rarely venture very far from the ringing sites, with only three out of the 164 known movements exceeding 100km. However, interchange between the Dutch polders and Suffolk has been confirmed by a well-travelled individual, ringed in Friesland, the Netherlands, in April 1974 and seen in Ipswich Docks and Mistley during following winters. There have been three other sightings of Dutch-ringed individuals and a Danish-ringed bird was found dead at Aldeburgh during the severe weather of February 1979. A ringed swan found in Holbrook Bay on 24th November 1979 that had been trapped at Abberton Reservoir, Essex, on 2nd March 1958, provides an example of longevity. This bird was at least two years old when trapped thus making it at least 23 when recovered, a British record.

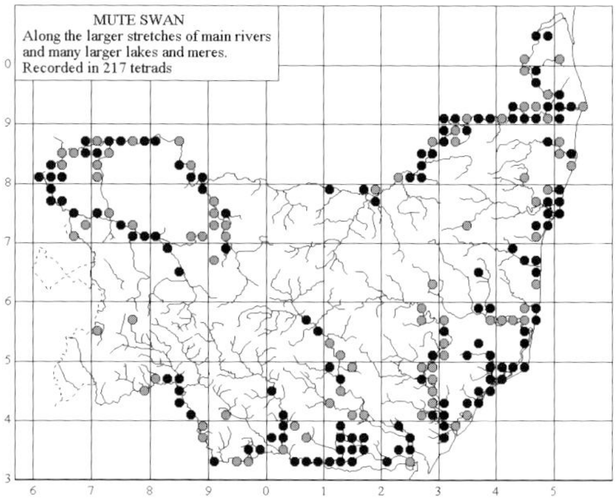
MUTE SWAN
Along the larger stretches of main rivers and many larger lakes and meres.
Recorded in 217 tetrads

Bewick's Swan (Tundra Swan) *Cygnus columbianus*

A locally common winter visitor and passage migrant

Bewick's Swans are noted annually in herds of normally less than 60, chiefly at coastal grazing marshes, but also at inland gravel pits such as Lackford Wildfowl Reserve In recent years, large herds have frequented arable fields on the fens near Mildenhall.

The East Anglian wintering population has increased dramatically during the 20th century. The species was scarce during the 1880s and considered by Babington to be decidedly less common than the Whooper Swan. Occurrences were less than annual in the 1920s (Ticehurst 1932) and its arrival much depended on the severity of the winter. Up to the early 1950s, a single bird was worthy of note and a herd of 92, amongst White-fronts and other wildfowl on a flooded marsh near Lowestoft on 22nd March 1942, was considered exceptional. Gatherings of 42 and 51 noted in 1955 and 1956 respectively were a prelude to wintering on a regular basis and by the end of that decade herds of 30-40 were not uncommon.

Bewick's Swans (*Brian Small*)

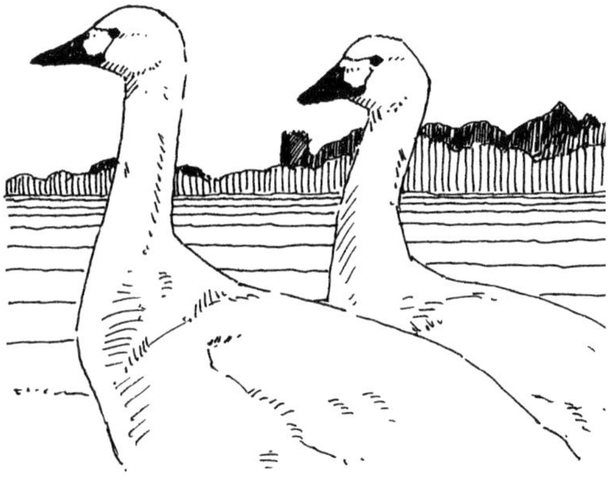

The Ouse Washes, in Cambridgeshire, are now the most important wintering site in the species' range and numbers have risen from a handful in the 1940s to over 5,000 by the 1990s (Kirby *et al.* 1991). Better protection, the provision of refuges and artificial feeding are thought to be the principal reasons for this increase. This extensive area of natural grassland regularly floods in winter and provides an ideal feeding habitat. However, when these shallow waters freeze, the swans will move to feed on arable land. In December 1989, a record gathering of 1,360 fed on discarded sugar beet tops at Kenny Hill, Mildenhall, and almost repeat performances were noted in December 1991 when 1,000 swans, mainly Bewick's, were noted at Sedge Fen, Lakenheath and in 1997 when 1,350 went to roost on an irrigation reservoir at Kenny Hill on January evenings.

On the coast, the number of flocks and flock sizes has also grown. Traditionally, feeding sites include: Shipmeadow, Kessingland Levels, Tinker's Marshes, Walberswick, Minsmere Levels, Aldeburgh, Sudbourne, Orford, Gedgrave, Boyton and Falkenham Marshes. Flocks arriving or moving south are regularly noted at migration watch-points from mid-October onwards and numbers steadily increase at feeding sites as the winter progresses. The majority leave by mid-March, but some linger into April. One that oversummered in the Gipping Valley in 1975 was probably sick.

Since the mid-1960s, emigrating swans have used Breydon Water as a staging post on their return to northern breeding grounds. As with other sites, there has been a spectacular increase in flock sizes and counts of 400+ are noted almost annually. Allard (1990) referred to a gathering of 700 on 21st February 1988 and to an easterly exodus over Great Yarmouth and Breydon Water from 5th-28th March 1985, which totalled 1,200. Away from Breydon Water, the largest herd for eastern Suffolk was 170 at Shipmeadow in December 1990.

Bewick's Swans fitted with inscribed colour-rings have demonstrated the species' mobility. Singles at Westleton in 1985 and Kenny Hill, Mildenhall, in 1990, had been ringed at the WWT Refuge at Slimbridge, Gloucestershire, two years previously. The latter individual had visited sites in Norfolk, Leicestershire and Cheshire during the 1989 winter. Five individuals ringed in arctic Russia have been noted amongst coastal herds in the period 1993-1997. The migration path of each bird can be plotted from the numerous reports from elsewhere in Europe, with multiple sightings from Russia, Estonia, Germany and Holland.

Whooper Swan *Cygnus cygnus*

An uncommon winter visitor and passage migrant

Small herds of Whooper Swans, usually no more than five birds together, are regularly reported, mostly on coastal marshes and often in the company of Bewick's or Mute Swans. Kessingland Levels, Sudbourne Marshes and Felixstowe Ferry have been the most favoured sites in recent years. It is scarce at inland localities.

Ticehurst stated that "there are few birds so truly hard weather visitors as the Wild Swan" and he listed the severe winters of 1819, 1837/8, 1870/1 and 1890/1 when "considerable flocks of 30-50 have been noted".

In recent years, double-figure herds have been rare, the county's largest being 48 which frequented Poplar Farm, Boyton, for two days in early January 1970. A herd of 43, perhaps the same birds, was noted over Havergate Island on 14th March of that year. Several reports of large herds either flying over or arriving from offshore must be treated with suspicion, as it is likely that Bewick's Swans are sometimes confused with this species.

Whooper Swans are rarely seen before November and one on Orfordness on 21st August 1962 was exceptionally early. Most leave by April, although lingering birds occur more often than Bewick's. Excluding those obviously sick or injured, individuals have been noted in May and June at Breydon Water (1880 and 1891), Hopton-on-Sea (1920), Benacre and Walberswick (1946) and Aldeburgh (1993).

Three at Sudbourne and another at Falkenham in January 1997 were wearing neck collars confirming that they had been ringed near Tampere in southern Finland. The Sudbourne birds were part of a brood of six cygnets, all of which wintered in the Norfolk Broads in 1995/6 and one was subsequently noted at Oulu, Finland, in October 1996.

The coastal marshes between Kessingland and the Alde/Ore became the species' favoured wintering localities during the 1970s, with Sudbourne Marshes hosting the largest concentrations. Flocks of 200 or more were regularly reported at the latter site from 1977 to 1986 and numbers increased dramatically during harsh-weather periods. This became particularly evident in early 1979, when a gaggle of 200 (14th January) increased to 700 (4th February), 1,250 (24th February) and peaked at 1,500 (3rd March). Unfortunately, changing land use, as a result of an ESA grant, has encouraged farmers to fence and graze extensively, proving detrimental to the species which no longer occurs there in large numbers.

Birds shot at Carlton Colville and Kessingland, in 1970 and 1972 respectively, which had been ringed in the Netherlands, proves interchange between wintering flocks on the Dutch polders and the coastal marshes of Suffolk.

White-fronts occasionally venture up the River Waveney to graze on flood plains near Beccles, although skeins of 45 over the town on 24th November 1990, and 65 over Ellough on 8th December 1991, were probably from nearby Haddiscoe and Berney Marshes, Norfolk, where wintering flocks have gathered in recent years. Six skeins totalling 200 geese, over Brampton on 4th February 1949, represent the largest count away from the coast and estuaries. Except for the resident Greylag population, the White-front is the commonest grey goose in West Suffolk, with flocks of 5-10 being reported more or less annually at scattered sites.

White-fronts occasionally arrive in late October, although rarely occur in any numbers before late December with peaks most often noted in January and February. Most leave in late February or early March.

In recent years, ones and twos, almost certainly injured or feral individuals, have regularly oversummered with Canada Goose flocks. Since 1988, one or two pairs have nested successfully at Cley, Norfolk, so future establishment of a feral breeding population is a possibility.

Greenland White-fronted Goose *A. a. flavirostris*

Accidental: five records involving 17 individuals

1890	Ramsholt: Ramsholt Marsh, "shot" n.d.
1956	Hartest: ten on 20th February
1975	Gt/Lt Livermere: Livermere Park, 20th February
1982	Gt/Lt Livermere: Livermere Park, three (two ads & an imm.) on 7th-13th December
1985	Minsmere: 9th March
1990	Breydon Water/Burgh Castle: 16th-25th November and 1st December
1999	Southwold: Town Marshes, 7th February and 5th March

The Greenland White-fronted Goose winters in substantial flocks in Ireland, western and northern Scotland and Wales (Lack 1986), although it is very much a rarity in East Anglia. It has been noted in Suffolk on only seven occasions.

Ticehurst makes no mention of this race and, curiously, Payn expressed some doubts over the Hartest record, despite two of them being shot and one examined by the curator of Bury Museum. The orange bill is a diagnostic feature of Greenland White-fronted Goose. The Ramsholt record constitutes the first of this race for East Anglia and the specimen is in the vaults of the Chelmsford & Essex Museum.

Lesser White-fronted Goose *Anser erythropus*

Accidental: three records

1949	Breydon Water: ad. male shot 24th January
1964	Breydon Water: imm. 5th January and ad. with White-fronted Geese 15th January

The above records represent the only likely genuine vagrants. The first was reported as "a goose new to Suffolk" in the *SNS Transactions* following a report in *The Times* newspaper (Giles 1949).

During a survey of introduced and escaped geese in Britain, conducted by the WWT in late June to mid-July 1991, 24 of the 29 Lesser White-fronts located were in East Anglia. They included 15 full-winged individuals at The Otter Trust near Bungay (Delaney 1993). The species is frequently found in association with large flocks of Canada and Greylag Geese, and Lackford and Alton Water are the most favoured sites. A group of four at the former site from 2nd July to 8th September 1991 is the largest reported.

The species' breeding range is restricted to northern Scandinavia and north-east Siberia, and the normal migration is to the Caspian Sea. This goose is a rare annual visitor to the British Isles, with 136 individuals being noted up to the end of 2000 (BBRC). However, there is now so much confusion over origins that it is almost impossible to differentiate with any certainty between wild birds and escapes.

Greylag Goose *Anser anser*

A locally common and increasing resident, and scarce winter visitor

A feral population of Greylag Geese has become well-established on some coastal marshes, lakes, reservoirs, gravel pits and ponds. Outside the breeding season, Greylags congregate in large feeding flocks. Southwold, Minsmere, North Warren, Trimley Marshes, Alton Water and Livermere regularly host the largest concentrations. Small numbers are occasionally noted at migration watch-points.

Bones of this species have been found in the peat of the East Anglian fens where it bred until at least 1773 (Ticehurst 1932, Bircham 1989). Ticehurst had little doubt that it nested in Suffolk and referred to wild geese being taken for fattening from the fens around 1770. He suggested that the taking of goslings and rearing them for market gave name to the gozzard's occupation (one who tends geese and leads them to market).

After its disappearance as a county breeding species, the Greylag became a very rare visitor, noted principally during passage periods. Tuck (1891) considered it the rarest of the four grey geese, but Hele (1870, 1890) stated that it appeared very regularly every season in October and November. These birds were said to have frequented the Iken and Sudbourne Marshes, and several specimens were obtained. Ticehurst, however, questioned the records and suggested that there might have been confusion with Pink-footed Goose by some observers. He referred to only 15-16 Suffolk records with precise dates and considered the Greylag to be a passage migrant. All records were for the period September-November and March-May with the exception of a single winter occurrence – one shot at Breydon Water during the harsh winter of 1906.

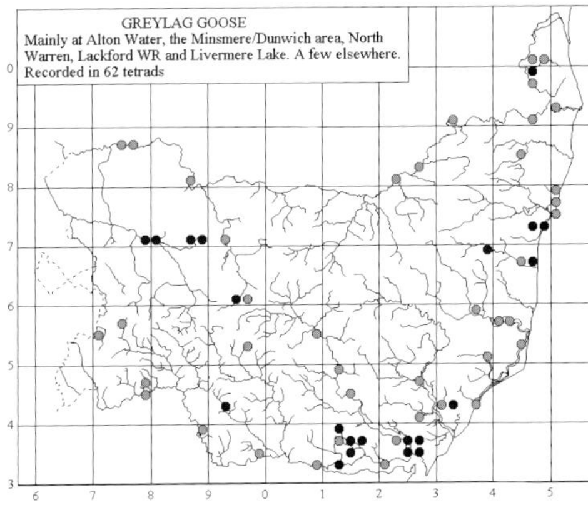

The species was reintroduced to the Norfolk Broads from Scotland in about 1933 (Kelly 1986, Taylor *et al.* 1999) from where its population expanded, at first slowly, but soon very rapidly. Around 200 birds were released in Essex in the 1970s (Cox 1984). Perhaps surprisingly, breeding was not proven in Suffolk until 1976, when a pair reared a brood at Minsmere. Thereafter, numbers increased rapidly and, by 1990, 30 broods were reported at nine widely spread localities. It is likely that the county's population originated from Norfolk stock as there are no known artificial introductions in Suffolk.

Large flocks of 350 or more have been noted at Minsmere and Alton Water between 1987 and 2001, with 815 at the latter site on 10th December 1995. The largest gathering to date involved 1,150 birds on Loompit Lake, Trimley St Mary on 9th January 2000. The county's wintering population in 1990/1 was considered to be in the region of 650-800 (SBR), but by early 2002 this had increased to around 2,500 individuals.

Although the British and Irish populations are generally resident, most other northern populations are migratory, with Icelandic birds wintering in Scotland and Scandinavian birds wintering in the Netherlands. It is difficult to recognise genuine wild birds amongst the county's large wintering flocks except for those that have been colour-marked in some way. A recent example of vagrancy from Scandinavia involved a female marked with an inscribed neck-collar, that was at Minsmere in December 2001 and subsequently at Loompit Lake, Trimley St Martin, on 14th January 2002. It had been captured whilst in moult at Tromso, Norway on 23rd July 2001. The populations of west and north-west Europe are of the nominate race *A. a. anser* and the East Anglian population was derived from this stock. There have been no Suffolk reports of the pink-billed East European and Asian race, *A. a. rubrirostris.*

Snow Goose *Anser caerulescens*

A scarce and wandering feral resident

It is becoming almost impossible to decide whether individual Snow Geese are of wild origin. Known feral groups, of both white and blue colour phases, are noted annually amongst Canada Geese flocks and a white-phase pair nested at Barton Mere in 1990.

Genuine vagrancy from North America to western Europe was confirmed by a flock of 18 in the Netherlands in April 1980, which included a bird ringed in Canada three years previously (Lack 1986). Suffolk's best claims of truly wild vagrants involved three (white phase) adults and a juvenile on Southwold Marshes on 18th-20th March 1982, an immature (blue phase) at Falkenham on 20th-23rd January 1987 and two (white phase) flying with three White-fronts at Middleton on 29th January 1995.

Canada Goose *Branta canadensis*

A locally common resident

Feral Canada Geese are widely distributed throughout the county, breeding by lakes, ponds, reservoirs, gravel pits and rivers, and in coastal grazing marshes, saltings and reedbeds. The size of non-breeding flocks in Suffolk is dramatically increased in midsummer by the addition of breeding pairs and their young from elsewhere in East Anglia. A vast increase in numbers has been noted over the past 30 years, in line with the national trend, resulting in the need to control numbers in some areas, as the goose is sometimes responsible for damage to crops.

Agents of King Charles II introduced the species into England from North America as an ornamental waterfowl around 1665 (Kear 1990). Babington listed a handful of flocks, noted mostly on the coast in spring and summer, which presumably were escapes from local collections. Ticehurst made scant reference to the species and was of the opinion that full-winged individuals, breeding on various private waters, occasionally ventured to the estuaries and inland waters. Payn stated that the species colonised or was introduced to several localities soon after the Great War and by the early 1930s was well-established at Livermere and Redgrave. Breeding was also noted at Culford, Barton Mere, several localities on the Little Ouse, Fritton Lake and two places in the Waveney Valley. Numbers declined during the Second World War, although breeding continued at Livermere and Redgrave from where former haunts were recolonised. The Breckland wintering population (including Norfolk) was estimated to be around 157-225 in 1953 and a link with the north Norfolk flocks was suspected (Ogilvie 1969).

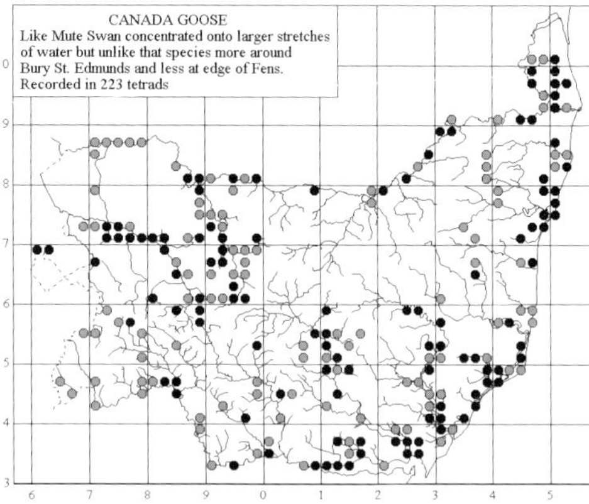

CANADA GOOSE
Like Mute Swan concentrated onto larger stretches of water but unlike that species more around Bury St. Edmunds and less at edge of Fens.
Recorded in 223 tetrads

Wintering numbers rose rapidly from the late 1960s, from 30 on the coast and 300 in Breckland in 1967-1969 (Ogilvie 1969) to a county total of 1,800 in 1972 (Payn 1973). Redgrave Lake held 40-50 breeding pairs during the 1960s and Livermere Lake then hosted about 25-30 pairs. Countywide censuses in 1972 revealed a nesting population of 105 pairs with 229 non-breeders and, by 1988, 192 pairs were present. The latter total was split between 125 pairs on river estuaries (Beardall 1989) and 67 pairs elsewhere. In 1989, the county's wintering population had increased substantially to an estimated 5,000 birds.

Understanding the discrepancy in numbers between the summer and winter populations has been aided by ringing. Bamber (1985) discussed the mobility of large wintering flocks in north-west Suffolk and an extensive study of birds colour-ringed in the Lark Valley confirmed interchange between Breckland, the Suffolk coast and north Norfolk (Martin 1988). Several hundred flightless geese were captured while completing their midsummer moult and, in addition to the many local recoveries, geese were found as far afield as Sutton Bingham Reservoir, Somerset, and Cherbourg, France. Four geese, all ringed at their moulting grounds at Beauly Firth, Scotland, on 12th July 1980, were recovered in the Southwold/Minsmere region between 1980 and 1985.

Barnacle Goose *Branta leucopsis*

An uncommon winter visitor and passage migrant, and an increasingly common feral resident

Large flocks of wild Barnacle Geese visit coastal marshes every few years, principally in late February and often coinciding with harsh weather. In recent years, the status of the species has become clouded by the presence of feral birds, some of which breed. Babington listed only a handful of records and the species was a very rare winter visitor in his day. Ticehurst could add only 11 more occurrences, which he considered were associated with hard weather, particularly snow and easterly gales.

Small groups were noted irregularly during the 1950s and 1960s between October and March, and the first double-figure flock was of 13 at Minsmere on 14th-15th March 1968. In 1970, 17 were noted with White-fronts at Sudbourne on 4th January and during the following week there were 30 at Minsmere, where an additional 43 flew south. Large flocks have since occurred more regularly at several coastal localities, normally in late February. Flocks in the second half of February have included: 60 at Southwold and up to 109 at Sudbourne, both in 1969, 74 flying south off Landguard Point in 1981, 150 at Boyton Marshes in 1981 and up to 66 at Sudbourne in 1991. One found long dead at Havergate Island in April 1991 was presumably from the latter flock and had been ringed two winters previously at Gaastmeer in the Netherlands, the favoured wintering area of the Russian population (Ogilvie 1978).

Unseasonal records in the 1960s, presumably involving feral birds, were from Iken on 2nd-10th May 1964 and Minsmere (a pair) in June 1969. Throughout the 1970s, one or two known escapees commuted with the Canada Goose flocks and it became increasingly difficult to distinguish between wild and feral birds. Feral birds readily hybridised with Canada Geese and their offspring were sometimes mistaken for the small race of Canada Goose *B. canadensis hutchinsii*. Since 1984, breeding pairs of Barnacle Geese have been noted at Cavenham, Havergate Island, Heveningham Hall, Weybread and Sotterley Park. A large semi-resident flock of non-breeding individuals has built up on the Kessingland Levels. Numbers here regularly reach three figures, with a peak occurring in midwinter, presumably due to the arrival of wild birds. A flock of 300 going to roost at Benacre on 30th August 1999 is the largest ever recorded in Suffolk. It had been widely assumed that breeding pairs and summering flocks were of feral origin, but two birds amongst c.20 full-winged Barnacles at Lound and later Fritton Lake, in April and June 1993 respectively, threw this theory into confusion. The former had been ringed in Svalbard in 1986 and had subsequently wintered at Caerlaverock, and the latter had been ringed in Sweden in 1989. Other non-marked birds may well be of similar origin.

Dark-bellied Brent Goose *Branta bernicla bernicla*

A locally common winter visitor and passage migrant

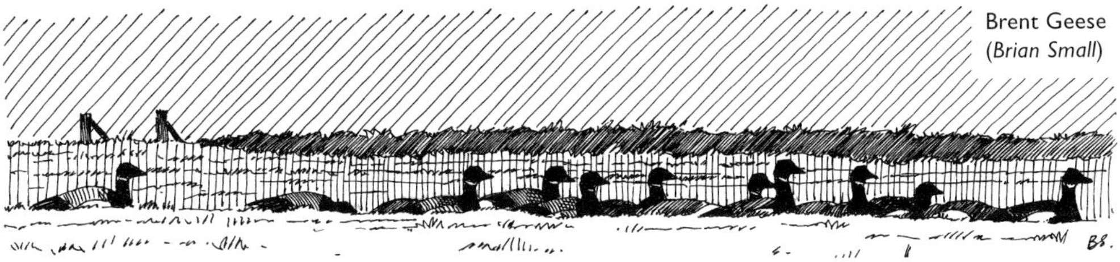

Brent Geese
(*Brian Small*)

Brent Geese are almost exclusively maritime, wintering in huge flocks on larger river estuaries and coastal marshes. The East Anglian wintering population is predominantly of the dark-bellied race *B. b. bernicla*. They traditionally feed on mudflats, foraging for eelgrass or algae at the tide edge (Owen 1980). When food is in short supply, flocks will venture to new areas. Many former grazing marshes are now under cultivation and the tender young shoots of winter wheat provide an ideal substitute. As numbers have increased, there have been the inevitable protests from the farming community and, when dispersal techniques have failed, the former Ministry of Agriculture, Fisheries and Food has issued licences for a small cull. The largest concentrations are found on the Orwell, Deben and Stour, although smaller numbers frequent other coastal sites. The geese seldom move far from tidal waters, although those on the Felixstowe peninsula regularly feed two miles away from either the Deben or Orwell.

Payn stated that it was formerly "very plentiful" on Breydon Water and there is evidence to suggest that the species occurred regularly on the Orwell and Stour estuaries during the 19th century. Numbers crashed markedly in the 1930s due to a disease affecting eelgrass (the staple winter diet), persecution on its breeding grounds on the arctic coasts of Siberia and extensive wildfowling, and the East Anglian population was at its lowest ebb in the 1950s. Following special protection measures and a series of exceptional breeding seasons, the population recovered well. By the mid-1960s, gatherings of 750 were recorded on the Stour and, 20 years later, four-figure flocks were regularly reported in the county, the largest being 4,000 on the Deben in February 1986.

The immigration of Brent Geese can be charted from vantage points all along the coast and can be one of the most spectacular events of the autumn. Small flocks normally appear in mid-September and numbers steadily increase through to November. A strong onshore wind in late October encourages skeins to pass close inshore and day-counts of several thousand are not uncommon. The largest day-counts were 15,000 off Pakefield on 5th November 1982 (Piotrowski 1983b) and 16,000 off Landguard Point on 11th November 1983.

Movement between the major estuaries is frequent. Ringing recoveries prove that the county's wintering flocks stop off in northern Europe on their return to arctic breeding grounds. Eight birds ringed in spring in Germany and ten in the Netherlands have been found wintering in south-east Suffolk and some have regularly alternated between sites. An individual ringed in Germany in 1983, was present there again in 1988 and then at Trimley Marshes in 1989. It was back at its nesting site at Taimyr, Russia in 1991 and then in the Netherlands the following winter.

Inland records are scarce. Up to 1984, a single bird feeding at Newton Green, near Sudbury on 31st January 1976 was the only one for West Suffolk. Flocks of 1-5 have since been noted in most years, with Livermere and Lackford Wildfowl Reserve being favoured localities. The largest inland flock involved a party of 50 that flew south-east over Eriswell on 13th January 1987.

Oversummering used to be extremely rare and the few May or June records mostly related to injured birds. Ticehurst referred to a flock off Aldeburgh that arrived exhausted from offshore after battling against a north-easterly gale on 10th June 1923. Brent Geese usually begin their spring migration before the end of March but, in the 1990s, spring migration off Landguard Point has become progressively later each year, for example 227 on 18th-20th May 1991 and 320 from 25th May to 1st June 1995. Ones and twos are now noted in midsummer during most years.

Pale-bellied Brent Goose *B. b. hrota*

An uncommon winter visitor

A scan through large Brent Goose flocks will often reveal pale-bellied individuals and sometimes they occur in single-race groups. Flocks of six or more are rare, being reported on only eight occasions between 1970 and 1995. The largest groups of that period involved 20 that frequented Lowestoft during harsh weather in February 1979 and at least 20 at Sudbourne/Orford on 13th September 1987. However, all previous records were eclipsed by the numbers observed in February/March 1996, when 50 pale-bellied birds were recorded within a flock of 400 Brents at Aldeburgh on 3rd February. In addition, there were 32 at Hollesley on 14th February and at Benacre on 23rd February, 80 at Tinker's Walks, Walberswick on 23rd-25th February, 59 at Gisleham on 3rd March and six at Boyton on 9th March. The 1996 records were part of an unprecedented influx into northern Europe which included c.2,000 birds in the Netherlands (Anon. 1996). The earliest autumn arrivals were eight that frequented Minsmere and the Blyth from 28th August to 5th September 1970.

Black Brant *B. b. nigricans*

Very rare winter visitor: 18 records

Individuals showing characteristics of the North American and East Siberian race colloquially known as the Black Brant, have regularly been noted among the Brent flocks in south-eastern counties since 1975. The race is noted more or less annually in Suffolk and has been found in Britain and Ireland on 129 occasions up to the end of 2000 (BBRC).

Records involving a particularly bulky adult, seen in consecutive winters at two sites on the Orwell Estuary from 1975 to 1978, were the first for Suffolk and almost certainly referred to the same individual returning with the same flock year after year (M. Marsh pers comm.). The next bird, at Levington in 1979, was noticeably smaller.

An adult at Boyton Marshes on 3rd January 1982 was the only record for that decade but, between 1991 and 2001, Black Brants were noted annually except in 1999. The many sightings each winter probably related to one individual, although up to three frequented the Deben and Orwell Estuaries during the winter of 2000/1.

Red-breasted Goose *Branta ruficollis*

Accidental: the records possibly involve only three individuals

1983/4	Deben/Orwell/Stour: ad. 11th December to 19th February
2000	Deben/Orwell: Waldringfield/Kirton/Wherstead Strand, 2nd-9th January
	Felixstowe: Landguard Point, S 17th January
	Southwold: 7th-17th January
	Lound: Waterworks, 20th-21st January
	Aldeburgh: North Warren, 2nd-30th December
2001	Aldeburgh: North Warren, 9th-13th January
	Minsmere: 3rd, 18th, 19th and 25th January

Despite their distinctive markings, Red-breasted Geese are notoriously difficult to locate amongst compact and constantly moving feeding flocks of Brents. The 1983/4 individual demonstrated the mobility of the wintering Brent Geese, presumably being present with the same flock at Falkenham, Ramsholt, Holbrook Bay, Levington and Trimley Marshes. The January 2000 bird frequented a Brent Goose flock on the Deben, but was also seen on the Orwell, off Landguard Point and at Southwold. The December 2000 bird arrived with Brents but later associated with a flock of White-fronted Geese.

A further five occurrences have involved presumed escapees. An adult, found amongst Canada Geese at Gedgrave on 16th November 1986, was subsequently seen at Falkenham from 25th November to 6th March 1987, before it moved up the coast to the Benacre/Kessingland and Weybread areas and was last reported on 29th July 1990. This bird was nearly always in the company of Canadas, except at Falkenham, where it initially associated with Brents before joining another Canada flock. Other adults have been reported with Canada flocks at Minsmere on 16th October 1994, Bramford on 25th-26th December 1996, two at Lound Waterworks on 14th September 1999 and one on Tinker's Marsh, Walberswick on 4th-21st June 2001.

The Red-breasted Goose breeds in west-central Siberia and winters mainly on the shores of the Black and Caspian Seas (Owen 1980). Its status has become slightly obscured by the presence of wanderers from wildfowl collections. Wild birds have been noted in Britain and Ireland on 61 occasions up to 2000 (BBRC).

Egyptian Goose *Alopochen aegyptiacus*

A locally common resident

Large, old trees, short grass and areas of standing freshwater are the breeding requirements of the Egyptian Goose, all of which are features of many stately homes in rural Suffolk. The main concentrations of Egyptian Geese are found around the parkland estates of Somerleyton and Sotterley in north-east Suffolk, and Euston, Ixworth and Livermere inland. The breeding range has expanded slowly and nesting sites now include gravel workings in the Waveney and Blackbourne Valleys. The Egyptian Goose remains faithful to traditional sites and wanders little during winter.

Its introduction into Britain dates back to 1678, when the species was noted in King Charles II's menagerie in St James's Park, London. It soon became popular in ornamental wildfowl collections on larger estates, from which it undoubtedly escaped. By the 19th century there were unpinioned, breeding groups in Norfolk, Bedfordshire, Devon and East Lothian (Holloway 1996). It was then considered to be an annual winter visitor to Suffolk and was sought after by local gunners. Babington listed many records, but Ticehurst made only scant reference to full-winged birds that were kept on various private waters.

Early records include a pair shot by fishermen off Great Yarmouth in 1851, two obtained at Thorpe Mere in 1857 and another eight in 1862, and one at Falkenham on 10th March 1936. Occurrences on the Norfolk coast, following easterly gales, prompted Lubbock (1845) to suggest that such birds could well be stragglers from the Netherlands, where there were also large collections.

Nesting was confirmed for the first time in Suffolk at Church Farm Marshes, Aldeburgh in 1973. The site became the county's stronghold for the species throughout the decade, with 2-3 pairs breeding annually and flocks of up to 17 reported. Wanderers from here were probably responsible for a number of records at other coastal localities. Broods were also noted at Lound in 1978, Lackford in 1979, Gunton in 1980 and Livermere in 1981. Breeding numbers increased steadily during the 1980s and Egyptian Geese now nest annually at Lound, Somerleyton, Sotterley Park, Weybread Pits, Wickham Market, Ixworth Thorpe, Euston, Lackford and Livermere. Birds normally pair in December and nest in late winter, with broods often appearing in early March. The county's breeding population is likely to be in the region of 20 pairs, although the number actually reported remains in single figures, with early nesters possibly overlooked. A pair, which nested in a cavity of an old oak and then in the main fork of an adjacent tree, is the only specific reference to a nest site in Suffolk (Tomlinson 1994).

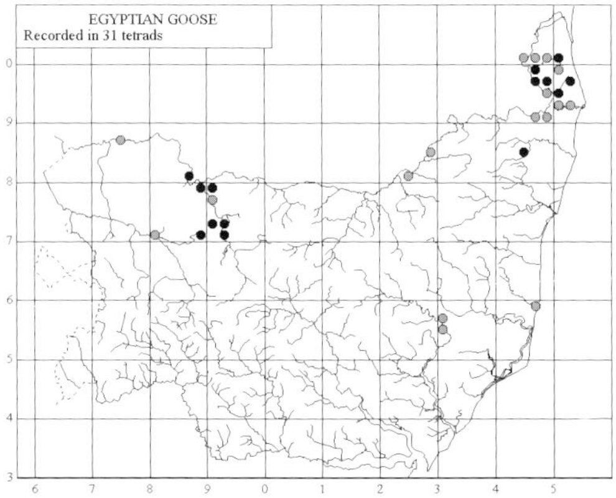

Moulting congregations are frequently noted in late summer and early autumn, with the largest number being 97 at Somerleyton on 11th September 1993.

Ruddy Shelduck *Tadorna ferruginea*

Accidental and escapee: c.75 records

1892 Aldringham-cum-Thorpe: Thorpe Mere, eight in from sea 5th July

The vast majority of records of Ruddy Shelduck are presumed to relate to escapees or birds of feral origin. The species is noted annually in small numbers, most often singly and usually in the company of other wildfowl.

Ticehurst quoted the only record assigned to genuine vagrancy from wild origins (see above). This flock was seen at a considerable height arriving from the sea off Thorpe. They alighted on a wet marsh at Thorpe Mere, where three were shot and now form part of the Ogilvie Collection at Ipswich Museum. Their arrival coincided with a considerable influx into Britain, involving 40-50 birds in parties of up to 20. The possibility of escapes was recognised as early as 1889, "the species was long ago introduced on many ornamental waters" (Rogers 1982). It has been suggested that autumn arrivals may relate to pre- or post-breeding flights from feral populations in northern Europe, where they sometimes breed in the wild. Vinicombe *et al.* (1993), on behalf of the BOURC, examined this possibility and found that breeding attempts were sporadic and there were no fully self-supporting populations. The large number of young produced in captivity was discussed, as well as the habit of continental wildfowl breeders of releasing excess young at the end of the season. Vinicombe & Harrop (1999) reviewed British and Irish records for the period 1986-1994 and it was concluded that the species should be regarded as an irruptive vagrant to north-western Europe.

Nearly half of the Suffolk occurrences have been noted in summer to early autumn (July-September), so some records are likely to relate to birds of wild origin, possibly displaced by droughts in their breeding haunts in south-east Europe and south-west Asia. Three that flighted in and out of Minsmere on 14th August 1989 (SBR), coincided with flocks of four in both Leicestershire from 17th August and Yorkshire on 18th August (Vinicombe & Harrop 1999), perhaps indicating a genuine influx.

Shelduck (Common Shelduck) *Tadorna tadorna*

A locally common resident, winter visitor and passage migrant

During the winter months, Shelducks are almost exclusively maritime, with large numbers inhabiting estuaries and coastal marshes. Nesting usually takes place near water, chiefly at coastal localities south of Aldeburgh but also in the Minsmere area and inland, notably around Livermere Park and Lackford. Large offshore movements are reported each autumn.

Rabbit burrows on dunes and heaths are traditionally chosen as nesting sites, although, nowadays, nests are more often found in hollow trees and amongst thick ground cover. In early April, territorial pairs leave the estuaries for drilled fields, woodland clearings or rides close to their intended breeding sites.

The Shelduck became rare as a breeding species during the late 19th century. For example, Babington stated that it "perhaps still breeds" and Tuck (1891) stated "a pair or two nest near the coast, but seldom bring off their young". Its demise was attributed to persecution by rabbit-warreners who blamed Shelducks for disturbing their stock (Holloway 1996). Rabbit farming declined early in the 20th century, and a recovery in the numbers of Shelduck followed. An estimated 187 pairs bred annually in the period 1925-1927 (Ticehurst 1932). In 1941, c.900 breeding pairs were counted on five estuaries, including 375-400 on the Orwell (Hollom 1941). Numbers remained relatively stable over the next 25-30 years – the *1968-72 Atlas* showed breeding in 21 10-km squares within the county and it probably bred in two others. A survey of Suffolk's estuaries in 1988 revealed 531 pairs (Beardall 1989) and a national census completed four years later found 1,129 pairs in Suffolk, representing 9.5% of the British breeding population (Wright 1994). In addition, there were 1,403 non-breeding Shelduck of which 42% were on the Orwell.

Although great numbers nested in Norfolk during the 17th century, often far inland, the Shelduck's expansion into West Suffolk occurred only comparatively recently. Three pairs nested at Lakenheath in 1947 and there were sporadic breeding attempts up to the mid-1970s. Thereafter, numbers increased steadily, particularly at Livermere, where, in 1992, 45 pairs raised 84 young. Breeding now takes place annually at Ixworth, Elveden and Lackford. Payn expressed the view that the Livermere birds were progenies of a captive pair released at East Wretham, Norfolk, some time before 1957. However, as the Breckland population disappears during the winter months and, as the increase in numbers corresponds to that in the Cambridgeshire Fens (Bircham 1989), natural inland expansion from the Wash would appear to be a more likely explanation.

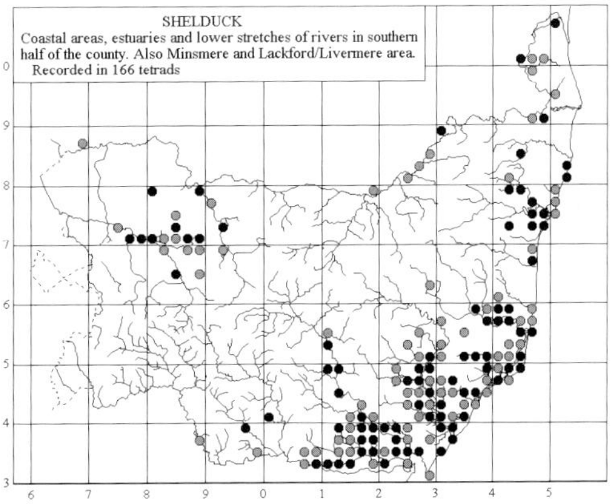

SHELDUCK
Coastal areas, estuaries and lower stretches of rivers in southern half of the county. Also Minsmere and Lackford/Livermere area.
Recorded in 166 tetrads

Most British adults move to the Heligoland Bight off Germany each July to moult, although, in recent years, other moulting flocks have been found in the Firth of Forth, the Wash and Bridgewater Bay (Gibbons *et al.* 1993). These include parents of dependent young, but a few adults remain to tend the combined broods, herding the ducklings into large crèches. The largest of these was 97 at Livermere in 1983. Returning flocks are noted daily at offshore localities in October and November, and such movements are often substantial with four-figure day-totals not uncommon. A total of 2,000 was logged off both Lowestoft and Southwold during a four-hour period on 27th October 1989. Huge southerly movements are sometimes recorded at the onset of harsh weather, the largest being 9,000 off Minsmere on 21st December 1969 and 2,800 off Landguard Point on 9th January 1986.

The larger river estuaries of south-east Suffolk hold the bulk of the wintering population and 1,000 or more are regularly reported. The Stour has traditionally held the highest populations, where the largest counts have been 3,370 in December 1959, 2,762 in January 1986 and 2,967 in February 1994. The highest count from the Orwell was 2,500 on 4th March 1979. The species' susceptibility to freezing conditions was demonstrated by the discovery of 99 corpses during the arctic spell in February 1991. These were found on three estuaries including the Orwell and Deben, for which they represented 5% and 3% respectively of the wintering populations.

Ringing returns show that immigrants from the near continent augment the breeding population in winter. Shelducks ringed, mostly in late summer, in Estonia, Poland, Denmark (4), France (3) and Germany (16) have been found on Suffolk estuaries. Birds ringed on the Suffolk coast, mostly in autumn, have been recovered in Belgium, the Netherlands, Germany and France. Britain's oldest Shelduck was found dead at Manningtree, Essex, on 4th April 1986, 15 years after being ringed as a juvenile at Butley Creek.

Mandarin Duck *Aix galericulata*

An uncommon feral visitor – has bred

The Mandarin Duck was introduced into Britain before 1765 and is a prized exhibit of many wildfowl collections. A thriving feral population has been building up for many years in southern counties and is currently estimated to be in excess of 7,000 (Gibbons *et al.* 1993). Occurrences in Suffolk were largely ignored until its promotion to 'Category C' of the British list in 1971. One on Fritton Decoy in October 1898 was the only record mentioned by Ticehurst.

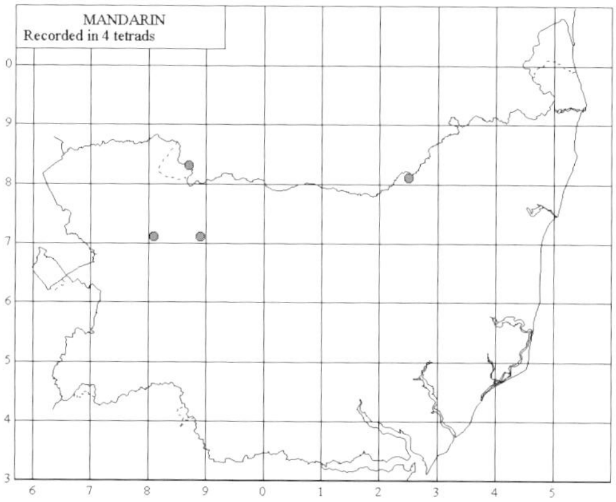

Numbers have increased steadily since the mid-1980s, although there are only four breeding records. In 1986, a female was discovered incubating a clutch in a cavity of a beech tree at Foxhall and, in the same year, two ducklings were reported on a small pond at Wherstead. Breeding was repeated at Wherstead the following summer and again two young were reared. Finally, a pair with eight ducklings were picked up in an Ipswich car park and released in Holywells Park in 1996.

There is little doubt that many records relate to birds that have recently escaped from local wildfowl collections. However, numbers increase during periods of harsh weather and it is possible that some are forced from their breeding areas when lakes and ponds become frozen. A count of 21 (13 males and eight females) on Christchurch Park, Ipswich on 25th November 2000 is by far the largest flock to date. A small population has become established in north-west Norfolk and the recent run of records in Breckland may well relate to post-breeding dispersal from that area.

Interchange between Suffolk and the near continent is proved by an extraordinary ringing return, involving a male ringed at Bennebroek, the Netherlands, on 9th April 1989 and noted at Lound exactly a year later.

Wigeon (Eurasian Wigeon) *Anas penelope*

A locally common winter visitor and passage migrant – a few oversummer and occasionally breed

River estuaries and coastal marshes host large flocks of Wigeon during winter with smaller numbers at Alton Water Reservoir and a few traditional inland sites.

There are two references to breeding during the 19th century. A clutch of eggs was taken from a site on the River Waveney near Bungay in April 1837 and adults with six young were noted on Ramsholt Marshes in early June 1882. Small numbers oversummering at coastal localities have become increasingly regular since the 1950s. In June 1973, a female with at least one young was noted at Reydon Marshes. Five ducklings accompanied a female at Southwold in 1975 and, during the following summer, two pairs bred successfully at Walberswick. Broods were seen at Minsmere in 1981 and 1990. A female with young at Glemsford in 1980 was thought to have been of feral origin.

Wigeon arrive in their thousands during the autumn and numbers increase dramatically during harsh-weather periods, especially when the Baltic Sea and waters on the near continent become ice-bound. The largest concentrations are found on the Stour and Alde/Ore/Butley complex where totals of 8,000 or more have been reported on 16 occasions since 1952. The county's highest counts were all from the Stour, with an early season peak of 11,800 in October 1966 and 13,000 in December 1959 and 1965 (Cox 1984). Most wintering birds depart in March.

Small flocks are normally noted moving south offshore in mid-August and these increase in number through September and October, to peak in early November. Landguard Bird Observatory logged a remarkable southerly movement of wildfowl, involving 27,900 Wigeon at the onset of severe weather on 10th January 1987.

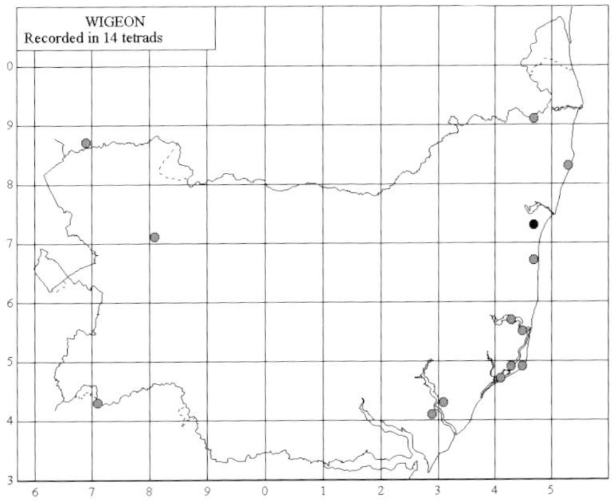

Wigeon were formerly almost exclusively marine, feeding on eel-grass (listed by Ticehurst as "Wigeon-grass"), algae and other plants associated with mud-flats and saltings. In the 1930s, a disease which attacked eel-grass forced the duck to seek an alternative food supply and soon small flocks were noted feeding on stubble grain and the young shoots of wheat. Thousands frequented stubble fields in the Iken area in February 1963, during the severe weather that winter. Wigeon do still feed extensively on algae, particularly *Enteromorpha* which is abundant at Butley River, Levington Creek, Holbrook Bay and other estuarine localities.

Daytime roosting of large flocks on the sea, which has become increasingly regular since the early 1970s, is probably due to disturbance on the coast during daylight hours. It is likely that these ducks return to feeding grounds after dark. Congregations of several hundred are regularly noted in Sole Bay but the largest count was 1,200 off Covehithe on 1st December 1973.

Wigeon were rare in West Suffolk early in the 20th century, despite the species being the commonest duck on the Cambridgeshire Washes (Bircham 1989). Ticehurst made no reference to inland occurrences and Babington listed only three records. Small parties were occasionally seen on inland waters in the early 1950s and a flock of 120 at Livermere on 30th January 1972, was considered exceptional. However, by the mid-1980s, three-figure flocks were a regular feature with Livermere and Lakenheath Washes being the principal sites. The largest inland gathering involved 1,000 feeding at Higham, in the Stour Valley, on 7th January 1980.

Most Wigeon are highly migratory as ringing recoveries demonstrate. Nacton Decoy was for many years one of Britain's premier wildfowl ringing sites and it is perhaps not surprising that Suffolk has received an impressive number of recoveries. Of the 1,833 Wigeon ringed at Nacton, there have been recoveries from the former USSR (59), Baltic States (7), Poland (1), Finland (30), Norway (1), Sweden (6), Denmark (21), Germany (6), the Netherlands (11), Belgium (1), France (15), Spain (1), Italy (3), Romania (1), Tunisia (1), Morocco (1) and Ireland (19). A further 92 birds have been recovered elsewhere in Britain, and Wigeon ringed in Iceland (2), Finland (1), the former USSR (1), Denmark (1), the Netherlands (13) and Belgium (1) have been found in Suffolk.

American Wigeon — *Anas americana*

Accidental: 13 individuals

1974	Minsmere: pair 21st May to 7th June, male only 8th-26th June then rejoined by female 27th June to 2nd July
	Benacre: 20th May
1979	Breydon Water: ad. male, with Wigeon, 19th February
1988	Minsmere: The Scrape, first-winter male and female 27th-28th January
1996	Levington/Trimley St Martin: River Orwell/Loompit Lake, male 3rd-8th November
2000	Minsmere: 10th January to 17th April
2001	Minsmere: ecl. male 20th-21st September
	Southwold: 22nd October
2002	Cattawade: male 2nd-28th March
	Minsmere: male 12th April-31st May, again intermittently from 2nd-17th June, and female 30th May-14th June

A high proportion of British records for the American Wigeon relate to late September and early October, coinciding with the main arrival of Wigeon. Drakes in eclipse plumage at this time of year could go unnoticed.

The duck from the long-staying 1974 pair disappeared for three weeks in June and there was speculation that incubation was taking place. However, on her return no young were seen.

The American Wigeon breeds in North America and winters as far south as Panama. Of the 423 records for Britain and Ireland, for the period 1958-2000 (BBRC), at least four had been ringed in Canada (Mead & Clark 1993), proving that genuine vagrancy occurs. However, free-flying American Wigeon are not uncommon in wildfowl collections and, in consequence, some of the listed records may refer to escapees. An eclipse male on the River Stour at Long Melford, from 28th August to 12th September 1994, was of uncertain origin and is consequently omitted from the list of occurrences.

Gadwall *Anas strepera*

A common resident and winter visitor

The breeding population of the Gadwall is almost exclusively confined to the stretch of coast from Minsmere to Benacre, and along the River Lark and Little Ouse, with nesting taking place near lakes and rivers. Large flocks winter at a few favoured sites, particularly in West Suffolk. Although numbers probably increase in winter as a result of immigration, the Gadwall is rarely seen moving offshore.

The present breeding population in Britain derives very largely from introduced stock (Fox 1988) and this is known to be the case in West Suffolk. The Breckland population originated in Norfolk where, in 1850, a pair of decoy-caught birds was released on Narford Lake, near Swaffham. A breeding population soon became established and gradually spread. Nesting was recorded in Suffolk for the first time in 1897 (Ticehurst 1932), at Euston, Elveden and around Thetford. It is likely that wild birds supplemented this feral population.

The origin of the coastal population is not so clear-cut. In the 19th century, the Gadwall was a scarce winter visitor and Babington listed only a handful of records. The situation changed little during the early part of the 20th century and Ticehurst doubted whether it occurred annually. A flock of ten visited Breydon Water on 17th May 1901, a pair probably bred at Aldeburgh in 1913 and breeding was confirmed at Barnby Broad the following year. In the early 1930s, there was a marked acceleration in colonisation with pairs present during the breeding season at several coastal localities. By the late 1940s, it was probably nesting annually. At least ten pairs bred at Minsmere in 1950 and by the end of the decade this population had risen to 40-50 pairs. In 1982, the county's breeding population had reached 100 pairs at 13 sites. A significant proportion of these nested on the River Lark, and the section between West Stow and Mildenhall hold one of the highest concentrations in Britain.

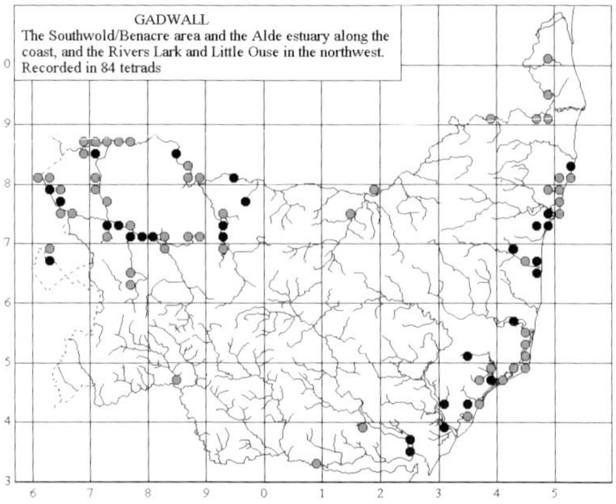
GADWALL
The Southwold/Benacre area and the Alde estuary along the coast, and the Rivers Lark and Little Ouse in the northwest.
Recorded in 84 tetrads
0
9
8
7
6
5
4
3
6
7
8
9
0
1
2
3
4
5

Large autumn and winter gatherings became a regular feature at Minsmere in the late 1940s, the first three-figure count being 100 on a single pool on 5th September 1948. Ten years later, the site's peak was 160 and, in 1969, 200 were present. Numbers were also increasing in the Lark Valley, in West Suffolk, with peak counts at Lackford of 120 in October 1975, 186 in February 1986, 320 in January 1990, 315 in January 1991, 302 in December 1992, 200 in January 1993, 247 in December 1994, 166 in December 1998, a county record of 375 in December 1999 and 288 in January 2000. At Lackford, the Gadwall has benefited greatly by the transformation of working gravel pits to a wildfowl reserve of national repute and the Lark Valley is now one of the most important wintering areas for the species in Britain. The development of wetland habitats in south-east Suffolk, since the 1970s, has resulted in further colonisation in an area where it was formerly scarce. Three-figure wintering flocks are now regularly noted at sites such as Alton Water, Trimley Marshes and Loompit Lake. A count of 355 at Alton Water on 11th December 1997 constitutes the county's largest gathering away from Lackford.

Relatively few Gadwall have been ringed in Suffolk, although recoveries have been reported from France (7), the Netherlands (4), Spain (1) and Ireland (2).

Teal (Common Teal) — *Anas crecca*

A locally common resident, common winter visitor and passage migrant

A large winter population of the Teal frequents coastal marshes and estuaries, and smaller flocks are common at inland waters. The small breeding population is almost entirely coastal and is diminishing rapidly. Passage flocks are regularly logged at migration watch-points.

Ticehurst stated that the Teal had undergone a considerable increase since the late 19th century and that it was common as a breeding bird between Lowestoft and Orford. Nesting was also recorded in West Suffolk, especially in the Lark Valley area, and was increasing at Euston. Early SBRs (1950-1951) list the species as a widespread resident and in 1960 a total of 45 pairs bred at Minsmere. Breeding pairs show a preference for waters surrounded by thick cover, such as reedbeds at coastal marshes, although the actual nesting site is often amongst heather on adjacent heaths. The drainage of marshes and meadows in the 1960s resulted in a decrease, but breeding continued on the coast and in Breckland, and sporadically along the Stour Valley (Payn 1978). The decline became more marked in the 1980s and by the end of that decade nesting occurred in only a few areas. From 1988-1994, Walberswick, Minsmere and Lackford were the only sites to host broods and the current breeding population is less than ten pairs. Nationally, a conservative assessment of the change in breeding numbers, between the periods 1968-1972 and 1988-1991, showed a reduction of one third (Gibbons *et al.* 1993). This surely understates the situation in Suffolk. It remains to be seen whether new wetland reserves at North Warren, Hazelwood Marshes and Trimley will support any recovery.

Whilst there has been a decrease in the number of breeding pairs, there has been an increase in wintering numbers on the coast. Flocks of 2,000 or more are now regular on the Alde/Ore estuary complex, but the county's largest gathering of 6,000 was on Havergate Island in January 1956.

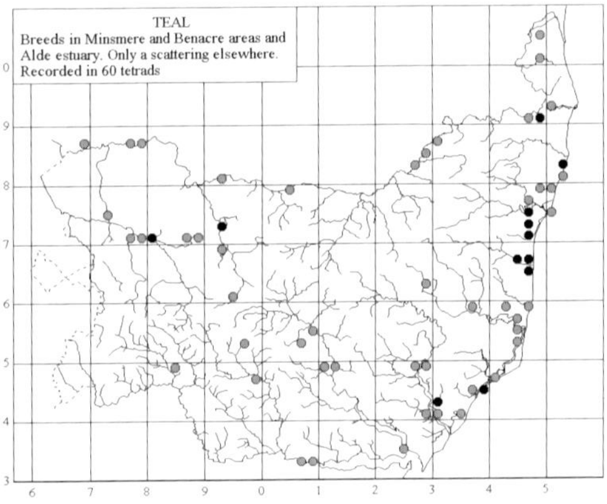

Most of the wintering population leave in March. Returning birds, in particular moulting males, start to appear as early as late June. The Teal is regularly logged during wildfowl movements and a southerly passage involving 1,500 off Southwold on 1st September 1994 far exceeds any other count.

Teal have traditionally been shot and trapped, and many older records relate to wildfowlers' bags and decoy captures. Ticehurst referred to the waters of Ashby (Fritton Decoy), where, in the reign of Elizabeth I, the tenant's 'fowling rent' of "100 couple of teals" was paid to the Lord of the Manor. Decoys have long been used to capture ducks for the table and, during the late 19th century, 1,000 Teal were taken annually at both Iken and Lakenheath Decoys (Payn 1978). During the period 1967-1981, 2,743 Teal were trapped for ringing purposes at Nacton Decoy and the presence of foreign-ringed birds revealed their origins. The recovery rate of Teal has always been high because of shooting. Of the 470 recoveries of Suffolk-ringed birds during the period 1909-1995, the following were from overseas: the former U.S.S.R (15), Finland (19), Denmark (17), Sweden (2), Baltic States (3), Poland (2), Germany (8), Iceland (1), the Netherlands (9), France (33), Italy (1), Portugal (1) and Ireland (17).

Green-winged Teal — *Anas carolinensis*

A very rare winter visitor and passage migrant: 17 records

For most of the 20th century, the Green-winged Teal was treated as a sub-species of the Teal. However, taxonomic studies indicate that it should be treated as a separate species (Sangster *et al.* 2001).

There is a predominance of spring records with most between mid-March and late May. However, its true autumn status remains uncertain, as Green-winged Teal and Teal are almost inseparable whilst in eclipse plumage in August and September. Females are always difficult to separate from female Teal and, in consequence, all records involve drakes in breeding plumage.

Red-breasted Merganser *Mergus serrator*

An uncommon winter visitor and passage migrant

Coastal localities, principally the river estuaries, are favoured winter retreats for the Red-breasted Merganser, although offshore records are commonplace. It is scarce away from salt water. The deeper waters of the Orwell estuary have traditionally been favoured, significant numbers first being noted in 1955 when a peak of 35 occurred in mid-March. During February of the following year, a peak of 85 was recorded, based on a count of birds flying to sea at dusk – behaviour that has been noted frequently since. This wintering population remained relatively constant at around 30-40 birds from the late 1950s to the mid-1980s, but during the 1990s the population has declined, with the Stour taking over as the principal site. The county's highest ever count of 169 occurred on the Orwell on 4th March 1979 during the severe weather of that winter. Small flocks are regularly reported elsewhere, but these rarely reach double figures.

Southerly movements of passage birds are regularly logged at migration watch-points, with numbers increasing dramatically during strong northerly gales in the first half of November. The highest counts are 160 off Pakefield on 6th November 1982, 78 off Benacre on 12th November 1983, 65 off Landguard Point on 9th November 1992 and 94 off Minsmere on 3rd November 1994. Spring passage is usually light with small groups passing north from late March to mid-May.

Most birds depart by early April, although some linger into May and June, and July occurrences are almost annual, with Benacre Broad and the Alde/Ore estuary being the most favoured localities. Almost all records in the summer months refer to singles, although groups of two or three are occasionally reported. A flock of six at Minsmere on 17th July 1975 was exceptional. Oversummering birds have been noted at Orford (1956), Butley (1968), Shingle Street (1970) and on the Orwell (1975).

Goosander *Mergus merganser*

A locally common winter visitor and passage migrant

Singles and small flocks of Goosanders usually winter at freshwater localities, with the larger inland lakes hosting the highest concentrations. Small parties are not uncommon at coastal localities and birds often seek refuge in tidal waters during harsh-weather periods. The most favoured wintering sites are Alton Water reservoir, flooded gravel workings in the Gipping, Lark and Waveney Valleys and, during freezing conditions, Ipswich Docks.

Although Goosanders were noted annually from 1900 to 1930, it was only during severe weather that numbers increased and even then were very much restricted to tidal waters (Ticehurst 1932). Such birds would have been of foreign origin, as at that time the Goosander was only just beginning to colonise Britain as a breeding species. There has since been a substantial increase and a southerly expansion in range of the British breeding population. The construction of reservoirs, and an increase in the number of flooded gravel workings, during and since the 1970s, have provided an abundance of suitable wintering habitat in Suffolk. Nowadays, concentrations of 20-30 are noted annually at Lackford Wildfowl Reserve, which is currently the county's principal site. A peak of 42 birds was logged at Lackford in February 1987. Wintering Goosanders are extremely mobile and there is much interchange between sites in north-west Suffolk, and probably also further afield. Those at Lackford Wildfowl Reserve often disperse during the day to feed at Livermere, Cavenham and on the adjacent River Lark, returning to roost on the pits just before dusk. A swift exodus to the coast takes place when inland waters become frozen.

The main arrival occurs in late December and peak numbers are normally noted in February and early March. However, there are a few August records and occasionally birds linger into May. There are also four occurrences in June and two in July, including one present at Havergate throughout July and August 1975.

Offshore movements are not uncommon in late October and November – the largest being a flock of 15 south off Minsmere on 18th November 1974. A flock of 28 flying south off Landguard Point on 2nd January 1996 heralded an unprecedented influx that involved more than a hundred birds. Groups of 1-7 were reported from over 20 sites, with the highest counts being a single flock of 50 south over Ipswich Docks, a group of 43 flying inland at Aldeburgh and 29 at Minsmere, all on 2nd January, and 17 at Alton Water three days later. A peak of 27 was reached at Lackford during the same month.

During severe weather periods, Ipswich Docks and Breydon Water become the most favoured refuges and 20 at the latter site on 29th-30th March 1992 was a high estuarine count.

Birds ringed in Finland and Sweden have been recovered in Suffolk. This indicates that at least part of the wintering population originates in Fennoscandia.

Ruddy Duck *Oxyura jamaicensis*

An uncommon resident, winter visitor and passage migrant

Ruddy Ducks breed on small reed-fringed lakes but can be most secretive, hiding for long periods in dense clumps of reeds. The species winters on larger, more open waters usually in association with large wildfowl flocks. Minsmere, Walberswick, Loompit Lake, Trimley Marshes, Alton Water, Livermere Lake, Ampton Water and Lackford are the most favoured sites. Freezing conditions will sometimes force wintering birds to seek refuge at estuarine localities, but this species is rare on the open sea.

Three pairs of this North American 'stiff-tail', were added to the wildfowl collection at Slimbridge, Gloucestershire in 1948 and this provided a base from where it colonised south-western counties. There has been a massive increase in the British population since 1971, reaching an estimated 350-400 breeding pairs in 1988 (Marchant *et al.* 1990). The WWT's National Wildfowl Counts showed a further increase to reach a peak winter population of around 3,500 in January 1992, although figures for subsequent years have shown an apparent decline (Cranswick *et al.* 1995).

One at Minsmere in June 1976 and another at Alton Water later in that year were the first for the county. Over the next five years, the species was almost an annual visitor to Suffolk and, in 1981, a pair nested at Abberton Reservoir, Essex, the first proven breeding in eastern England. Freezing conditions during the following winter resulted in an unprecedented influx of around 16 to the Suffolk coast from where a pair subsequently oversummered at Minsmere. Although nesting was not proven in 1982, up to five frequented Alton Water from August to December. Suffolk's first brood was noted on Livermere Lake in 1983 where a small population of nesting pairs has since established itself. During the late 1980s and early 1990s, one or two pairs bred annually on Westwood Marsh, Walberswick, a pair bred at Loompit Lake, Trimley St Martin in 1998 and three pairs bred at Trimley Marshes in 2000, by which time the county's breeding population had risen to around eight pairs.

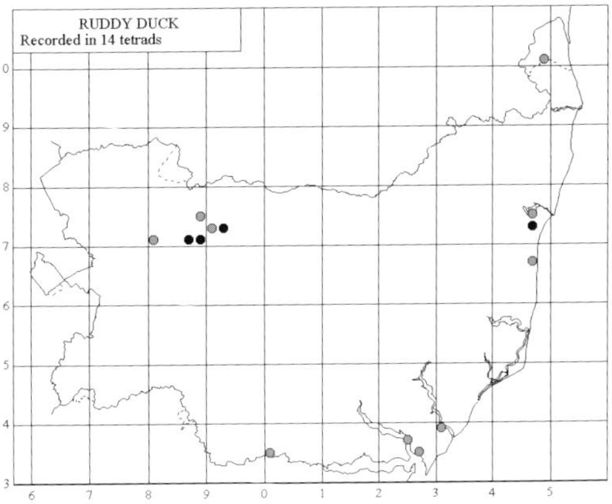

Except for very occasional influxes, the wintering population depends largely on the breeding success of the previous season and seldom exceeds 30 individuals. During the winter of 1999/2000 Ruddy Ducks built-up at Alton Water to reach a peak of 31 on 29th January and, by late February 2002, Trimley Marshes held 46, the county's largest gathering to date.

The species' success may be short-lived, as conservation bodies have introduced control measures. The Ruddy Duck has spread to other European countries and in southern Spain it interbreeds with the White-headed Duck, thus potentially threatening the survival of the latter species.

Honey Buzzard (European Honey-Buzzard) *Pernis apivorus*

Scarce passage migrant – has bred

The number of nesting pairs of Honey Buzzard in Britain increased steadily between 1989 and 1999, peaking at 43 in the latter year (Ogilvie *et al.* 2001). It occurs in Britain as a summer visitor and migrating birds are noted annually in Suffolk, chiefly at coastal localities. In recent years breeding pairs have graced Norfolk woodlands, while in Suffolk between 1966 and 1999 there were several reports of birds in June and July frequenting suitable breeding habitat, although nesting was not suspected.

Honey Buzzards formerly bred in Suffolk, although Ticehurst admitted that information regarding nesting was "very meagre" and most claims of breeding were based on females with well-developed ovaries killed during the summer months. The county's last breeding record was a pair shot at Melton in 1922 and delivered, with their nest, to Ipswich Museum (Payn 1978).

Of the 44 records for the period 1835-1881 (Babington 1884-1886), almost all referred to birds shot or trapped and the species remained relatively common up to the beginning of the 20th century. The most frequent months for dated records were September and October. Three specimens were obtained in June or July, but, surprisingly, there were no records for May. One shot in early November and two in December are likely to have been birds lingering rather than attempting to overwinter.

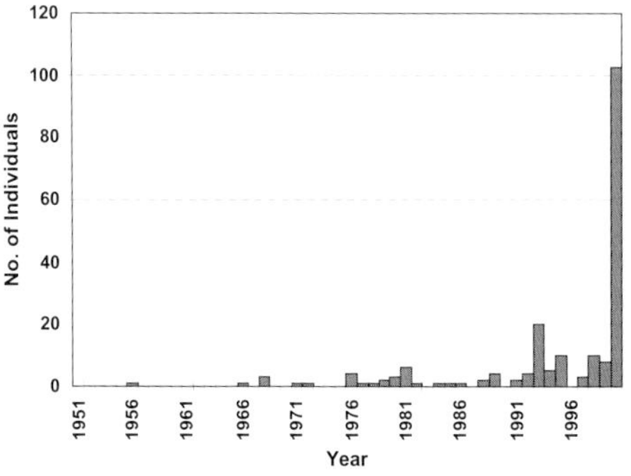

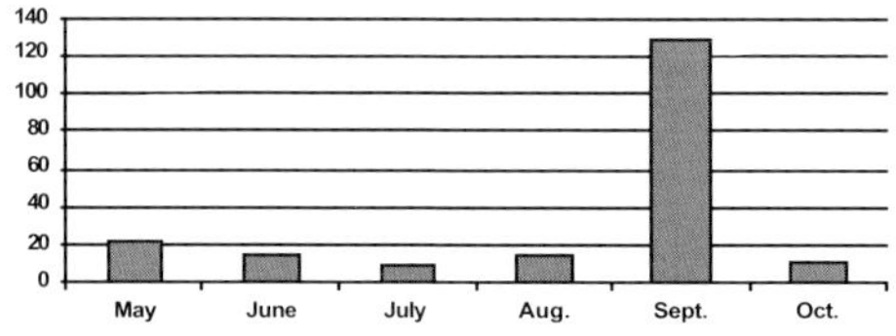

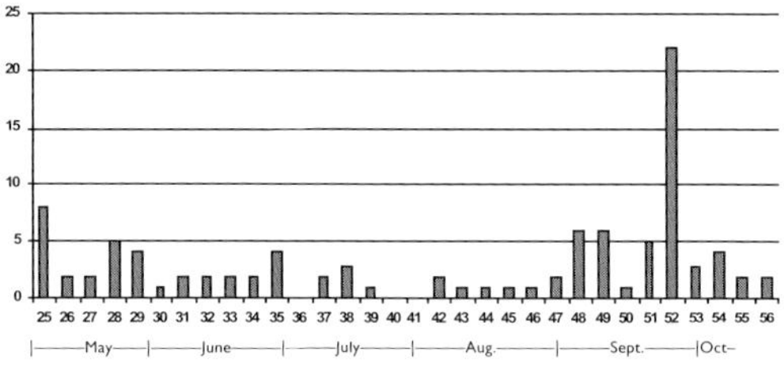

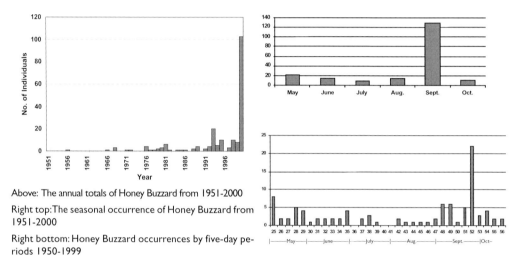

Above: The annual totals of Honey Buzzard from 1951-2000

Right top: The seasonal occurrence of Honey Buzzard from 1951-2000

Right bottom: Honey Buzzard occurrences by five-day periods 1950-1999

Ticehurst stated that "between 1850 and 1913 there were few years in which it did not appear" but, thereafter, it became rare with only three records for the period 1914-1966. These included one trapped near Bury St Edmunds in 1948 and hung on a scarecrow. Honey Buzzards were reported more regularly during the 1970s and six in 1981 was exceptional for that period. More than 70 individuals were recorded between 1956 and 1999, the majority between late August and mid-September, and mainly along the coastal strip between Benacre and Minsmere. Birds on spring passage are rarely sighted in Suffolk and, from the 20 or so records for May, eight occurred in 1995, including six remarkably early birds over North Warren on 1st and 2nd of that month. Extreme dates since the 19th century are 20th April 2002 and 15th October 2000 – the former individual circling from the east and then gliding south over Felixstowe. This is the only April record for the county to date.

Ticehurst noted the autumn of 1876 as being "rather remarkable for the number of Honey-Buzzards", but this was surpassed by the events of September 1881 when there was an "exceptional migration". Unfortunately, documentation of both invasions was poor and exact numbers involved are unknown. Babington listed five specimens for 1876 and six for 1881, but these small samples confirm that the influx was substantial bearing in mind that all these birds came within range of the shooters and trappers. A total of 11 Honey Buzzards was noted in a southerly movement of raptors at Minsmere on 16th September 1993 (Robertson 1994) and four others were reported from elsewhere during the same period. However, this was eclipsed by an extraordinary influx in late September 2000 that involved at least 100 individuals. Flocks of up to nine were noted at coastal and inland localities, and birds were logged almost daily from 20th September to 1st October (Piotrowski 2002). The birds were forced off their normal migration path by persistent, strong south-easterly winds.

Black Kite *Milvus migrans*

A very rare passage migrant: 24 records – all since 1971

The Black Kite occurs in much of Europe as a summer visitor and in Britain mainly as an overshooting migrant. The species now breeds regularly in Belgium and France (Cramp *et al.* 1974-1994) and the recent spate of reports is probably a result of range expansion in western Europe. Since the late 1980s, this kite has visited Suffolk almost annually and is most often seen on the immediate coastline. The majority of records refer to birds flying over and, due to inadequate descriptions, the rejection rate by the BBRC is one of the highest for any species. Nationally, 302 records had been accepted up to the end of 2000 (BBRC).

The Black Kite was added to the county list as recently as 9th May 1971, with one at Westleton, followed by another one month later at Blythburgh on 6th June. One flew over Walberswick on 12th May 1979 and another remained at Cove Bottom on 20th-22nd May. This was a well-watched individual and roosted in a large oak tree. Another tussled with Marsh Harriers over the reedbed at Eastbridge on 10th June 1981. From 1987 to 2001, a further 19 individuals were noted including singles in the Benacre area on the early dates of 23rd March 1996 and 16th March 1997. All accepted records for Suffolk refer to spring and early summer. Two other sightings, claimed as part of the raptor movement at Minsmere in September 1993 (Robertson 1994), were not accepted by BBRC. One at Haverhill on 13th June 1988 is the only accepted record for West Suffolk.

Red Kite *Milvus milvus*

Scarce winter visitor and passage migrant – has bred

The Red Kite is reported annually at coastal localities and occasionally further inland. Although there are many records for the winter months, there is a pronounced spring passage and late March to mid-April is the peak period.

Up to the early 19th century, Red Kites bred over much of Britain, including Suffolk. It was then comparatively common in eastern England (Montagu 1813) and Babington thought that it last bred in Suffolk at Bures around 1830. Its extinction in England was undoubtedly due to human persecution and records show that falconers contributed greatly to its final demise. Ticehurst quoted a notice that appeared in a newspaper dated, Swaffham, 5th February 1783 "The gentlemen of the Falconer's Society are hereby acquainted that the hawks will be in England in the first week in March and will begin Kite and Crow hawking immediately after their arrival. Their quarters are fixed at Bourn Bridge, Cambridgeshire... until the first April meeting when they will go to Barton Mills and Brandon till the 31st of May when the season will finish".

The Red Kite had become very rare by 1846 and was seen only sporadically in the latter half of the 19th century, being reported on a dozen occasions. Following one in 1901, 57 years were to pass before the next record. The species was reported more regularly during the 1960s, and between 1972 and 2001 there has been only one blank year. The majority of records refer to single-day observations, but long-staying, overwintering birds were noted on the coast in 1974-1975 and in 1976. The latter individual was reported irregularly until 19th July.

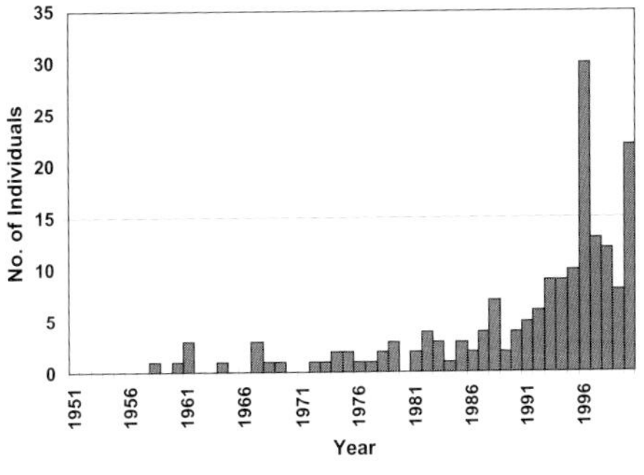

The annual totals of Red Kite from 1951-2000

Efforts to introduce the Red Kite to former haunts began in 1989 and resulted in two breeding populations becoming established in southern England and northern Scotland (Carter 1998). The second phase of the programme began in the Midlands in 1995 and the third, in Yorkshire, in 1999 (Rafe & Carter 2000). Dispersal from these sites has resulted in several wing-tagged birds in both East and West Suffolk, which prompted speculation that this graceful raptor would recolonise the county. Courtship was noted at Dallinghoo in February 1995 when another joined the overwintering, wing-tagged bird. An excellent spring passage in 1996 resulted in an untagged-tagged pair, probably continental migrants, nesting in north-east Suffolk and successfully rearing two young. The pair nested again at the same site the following summer and three chicks were reared. All five chicks were wing-tagged and four were subsequently noted elsewhere: one at a communal roost site in the east Midlands and then in the Wroxham/Hoveton area of the Norfolk Broads, two at different Red Kite feeding stations in west Wales (one of these birds was subsequently seen in the Netherlands), and another at a communal roost site in the Chilterns (Carter 2000).

Hopefully, Red Kites will soon become a regular feature of the Suffolk countryside, and recolonisation may be aided by further introduction schemes. However, as game preservation is still carried out in many areas at the expense of other living creatures, it will be an uphill struggle.

White-tailed Eagle *Haliaeetus albicilla*

A very rare winter visitor: c.80 records, but only 11 individuals during the 20th century

1931	Blaxhall: 26th December
1934	Euston: February
1958	Walberswick: 3rd January
	Snape: same 18th January
	Orford: Havergate Island, 28th February to 3rd March
	Butley: 2nd March
1962	Orford: Havergate Island, 14th February
1982	Dunwich/Leiston-cum-Sizewell: 21st-30th January
	Martlesham: 1st February
1984	Oulton/Covehithe/Easton Bavents/Walberswick: 15th April
	Halesworth/Walberswick: 17th April
1985	Benacre: Benacre Broad, second year bird 12th and 29th November and December 18th
	Walberswick/Dunwich: 13th-16th November
1988/9	Helmingham: Helmingham Park, first-winter 20th November to 10th December
	River Alde area: 12th December to 23rd February
1990	Fritton: Fritton Warren, imm. (roosted in pine trees) 11th February to 15th March
	Walberswick: Westwood Marsh, 11th March.
	Minsmere: 2nd and 15th February and 12th March
1999/2000	Benacre/Minsmere: imm. 26th October to 19th February
	Aldeburgh/Sudbourne: North Warren/Orfordness, two on 13th February and singles 15th and 20th
	Boyton: 13th and 23rd February

The White-tailed Eagle was a regular visitor to Suffolk throughout most of the 19th century (Ticehurst 1932). Reports came from coastal and Breckland localities, and most were trapped or shot. There were no records for the period 1899-1930, but since then the species has been noted as above (apart from the two birds seen together in February 2000, it is thought that only one bird was involved in each of the winter or spring periods).

The occurrence of a White-tailed Eagle creates widespread interest amongst both birdwatchers and the general public. The 1958 bird was observed feeding on a dead swan and the 1985 individual pursued ducks on Benacre Broad.

The run of records in the 1980s could possibly be the result of the reintroduction programme started in Scotland in 1975. However a bird shot in Norfolk in May 1984 had been ringed as a nestling in Germany the previous year, suggesting a continental origin for some of the winter visitors.

Marsh Harrier (Eurasian Marsh Harrier) *Circus aeruginosus*

A local breeder, summer visitor and uncommon passage migrant – a few overwinter

Marsh Harrier
(*Stuart Ling*)

Each summer, the extensive reedbeds of coastal Suffolk provide the Marsh Harrier with a rich feeding and nesting habitat. Although still a rare breeding species, numbers have increased steadily in recent years, rising to 156 nesting females in Britain in 1995 (Ogilvie *et al.* 2001). A few, mainly females, overwinter annually in the central coastal zone of Suffolk but this harrier is rare elsewhere. Birds are widely reported during passage periods.

The species was widespread in Britain and Ireland 200-300 years ago and probably nested regularly in the East Anglian fens. However, there is no conclusive evidence to confirm that it bred in Suffolk, although Babington referred to "a nest and three young ones" which were taken in the neighbourhood of Great Yarmouth in 1862 and, in all probability, it nested in the reed-covered fenland around Mildenhall. Migrating birds were reported widely during this period.

The Marsh Harrier became extinct as a British breeding species in the late 19th century, returning to nest intermittently in the Norfolk Broads from 1911 and annually from 1927. In the 1930s, the species began to settle in Suffolk's coastal marshes, where it probably bred. The sudden abundance of reedbed habitat, provided by wartime flooding of grazing meadows at Kessingland, Walberswick and Minsmere was soon exploited. A nest near Lowestoft in 1945 produced four young and heralded a slow recolonisation, with breeding taking place annually, except in 1951. Kessingland marshes were reclaimed for agriculture soon after the war, but reedbeds at Lowestoft, Walberswick and Minsmere proved ideal for nesting and there was a steady increase in breeding attempts. Numbers fluctuated in those early years rising to a maximum of eight pairs, out of 15 in Britain, in 1958 and then declining during the early 1960s as organochloride pesticides entered the food chain. A single pair at Minsmere in 1971 constituted the sole British breeding record for that year. The species has since recovered and now nests at many suitable reedbeds along the Suffolk coast. Males are well known for their bigamous behaviour and this contributes greatly to the high concentrations at larger marshes. Such sites may hold up to ten nests and a few breeding pairs have ventured up river estuaries to occupy smaller reedbeds. Between 20 and 40 nests produced 50-70 young per annum in the early 1990s. Since the late 1970s, one or two pairs have bred intermittently in north-west Suffolk, the only record of nesting away from the immediate coastline.

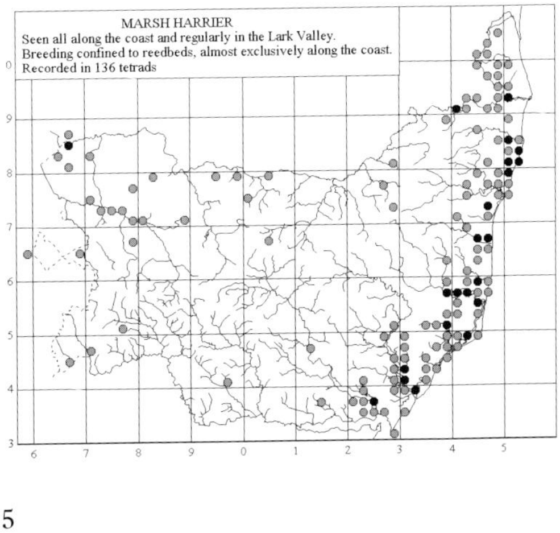

MARSH HARRIER
Seen all along the coast and regularly in the Lark Valley.
Breeding confined to reedbeds, almost exclusively along the coast.
Recorded in 136 tetrads

The withdrawal of damaging pesticides contributed greatly to the species' revival, but the creation of wardened nature reserves, offering better protection, is also a significant factor. It has been suggested that young birds could have been recruited from the Dutch polders, which in the 1980s held an estimated 900 nests (Moore 1987). However, although this may well have been a significant factor during the early years of colonisation, the period 1945-1998 has seen no fewer than 1,191 young fledge from 532

Suffolk nests (Wright 2001), which is arguably a more likely reason for the increase in numbers. Although this harrier has utilised almost all available reedbeds as a breeding habitat, there has yet to be a record of nesting amongst arable crops – a practice noted annually in neighbouring counties and on the continent.

Passage birds are widely reported from early April to mid-May, and in August and September. However, with so many breeding pairs on the coast, it is often difficult to distinguish birds on passage from those wandering from their breeding sites. Nevertheless, the number of reported movements is surprisingly low, bearing in mind the numbers of birds flying to and from their nesting sites. For example, in 1995, 67 young fledged from four coastal sites alone and it is likely that more than 200 East Anglian-bred birds moved south during that autumn, of which relatively few were logged at migration watch-points. The largest reported movement involved about 40 birds in September 2000, coinciding with the Honey Buzzard influx of the same period (Piotrowski 2002).

Ringing returns suggest that the majority of birds reared in Suffolk winter in north-west Africa and their migration path can be plotted by recoveries. A juvenile, discovered in an emaciated condition in a coypu trap at Walberswick in 1966, was nursed back to health at Minsmere and ringed prior to release. The following spring, it was found dead in Mauritania, close to the Senegal border, which represents the most distant recovery of a British-ringed bird. Others, mostly from Minsmere and Walberswick, have been recovered in the Netherlands, Spain, Portugal and Morocco (3). Marsh Harriers ringed in Germany and the Netherlands have been found during passage periods on the Suffolk coast.

Hen Harrier *Circus cyaneus*

A fairly common winter visitor and passage migrant – formerly bred

Breeding of the Hen Harrier occurred annually in the fens of north-west Suffolk in the 1830s and a nest with three broken eggs was found on Cavenham Heath on 15th May 1871 (Ticehurst 1932). A clutch of six eggs was taken on this heath in 1918 and the female killed and sent to a local taxidermist. In 1929, the same fate met Suffolk's last breeding pair that had a clutch of four eggs on nearby Tuddenham Heath. The Hen Harrier has traditionally been the gamekeepers' enemy and is mentioned in the Bedingfield Parish Accounts as early as 1568. Under the Vermin Act, one penny was paid for the head of each "Ryngtale", as the Hen Harrier was then called (Ticehurst 1932). Its liking for game birds was demonstrated by an analysis of pellets found at a Breckland roost site (Clarke & Palmer 1987). Birds formed over 50% of the diet, of which 13.4% were Pheasants and partridges. However, passerines were taken far more frequently, with prey items consisting of 27% Reed Buntings, 12.4% Greenfinches and 11.3% each for Wrens and Yellowhammers. Field Voles formed the major part of the non-avian diet.

This harrier has always been a regular winter visitor, arriving in late September and leaving in March. A few linger into April and there are occasional May records, presumably relating to passage birds. A male was present at Cavenham Heath in June 1977 and breeding behaviour, including displaying pairs at Minsmere in April 1982 and April 1983, raised hopes that the species might return to breed in Suffolk. However, there are no recent July records. The earliest birds to return to Suffolk have been a female that hit telegraph wires at Bradwell on 13th August 1961 and singles in the Benacre to Easton Bavents area on 2nd-17th August 1980 and at North Warren, on 16th-18th August 1992. This harrier migrates diurnally and is sometimes observed offshore battling its way landwards, often being harassed by passing gulls.

Coastal heaths and marshes, as well as Breckland localities, are frequented throughout the winter months and communal roosting occurs at several sites, most often amongst tall heather or in reedbeds. Ticehurst described the extensive heathlands around Sudbourne, Rendlesham and Sutton as favoured winter haunts and he considered eight on one heath in 1921/2 as noteworthy. Roost counts have shown that the winter population fluctuates greatly from year to year and harsh weather encourages further immigration. During the arctic conditions in January 1979, a total of 95 (out of 753 in the whole of England) were roosting at eight sites in Suffolk (Davenport 1982). Other January counts for Suffolk have included 48 in 1984, 30 in 1985, 37 in 1986 and 13 in 1987 (Clarke 1988). This diurnal hunter is normally noted in ones and twos at coastal heaths and marshes, with the Walberswick to Minsmere area being the most favoured. In Breckland, this species is regularly recorded on heathland and arable land.

The origins of some of the county's wintering birds are shown by three recoveries of nestlings ringed in the Dutch polder region.

Pallid Harrier *Circus macrourus*

Accidental: one record

1999 Bramford: Suffolk Water Park, male 7th May

The above record coincided with an influx of at least 15 birds into Denmark (Sharrock & Davies 2000). The bird was seen briefly by only two observers.

The Pallid Harrier breeds in eastern Europe through to central Asia, wintering in south Asia and Africa south of the Sahara. It had been recorded in Britain and Ireland on ten occasions up to the end of 2000 (BBRC).

Montagu's Harrier *Circus pygargus*

A rare passage migrant and former summer visitor

The Montagu's Harrier is recorded annually in Suffolk, principally at coastal marshes but in diminishing numbers. The British population declined by 36% between the 'Atlas' periods (1968-72 and 1988-91) and it is now a very rare breeding species. Nesting was confirmed at only 9-16 localities between 1989 and 1999 (Ogilvie *et al.* 2001).

Early in the 19th century, the Montagu's Harrier was considered to be the commonest harrier in East Anglia and small numbers bred on the county's heaths and marshes (Ticehurst 1932). It was extensively persecuted, however, with the adults shot and nests destroyed year after year until, by the end of the 19th century, it was on the verge of extinction. Ticehurst passionately appealed to landowners to allow birds to breed unhindered but, sadly, the slaughter continued. In one case, he tried to enlist the help of three coastal landowners to provide sanctuary for two pairs. One responded to the effect that he did not blame his keepers if they killed every 'hawk' and he certainly would not give instructions to the contrary.

Afforestation during the 1930s may have been beneficial to the species initially, but the fragmentation of heathland eventually contributed to the harrier's demise. This was particularly evident in Breckland where it ceased to breed regularly in the 1940s. Nesting continued sporadically on the coast during the 1950s and 1960s, and it was during the latter decade that a new threat became apparent – DDT poisoning. Analysis of eggs, from a failed Breckland nest in 1963, revealed residues of five chemicals, including dieldrin (Payn 1978). Unlike other raptors, the Montagu's Harrier never recovered when the use of this pesticide declined. Disturbance may well be the principal factor in the species' reluctance to recolonise Suffolk. Few areas of open space remain which are not 'swamped' by people on fine summer days. Elsewhere in East Anglia, the species has recently taken to nesting amongst arable crops (Gibbons *et al.* 1993) and this may be the key to its future success.

The Montagu's Harrier last bred in Suffolk in 1967 when nine young fledged from four nests (one unsuccessful). However, a male established a territory at Minsmere in May and June 1979 and was seen carrying nesting material as part of its display. Two years later, a pair, plus a second female, were present at sites in July and two juveniles were seen elsewhere in August, giving rise to speculation that breeding had occurred. A pair may have bred in 1986. Records in the 1990s are limited to the occasional passage birds in May or June and, to a lesser extent, August and September, with the reedbed habitats of Walberswick and Minsmere being the most favoured localities. Extreme dates are 15th April 1951 (Walberswick) and 4th November 1956 (Redgrave). The latter record involved an adult male which makes the record even more surprising. One ringed as a pullus in Texel, the Netherlands, on 28th June 1928 was recovered in Suffolk almost exactly a year later. A dark morph male frequented Minsmere on 10th-16th May 1997.

Goshawk (Northern Goshawk) *Accipiter gentilis*

Scarce resident, winter visitor and passage migrant

Woodlands in Breckland and more rarely on the coastal strip, harbour a few nesting pairs of Goshawks, although the species is often elusive during the breeding season. Consequently, sightings are few and far between. The population of north-west Suffolk is largely confined to conifer forests, although those on the coast favour mixed woodland. Goshawks pose considerable identification problems and claimed sightings have the highest rejection rates of any species in Suffolk (Crewe 1996). Large, female Sparrowhawks flying over distant canopies are regularly misidentified as Goshawks.

Relentless persecution by gamekeepers, falconers and egg collectors persists, so much so that the RSPB and other conservation bodies employ extreme protection measures. For this reason, information on nesting is rather meagre and site locations are treated with the utmost secrecy. The national breeding population has increased steadily in recent years, from a maximum of 61 pairs in 1983 to 299 a decade later (Ogilvie *et al.* 1996).

Since the early 1970s, Goshawks have been recorded more regularly and breeding was confirmed for the first time in 1983. Up to six pairs now breed annually at Breckland sites, those in and around Thetford and the King's Forest being the most successful. Suffolk's share of a national breeding population, which ranged from 166 to 347 between 1989 and 1999 (Olgivie *et al.* 2001), is likely to be less than ten pairs (Wright 2001).

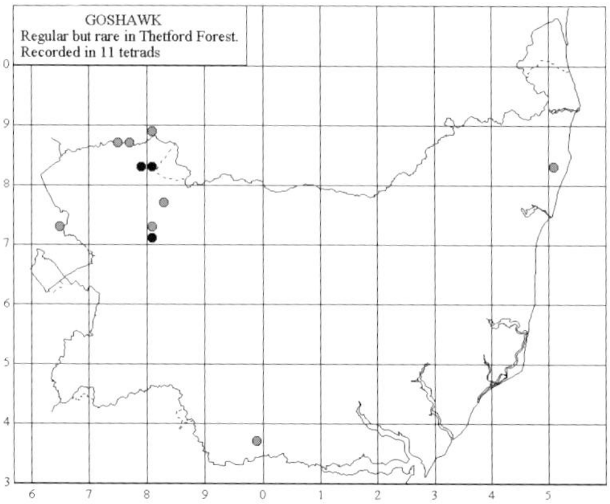
GOSHAWK
Regular but rare in Thetford Forest.
Recorded in 11 tetrads

Goshawks were breeding in Suffolk prior to the 17th century as recorded by Reyce (1618) when he wrote: "the Sparhauk and Gossehauk are found here in diverse places offtimes to breed butt nothing so commonly as in former times". By the 19th century, however, it had become very rare and Babington lists only 18 records. An immature male, shot at Saxham in October 1946, was the first record for the 20th century and there were only ten records over the next 25 years.

The current British population is thought to have derived from falconers' escapes or deliberate introductions (Marquiss & Newton 1982, Vinicombe *et al.* 1993). Ringing returns have shown that British-reared Goshawks are highly sedentary with birds rarely venturing far from their natal areas even in winter (Crewe 1996). In consequence, any future colonisation of new sites will be slow.

Passage birds are occasionally noted at coastal localities and immigrants from the continent increase the winter population in some years. The Goshawk has been recorded at offshore localities on five occasions, including one caught on the rigging of a trawler and brought into Great Yarmouth in November 1843.

Sparrowhawk (Eurasian Sparrowhawk) ***Accipiter nisus***

An increasingly common resident, winter visitor and passage migrant

The Sparrowhawk is the county's second-commonest raptor, although its secretive nature makes population estimates difficult. It prefers well-wooded habitats, especially coniferous forest, but will also frequent open countryside during winter. Sparrowhawks are most often seen soaring overhead, gliding along woodland edges or flying fast and low in pursuit of prey. In recent years, it has increasingly entered urban environments. Populations have fluctuated enormously over the last 100 years. During the 19th century, its numbers were kept constantly in check by the activities of gamekeepers. Over the autumn and winter of 1911, more than 100 were killed on a single estate near Lowestoft. This demonstrates the species' abundance at a time when huge finch flocks would have helped sustain populations of this raptor. Numbers increased during the First World War, probably due to reduced keepering and, thereafter, remained relatively stable until 1950.

A sudden decline was experienced in south-east England in the 1950s (Newton & Haas 1984) and, during the 1960s, the Sparrowhawk became extremely scarce over much of Britain. DDT and other pesticides were applied as sprays or seed dressings and were picked up by pigeons, thrushes, starlings, sparrows, finches and other prey species, and these were undoubtedly responsible for the Sparrowhawk's decline. The effect of this was greatest in the open arable districts of eastern England where the species became virtually extinct. It was estimated that in Suffolk no more than four pairs bred annually from 1960 to 1977. As the use of these chemicals was restricted, it recovered and the raptor has now reappeared in many of its former haunts. Nationally, a population increase of 19% was noted between the *'Atlas'* periods

(1968-1972 and 1988-1991), although the increase started later in the eastern counties and was more marked (Gibbons *et al.* 1993). The species was noted in 328 tetrads during the Suffolk Survey of breeding raptors and owls (1995-1998) and the county's breeding population was estimated to be between c.480 and c.700 pairs (Wright 2001). Densities appeared to be low in Thetford Forest with greater numbers in the surrounding wooded farmland. The greatest concentrations appear to be in the coastal belt, between the River Alde and Lowestoft, in central Suffolk around Stowmarket and on the Shotley peninsula. The raptor is scarce in the Stour Valley and in south Suffolk generally, in spite of an abundance of suitable habitat. It is likely that this is related to more vigorous keepering.

The British resident population is extremely sedentary (Newton 1986). Immigrants from the continent supplement numbers each winter and studies at Landguard Point show distinct peaks in occurrences during the third week of April and again from late September to mid-October (Odin 1996). Ticehurst referred to the raptor invasion of September 1881, when Sparrowhawks were very numerous, and to birds caught on boats in the North Sea during the autumn. Nowadays, this species is frequently seen arriving from offshore at migration watch-points such as Southwold and Landguard Point. One ringed in Germany in 1945 was found at Trimley the next year and others (mostly young females) have been found bearing rings from Denmark, Finland, Norway and the Netherlands (2). A young male trapped at Landguard Point on 8th November 1994, was recovered in Denmark the following spring. The county's annual ringing totals are indicative of the upsurge in the population; only 33 were ringed during the period 1986-1990, compared with 167 for 1991-1995.

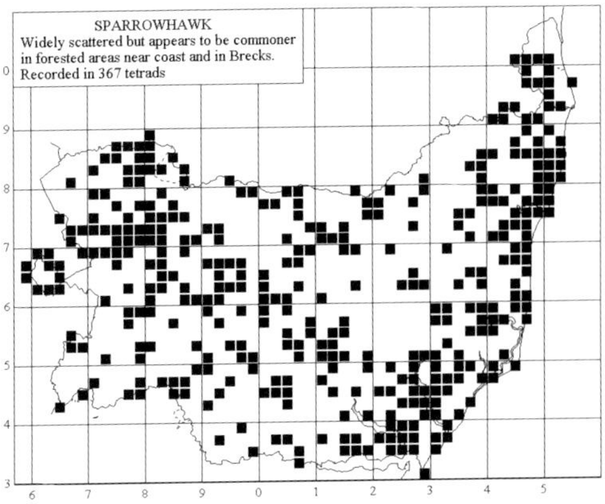

Ticehurst was convinced that damage inflicted by the Sparrowhawk on game stocks was much exaggerated and studies at the time supported this view. Even so, its reputation as a ruthless killer remains to this day and there are moves by the shooting fraternity to reinstate control measures under the guise of concern for songbird populations. There is no doubt that many birds are predated each year and a successful breeding pair of Sparrowhawks could account for 55kg of meat per annum (Newton 1986). Finches, thrushes and pigeons make up the bulk of the diet, but unusual prey items recorded in Suffolk have included Wood Sandpiper, Green Woodpecker and Kingfisher.

Buzzard (Common Buzzard) — *Buteo buteo*

Uncommon winter visitor and passage migrant – breeds infrequently

The Buzzard is noted as a passage migrant, principally at coastal localities, and a few birds overwinter. It became extinct as a breeding species towards the end of the 19th century, but successful breeding in 1999 and 2001 could be a prelude to future recolonisation.

This raptor has long been regarded as vermin. Entries in the Parish Accounts of Bedingfield (1st March 1568) and Cratfield (1580) offered bounties for buzzards' heads (Ticehurst 1932). It was probably as a result of such persecution that the species was lost as a breeding species, its demise typifying the wholesale slaughter of raptors in the late 19th century. As Ticehurst said "Little wonder that this fine bird has died out as a nesting species, every gamekeeper's hand was against it, no one seems to have given it any sanctuary". The fate of a breeding pair at Monkspark Wood, Felsham demonstrates the treatment that was then meted out by landowners and their employees. Its nest was shown to Babington in 1874, after the gamekeeper had killed one of the adults and thrown it to the foxes. In spite of this, a pair returned the following year, but the female was "wounded" on her nest.

Although Ticehurst had little doubt that the Buzzard formerly bred in Suffolk woodlands on a regular basis, the records show that by the middle of the 19th century it was no more than an infrequent breeder and, by the beginning of the 20th century, its status was reduced to that of a passage migrant of somewhat irregular occurrence. Despite an abundance of nesting habitat, the only possible breeding up to 1998 occurred at Brandon in 1922 when five were together in August. During the 1980s and 1990s, birds occupying suitable breeding habitat in high summer were noted almost annually and, in 1998, up to three birds were regularly seen and breeding was suspected. The Buzzard was finally reinstated to the county's list of breeding birds in 1999 when a pair raised two young at a West Suffolk site. Up to two pairs bred successfully in the area from 2000 to 2002 and displaying birds were also noted in north-east Suffolk. Although recolonisation of old haunts now appears to be a good possibility, persecution would be a likely reason for its failure. The *New Atlas* highlights conspicuous gaps in the eastern fringe of the Buzzard's breeding distribution that "coincide with well-keepered estates".

Autumn migrants occasionally appear in large groups. The Buzzard was described as "extraordinarily abundant" during the immigration of raptors in September 1881 but numbers involved were not documented. During a remarkable raptor movement on 16th September 1993 (Robertson 1994), 11 flew south over Minsmere. Autumn passage can begin as early as July, although most birds occur in late August and September.

Buzzards winter annually, mainly along the coastal strip and in Breckland. Assessing numbers is difficult due to the wide-ranging nature of the birds and it is likely that no more than ten birds are present in any one winter. One seen at Snape on 30th March 1997 had a distinctive pattern of missing wing feathers and had been identified at Benacre two weeks previously. Two separate groups of eight and seven circling near Cavenham and over the King's Forest area on 13th February 2002 is the largest total for West Suffolk.

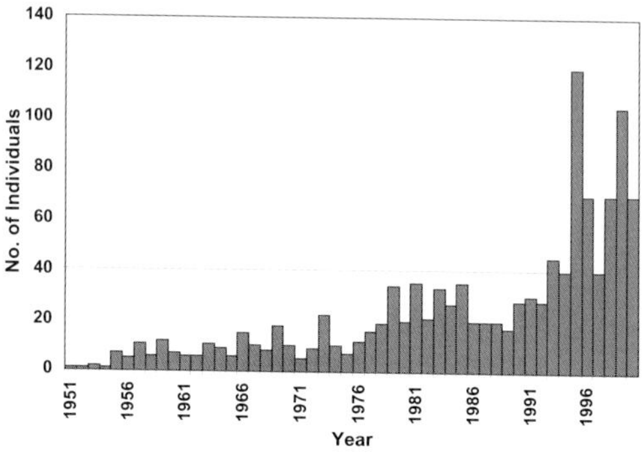

Occurrences of Common Buzzard from 1951-2000

Most overwintering birds leave in late March or April, but a few linger into May. Ticehurst referred to only four spring records, but recent observations reveal that Buzzards are regular passage migrants with northerly movements occurring in March and early April in most years. The species is normally observed singly and groups of three or more are rare. Exceptional movements include a flock of ten drifting over Minsmere on 29th April 1973, 30 in from the sea at Benacre on 4th April 1995, 13 spiralling over woods and drifting out to sea on 28th March 1996, ten over Benacre on 20th March 1997, and 15 over Oulton Broad and 17 over Covehithe on 14th March 1999. The 1995 movement started with a group of nine at 09:30 hrs, followed by several groups of up to five through to the afternoon. Although these birds arrived from offshore, a direct crossing over the North Sea from the Low Countries is unlikely. The first group arrived far too early in the day and a more likely explanation is that the birds were coasting northwards after leaving their roost, perhaps taking the shorter seaward route from Kent before making landfall to pick up thermals. The movement is difficult to interpret as ringing evidence suggests that the British breeding stock is extremely sedentary and up to the end of 1994, only one continental-ringed Buzzard had been recovered in Britain (Appleton *et al.* 1997). However, there are significantly more Buzzards around in good Rough-legged Buzzard years, so there is a suspicion that at least some of Suffolk's wintering birds originate in Scandinavia. The relative frequency of pale-phase birds, which are scarce in the British breeding population, also points to birds of continental origin.

Rough-legged Buzzard *Buteo lagopus*

A scarce winter visitor and passage migrant

Suffolk's wintering population of Rough-legged Buzzards normally fluctuates between five and eight birds, but a few major influxes have taken place, while the species is totally absent in some years. The majority frequent the coastal strip between Walberswick and Boyton but they are also regularly reported in Lothingland and Breckland.

Rough-legged Buzzards were particularly abundant in 1839 (47 were killed around Thetford), 1858, 1875, 1876, 1880, 1881, 1891, 1910 and 1915 (Ticehurst 1932). Wintering numbers were low between the 1930s and early 1970s although there were 'mini peaks' in the winters of 1960/1, 1966/7 and 1973/4. During the autumn of 1974 an immigration of enormous proportions took place. In a 4-hour period on 22nd October, a total of 45, mostly in groups of 1-3, but including 11 together, arrived from offshore at Dunwich and headed south over Minsmere. On the same day, a single flew south over Felixstowe. Two days later, 40 flew south-west from Walberswick, including a party of 13, and again one was sighted at Felixstowe (Scott 1978). Many, if not all, of these birds were likely to have been the same as those seen two days earlier. Many dispersed but about 30-40 overwintered in Suffolk, including five in Breckland.

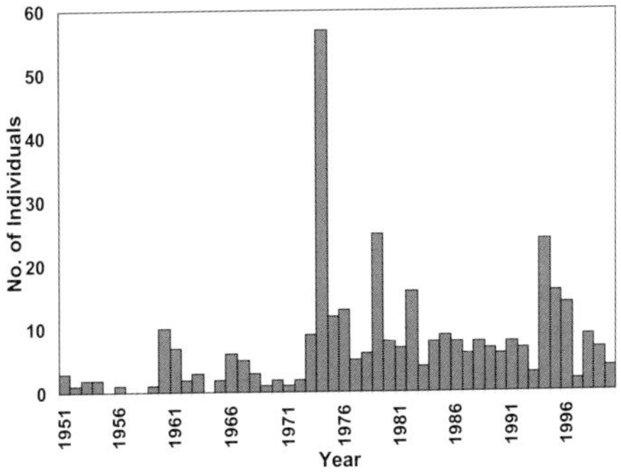

Occurrences of Rough-legged Buzzard from 1951-2000

Ringing recoveries, including one trapped in Denmark in October 1979 and found dead four autumns later near Elveden, show movements between Scandinavia and Britain (Mead & Clark 1993). The first immigrants normally arrive in late October, so one at Walberswick on 13th August 1980 was exceptionally early. Most leave in April and departing groups of four and seven were observed off Minsmere on 20th April 1975 and 14th April 1979 respectively. There have been six May records since 1967 and singles were noted at Minsmere on 5th June 1975 and Ashby Warren on 22nd-26th June 1987.

Spotted Eagle (Greater Spotted Eagle) *Aquila clanga*

Accidental: three 19th century records involving four individuals

1875	Elveden: shot
1891	Sudbourne: Sudbourne Hall, two (one shot) 4th November
1892	Reydon: shot 2nd January

The omission of the Elveden record by authors of previous county avifaunas is puzzling. The specimen, which is currently on display in the Elveden Estate Office and clearly labelled "shot at Elveden 1875", has been examined and the identification confirmed by Howard Mendel formerly of Ipswich Museum.

An autopsy on the bird shot at Sudbourne revealed that it had fed on a water vole and a partridge. The specimen is now exhibited at the Norwich Castle Museum. There are 12 records (of 14 individuals) for Britain and Ireland, and the Sudbourne and Reydon birds were part of a small influx into western Europe, which also included two in Essex (Cox 1984).

The Spotted Eagle breeds in eastern Europe across Siberia and winters in Turkey, northern Israel and Egypt, discontinuously to south-east Asia. Very occasionally, birds venture to western Europe, but the species has not been recorded in Britain since 1915.

Osprey *Pandion haliaetus*

Uncommon passage migrant

Estuaries, lakes, reservoirs and even small ponds may attract this fish-eating raptor. Ospreys move through Suffolk en route to northern nesting grounds and, although most pass through quite quickly, a few linger for several weeks. The most favoured localities are the River Blyth, Minsmere, Lackford and Livermere. Oversummering individuals have become increasingly frequent in recent years and the introduction attempts at Rutland Water since 1996 may well have a bearing on future records.

During the middle of the 19th century, the Osprey was a common passage migrant but, as a result of persecution in its breeding grounds and whilst on passage, it became extremely rare. The Scandinavian population went into steep decline at the turn of the 19th and 20th centuries and it became extinct in Scotland in 1916. The lack of passage migrants in Suffolk (only ten records during the period 1920-1947) was a sad reflection of this decline. The Osprey began to appear more regularly during the late 1940s with around 5-6 being noted annually during the period 1947-1985. Sightings have since increased further with around 10-20 records each year.

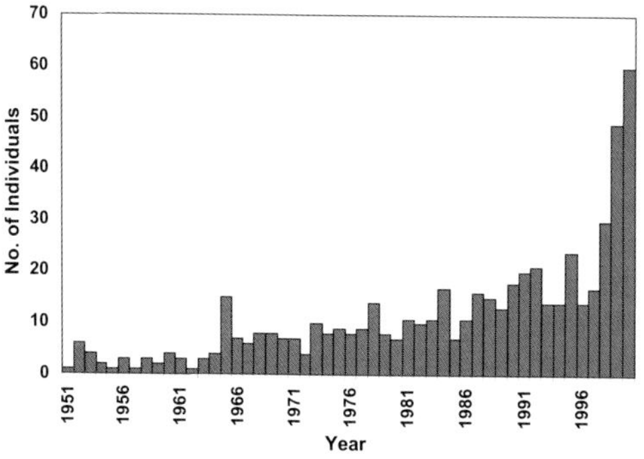

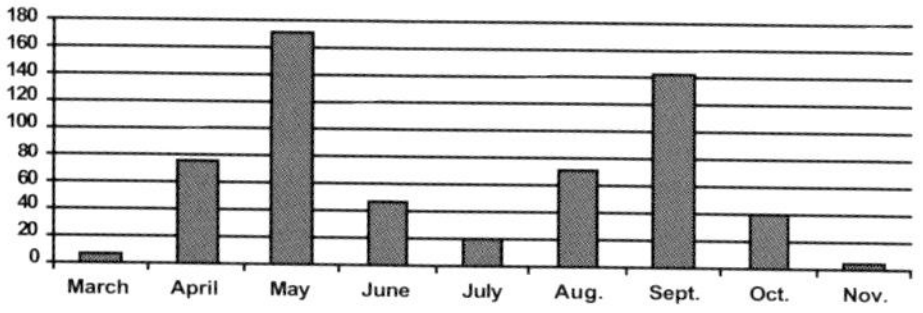

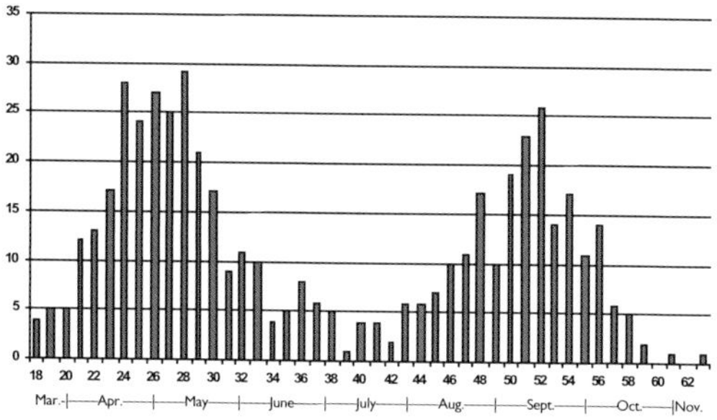

Above: The annual totals of the Osprey from 1951-2000
Right top: The seasonal occurences of the Osprey from 1950-2000
Right bottom: Osprey occurrences by five-day periods 1950-1999

The majority passing through the county are likely to be moving to and from Scandinavia. Most spring occurrences are from the last week of April to the third week of May, when Scottish birds would be incubating. Ospreys have been noted in the last few days of March on only four occasions, the earliest being singles on 29th March over Tunstall Common in 1986 and Westleton Heath in 1997.

September is the most favoured autumn month, although Ospreys are regularly seen in August and October. The largest day-total was six, all of which passed over Landguard Point on 16th September 2000, part of a protracted movement that involved at least 40 individuals (Piotrowski 2002). Singles near Slaughden on 30th November 1874, at Mendham on 14th November 1888, at Thorington Street on 9th November 1999 and at Minsmere on 19th November 2000 are the only records for that month. An immature female, shot at Blundeston on 19th October 1942, had been ringed as a nestling in Sweden earlier that year.

Oversummering pairs in the Lackford area in 1990 and 1991 gave rise to speculation that the Osprey may one day be added to the county's breeding list. Consideration has been given to the erection of artificial nesting platforms – a practice that has proved successful in the Scottish Highlands (Gibbons *et al.* 1993) and elsewhere. However, as some oversummering birds were immatures, it is likely that they were prospecting new areas in their first summer, returning to more traditional northern habitats the following year. Earlier in the 20th century, the majority of Suffolk's Ospreys frequented the coastal estuaries and larger estuaries, where their chief food was grey mullet (Ticehurst 1932). An Osprey fishing at Minsmere's Island Mere on 29th June 1984 was seen to catch two fish in a single dive (Turnbull 1986).

Kestrel (Common Kestrel) *Falco tinnunculus*

A common resident, winter visitor and passage migrant

Kestrels hovering over roadside verges are a familiar sight, as this is Suffolk's most numerous raptor. It remains relatively common throughout the county's more open habitats and it is also a regular breeder in urban environments. Migrants regularly pass through coastal watch-points and are most obvious during autumn. Nationally, there has been a 40% decline in the breeding population since the early 1970s (Gregory *et al.* 1996).

Prior to the 1950s, the Kestrel was widespread throughout Suffolk, but its numbers plummeted about 1959-1960 as a result of the ingestion of harmful agricultural pesticide and herbicide residues in its prey. In the 1960s, it had become a rare breeding species and by 1968 only 12 pairs were known (Payn 1978). Following restrictions on the use of the more damaging agrochemicals, the population recovered well and by 1978 an increase was widely reported. Kestrels are once again widespread throughout the county, the highest concentrations being in Breckland and on the coast. The species is least abundant in the cereal-growing areas of central and south-west Suffolk.

Village (Gibbons *et al.* 1993) estimated that, on average, a 10-km square would contain 20 territorial pairs, 36 in the best grassland areas and ten in many arable ones. Much of Suffolk is arable, but the *New Atlas* suggests that the county holds some of the highest densities in the country, so an estimate of 1,200 pairs seems reasonable. Calculations by Wright (2001) gave a breeding population of 660-970 pairs for the period 1995-1998.

Southerly movements of this species are regularly recorded off Landguard Point, principally between mid-August and November. In some years, up to 25 migrants are logged passing through the site. Nestlings ringed in the Netherlands (2) and Denmark have been recovered in late summer in Suffolk and an adult female ringed at Bawdsey in 1961 was found dead at Maine et Loire, France, one year later.

The Suffolk wintering population is largely determined by the local survival rate, although the above ringing recoveries suggest that a few immigrants from the continent reinforce numbers. There is no evidence to suggest that substantial influxes occur. WeBS counts show increased numbers at estuarine localities during winter. No doubt birds are attracted by better feeding opportunities in these areas, although information for inland arable districts is limited. In the autumn of 1995, a high count of 29 on the grasslands on Orfordness on 10th September probably included some migrants.

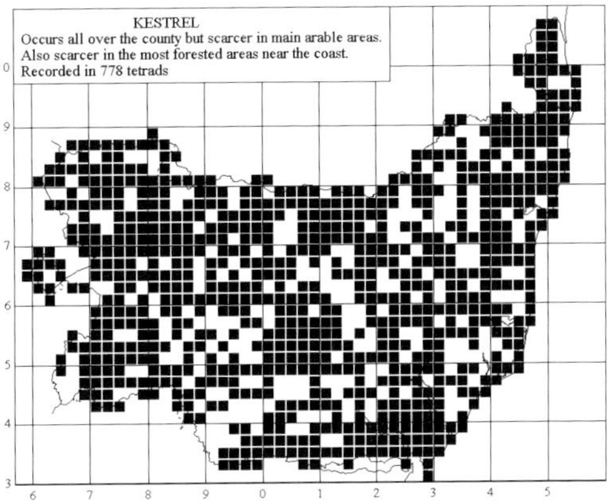

The Kestrel's dietary habits have attracted interest over the years although, surprisingly, there are no fully documented studies for Suffolk. Voles, insects and birds form the bulk of the prey. In addition, there are numerous references to Kestrels grubbing for earthworms and a party of five following the plough at Shotley in September 1993 is noteworthy. Birds taking slow-worms were noted at Kelsale in March 1981 and at Felixstowe in October 1992 (SBR). Kestrels have been noted feeding on a dead coypu at Iken on 31st December 1980, caching fish heads at Landguard Point in 1987 and taking bread thrown to gulls at Southwold on 23rd January 1990. This normally diurnal species has been reported hunting on clear moonlight nights (Payn 1978) and has been observed pursuing and capturing bats at Somerton in 1933, Saxmundham in 1981, and Timworth and West Stow in 1985. One was seen to steal a mouse from a stoat at Hasketon in 1977.

Red-footed Falcon *Falco vespertinus*

A very rare passage migrant: 37 records

Formerly an extremely rare vagrant, the Red-footed Falcon is now almost an annual visitor, frequenting heathland, grassland habitats and, occasionally, cultivated areas. Overhead power-lines are frequently used as vantage points for hunting forays. An adult female, on Orfordness in May 1992, was seen to rob a Kestrel of its prey (Piotrowski 1994). The falcon was recorded in Britain and Ireland on 732 occasions up to the end of 2000 (BBRC).

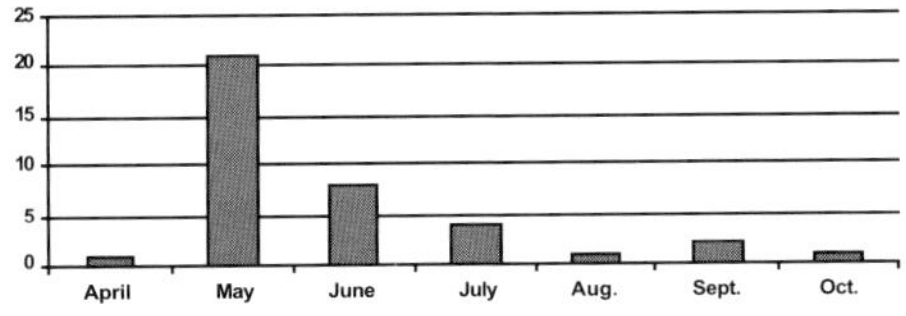

The seasonal occurrences of Red-footed Falcons (1862-2000)

An immature male shot at Somerleyton on 12th July 1862 was the first record for Suffolk, but nearly a century passed before the second – an immature female that frequented Southwold Golf Course on 9th-14th June 1958. In 1973, there were three records, thereafter, 1-2 have been noted in most years, mainly at coastal and Breckland localities. In 1992, ten visited Suffolk, part of a national influx of unprecedented proportions (Rogers *et al.* 1995).

Occurrences coincide with periods of easterly winds and more than two-thirds of Suffolk records are for May and June. An adult male at Cavenham on 21st-22nd April 1992 is the only report for that month and there are four reports for early July. Of the 31 records, only four have occurred during autumn (after mid-July): at Minsmere on 1st-5th September 1973 (adult male), at Eastbridge on 28th September 1975, at Kessingland on 6th August 1976 and at Cavenham on 2nd October 1987 (immature male).

Merlin *Falco columbarius*

An uncommon winter visitor and passage migrant

Coastal heaths and marshes are feeding grounds for this agile little falcon. One or two individuals also winter annually in north-west Suffolk in the fens and breck, and passage birds regularly pass through this region in autumn and spring. Although Merlins breed on upland moors in northern and western Britain, immigrants arriving at coastal watch-points are just as likely to have originated in Scandinavia.

Described by Ticehurst as "at all times a rare bird", the Merlin is now a regular visitor noted most frequently from December to March. Some birds linger into April and passage birds are occasionally observed as late as May. Passage birds are again noted from late July, but more often the first of the autumn occur in September or October. Singles at Minsmere on 12th June 1954 and at Walberswick on 16th June 1976, are the only records for that month.

Like other raptors, the Merlin has suffered a widespread decline during the 20th century, especially during the 1950s due to organochlorine pesticides. The species failed to recover when the use of these chemicals was restricted and the *New Atlas* shows further range contraction. The reduction in the British breeding population is paralleled in the county's records and it has become less common than in the late 1970s and early 1980s.

The falcon is most often recorded singly, although hunting pairs are not uncommon and up to four regularly roosted in the Walberswick reedbed during the early 1980s. Merlins are increasingly noted on arable lands away from the coast and Breckland, but whether this is a genuine change in the falcon's habits, or an increase in observer awareness, is unclear.

Hobby (Eurasian Hobby) *Falco subbuteo*

A fairly common summer visitor and passage migrant

Hobbies and Sand Martins
(*Adam Kennedy*)

The Hobby is now a regular feature of a Suffolk summer. This dashing falcon is most frequently observed on open heathland and over conifer belts on the coast and in Breckland, but it is not uncommon in farmland, parkland, mixed woodland and urban areas.

Suffolk's first reported nest was at Stoke-by-Nayland in 1830 and there were eight more breeding records, from widely scattered localities, up to 1884 (Babington 1884-1886). They included a pair that occupied an old Raven's nest at High Grove, Beccles, adding a touch of nostalgia for those lamenting the loss of the latter species. Ticehurst thought that it still bred on both sides of the county and, although he gave no precise details, the *Transactions of the SNS* reported nesting in East Suffolk in 1932. In August 1933, an adult was seen feeding three young on a Sandling heath. The Hobby continued to breed sporadically until the mid-1970s, when there was a steady expansion in numbers.

The *New Atlas* reported a sevenfold national increase in breeding numbers between 1973 and 1990. Maximum numbers ranged from 390 to 675 pairs during the period 1989-1999 (Ogilvie *et al.* 2001). The county's records show an increase from between 5 to 10 pairs during the 1980s to between 15 and 25 pairs in the late 1990s (Wright 2001), although the number of midsummer sightings suggests that the latter figure may be vastly under-estimated.

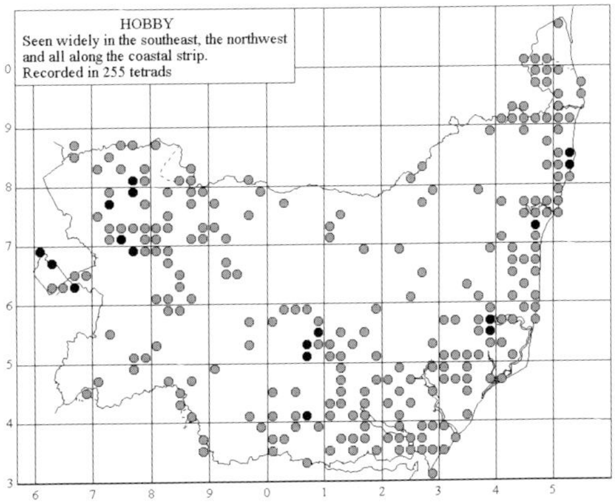

In many cases, it is difficult to separate lingering passage birds from those setting up territory. One at Reydon on 11th April 1954 is particularly early, although reports later in April are not unusual. Most Hobbies leave in September, but the species is increasingly reported in October and there are five November records, with the latest at Knettishall Heath on 20th November 1983.

The aerial spectacle of Hobbies outmanoeuvring Swifts has become a regular sight in Suffolk. Hobbies also make regular forays into Sand Martin colonies, especially as the young martins begin to fledge. This species' crepuscular habits are well-known, along with its taste for bats (Cramp *et al.* 1974-1994). A Hobby was seen to capture a noctule bat at a Breckland breeding site in 1989 (SBR). Dragonflies also form a significant part of the Hobby's diet as demonstrated by a juvenile that captured nearly 100 migrant hawkers during a relatively short stay at Landguard Point in 1985 (Piotrowski 1988). The populations of migrant hawker and common darter have exploded in recent years. Both of these dragonfly species peak in August and September, which may have contributed to the Hobby's post-fledging survival in southern England (Prince & Clarke 1993). The northward shift in the Hobby's breeding range is possibly a result of global warming.

Gyr Falcon *Falco rusticolus*

Accidental: four records

pre-1825	Bungay: Bungay Common, "shot... slightly wounded" n.d.
1867	Sudbourne: imm. shot "while eating fowl", 14th October
c.1875	Ipswich: Westerfield Park. n.d.
1883	Thetford: Thetford Warren, imm. killed "spring"

Of the seven records listed by Ticehurst, only the above four can be considered in any way authentic and even then the possibility of falconers' escapes cannot be ruled out. Falconry was popular from the Middle Ages to the early part of the 19th century. The townsmen of Dunwich paid 300 marks, ten falcons and five Gyr Falcons in 1199 for a charter from King John (Ticehurst 1932). These 'falcons' were thought to be Peregrines, which had been taken locally, but the Gyrs were from Iceland, collected by east coast boats during fishing trips to the island.

The Sudbourne bird was of the Norwegian race *F. r. rusticolus* and is one of only two examples of this race recorded in Britain (Snow 1971). It was said to be "so glutted", after its meal, that it allowed "an easy approach" (Hele 1870). The specimen is now on display at Ipswich Museum. The Bungay bird was assigned to the Greenland race *F. r. candicans*, and the Ipswich individual considered as either *F. r. candicans* or *F. r. islandus*. The latter falcon stooped at a bird flying over a pond, missed it and fell into the water. A man who threw his coat over it caught the bedraggled individual! The young Gyr Falcon killed at Thetford could not be racially assigned with any certainty (Babington 1884-1886).

The Gyr Falcon has a circumpolar distribution around or above the Arctic Circle. It had been recorded in Britain and Ireland on 137 occasions from 1958 to the end of 2000 (BBRC).

Peregrine (Peregrine Falcon) *Falco peregrinus*

An uncommon winter visitor and passage migrant – formerly bred

Coastal marshes and estuaries provide the favoured habitats of this spectacular falcon. Lothingland, Minsmere to Benacre, the Alde/Ore and Deben/Orwell/Stour estuary complexes form the wintering territories of a few birds each year. Peregrines are normally seen singly, although pairs are sometimes reported. Passage birds are regular on the immediate coastline and wintering birds occasionally frequent Breckland. The species is most often recorded from October through to March, but sightings as late as May are not uncommon and immatures are sometimes reported as early as late July. Singles at Walberswick on 28th June 1946 and over Princes Street, Ipswich on 4th June 1995, were the only 20th century records for that month. One over Trimley Marshes on 30th June 2000 and a female that oversummered on Orfordness in 2002 are hopefully preludes to successful breeding on the Suffolk coast. During the protracted stay of the latter individual, it was initially accompanied by a male Peregrine but then by a presumed escaped Lanner Falcon that also frequented the site. Suffolk's only documented breeding record was of a pair that nested in the steeple of Corton Church around 1800. To ensure that falconers left the nest undisturbed until the nestlings were ready for collection, the Parish Clerk was paid a retaining fee (Ticehurst 1932). Reports of nesting near Bentley and in the Waveney Valley early in the 20th century are not fully substantiated.

Due to human persecution, the species suffered a national decline in the 19th century, but about 700 pairs still bred in Britain and Ireland from 1930 to 1939. To counter the threat to racing pigeons carrying important messages during the Second World War, control measures were introduced as a precaution. Pesticides substantially reduced the population to only 62 breeding pairs in 1962 (Cramp *et al.* 1974-1994). The 1950s' crash is paralleled by the decline in the county's records. No more than three birds per annum were recorded from 1960 to 1984. In parallel with a moderate recovery, nationally, the Peregrine is again a familiar sight in Suffolk and there has been an obvious increase in the wintering population. However, wintering Peregrines appear to hold huge territories and its wide-ranging nature means that estimating the numbers involved is difficult. For example, regular but sporadic sightings on the Orwell, Stour and Deben each winter during the 1990s could have possibly related to just one individual.

The Peregrine may seem an unlikely Suffolk breeding species, but a pair that wintered near the Orwell Bridge, from 1991 to 1997, raised speculation that this may be a possibility. In 1997, these birds were seen displaying over Ipswich Docks in the spring, the male almost certainly oversummering in the area, although it was only reported up to 15th May and again from 9th July.

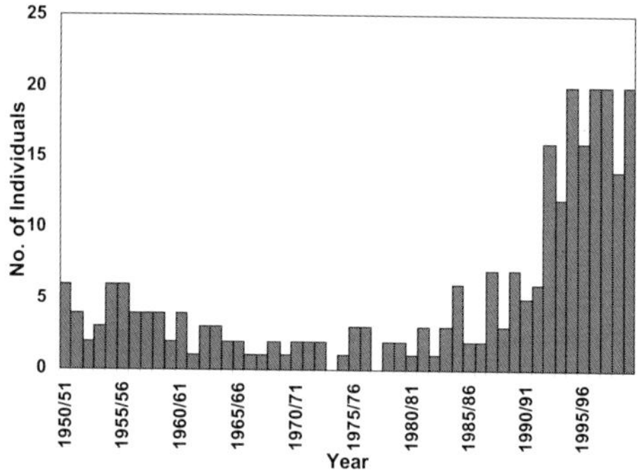

The annual totals of Peregrines from 1950/51-1999/2000

Peregrines take a variety of avian prey. Feral Pigeons form a significant part of the species' diet and the falcon regularly harasses wader flocks on estuarine mudflats. One was seen chasing and catching Little Auks at Benacre on 18th November 1995 and a pair was watched attacking a flock of Teal off Orfordness on 15th December 2001. There are two reports of Peregrines attacking other raptor species. One took a Sparrowhawk on the wing and then plucked it on a haycock at Hopton-on-Sea in 1947 and another killed a Kestrel on a track within a few metres of observers at Fagbury Cliff in 1992. Whether these two incidents were the end results of territorial disputes, attempts to eliminate competition for food or merely birds taken as prey, is open to speculation.

In autumn, Peregrines are occasionally observed arriving from offshore and it is likely that these birds are of Scandinavian origin.

Red-legged Partridge *Alectoris rufa*

An abundant resident

The Red-legged Partridge occurs in a variety of habitats, particularly heathland and farmland, although marshland and dense conifer forests are largely avoided. Numbers are augmented each year by large-scale releases for shooting. In the late 1980s, the release of Red-legged Partridge x Chukar (*A. chukar*) hybrids complicated records. Extensive studies at that time showed purebred Red-leggeds to be very rare, although, in recent years, increases have occurred as a result of licences for such releases being withdrawn.

The species was introduced into several British counties as a game bird from 1673, but it was in Suffolk where the first successes were achieved (Sharrock 1976). Eggs were imported from France for local rearing, hence the common names French Partridge or Frenchman. Releases took place at Sudbourne and Rendlesham around 1770 and at Culford, Fornham and Cavenham in 1823. By the late 1820s, it had become plentiful over much of the county, exceeding the indigenous Grey Partridge in numbers on coastal heaths. A population decline in both species was noted around 1945 (Payn 1978), but Red-leggeds were more able to adapt to the loss of grassland and with other agricultural changes that took place in subsequent decades. Nationally, Greys outnumbered Red-leggeds by 20:1 up to the 1950s whereas nowadays the respective populations are approximately equal (Gibbons *et al.* 1993).

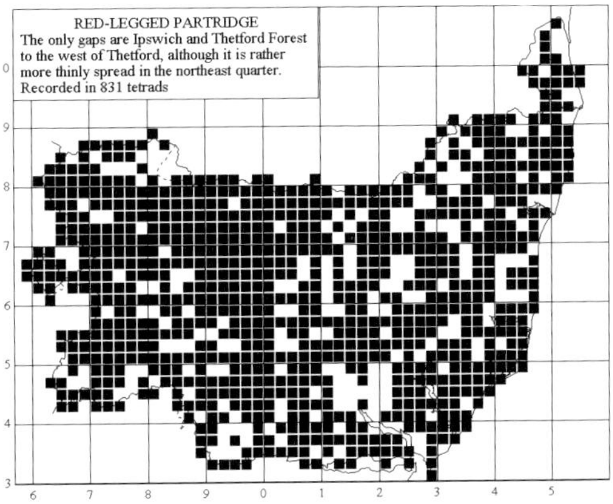

The Red-legged Partridge nests amongst heather, along field edges, in woodland, and on sand dunes and shingle banks. In winter it congregates in large coveys, especially on arable fields. A group of 150, at Iken in January 1969, is the largest covey recorded. The species is largely absent from urban environments, although it will occasionally venture into built-up areas to occupy relatively undisturbed land. For example, a pair bred at the disused gas works close to Ipswich town centre in successive summers during the 1970s. Red-legged Partridges are extremely sedentary and movements of any distance are rare. However, one was captured on-board a trawler off Lowestoft and brought in alive to the port about 1965.

Grey Partridge *Perdix perdix*

A fairly common resident

Suffolk was once regarded as one of Britain's best counties for the Grey Partridge (Payn 1978). It used to be widely distributed and numerous on most large shooting estates. No fewer than 846 were killed in a day at Elveden in September 1885 and a bag of 3,344 collected over a four-day period at Orwell Park, Nacton in October 1912, demonstrates its abundance on both sides of the county in those days. Breckland and north-west Suffolk currently hold the largest populations.

A sharp fall in numbers was widely reported as early as 1945 and by 1950 the Grey Partridge had disappeared altogether from most of central and south-west Suffolk. The decline became more rapid during the 1970s and 1980s. Agricultural change, such as early mowing of hay, stubble burning and autumn ploughing were considered to have been the principal reason. There was also a substantial loss of both grassland and hedgerow habitat, and the

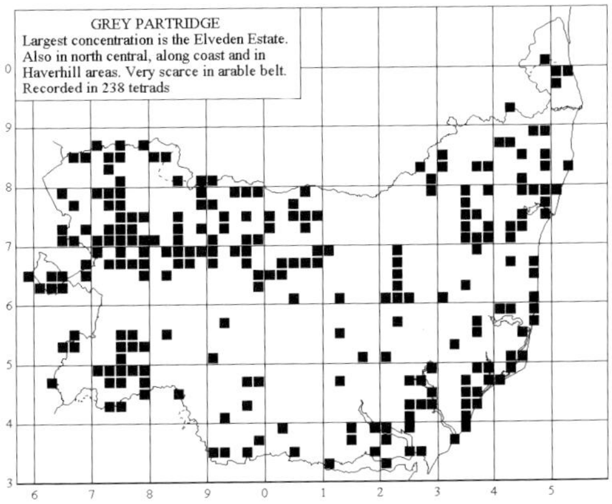

widespread use of pesticides and seed-dressings is thought to have reduced the quantity of invertebrate food available. Colder and wetter springs would also have contributed to the decline in chick survival (Potts 1986, Gibbons *et al.* 1993). The Reydon Grove Farm study from 1964 to 1971 found between three and 11 pairs annually (Benson & Williamson 1972) but the species had been lost by 1997 (Pearson 1998).

Quail (Common Quail) *Coturnix coturnix*

A scarce summer visitor and passage migrant, subject to occasional influxes

The Quail is Britain's only migratory game bird. Although small numbers are reported annually in Suffolk, it is difficult to assess just how many actually breed. The majority of records are of singing males, few of which are seen, and most are probably just stopping off briefly during migration. Criteria for fieldwork for the *New Atlas* interpreted males holding territory on successive visits as 'confirmed' breeding. However, breeding was not conclusively confirmed between 1966 and 1996. A nest of seven eggs was found at Risby in 1966 and four clutches were discovered near Newmarket in 1997. Numbers fluctuate greatly each summer, with 1-5 birds heard in most years to, very occasionally, 30 or more. It is relatively rare for no birds to be reported in a year.

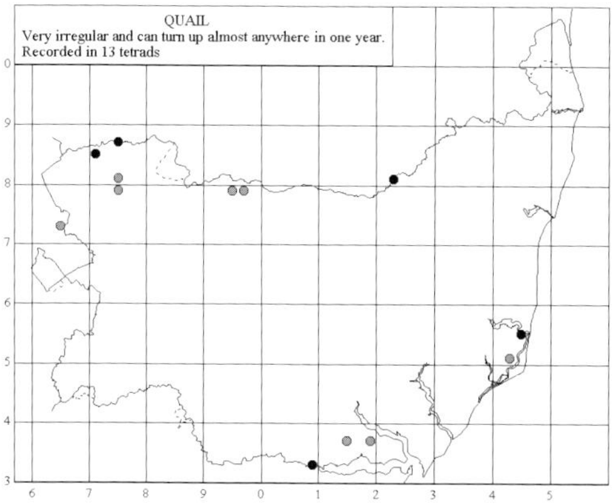

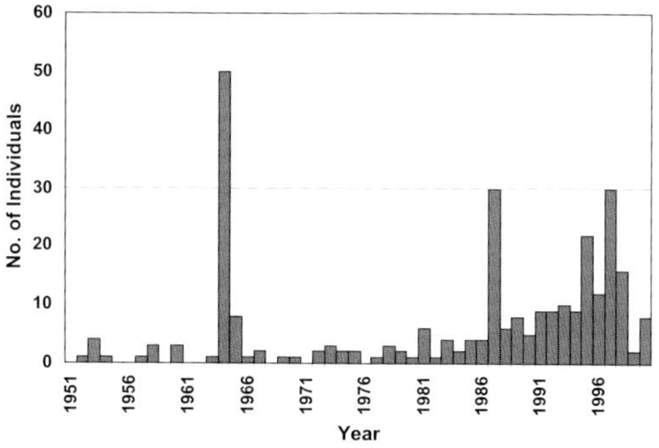

The annual totals of Quail from 1951-2000

Up to the 17th century, the Quail figured prominently on banquet menus and poultry price lists, perhaps suggesting that it was more numerous in Britain at that time (Marchant *et al.* 1990). However, there is no hard evidence to suggest that the species was ever plentiful in Suffolk. A bag of 14 obtained on common land, near Newmarket in 1860, was considered exceptional.

'Quail years', when invasions to Britain from the continent have taken place, have been well documented and occurred in 1870, 1893, 1947, 1952, 1953, 1964, 1970, 1983 and 1989 (Gibbons *et al.* 1993). However, except for 1964, when the county's share of a national influx of some 600 birds was about 50, there is little correlation between these and numbers in Suffolk. Quail are late migrants, rarely reported before mid-May. One flushed from Gunton Cliffs on 15th May 1992 and another that ran around the shingle beach at Landguard Point on 23rd May 1994 are two of the few examples from coastal watch-points. Singing males are most often reported in late May, June or July and, occasionally, they continue through to August. New arrivals sometimes reach their breeding areas in June or later (Cramp *et al.* 1974-1994), especially during influx years. One found freshly dead on a flat roof in Felixstowe on 15th June 1983 was probably a late immigrant. Returning birds are occasionally noted in September and October, although autumn reports are generally rare. Tardy individuals include one shot at Thorpe Fen in November 1859, one killed on the Shipwash light-vessel on 22nd October 1886, an injured bird that was hand caught at Worlingham on 30th November 1982, one which survived after hitting a window at Framlingham on 19th October 1984, one found in a Nacton garden on 15th October 1991 and another flushed at Aldringham Walks on 8th November 2000.

Although predominantly a summer visitor, the Quail has been reported in all months of the year including seven records between December and February. The most recent of these involved singles at Benacre from 17th January to 23rd March 1970 and at Martlesham on 24th February 1978.

Quails are most often heard calling from cereal crops and in areas rarely frequented by birdwatchers. Consequently, it is likely that many go unnoticed. The flat, arable fields in north-west Suffolk have long been favoured sites and singing males have traditionally held territories on the Shotley Peninsula. Two males calling from set-aside fields at Wherstead in July 1991 is a hopeful sign that this regime has created additional breeding habitats for Quail to exploit.

Pheasant (Common Pheasant) *Phasianus colchicus*

An abundant resident

The Pheasant is common and widespread throughout Suffolk, frequenting all habitat types, but showing a preference for woodland edges, marshes, reedy dykes and areas of scrub. It even breeds on Havergate Island and the only obvious gap in the range is in the centre of Ipswich. During winter, it is frequently observed feeding in small flocks on open arable land. Its abundance depends entirely on the game preservation policy in each area and numbers are augmented by large-scale introductions of hand-reared birds.

The species was believed to have been introduced to Britain by the Saxons during the early years of the reign of Edward the Confessor (1042-1066) and there is documentary evidence detailing rations specified for the household at the monastery of Waltham Abbey in Essex (Lever 1977), which proves that it was eaten at East Anglian tables at that time. The first reference to its existence in Suffolk is logged in the Accounts of the stewards of Acton Hall, dated 1419 (Payn 1978), although it probably remained a fairly rare bird in the county till the mid-19th century. The original stock was of the nominate race *P. c. colchicus* from the Caucasus, but the ring-necked variety *P. c. torquatus* was introduced from China in the late 19th century and is currently the dominant race.

Although the species commands little interest amongst birdwatchers, there is a considerable amount of time and effort spent on rearing Pheasants for shooting and, as such, the interest in the preservation of the Pheasant has undoubtedly shaped our countryside for a number of centuries. Arguably, small copses would not have been retained had it not been for these interests, but many of the species, particularly raptors, have suffered as a result of over-zealous protection measures. Nationally, the population of the Pheasant is stable or increasing depending on releases, although 'wild' birds are declining (Marchant *et al.* 1990). The Reydon Grove Farm study from 1964 to 1971 revealed an average of 25 pairs per annum (Benson & Williamson 1972) although none were found in 1997 (Pearson 1998).

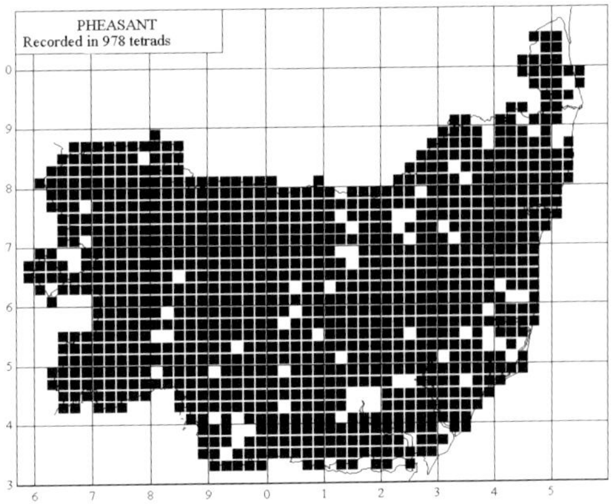

The larger, well-keepered estates such as those at Elveden and Euston in Breckland, produce ideal sporting opportunities for shooters and four-figure bags have been reported from time to time. A total of 1,128 Pheasants shot at Euston on a November day in 1895 is the largest reported bag in Suffolk. Nowadays, most rearing occurs off-site at game farms with birds transported to release pens in wooded areas of the estate. A release of around 5,000 birds on a single estate is not unusual, from which bags of 100-200 would be expected on a day's shoot.

Wing-tagging experiments by the Game Conservancy have proved that Pheasants are very sedentary, with less than 1% dispersing further than 2km and 61% being shot within 400m of the release point (Lack 1986). However, two ringed and released as juveniles at Framlingham moved approximately 16km to the Tunstall Common area (Banks 1971). They were ringed as juveniles during the summers of 1963 and 1965 and were recovered in the following August and January respectively. Birds occasionally penetrate built-up areas and there are a number of records from Ipswich housing estates. Pheasants sometimes 'pass through' Landguard Point, probably reaching the site from Trimley St Mary by overflying Felixstowe Docks.

Subsequently, only passage birds have been noted, with the vast majority occurring in September. Arrivals have been reported as early as 9th April (in from the sea at Benacre in 1955) and most depart by October. However, there have been three winter records: Thorpe Fen on 17th December 1861, Leiston on 16th December 1872 and Mildenhall on 10th January 1971.

Since 1990, two birds have been recorded in midsummer: one running ahead of a combine harvester at Swilland in June 1991 and two calling at Martlesham on 4th-5th July 1995.

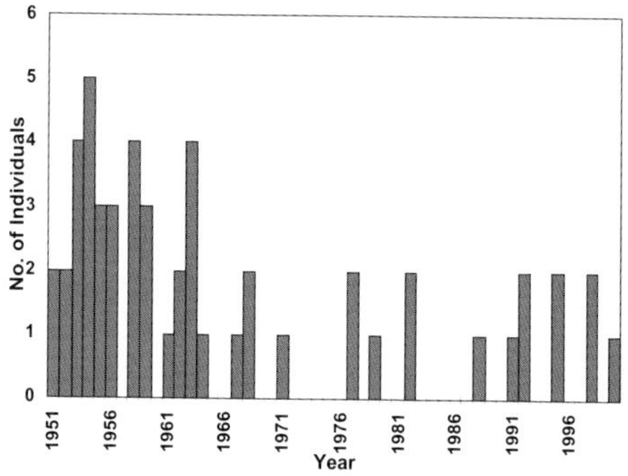

The annual totals of Corncrake from 1951-2000

An alarming decline has been noted in Scotland and Ireland, and the Corncrake is on the brink of extinction as a breeding species in England and Wales (Gibbons *et al.* 1993). This decline has been reflected in the number of passage birds recorded in Suffolk with only 14 reported during the period 1970-1999. Conservation measures at breeding sites on the Western Isles appear to be successful and there are early signs of a recovery in that area.

Moorhen (Common Moorhen) *Gallinula chloropus*

An abundant resident, passage migrant and winter visitor

The Moorhen breeds prolifically in all freshwater habitats throughout the county from the margins of large reservoirs to the middle of the smallest farmyard or industrial pond. A few nest on saltings and saline lagoons on river estuaries. Resident birds may vigorously defend their breeding territories throughout the winter, but will also feed in loose flocks, normally of less than 20. Moorhens sometimes feed gregariously on open meadows or drilled fields, particularly when dykes and ponds become frozen. Coordinated counts at the larger sites sometimes reach three figures, but flocks of this size are uncommon.

The larger coastal nature reserves hold substantial breeding populations. In 1993, Minsmere and North Warren held 29 and 72 pairs respectively, and Benacre and Walberswick are also known to hold good numbers. However, Moorhens are not always welcome residents as they are notorious egg thieves and can cause damage to wader and tern colonies. At Minsmere, in 1989, one was watched taking Little Tern chicks.

The distribution map shows that breeding occurs in every 10-km square and the gaps in distribution correspond to the dryer heathland areas and forestry belts. The species has a long nesting season usually beginning in late March and continuing through to the autumn. Each pair normally produces two and often three broods each year. A pair with small young was noted at Woodbridge in December 1945 (Payn 1978). The Reydon Grove Farm study from 1964 to 1971 revealed a range of 3-11 pairs annually (Benson & Williamson 1972) compared with only two pairs in 1997.

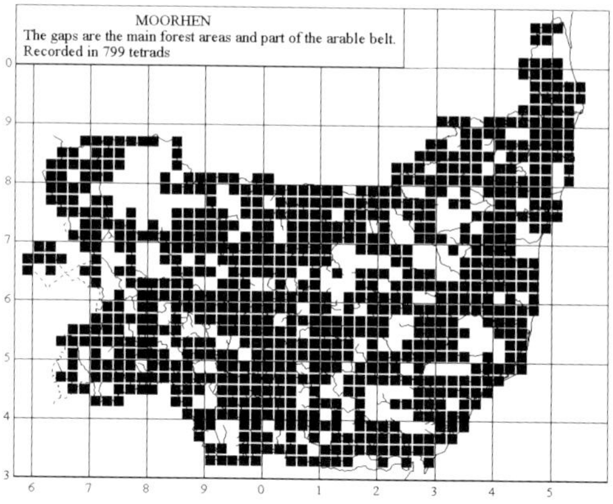

A Moorhen flew aboard a steam drifter 50 miles off Lowestoft on 22nd November 1951 and birds are regularly reported at migration watch-points, with LBO logging several records in recent years. Wintering numbers are supplemented by immigrants from Scandinavia and the near continent (Cramp *et al.* 1974-1994), as proved by the county's ringing returns which include three birds from Germany, seven from the Netherlands, two from Denmark and one from Belgium. Evidence of regular movements from north Essex to Suffolk includes four birds trapped at Abberton Reservoir during the autumn and subsequently found wintering in Suffolk.

A flock of 190 fed on drilled fields at Butley on 3rd January 1982, but the highest totals have been in the Long Melford/Glemsford area, with 200 in February 1987 and 250 in January 1989.

Allen's Gallinule *Porphyrula alleni*

Accidental: one record

1902 Hopton-on-Sea: juv. 1st January

Britain's first record of Allen's Gallinule involved an exhausted individual that was found on a fishing boat off Hopton following strong south-westerly winds. It was taken alive to a local taxidermist who fed it on mealworms for two days before it was preserved (presumably it died rather than being killed).

The species was not admitted to the British list until 1974, following research by Hudson (1974). He found that no fewer than five of these African wanderers arrived at Palearctic sites in 1902, following an anticyclone over Algeria that produced strong south-westerly winds from north-west Africa to Britain. Britain's only other record involved an exhausted individual picked up near Portland Bill, Dorset, in February 2002, a century after the Suffolk occurrence.

The Allen's Gallinule is a 'rains migrant' breeding in Africa south of the Sahara and also Madagascar. The West African population moves south during the dry season.

Coot (Common Coot) *Fulica atra*

A common resident and winter visitor

Larger lakes, reservoirs and slow moving rivers provide the Coot with breeding and wintering haunts. Overwintering is attempted at the nesting areas and small groups are recorded at most areas of standing freshwater. When lakes and rivers become frozen, huge congregations of immigrant birds will join local birds that frequent larger sites such as Alton Water, Lackford Wildfowl Reserve and the Orwell estuary. The species will also nest on smaller ponds, rivers and borrow-dykes, but the breeding population is concentrated onto the larger river valleys and coastal marshes.

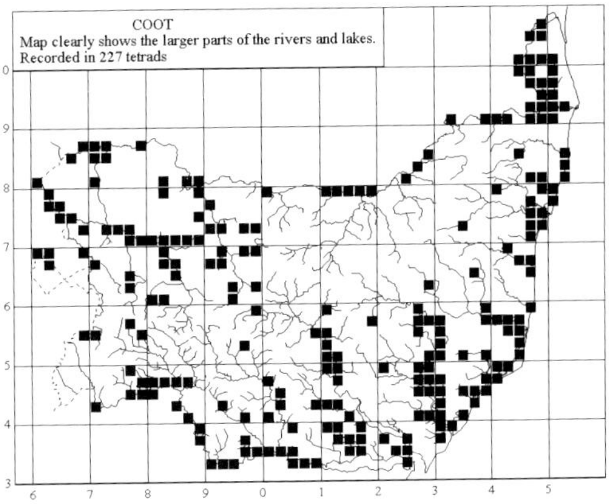

Sheppard & Whitear (1824-1825) described a flock of "several thousands" resting on the Stour in January 1819 and similar sized gatherings were regular on this estuary in the 19th and early 20th centuries (Cox 1984). Ticehurst considered the Coot as "very largely a winter visitor" arriving in July and August, and departing in March. Up to the late 1950s, the tidal waters of the Alde and Orwell hosted large wintering populations and the former locality was recognised for coot shooting during hard weather. About 2,000 were present on the Alde in December 1952 and, during the next few years, flocks of up to 750 wintered in the Freston-Woolverstone area on the Orwell. Estuarine flocks dwindled during the 1960s, probably due to the disease affecting eel-grass, the species' favoured winter food. The construction of a freshwater, trout fishing lake beside the Orwell, at Trimley St Martin (Loompit Lake) late in that decade, provided an alternative feeding area for wintering flocks. The vast majority of birds, in a record estuary count of 1,003 in November 1984, were on Loompit Lake. Increasing numbers of birds have wintered at Alton Water where annual peak counts include 1,427 (December 1994), 2,845 (8th October 1995), 2,003 (January 1996), 2,135 (December 1997), 1,465 (December 1998), 3,090 (November 1999) and a record 4,778 (December 2000). The 1995 concentration was attracted by an abundance of submerged vegetation that flourished during a summer that saw extensive periods of sunshine (Piotrowski 1996).

Coots are long-distance, nocturnal migrants and European ringing recoveries show a general movement south and west in autumn (Lack 1986). Ticehurst referred to individuals killed on lightships and the species is occasionally found at Landguard Point during hard-weather periods. One ringed at Boyton on 16th August 1969 and recovered at Charente-Maritime, France on 19th December 1986 demonstrates both the movement and longevity of the species.

The presence of a Moorhen x Coot hybrid at Alton Water from 27th February 1981 to March 1982 caused quite a stir, due to speculation by some that it showed characteristics of American Coot *F. americana* (Moore & Piotrowski 1983).

Crane (Common Crane) *Grus grus*

A rare passage migrant: (75+ records) – formerly bred

The Crane occurs in ones and twos at coastal sites almost annually and very occasionally in small flocks. Occurrences are normally during passage periods with May and September being the most favoured months, although there are also records for midwinter and, occasionally, lingering birds remain throughout the summer.

The species bred commonly in East Anglia up to the start of the 17th century, but was wiped out by shooting (Payn 1978). Ray (1678) referred to great flocks in the Cambridgeshire and Lincolnshire fens, but these were probably passage or wintering birds. Previous authors have considered that the species was also present in the Suffolk fens.

There were only two records for the 19th century: one killed at Kirkley, Lowestoft in April 1845 and another shot on Benacre Marshes in June 1894. During the first half of the 20th century, there were only five more occurrences. The 1950s saw an increase in records and a wintering flock of five at Waldringfield from 8th January to 2nd March 1958, were the first to occur south of Minsmere and the first group to exceed two birds. Suffolk's most spectacular record involved a migrating flock of 26 that flew south over Higham on 16th October 1977. These were the first to be noted away from the coast and estuaries, and the same flock was seen later that day over Essex and Kent. Since 1983, Cranes have been noted annually except for 1993 and 1994. One that frequented a number of Breckland sites from 22nd June to 1st November 1995 is the only record for north-west Suffolk.

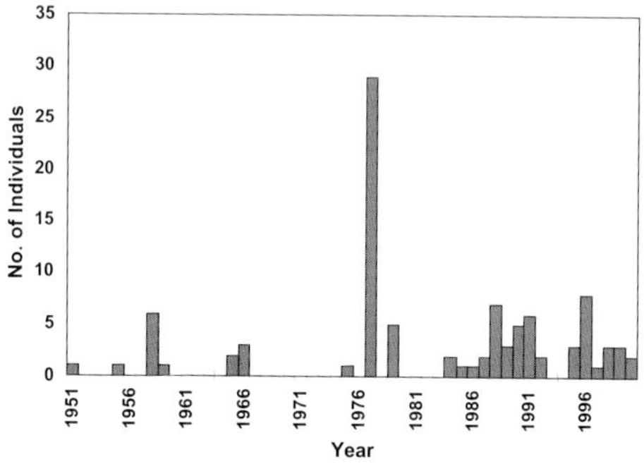

The annual totals of Crane from 1951-2000

Since 1981, breeding has been attempted on a number of occasions in the Norfolk Broads, with at least one pair raising four young in their first eight years (Gibbons *et al.* 1993). It is likely that some Suffolk records refer to wanderers from this nesting area.

Little Bustard *Tetrax tetrax*

Accidental: 21 records involving 23 individuals

1912	Wickham Mkt: December.
1959	Leiston cum Sizewell: female shot 3rd December
1960	Orfordness: 20th June
1987	Sudbourne: three 20th December

There were only four records of Little Bustard during the 20th century in Suffolk. However, no fewer than 17 records of the species occurred during the 18th and 19th centuries. The first example involved a female captured on Newmarket Heath and kept alive for some weeks, sometime prior to 1797. There was a concentration of five records between 1858 and 1866. With the exception of two – a male in full summer plumage shot at Kessingland on 3rd May 1898 and another bird on Orfordness in June 1960 – all have occurred between October and March.

The breeding range extends from France through Iberia to north-west Africa and eastwards through southern Europe to Kazakstan. The Little Bustard is a rare visitor to the British Isles, having been noted on 109 occasions up to the end of 2000 (BBRC).

It has been proved that both western (*T. t. tetrax*) and eastern (*T. t. orientalis*) races occur in Britain (Dymond *et al.* 1989), but those specimens examined in Suffolk have been of the latter race.

MacQueen's Bustard *Chlamydotis macqueenii*

Accidental: one record

1962 Blythburgh: Hinton, 21st November to 29th December

The above occurrence was arguably one of the most exciting ornithological events of the 20th century, with this long-staying rarity causing quite a stir even in the 'non-twitching' 1960s. This was the fifth and most recent British record, and it may well be the last, as the populations of Macqueen's Bustard in Arabia and Pakistan are being decimated by Arab falconers (Dymond *et al.* 1989). The bird was most confiding – frequenting mustard and stubble fields and occasionally using roads to walk to another feeding spot (Axell 1964). Two observers looking for the bird early one morning were surprised when one of the piles of frost-covered weeds in the field suddenly stood up and started feeding (B. J. Brown pers. comm.).

Macqueen's Bustard has until recently been treated as a race of the similar Houbara Bustard *C. undulata*. However, following a review by the taxonomic sub-committee of the BOURC, Macqueen's Bustard now warrants full species status. The Suffolk bird showed the plumage features, in particular the dark crown stripe and spotted mantle, of Macqueen's Bustard. Macqueen's Bustard is found from the Sinai Peninsula and east Turkey through to Mongolia. The species is migratory, moving to the Persian Gulf and Pakistan during winter.

Great Bustard *Otis tarda*

Accidental: recorded in two winters (ten individuals) in the 20th century – formerly resident in Breckland

1925	Cockfield: four (one shot) c.10th December
1987	Harkstead: Harkstead Hall, four 16th-20th January
	Kirton/Hemley: three intermittently from 18th January to 7th February
	Orford: Raydon Hall, same 20th January to 27th February, single to 7th March
	Kessingland/Benacre: two 7th February
	Horham: two 14th-25th February
	Theberton/Blythburgh: three 10th-21st February

The Great Bustard represents one of the greatest losses to the breeding avifauna of Suffolk and Britain. This magnificent bird roamed the Breckland plains up to the early 19th century and possibly bred on the coastal sandlings as well, although evidence for the latter is scant. The planting of fir belts and cultivation broke up the wide open spaces of Breckland and was probably the root cause of the bustard's extinction in the county. Hunters exterminated the last few remaining birds.

Greyhounds hunted Great Bustards on Newmarket Heath as early as 1656 and there were about 40-50 frequenting the Icklingham area in 1812 (Ticehurst 1932). Great Bustards were offered little protection and winter flocks were decoyed to piles of turnips and blasted by duck-gunners. One notorious keeper killed seven birds with a single shot (Payn 1978). This wanton slaughter had a disastrous effect on the population with numbers dwindling rapidly during the early decades of the 19th century. The last nest was found in a rye field at Icklingham in 1832. Records at Wherstead and Martlesham in the early 19th century perhaps suggest that breeding also took place around Ipswich, although wanderers from the resident Breckland population is a more likely explanation (Ticehurst 1932).

Since its extinction, one frequented Wangford and Lakenheath Warrens in August 1873 and a male was seen at both Eriswell and Elveden on 24th-25th February 1876. A female was killed at Mildenhall Fen on 5th February 1891 in a winter when several were obtained elsewhere in England. There was a failed attempt to introduce Spanish-reared birds to Elveden in 1900. Excluding the latter, 20th century records involve just ten individuals (see above).

The Cockfield birds flew over a shooting party and one was collected. The 1987 occurrence was a frustrating experience for many birdwatchers, with probably as many as six to nine birds proving notoriously difficult to locate – large and conspicuous though they might appear. The birds frequented a number of oil seed rape fields and, when disturbed, would fly many miles to a new feeding area. All were males, of various ages, which conforms to the species' behaviour pattern of single sex flocks appearing at regular wintering sites elsewhere in Europe (Snow & Perrins 1998). Whilst at Theberton, the birds frequently displayed to one another.

Oystercatcher (Eurasian Oystercatcher) *Haematopus ostralegus*

A locally common winter visitor, passage migrant and common resident

Red-necked Phalarope and Oystercatcher
(*Adam Kennedy*)

The extensive mudflats of the lower Orwell and Stour estuaries host a combined wintering population of some 2,000-3,000 Oystercatchers. Small groups explore exposed mudflats and roosts of several hundred form on adjacent fields at high tide. Grassland areas such as playing fields and mown cliff-tops at seaside towns are probed for earthworms, the birds often being oblivious to the presence of humans. Nesting occurs on saltings, beaches and adjacent arable land and, in recent years, a few pairs have colonised inland gravel pits.

Regular breeding occurred at only one site during the 19th century (Babington 1884-1886) with "large numbers" nesting around the "mere land" at Thorpe (Hele 1870). As the mere land was lost, the birds disappeared. Ticehurst listed the Blyth, Dunwich and Orfordness as sites where nests had been found, but generally thought that the Suffolk coast offered few inducements to the species. The breeding population began to increase in the late 1930s (Payn 1978) and by 1960 at least 20 pairs were nesting between Breydon Water and the Stour, most being confined to the immediate coastline, but a few pairs became established on the larger estuaries.

A full census of coastal sites in 1988 and 1989 revealed 478 breeding pairs. Nearly half were on the Butley/Alde/Ore complex (Holzer *et al.* 1993) with a significant proportion of these on Orfordness, which forms the eastern bank of this estuary. A breeding density of 28.2 pairs/km^2 was recorded on the shingle spit compared with 24.2 pairs/km^2 on saltmarsh and 7.5 pairs/km^2 on grazing marsh.

This wader's range has been extending into inland Britain since the late 19th century (Gibbons *et al.* 1993), but nesting was not reported in West Suffolk until comparatively recently. There were only four records from 1950 to 1975 (Last 1976), but since 1987 up to five pairs have bred annually in Breckland. Inland nesting has also occurred in the Gipping and Waveney Valleys and it is likely that the colonisation of inland habitats will continue.

According to Ticehurst, normally few, if any, wintered during his time, although flocks would appear during spells of severe weather, gales and snow. Wintering numbers began to increase during the 1950s, although flocks of 20 on the Stour in 1953 and 55 on the Orwell in 1955 were still noteworthy. However, the population increase was poorly documented, with the species hardly mentioned in SBRs throughout the 1960s. WeBS counts demonstrate the growth in the wintering population that has more than doubled

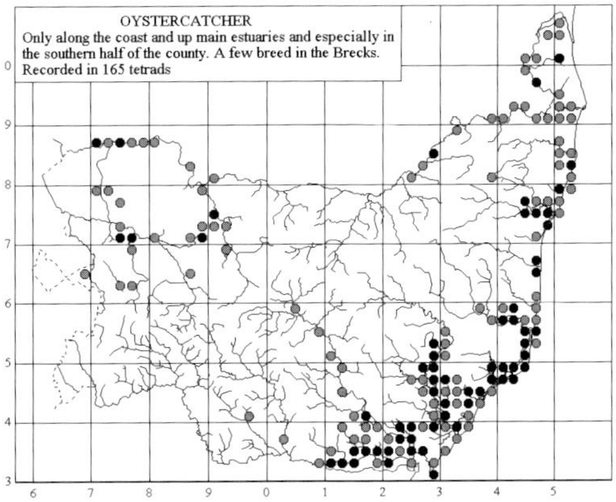

at most sites since the early 1970s (Wright 1989). The Orwell held the county's highest densities up to the late 1980s. Four-figure gatherings were noted in consecutive years from 1984 to 1988 with most of the birds frequenting Fagbury Flats. However, the loss of this site to the Port of Felixstowe development in the late 1980s resulted in an exodus to the Stour from where similar totals are now reported. Suffolk's largest site total was 2,053 on the Stour in November 1996.

OYSTERCATCHER
Only along the coast and up main estuaries and especially in the southern half of the county. A few breed in the Brecks.
Recorded in 165 tetrads

March and August are the peak passage periods, with small flocks of 20 or more occurring daily at coastal localities. The largest recorded movement involved 400 moving south off Minsmere on 22nd August 1988. From 1909 to the end of 1995, Suffolk-ringed birds have been recovered in Norway (4), the Netherlands (7) and France (7). Three Dutch-ringed birds have been found wintering in Suffolk. The months of ringing and recovery indicate that Norwegian and Dutch breeding birds winter in Suffolk and a bird ringed as a nestling at Texel, the Netherlands, in 1929 and shot at Pakefield 28 years later provided a remarkable example of longevity.

Black-winged Stilt *Himantopus himantopus*

A very rare passage migrant: 24 records involving 33 individuals

The coastal nature reserves provide ideal feeding habitat for this elegant wader and their creation may be a reason for the increase in records since 1976. Up to the end of 2000, 326 Black-winged Stilts had been recorded in Britain and Ireland (BBRC).

From 1823 to 1902, nine individuals were reported in Suffolk, all at coastal localities, and most were shot. Two at Dunwich in 1945 heralded a cluster of records, culminating in a flock of six in Buss Creek, Reydon in April 1949. A pair frequented flooded fields at Aldeburgh in June 1957 and one was at Minsmere the following year. A pair visited Felixstowe golf course in April 1965, presumably the same birds seen at Minsmere the following month. A pair seen briefly on the River Blyth in May 1979 was the only record for that decade. From 1988 to 1993, the species was noted on seven occasions, six individuals, and a pair that visited Alton Water and then Livermere on 6th-7th June 1988. Nine years followed before another pair was seen intermittently at Lakenheath on 8th-11th May 2002.

The Black-winged Stilt's breeding range extends from the Middle East and Asia Minor sporadically through western Europe. Numbers fluctuate, depending on water levels at breeding sites (Cramp *et al.* 1974-1994) and the wader may not nest at all in dry periods, which are regularly encountered in the south of its range. Displaced birds may then venture further north and probably account for British breeding attempts in 1945, 1983 and 1987 (Gibbons *et al.* 1993).

A colour-ringed individual seen at Bawdsey and Trimley Marshes in June 1993 was from France, the exact ringing location has yet to be determined.

Avocet (Pied Avocet) *Recurvirostra avosetta*

A locally common resident, winter visitor and passage migrant

The Avocet has a special place in the county's natural history. It returned to breed at Minsmere and Havergate Island after an absence of more than a century and from there colonised many other East Anglian sites. In the late 1990s, about 200-250 pairs bred annually on brackish coastal lagoons and saltings, and the wintering population was in the range of 1,500-2,000. Avocets winter in large flocks principally on the Alde/Ore/Butley complex, but also increasingly on the Blyth and Deben. Offshore movements have become increasingly frequent and passage birds are occasionally attracted inland to flooded meadows and lakesides.

In the early 19th century, breeding took place near Orford lighthouse and around Thorpe Mere. Elsewhere there were scattered colonies on the east coast between Kent and Yorkshire. It was never common

Avocets
(*Adam Kennedy*)

and was afforded little protection and, in consequence, was lost as a British breeding species. There was an isolated breeding attempt at Thorpe Mere in 1882, but the eggs were taken. A female with well-developed ovaries was shot at Thorpe Mere in May 1893.

During and immediately after the Second World War, a small colony became established at Minsmere, the habitat made suitable by flooding. Four pairs bred in April 1947 and, in July of that year, a second colony was found on Havergate Island where four or five pairs raised eight young. Breeding continued at the latter site, with numbers building-up gradually to 22 pairs in 1951 and c.100 by the end of that decade. There was limited breeding success at two or three smaller sites. Nesting did not take place again at Minsmere until 1963 but, thereafter, the colony steadily increased following the expansion of The Scrape, and by 1976 the number of nesting pairs had reached 51. A further 90 pairs were nesting on Havergate. Avocets currently breed with varying success at about ten coastal sites. Minsmere and Havergate remain the county's principal breeding sites, although small populations are growing elsewhere such as at Walberswick NNR and Trimley Marshes.

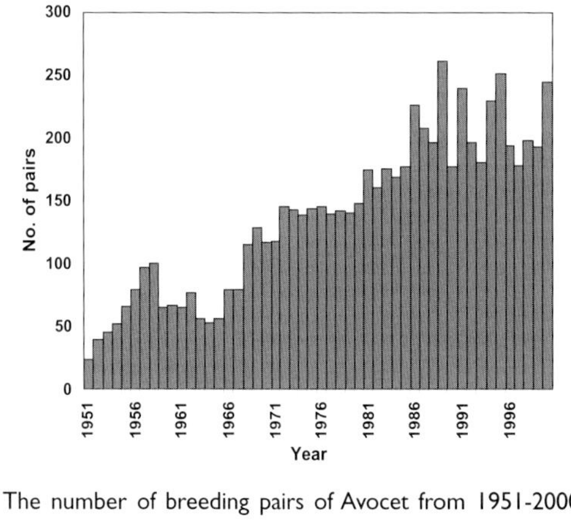

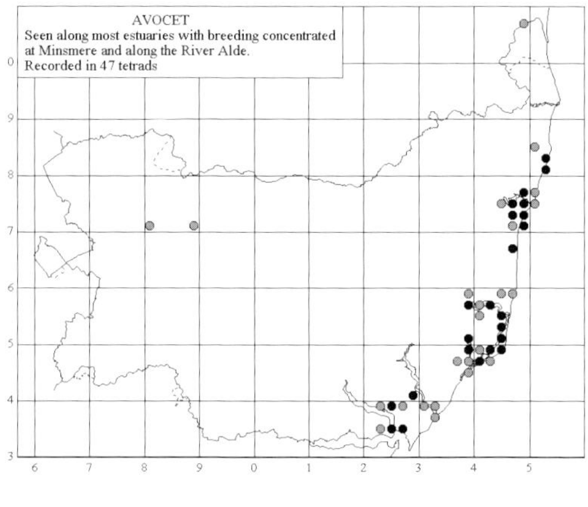

AVOCET
Seen along most estuaries with breeding concentrated at Minsmere and along the River Alde.
Recorded in 47 tetrads

The number of breeding pairs of Avocet from 1951-2000

Overwintering was not reported until 1976 when 23, from an August gathering of c.220, remained at Havergate. Thereafter, wintering numbers increased greatly to counts of over 300 in the 1980s to nearly 1,000 by the early 1990s. The Alde/Ore/Butley complex was the first British site to reach international importance for winter populations, having attained a five-year average of 700 birds (Waters & Cranswick 1993). A count of 946 in March 1992 probably consisted of both wintering and breeding birds, and 1,336 on the estuary in February 1999 is the highest count to date. Wintering numbers on the Blyth are also increasing with flocks of 600 or more reported in the late 1990s. Smaller numbers winter on the Deben.

Small parties, commuting between breeding sites during the summer months, account for the majority of offshore sightings. However, small movements are increasingly logged at Landguard Point, during the late autumn period, including an exceptional northerly passage involving 127 individuals on 6th November 1994.

Between 1970 and 1973, 140 chicks were ringed in Suffolk, of which nine were fitted with colour rings to distinguish those reared at Minsmere from those from Havergate (Cadbury *et al.* 1989). Interchange between breeding sites was confirmed. One ringed at Minsmere was found wintering on the Tamar estuary in four consecutive winters during the 1970s. Up to the end of 1997, Suffolk-ringed birds had been recovered in the Netherlands (2), France (3), Spain (3), Portugal (2) and Morocco, most of them between September and January. The exceptions are the two in Portugal found in June and August. Birds ringed in the Netherlands (4), Belgium (2) and Germany have been recovered in Suffolk. There are some good examples of longevity, the oldest bird so far being 17 years (Cadbury *et al.* 1989).

The Avocet has been noted in West Suffolk on 16 occasions, mainly in pairs and during the passage periods. At Lackford, one on 16th June 1992 and two on 22nd June 1996 were probably failed breeders from the coast, while another there on 4th January 1995 is the only winter record from an inland locality.

Stone Curlew *Burhinus oedicnemus*

A locally common summer visitor and rare passage migrant

Stone Curlews
(*Adam Kennedy*)

In Breckland, there is a stable breeding population, but numbers of Stone Curlew have dwindled to just one or two pairs on the coast. Passage birds are occasionally reported elsewhere. The breeding population currently ranges from 40-50 pairs. Stone Curlews are more active at night when their eerie calls echo across Breckland plains.

Formerly, there were healthy populations on the coast and Sandlings, and in Breckland. Ticehurst stated that it bred on every heath between Southwold and the River Orwell, although it was nowhere abundant. Nesting even took place in south Suffolk along the Stour Valley up as far as Sudbury. Agricultural reclamation and afforesation were responsible for the decrease of the species in Breckland that was noted as early as the 1840s and, by the end of that century, the population had declined to such an extent that its extinction was thought imminent. However, the species found the stony, arable fields increasingly to its liking and in many cases nested on these in preference to traditional heathland sites. Stone Curlews increased when marginal land was again taken out of cultivation between the two World Wars, but decreased again in 1939-1945.

A census of Breckland in 1949 located 634 individuals, but a rapid decline took place during the 1950s as the rabbit population was decimated by myxomatosis. This slowly allowed the remaining brecks to scrub up at a time when afforestation was continuing to take its toll. Stone Curlews decreased from over 300 pairs in 1948 to 60-80 pairs a decade later (Parslow 1967). The species became extinct in south Suffolk in the late 1960s and ten years later the coastal population was limited to a mere four pairs. Breeding numbers (1990-1993) ranged from 41 to 48 pairs in the Suffolk Breckland, demonstrating that the decline has, perhaps, bottomed out in this region. A single pair remains on the coast and, hopefully, the habitat restoration schemes, currently underway, will soon encourage birds back to their former haunts.

Stone Curlews form post-breeding flocks that are a good indicator of population levels. Such gatherings were formerly noted at both coastal and Breckland sites as early as late July, the majority forming between late August and the end of October. The largest autumn gatherings were all in the breck and include 300 on the Black Ditches, near Icklingham in the late 19th century, 150-200 on Troston Heath on 10th October 1914 and over 600 there during the 1940s (Green 1989) – what an amazing spectacle the latter must have been! Flock sizes decreased during the 1950s, although groups of 50-120 were reported almost annually, including 67 and 50 in the Minsmere/Westleton Heath area in 1952 and 1955 respectively. Nowadays, concentrations of 25-35 are a regular feature of a Breckland autumn, but groups of 52 and 50 in September 1993 and October 1994 respectively are now considered exceptional.

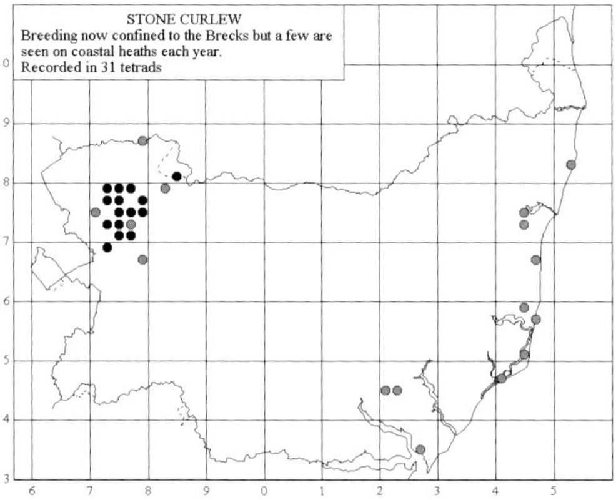

STONE CURLEW
Breeding now confined to the Brecks but a few are seen on coastal heaths each year.
Recorded in 31 tetrads

Previous authors have noted that some Stone Curlews fly several miles to feed in damper habitats each evening. This behaviour was confirmed during an intensive study by the RSPB (Green 1988), part of which involved fixing radio transmitters to some of the birds to monitor movements. One Breckland breeder was tracked for several miles and was eventually found on a football pitch in Bury St Edmunds (C. Bowden pers. comm.). It was also shown that the species searched for dung beetles and their larvae in fields occupied by livestock.

Stone Curlews normally arrive back at their Suffolk breeding grounds in mid-March. Four February reports probably relate to early immigrants, one at Levington on 11th February 1972 being the earliest. Most birds depart in September and October, but there are six records for November, up to 24th. In addition, there have been seven December occurrences and three in January. These may well have been overwintering attempts, although dated records refer only to single-day observations.

The perils of migration are aptly illustrated by ringing returns. Between 1976 and 1993, 19 Stone Curlews from Suffolk (mostly ringed as chicks) were recovered elsewhere. Seven out of nine birds recovered in Spain had been shot. Several also perished in France but one shot in Morocco represents the longest movement involving a Suffolk-ringed bird. The species is rarely encountered on passage and the following occurrences are considered to have involved migrant birds: one flying south off Landguard Point (19th August 1989), one at Alton Water (14th September 1990), two at Felixstowe Ferry (early September 1991), one at Havergate (20th July 1995) and one at Shingle Street (10th September 1995). One ringed in Hampshire in July 1976 and recovered in Breckland nearly 18 years later demonstrated the longevity of the species.

Cream-coloured Courser *Cursorius cursor*

Accidental: one record

1828 Friston: shot 3rd October

The Cream-coloured Courser is a rare vagrant to the British Isles with only 33 occurrences up to the end of 2000 (BBRC). All records are for the months of September through to December, with the majority in October (Dymond *et al.* 1989).

The breeding range is restricted to the desert regions of north and East Africa and south-west Asia east to Afghanistan. It winters in Arabia and in East Africa as far south as Kenya.

The Friston bird was shot by a shepherd and sent to the British Museum (Ticehurst 1932).

Collared Pratincole *Glareola pratincola*

Accidental: five records involving six individuals

1827 Breydon Water: two shot 21st May
1977 Alton Water: 30th May to 2nd June
1996 Dunwich/Minsmere: Shore Pools/The Scrape, 8th-9th June
1997 Burgh Castle: 15th May
Blundeston: 29th September

The Alton Water bird favoured an earth bank and was one of the site's two national rarities in as many days (White-winged Black Tern being noted on 28th May). The reservoir was at its initial flooding stage and the banks were sparsely vegetated.

The Dunwich bird could be recognised by a broken tail streamer and was recorded at a number of sites before and after visiting Suffolk. It was also seen in Warwickshire, Northamptonshire, Yorkshire, Norfolk and the Netherlands during the period 12th May to 25th July. It spent the afternoon of 8th June on a pool visited by the Oriental Pratincole in 1981 and was seen over Minsmere's Scrape the following day. The Burgh Castle and Blundeston records may relate to the same adult seen at several sites in east and north Norfolk between May and July 1997.

The Collared Pratincole breeds in Iberia and north-west Africa eastwards through the Middle East to Kazakhstan. In addition it nests to the south of the Sahara where it also winters. Records for Britain and Ireland stood at 84 to the end of 2000 (BBRC).

Oriental Pratincole *Glareola maldivarum*

Accidental: two records

1981 Dunwich: Shore Pools, first summer 22nd June to 8th July
1993 Orford: Havergate Is., 4th and 19th September

The long-staying Dunwich individual, which later frequented Old Hall Marshes, Essex, was Britain's first record. The two single-day observations at Havergate involved a well-watched bird that probably over-summered in Norfolk that same year. There were only five records for Britain and Ireland to the end of 2000 (BBRC). The breeding range extends from north India to east China and the species winters in Indonesia and Australia.

Black-winged Pratincole *Glareola nordmanni*

Accidental: two records

1985 Minsmere: 5th July
1993 Gt/Lt Livermere: Livermere Park, intermittently 6th-12th September

Suffolk's first record of the Black-winged Pratincole was on the day that observers awaited the reappearance of a Greater Yellowlegs that had been seen at Minsmere the previous evening. Consequently, the pratincole's two brief afternoon visits to the Scrape were well-recorded. Similarly, many ornithologists saw the relatively long-staying individual in the Livermere area.

The breeding range incorporates the steppe zone from Romania through to Kazakstan and as far south as the Caucasus, and the wintering areas lie in the Afrotropical region. It is a rare visitor to the British Isles, noted on only 34 occasions up to the end of 2000 (BBRC).

Pratincole sp. — *Glareola* sp.

Accidental: one record

1975 Covehithe: in from sea 22nd August

Of the 11 pratincoles recorded in Suffolk, the above individual could not be specifically assigned.

Little Ringed Plover (Little Plover) — *Charadrius dubius*

A fairly common summer visitor and passage migrant

Little Ringed Plover (*Stuart Ling*)

An increase in the number and extent of working gravel pits has provided this diminutive plover with new breeding habitats. Little Ringed Plovers currently breed annually in the Lark, Gipping, Little Ouse and Waveney Valleys. It is frequently noted on passage and gatherings of six or more are common at both coastal and inland localities.

The Little Ringed Plover was not recorded in Suffolk until 1948, when two or three nesting pairs were found at wartime gravel workings at Benacre Ness. The same year, a pair bred on the Minsmere Levels and another two pairs summered at a site near Lakenheath, although breeding was not proven. In 1949, nesting activity was noted at the same three sites and, thereafter, at least one pair bred annually till 1953 and then intermittently until 1959. Sitting birds remained unperturbed as the army practised landing manoeuvres at one of the sites in 1958. Few pairs were reported during the 1960s, but demand for sand

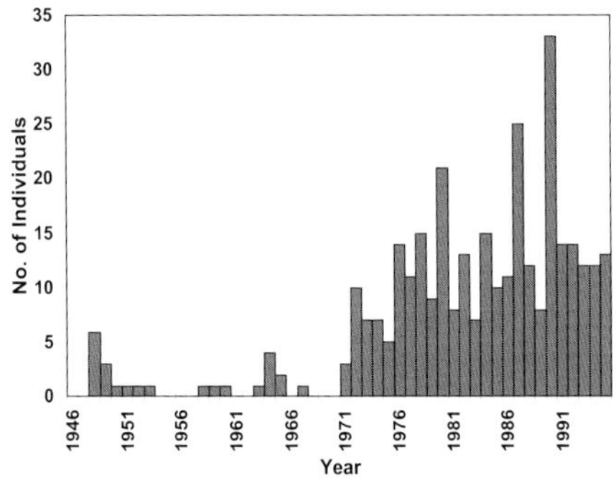

The annual totals of territorial pairs of Little Ringed Plovers from 1946-1995

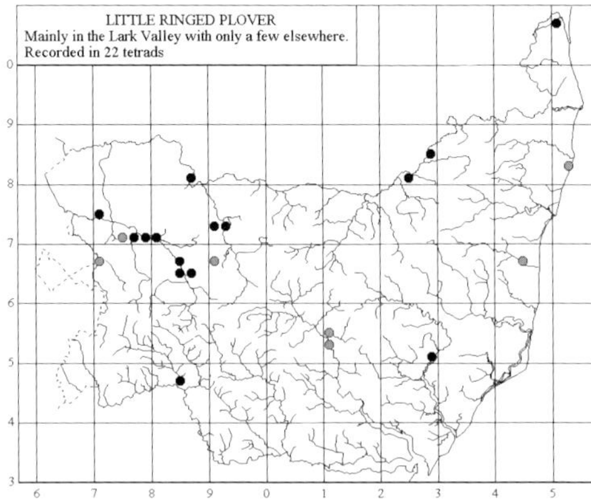

and gravel in the 1970s and 1980s resulted in an increase in working pits and a corresponding upsurge in breeding pairs. Ten pairs were located in 1972, increasing to 14 in 1976 and 33 in 1990. During the construction of Alton Water at least seven pairs bred but, generally, the species nests on recently disturbed gravel beds and prefers islands surrounded by deep water. The nest is often sited in close proximity to heavy machinery. Unfortunately, the plover's occupation is short-lived once aggregate extraction finishes.

As vegetation becomes established, the suitability of the site diminishes. However, careful management can prolong a site's attractiveness, as demonstrated at Ixworth Thorpe where six pairs nest annually, some amongst sugar beet and linseed crops adjacent to newly constructed lakes.

Little Ringed Plovers normally arrive in Suffolk in late March/early April, sometimes earlier. They have been noted between 3rd March (Trimley Marshes in 1997) and 15th on seven occasions. Autumn passage commences in late July and is over by mid-September. One at Alton Water on 16th October 1977 is the latest for the county. The largest gatherings occur on autumn passage when feeding groups frequent coastal lagoons and marshes, as well as inland reservoirs and gravel pits. Bury St Edmunds B.F. ponds traditionally attract good numbers in early August and 28 there in 1980 constitutes the largest recorded gathering. Post-juvenile dispersal accounts for an increase in numbers at coastal sites and ringing studies have proved that they are not all of Suffolk stock. Birds trapped at Minsmere in 1966 and 1967 were ringed as chicks earlier the same year in Oxfordshire and Kent respectively, and a chick ringed at Alton Water in June 1998 was controlled at Icklesham, Sussex in August of that year.

Ringed Plover *Charadrius hiaticula*

A common resident, winter visitor and passage migrant

Breeding pairs of Ringed Plover frequent the coast and estuaries during the summer months and a few nest at inland gravel workings. Concentrations of several hundreds are noted on the larger estuaries of south-east Suffolk during passage periods and the winter months.

Shingle beaches have always provided this plover with breeding habitat, but it formerly bred regularly on coastal heaths and in Breckland where it used to be abundant upon all the Thetford warrens (Salmon 1836). At the beginning of the 20th century, an estimated 400 pairs bred in the Breck (Clarke 1925). Its decline was more dramatic than that of the Stone Curlew. Although agriculture and afforestation fragmented the fragile habitat, the 1953-1954 myxomatosis epidemic was arguably the principal cause of the decline (Piotrowski 1980). Only 16 pairs were reported from north-west Suffolk in 1958 and, six years later, Breckland (including Norfolk) held only ten. Although a handful was present during the *1968-72 Atlas* study, none was found during the national Ringed Plover census of 1973-1974 (Prater 1976). There has been a partial return to Breckland, but not to traditional habitats. Nesting now takes place at gravel workings and on stony fields, often in close proximity to Little Ringed Plovers. Ticehurst reported nesting on many Sandling heaths including Belton, Fritton Warren, Walberswick, Blythburgh, Tunstall, Eyke, Bromeswell, Playford and Martlesham.

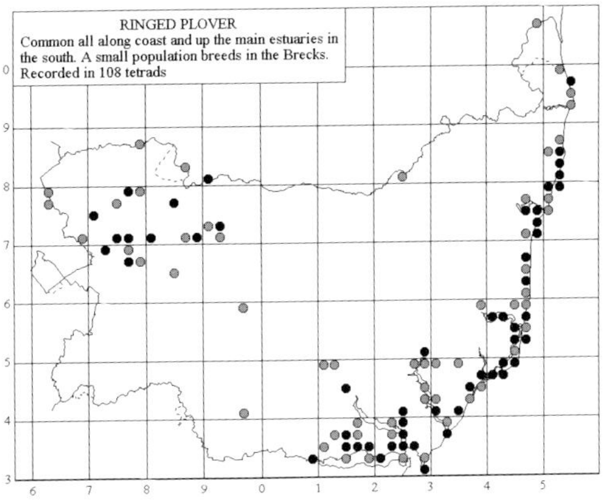

Scattered pairs formerly nested on the coastal strip from Gorleston to Landguard Point but during the second half of the 20th century the species faced considerable human pressure as beaches became more popular. From the 209 pairs located on the coast in 1979, 53 were on the desolate beaches of Orfordness compared with only three on the more popular beaches north of Kessingland (Piotrowski 1980). Breeding success at beaches protected by conservation bodies has also been limited. Predation is the greatest threat at these sites where the eggs often disappear a day or two before hatching, with marauding brown rats, Moorhens or crows being likely culprits. Chicks squeaking inside the shells undoubtedly attract their unwelcome attentions. Those that do hatch are often subject to aerial attacks from large gulls and Kestrels. Ringed Plovers occasionally venture into urban environments and have been found nesting in industrial areas. A total of 11 pairs was found in such habitats during the 1979 survey including one on hardcore, provided as a base for land piling rigs, and another tucked against sleepers beneath a rarely-used railway line in Ipswich Docks (Piotrowski 1980).

Ringed Plovers winter on river estuaries with the Orwell and Stour holding the bulk of the birds. The county held 2.3% of the north-west European population in 1989, being more or less evenly split between these two estuaries (Wright 1989). A coordinated count totalling 782 was reported on the Orwell in November 1985. Although local breeders form a significant proportion of the wintering birds, there is evidence to show that some are also drawn from the continent. Ringed Plovers ringed in Greenland (2), Finland, Sweden, Norway and Germany (4) have been found in the county and Suffolk-ringed birds have been recovered in Norway, France (3) and Spain.

The northern race, *C. h. tundrae*, is a regular passage migrant being noted annually at estuarine localities. Small flocks of this smaller and darker race are more conspicuous in the spring, when local birds are breeding. The race is most frequently reported from mid-May to early June.

Kentish Plover *Charadrius alexandrinus*

A scarce passage migrant – has occasionally bred

Passage birds have appeared annually, exclusively at coastal localities and normally in association with flocks of other small waders. The Kentish Plover is most often noted in May and June with Breydon Water, Minsmere and Havergate Island being the most favoured localities.

Historically, Kentish Plovers have never been plentiful, although there were nearly 20 occurrences between 1878 and 1890, with Breydon Water hosting most of them (Ticehurst 1932). Documentation of the species in the first half of the 20th century was minimal, but there was only one blank year from 1955 to 1995. During the early part of this period, records were equally divided between spring and autumn. The number of occurrences peaked during the late 1970s/early 1980s when the emphasis moved mainly to spring passage. Nowadays, most reports are from mid-May to early June, and there is an occasional April record. Singles at Havergate on 15th March 1983 and Minsmere on 29th March 1974 are the only reports for that month, and one at Breydon Water on 5th April 1980 is also exceptionally early. A group of five was noted at Breydon Water during May 1981, but a gathering of 14 on Havergate on 17th September 1960 is remarkable. Most autumn occurrences are confined to August and September, and one at Benacre on 7th October 1991 is the only record for that month.

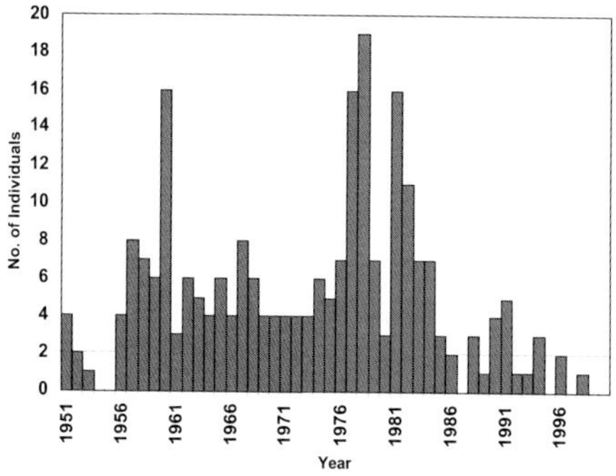

The annual totals of Kentish Plover from 1951-2000

The Kentish Plover is one of three breeding species which have been lost to Britain in the 20th century, the others being White-tailed Eagle and Red-backed Shrike. The county has witnessed just a single nesting attempt, at Walberswick in 1952, but sadly the eggs were predated a day or two before hatching.

Although primarily a passage migrant, there are six winter reports: two historic records for January and February (1834 and 1836 respectively), one on November 27th (pre-1932), one at Breydon Water on 15th-16th December 1968 and again on 16th February 1969 (Allard 1990), and another at Ness Point, Lowestoft on 22nd January 1979.

Greater Sand Plover *Charadrius leschenaultii*

Accidental: one record

1981 Breydon Water: 17th April

The county's only Greater Sand Plover frequented the Suffolk side of the Breydon Water Estuary. It was initially identified as a Kentish Plover after being distantly viewed from the northern shore.

This wader breeds in Asia Minor through to Mongolia and had visited the British Isles on 13 occasions up to the end of 2000 (BBRC), the first in Sussex during the winter of 1978/9 (Dymond *et al.* 1989).

Dotterel (Eurasian Dotterel) *Charadrius morinellus*

A scarce passage migrant

Dotterel
(*Adam Kennedy*)

Ones and twos occasionally frequent coastal localities, mostly during spring passage and more rarely during the autumn. Although arable fields are the most favoured habitats, Dotterels will occasionally frequent short-sward grassland such as golf courses and rabbit-grazed turves on the immediate coastline such as at Landguard Point and Kessingland. Double-figure trips were reported in west Suffolk in 1987 and 1994. The Dotterel was formerly a common passage migrant with groups recorded annually during both spring and autumn. Trips were not uncommon on Thetford Warren, sometimes involving a dozen birds and rarely as many as 20 (Clarke 1897). King James I was reported to have taken "dotterels" with a Sparrowhawk, whilst at his sporting retreat at Thetford on 8th May 1610 (Babington 1884-1886). Dotterels were also regular on the coast with Sizewell Walks, Sutton Heath and Bawdsey being favoured localities. The species returned to traditional fields, heaths or warrens each spring, spending a few days there before moving to more northerly breeding grounds. Ticehurst was of the opinion that the long-staying, early arrivals were of British breeding stock, whilst those making more fleeting visits later, were of Scandinavian origin. During the early 19th century, netters eagerly awaited the arrival of Dotterels as the species was considered to be "an excellent dish" (Babington 1884-1886). However, such persecution depleted their numbers and a decrease was noted in Breckland as early as the 1830s. By the end of that century, it had become rare with only 11 records from 1890 to 1930 (Ticehurst 1932). Dotterels remained scarce throughout the 20th century and was not recorded in 12 of the years during the period 1951-2000.

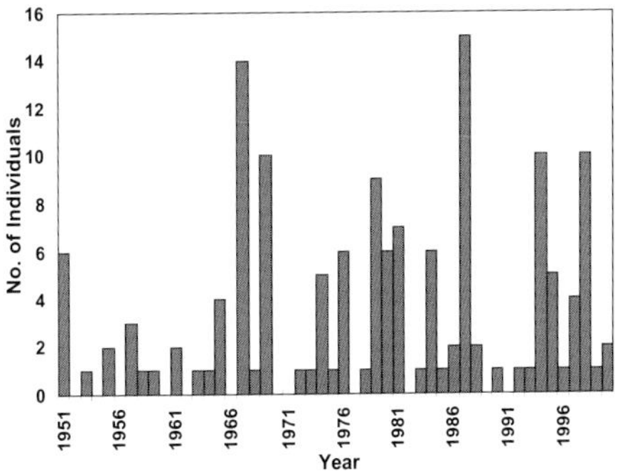

The annual totals of Dotterel from 1951-2000

Trips are no longer reported regularly, although annual, well-watched, spring gatherings occur just over the county border, between Royston and Newmarket, in Hertfordshire/Cambridgeshire. As the species often favours areas that are not popular birdwatching venues, it is likely that some, especially those frequenting tilled land, go unnoticed. Babington noted March arrivals and there were four April records between 1834 and 1881, the earliest on 21st April 1835. A male flying south over the brecks on 22nd April 1998 is the only modern day record for that month and, nowadays, spring passage occurs in a narrow period during May. Similarly, autumn passage is now restricted to September and two October records are both prior to 1932. However, Suffolk's latest occurred as recently as 1st November 2000, a year in which many summer migrants lingered.

American Golden Plover *Pluvialis dominica*

Accidental: one record

1997 Walberswick: Tinker's Marsh, 26th May

The above individual was observed briefly on Tinker's Marsh before it immediately took flight and flew past the observer to show the characteristic dusky underwings and axillaries. Although the observer was convinced that the bird was an American Golden Plover, insufficient details were submitted to the BBRC for it to be certain of the specific identification. It was therefore accepted as either American Golden Plover or Pacific Golden Plover *P. d. fulva*.

Up to 1986, American and Pacific Golden Plovers were considered to be conspecific, and were treated as Lesser Golden Plover *P. dominica*. The American Golden Plover breeds in arctic North America and in the north-eastern extremities of Asia, and winters in South America.

Pacific Golden Plover *Pluvialis fulva*

Accidental: one record

1992 Breydon Water: 28th May

The expansive mudflats of Breydon Water provided a brief refuge for this individual. It was initially seen amongst Grey Plovers, but disappeared after the flock was disturbed by a Peregrine.

The Pacific Golden Plover breeds in North Asia and Alaska, and winters in southern Asia, Australasia and western North America.

Golden Plover (European Golden Plover) *Pluvialis apricaria*

A common winter visitor and passage migrant

Large flocks of Golden Plovers, numbering several hundred, occur during the winter months and they are also regular on passage. The species is widely but locally distributed and most often accompanies Lapwing flocks. Flat arable fields are traditionally chosen and most flocks return to the same site year after year. Numbers may change dramatically during periods of harsh weather, when frozen ground forces birds to move further afield in search of food.

The status of this species has varied significantly over the years, apparently reaching a low ebb in the early 20th century, but, thereafter, increasing to become common and to occur in larger concentrations. Ticehurst said that it was uncommon or absent from districts where it was once numerous, although he mentions "huge flocks" on the Stour.

Although elsewhere in Britain the species shows a preference for permanent pastures (Lack 1986), the favoured winter habitat in Suffolk is arable land, holding recently germinated cereal crops. Flocks commute between a cluster of parishes to favourite fields known as "flock ranges" (Fuller & Youngman 1979). Such flock ranges include the Carlton Colville, Pakefield, Mutford and Ellough area, Metfield, the Worlingworth and Laxfield area, Falkenham, Trimley and Levington area, all parishes around Sudbury, Risby and the Pakenham, Ixworth and Livermere area. These regularly hold flocks ranging from 200-2,500. Some of these sites may have been used since time immemorial. Babington referred to "great numbers" at Walton and Levington – an area still favoured today. Changes in agricultural practices have probably benefited this species more than most, as the large open fields allow flocks more time to take evasive action when confronted by predators.

Flock sizes vary from 10-50 to sometimes a thousand or more. Gatherings exceeding 3,000 have been noted on eight occasions: 3,000-4,000 at Sizewell on 24th December 1906, c.4,000 at Walsham-le-Willows on 20th March 1982, 3,500 at Worlingworth on 12th March 1991, 3,800 at Long Melford on 20th December 1992, 6,000 at Blythburgh, on 22nd January 1995 and 1st January 1999, 6,000 at Livermere on 15th February 1995 and 7,500 on the Blyth Estuary on 4th December 1999. Some flocks of this magnitude have arrived as a result of cold-weather influxes, but there is a noticeable build-up in numbers in mid-March as birds gather prior to the spring exodus to their breeding grounds. Golden Plovers will move great distances and flocks will disappear overnight during periods of hard frosts.

The bulk of the wintering population departs at the end of March, but passage birds continue to be noted in small numbers through to mid-May. Normally ones and twos are recorded in midsummer, mainly at coastal localities, and return passage usually gets underway from mid-July. There are few flocks of any size before the end of September and the main influxes are noted between October and December.

Four foreign-ringed birds have been recovered in Suffolk: three from the Netherlands and one from Denmark, all of which were ringed during passage periods and recovered in midwinter.

A significant proportion of birds on spring passage show deep black underparts and cheeks – characteristics of the northern race *P. a. altifrons*.

Grey Plover *Pluvialis squatarola*

A common winter visitor and passage migrant

The estuaries of south-east Suffolk hold a significant wintering population of Grey Plovers with smaller flocks occurring regularly at other estuarine localities. Passage migrants occur in small numbers at other coastal sites and are reported regularly in flooded meadows and gravel pits in West Suffolk. The wader holds a winter feeding territory on mudflats and thus does not feed in flocks. However, large numbers mingle with other wader species at high-tide roost sites.

The expansive mudflats of the Stour have always held a large wintering population and flocks of 500-600 were noted as early as 1924 (Ticehurst 1932). The Stour estuary is of international importance for Grey Plovers, holding 1.7% of the western European wintering population (Wright 1989). The estuary's five-year average has risen steadily. For example, the wintering population averaged 356 for the period 1970-1975, 1,345 for 1984-1989 and 2,865 for 1989-1994. The last figures places the Stour in sixth place in the table of Britain's best sites for this wader (Cranswick *et al.* 1995). The Suffolk increase conforms to the national trend, where the population has undergone a fourfold increase over the last 20 years. An exceptionally high count of 4,253 was logged on the Stour in December 1994.

Grey Plovers are very susceptible to harsh weather but appear less inclined to move to warmer climes than other waders. Instead, most attempt to brazen out tough conditions and, as a consequence, many perish. For example, during a cold spell in early 1991, 54 tideline corpses were found on the Deben and it was estimated that 39% of the estuary's wintering population had perished.

Wintering flocks disperse in late March and April, and spring passage peaks in early May. Birds in superb breeding plumage are noted at coastal sites throughout May, although numbers are normally restricted to up to 20 and rarely reach three figures. Adults return to the estuaries in July, but oversummering individuals often complicate the recording of earliest dates. The bulk of the population arrives in September and the highest totals are reported in January. Movements are regularly logged at migration watch-points with peak southerly passage normally occurring from mid-August to mid-September. Monthly totals at Landguard Point are normally restricted to three figures, although, in favourable weather conditions, three-figure day totals are reported. A southerly movement involving 440 was logged off Southwold on 12th September 1993.

King (1838) stated that Grey Plovers were occasionally recorded in "immense flocks" on floods at Sudbury, but these were almost certainly Golden Plovers. It does seems incredible that up to 1980, there had been only four inland records involving singles at Lakenheath in 1879, Bury St Edmunds in 1905, Knettishall in 1972 and Barham in 1976. The latter two were the forerunners of annual occurrences during the 1980s and 1990s. Although most were at inland waters, a few were found amongst Golden Plover flocks on arable land in central Suffolk. Ten over Eriswell in October 1985 is the largest inland flock. There is no real pattern to inland occurrences, although there are slightly more records during spring passage, with the remainder equally divided between autumn and winter.

Sociable Plover (Sociable Lapwing) *Vanellus gregarius*

Accidental: four records of presumably three individuals

1968	Orford: Havergate Island, 4th October
1977/8	Little Cornard: 25th December to 17th January
2000	Aldeburgh: Town Marshes, 19th-20th October
	Walberswick/Minsmere: 22nd-24th October

The brief occurrence of a Sociable Plover at Havergate was compensated for by the long-staying individual at Little Cornard, which for three weeks accompanied a Golden Plover and Lapwing flock. Another well-watched bird was found on the Dingle Marshes during the autumn of 2000 and presumably was the same bird reported at Minsmere and North Warren.

The Sociable Plover had been noted in Britain and Ireland on only 42 occasions up to the end of 2000 (BBRC), with most arriving from their south-eastern Russian and central Asian breeding grounds, from mid-October onwards.

Lapwing (Northern Lapwing) *Vanellus vanellus*

An abundant winter visitor, passage migrant and common resident

Large open marshes and arable fields provide the Lapwing with winter feeding grounds. Wintering flocks of 1,000 or more are not uncommon and large-scale immigration is noted during the autumn. Nesting is mainly on heathland, meadows and tilled land, with marked concentrations along the coast up to about 15 miles inland, and in Breckland.

Climatic warming was thought to be responsible for a northward expansion in range in north-west Europe during the late 19th century (Marchant *et al.* 1990). Since then, there has been a marked decline in breeding numbers that has been largely due to habitat change and egg collecting. The Lapwing was formerly a common breeding species in both East and West Suffolk and was abundant in Breckland. Eggs were collected as a source of food and an indication of breeding numbers can be seen by the annual gatherings. At one Breckland estate 3,000 eggs were harvested each spring, and egg-collecting was thought to be responsible for a reduction in the breeding population around Thetford as early as the 1830s (Salmon 1836).

As part of the BTO's 1987 national Lapwing census, one tetrad in each of the county's 10-km squares was selected at random and surveyed for this species. The results showed that Suffolk's population was in the region of 1,840 pairs with 58.7% choosing semi-natural grassland and the remainder cultivated land (Wright 1988). A repeat survey in 1998 revealed that the Suffolk population had declined by 53% to around 860 pairs (Wright 2000).

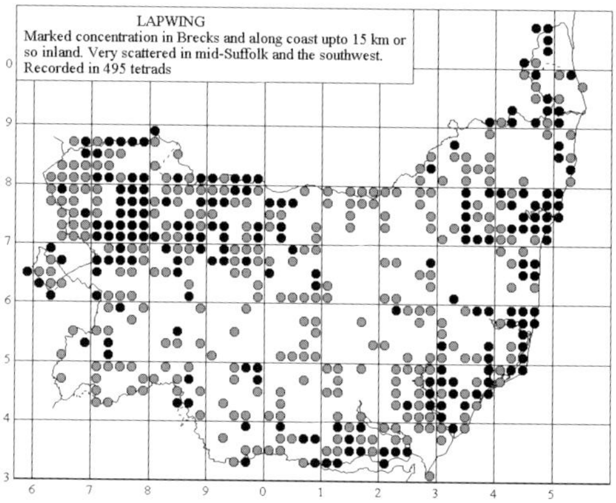

Lapwings congregate in loose flocks on meadows, drilled fields and mudflats during winter, sometimes in the company of Golden Plovers. Concentrations of 5,000 or more have been noted annually from 1987 to 1999, with counts of 10,000 at Claydon and 9,100 at Worlingworth, both in December 1990, demonstrating the vast numbers present during that winter. An estimated 40,000 were at Breydon Water on 13th December 1992, although a significant proportion of these were on the Norfolk side of the estuary. A count of 10,000 on the Blyth on 22nd January 1995 is the only other five-figure count. Harsh weather can have a significant effect on populations and there was a marked decline following the severe winter of 1963. Generally, however, Lapwings will try to escape such conditions and large flocks may disappear overnight during hard frosts. Some may seek temporary refuge on mudflats and then return, but many will move to more southerly counties. During a prolonged freeze, Lapwings may move to France and Iberia where they may remain for the rest of the winter. In fact, ringing recoveries suggest that some of Suffolk's breeding birds winter in that region, along with passage migrants ringed at estuarine localities during early autumn. A high proportion of Britain's wintering population originates in Scandinavia and northern Europe, and Lapwings ringed in Italy, Denmark (4), Finland, Germany (2) and the Netherlands (5) have been found in the county. Suffolk-ringed birds have been recovered in Ireland, France (16), Spain (5), Portugal and Morocco, all between November and February and, as the bulk of these were ringed as chicks, it shows that locally-bred birds tend to seek milder climes during winter.

Lapwings are one of the first birds to return from northern breeding grounds and autumn immigration normally gets underway as early as late May. Gatherings of 20 or more are common during June and July, and three-figure concentrations occur in August and September. The main influx is usually noted during November and small flocks arriving from offshore are a common feature at migration watch-points, where day totals of several hundred are regularly logged.

Knot (Red Knot) *Calidris canutus*

A common winter visitor and passage migrant

The larger, deeper estuaries of south-east Suffolk provide wintering areas where a significant population of Knots feed and roost in tightly packed flocks. During migration periods, smaller groups frequent other coastal sites, many attaining summer plumage during spring passage. Offshore movements are regularly reported at migration watch-points particularly during the autumn.

The Orwell and Stour hold almost all of Suffolk's wintering population and few birds are noted away from these sites. Feeding flocks of several hundred occur at favoured stretches of these estuaries, such as Freston, Fagbury, Holbrook Bay and Seafield Bay. Up to the early 1980s, the Orwell was Suffolk's principal site, but the loss of habitat, due to extensions to the ports of Ipswich and Felixstowe, has taken its toll and now the Stour hosts the highest numbers. Counts of 2,000 or more have been noted annually on the latter estuary since 1989, with a peak count of 4,748 logged in January 1996.

The migration of the Knot has been well studied. Although the precise breeding range remains uncertain, those wintering in Britain nest in arctic Canada (Cranswick *et al.* 1992). Some fly 3,000km over open oceans to the shores of Denmark, Germany and the Netherlands and others fly directly from Greenland to Britain, using Iceland as a staging post (Alerstam 1990). Sites in northern Norway are used as an alternative during spring passage. The north-central Siberian breeding population passes through East Anglia to winter in West Africa. Suffolk's eight ringing recoveries conform to this pattern and include one ringed on Butley River in September 1973 and found in Congo Brazzaville in October 1979. The latter constitutes only the third British-ringed Knot to be recovered south of the Equator. Four found dead in winter on Suffolk estuaries had been ringed on passage in Iceland, South Uist, Denmark and the Netherlands respectively and a Suffolk-ringed bird was found at the Norwegian staging post in spring.

Most wintering birds leave in March, with a few lingering until early April in some years. Spring passage normally commences in late April and small feeding groups are regular on shallower estuaries, such as the Blyth, and on coastal lagoons. The species is far more obvious during autumn passage, although few of the many thousands of birds that pass offshore actually stop off to feed. Small flocks begin to appear from early July, but estuarine flocks rarely build up before mid-September with the main influxes occurring in November.

Small groups passing south, often at some distance offshore, are noted almost daily from late August through to mid-October, although a day-total of 523 south off Landguard Point on September 1st 1988 was exceptional. An amazing movement during unseasonal weather on 30th August 1992 yielded the following counts: 2,400 off Benacre, 2,475 moving south (in 3 hours) off Southwold and 4,034 off Landguard Point. The timing of the counts suggested that at least 7,000 moved south that day.

The Knot was formerly an extreme rarity at inland localities, having been recorded on only four occasions up to 1970. This included one that was shot on a partridge drive at Wetheringsett in January 1914. Since 1983, the species has been recorded more regularly with gravel workings along the Lark Valley being the most popular localities. Most inland occurrences are logged during autumn passage and there are a few winter records. Singles at Bramford on 22nd-23rd April 1983 and Livermere on 23rd March 1996 are the only spring records, and four at Lackford on 15th October 1988 is the only inland record involving more than one bird.

Sanderling *Calidris alba*

A fairly common winter visitor and passage migrant

A small wintering population of Sanderlings frequents the sandy beaches around Lowestoft and south to Benacre Broad. The Sanderlings avoid the larger estuaries, although a small wintering population has built-up on the lower reaches of the Orwell, near Fagbury Point. However, as the expansion of the port of Felixstowe has gradually covered the beach and mudflats, these latter flocks have disappeared. The species is occasionally attracted to lagoons and short turves, immediately adjacent to the shore, and is regularly noted on passage.

Ticehurst described the species as a regular passage migrant, only appearing in winter during hard weather, especially when this was accompanied by north-easterly winds.

Small, mostly single-figure groups energetically feeding at the water's edge are now a regular winter sight on the sandy beaches of north-east Suffolk with flocks regularly peaking at 15 or more. Up to 1970, there were only two counts of 50 or more: 50-60 at Hopton on 1st January 1950 and 56 on the Lowestoft North Denes from January to March 1969. Since then, however, such gatherings have become more regular, the largest being at Breydon Water with 166 on 16th February 1974 and 121 on 29th December 1983, and at Kessingland with 110 on 3rd January 1997.

Passage birds are noted in small flocks from late April, throughout May and up to mid-June. A gathering of 65 at Walberswick on 19th May 1950 was exceptional. The species is normally less conspicuous during the autumn with singles and small flocks being seen irregularly at coastal sites in August and September. A southerly movement involving 77 passed Landguard Point on 30th August 1992 and a flock of 65 that settled on Aldeburgh beach on 9th September 1995 is quite remarkable for that season.

Like other wader species, the Sanderling was an extreme rarity at inland localities prior to the mid-1980s. Babington listed one at Pakenham in winter plumage as the only inland record, and up to 1985, ones and twos at Bury Beet Factory ponds in 1950, 1954, 1978 and 1981 were the only 20th century records. However, the creation of Lackford W.R., now one of Breckland's premier birdwatching sites, together with the availability of other suitable waters in the Lark Valley, has resulted in more frequent occurrences. For example, apart from 1987 and 1988, the Sanderling has been noted annually from 1985 to the end of 1994, with almost all records occurring in the first half of May.

Semi-palmated Sandpiper *Calidris pusilla*

Accidental: three records

1982/3	Felixstowe: Felixstowe Ferry, 30th October to 14th April
1986	Minsmere: 6th-15th August
1993	Trimley St Mary: Trimley Marshes, 13th-14th May

There will be few more controversial records than that involving the long-staying individual at Felixstowe Ferry. The bird was initially considered to be a Western Sandpiper *C. mauri*, the identification having been more or less agreed by all, with the exception of one or two doubters. The occurrence prompted two identification papers (Grant 1986, Millington & Vinicombe 1992), which proved beyond any reasonable doubt that it was in fact a Semi-palmated Sandpiper.

The record of a bird which visited Minsmere on 3rd-8th September 1971 was eventually withdrawn by BBRC after initial acceptance (Wallace 1979).

Semi-palmated Sandpipers breed in the Nearctic tundra and winter in coastal Central America and south as far as Ecuador. Up to the end of 2000, this wader had been recorded in Britain and Ireland on 114 occasions (BBRC).

Little Stint *Calidris minuta*

A fairly common passage migrant – occasionally overwinters

Coastal wetlands offer feeding opportunities to small flocks of Little Stints during passage periods and, although regular at estuarine localities, the most favoured sites are lakes and flooded meadows, and natural and man-made lagoon systems, such as Minsmere. In recent years, one or two have overwintered.

The status of this species has changed little over the past hundred years, except for a notable increase in the number of records in midwinter. It has always been rarer in spring than in autumn and has been subject to occasional influxes. It was unusually abundant in 1870, 1881 and 1898 (Ticehurst 1932). Between 3rd and 30th September 1881, 35 were killed on Breydon Water, including six in one shot (Allard 1990).

Little Stints are not uncommon on spring passage, although they are never plentiful. In some years only one or two are reported and flock sizes rarely reach double figures. A group of 20, which arrived at Benacre on 15th May 1980, is exceptional. The bulk of the records occur in a short period, from May through to mid-June, but, very occasionally, migration can start in April and sometimes as early as late March.

Autumn passage is normally much more protracted, with returning birds appearing in late July and continuing through to October, and lingerers are still present in November and December in some years. Much larger numbers occur during the autumn, but there is considerable variation in flock sizes. Groups of up to 10-15 are noted in most years but, occasionally, influxes can be more substantial. There was a pronounced autumn passage of Little Stints in 1960, 1973, 1976, 1978 and 1993, and the county's largest gatherings were in those years. A peak of 65 was noted at Havergate on 2nd October 1960 and Suffolk's largest flock of 142 occurred at Minsmere on 9th September 1978. The bulk of the occurrences are from mid-August through to October, although there have been 17 December records, of which five have involved birds that overwintered. Such records normally follow large autumn influxes and all, except one at Lackford in 1976, have found food and shelter at estuarine or coastal localities. A flock of 22 at Minsmere on 15th December 1961 was unusual. Overwintering was proven on the Orwell in 1990/1 and 1993/4.

A Little Stint at Breydon Water on 24th September 1964 had been ringed in Sweden earlier that month and one trapped at Sizewell on 20th September 1974 was found in France the following autumn.

There were no records from West Suffolk until 1964, when three visited Bury St Edmunds B.F. ponds. Thereafter, Little Stints frequented the site on six occasions up to 1984. Livermere was the only other inland locality to record the species during that period, with a maximum of nine in September 1970. This remained the largest inland gathering until up to 14 frequented Lakenheath Fen on 6th-12th September 1998. Since 1989, the Little Stint has become increasingly frequent at inland lakes and gravel pits, where it is now an almost annual visitor.

Temminck's Stint *Calidris temminckii*

A scarce passage migrant

Temminck's Stints occur annually at coastal localities, usually singly or more rarely in flocks up to four. There have been only four inland records. Muddy pools and saline lagoons on wetland nature reserves such as Minsmere, Havergate Island, North Warren and Trimley Marshes are the most favoured habitats and, although the species will sometimes frequent small pools on saltings, open mudflats are mostly avoided. Payn suggests that this stint was less plentiful than formerly, as evidenced by the large number listed by Babington for Breydon Water (then reed-fringed and less saline than today) and elsewhere, and Ogilvie's comment that it was very common at Thorpe Meare. A flock of ten, from which one was shot, was noted at Benacre around 1850 and similar numbers were noted during the 'Great Fall' of September 1965 between Walberswick and Havergate Island.

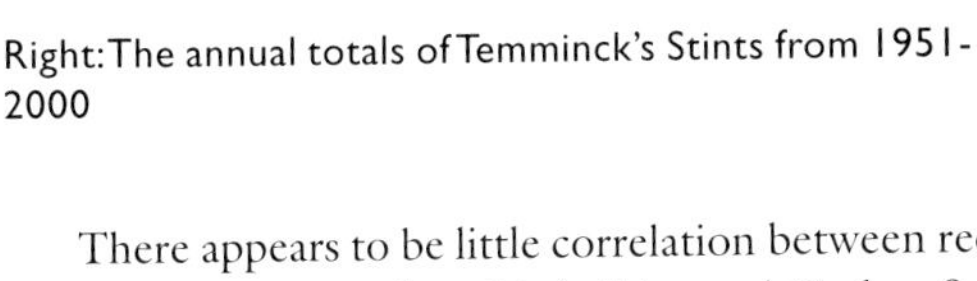

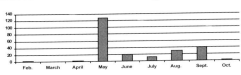

Above: The seasonal occurrence of Temminck's Stints from 1948-2000

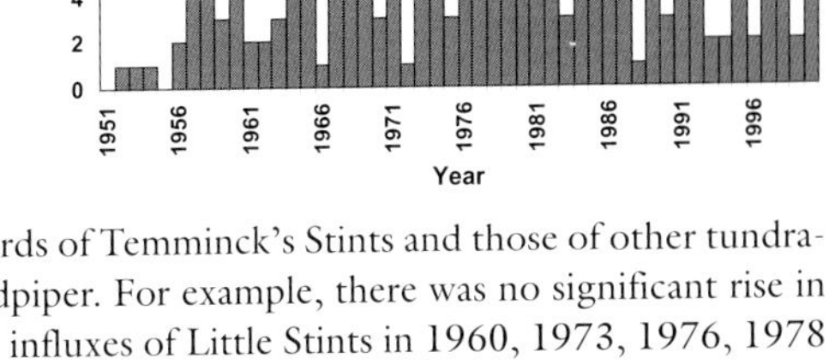

Right: The annual totals of Temminck's Stints from 1951-2000

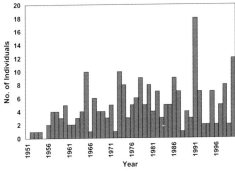

There appears to be little correlation between records of Temminck's Stints and those of other tundra-breeding species, such as Little Stint and Curlew Sandpiper. For example, there was no significant rise in the numbers of Temminck's Stints during the autumn influxes of Little Stints in 1960, 1973, 1976, 1978 and 1993, yet during the exceptional spring of 1991, when no fewer than 13 Temminck's Stints were reported, the Little Stint passage was described only as "reasonable" (SBR).

In spring, the vast majority of records are in a comparatively short period between mid-May and early June, with extreme dates of 21st April (2002) and 20th June (1967). Autumn birds have been noted from 14th July (1991) through to September. There have been only four October occurrences, all within the eight-year period 1954-1961, and one at Breydon Water on 23rd November 1861 is the only record for that month. One at Minsmere on 12th-14th February 1971 is a remarkable record and probably refers to an overwintering individual rather than an early migrant.

Most nest in the Arctic tundra of Scandinavia and Russia, but some breed further south in northern

Europe and a few pairs are found in Scotland. One bearing colour rings at Levington on 17th-19th August 1980, had been ringed as a chick in Norway on 1st July of that year.

Temminck's Stints have been noted in West Suffolk on only five occasions: at Livermere Lake on 26th July 1983 and 16th-21st August 1986, at Lackford and Cavenham from 29th April to 6th May 1991 and at Ixworth on 15th-16th May 1999 and 7th-9th May 2002. One at Sproughton pits on 19th May 1979 is the only record for the Gipping Valley.

White-rumped Sandpiper *Calidris fuscicollis*

A very rare passage migrant: 24 records

White-rumped Sandpipers have been recorded between 14th July and 20th October. Many of these birds have been found in flocks of Dunlin. There is a preference for coastal broads and lagoon-type habitats, as well as the mudflats at Breydon Water. Early arrivals are normally adults with juveniles noted later in the autumn. More than half of the occurrences have been at Minsmere, where the first for the county was present intermittently between 9th August and 7th September 1962. This individual commuted between Minsmere and Walberswick, and was trapped and ringed at the latter site on 25th August. Two were recorded at Minsmere during the autumn of 1966, and one there in early September 1971 was the first of ten records for that decade. There were only five records for the 1980s and, after an adult visited Minsmere in August 1990, the species was not noted again until up to four were sighted from Breydon Water's south bank from 16th July to 14th August 1996.

The species breeds in northern North America and winters in southern South America, and is an annual visitor to the British Isles. From 1958 to the end of 2000, there had been 491 records for Britain and Ireland (BBRC) of which Suffolk had hosted a mere 5%. Suffolk records have been exclusively autumnal.

Baird's Sandpiper *Calidris bairdii*

Accidental: five records

1965	Orford: Havergate Is., 4th-18th September
1967	Minsmere: 30th August to 13th September
1977	Benacre: 7th-18th September
1990	Benacre: juv. 23rd September
	Easton Bavents: juv. 27th October

This wader breeds in North America to north-west Greenland and north-east Siberia, and winters in southern South America. There were 229 records for the British Isles up to the end of 2000 (BBRC) with a clear bias towards south-west Britain and southern Ireland.

The 1990 records were considered to be different individuals.

Pectoral Sandpiper *Calidris melanotos*

A scarce passage migrant: 87 records

The Pectoral Sandpiper has been recorded more or less annually at coastal localities in recent years. It normally occurs singly with other wader species, but occasionally in groups of two or three. Minsmere is by far the most favoured site, although there are occasional records from Walberswick, Trimley Marshes and Alton Water.

It breeds in north-east Siberia and northern North America and is a regular visitor to the British Isles. Suffolk's and Britain's first record involved a female at Breydon Water on 17th October 1830 and was followed by six more records that century. From 1900 to 1925, there were a further four county records, but no more for 26 years. This wader's scarcity at that time was paralleled nationally – up until 1950 there were less than 100 records for Britain and Ireland (Sharrock 1974). Appearances in Suffolk were very irregular during the period 1951-1982, being limited to 28 individuals and involving no more than three in any one year. However, since 1981, Pectoral Sandpipers have been recorded annually, including ten in 1985, Suffolk's highest annual total.

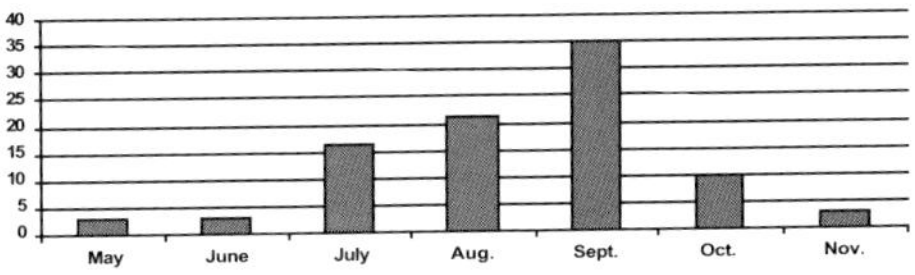

Above: The seasonal occurrences of Pectoral Sandpiper from 1951-2000

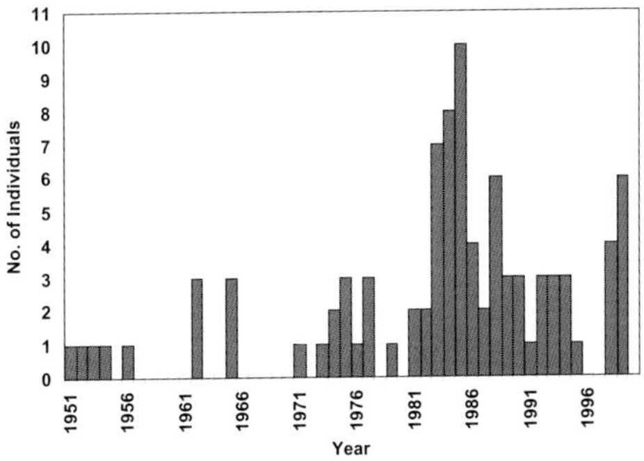

Right: The annual totals of Pectoral Sandpiper from 1951-2000

There are only six spring records, equally divided between May and June, although two late June records, including a male in full breeding plumage at Trimley Marshes on 30th June 1991, probably relate to birds returning from their Siberian breeding grounds rather than to late spring migrants. The bulk of the occurrences are in autumn between mid-July and late September. There have been eight October records, two at Minsmere on 1st-3rd November 1993, one at Alton Water on 2nd November 1984 and another at Minsmere on 3rd November 2001.

Three have visited West Suffolk: Bury St Edmunds B.F. Ponds on 10th-11th September 1977, Lakenheath on 14th July 1989 and Cavenham on 15th-17th May 1993.

Sharp-tailed Sandpiper *Calidris acuminata*

Accidental: one record

1892 Breydon Water: ad. shot 29th August

A record of Sharp-tailed Sandpiper listed under Siberian Pectoral Sandpiper *Erolia acuminata*, was included by Ticehurst and by Payn in the first edition of his book. It was then omitted by the latter author, in his revised edition, presumably due to county boundary changes. Although locations are not fully documented, its inclusion by Ticehurst was probably a result of it visiting the Suffolk side of the estuary. The species has now been reinstated on to the Suffolk list.

The species breeds in the low arctic and sub-arctic regions of north-east Siberia and winters in Australasia. The Sharp-tailed Sandpiper is a rare visitor to the British Isles, noted on 26 occasions up to the end of 2000 (BBRC).

Curlew Sandpiper *Calidris ferruginea*

A fairly common passage migrant

The Curlew Sandpiper has been recorded in small flocks on spring passage, but occurs more regularly, and in larger numbers, during the autumn. Occurrences are almost exclusively coastal with saline lagoons and estuaries being the species' preferred habitat. Walberswick, Minsmere and Havergate Island are the most favoured sites.

The migration of this species almost parallels that of Little Stint, occurring at roughly the same time each year and in similar numbers. Flock sizes are usually more substantial in autumn than in spring. Groups of up to five are regularly reported, but influxes may total several hundred at scattered localities along the coast. Gatherings of 50 or more have been reported on only 12 occasions, with a count of 500-600 at Thorpe Meare on 21st-22nd August 1892, being by far and away the largest ever for Suffolk. There are three other three-figure counts: 107 at Breydon Water on 18th September 1985, 104 at Minsmere on 1st September 1988 and 152 at Breydon Water on 30th August 1992. The species is sometimes absent altogether during spring, but single-figure groups normally occur from mid-May to early June. There are few April records. Autumn passage is more protracted, with failed breeders often returning as early as mid-June and, as with Little Stints, one or two juveniles sometimes linger into October, more rarely November and very

Buff-breasted Sandpiper *Tryngites subruficollis*

Accidental: seven records

1843	Breydon Water: 20th September
1961	Minsmere: 1st September
1975	Walberswick: Shore Pools, 28th August to 5th September
1997	Orford: Havergate Is., 16th-19th August
1999	Walberswick: Tinker's Marsh, 22nd September
2000	Corton: 20th September
2001	Walberswick: Tinker's Marsh, 4th-14th September

This Nearctic wader is an annual visitor to the British Isles, having been recorded on 495 occasions between 1958 and 1985. The south-western counties from the Isles of Scilly to Somerset, and Co. Cork and Wexford in Ireland, have hosted 55% of the autumn migrants (Dymond *et al.* 1989). Four out of the seven Suffolk records were from August to early September, conforming to the national trend.

Ruff *Philomachus pugnax*

A common passage migrant and scarce winter visitor – a few oversummer

Ruffs
(*Adam Kennedy*)

Large concentrations of Ruff occur at coastal localities in both passage periods, and during some springs the birds gather into leks. There is a clear preference for flooded meadows and lagoons rather than estuarine mudflats. Although one or two 'pairs' oversummer in Suffolk in some years, raising speculation of breeding, there was no conclusive evidence of successful nesting during the 20th century. Ruffs are frequently recorded at inland localities. During winter, singles or small parties frequent sites on or near the coast.

The Ruff declined as a British breeding species during the 18th and 19th centuries, largely as a result of drainage of marsh and fenland habitats. There is some evidence to suggest that breeding took place at Mildenhall Fen in the early 1800s and nesting certainly occurred at a marsh near Burgh Castle in that period (Ticehurst 1932). Chicks may also have hatched from a nest near Euston in 1898. There were unsuccessful attempts to introduce the species in Norfolk in 1939 and 1957 (Nethersole-Thompson 1986), but colonisation of the Ouse Washes, Cambridgeshire, began in 1963 with the number of breeding reeves peaking at 21 in 1971. The Ruff is an extremely rare breeding bird in Britain, with a maximum of seven pairs during the period 1989-1999 (Ogilvie *et al.* 2001). Nesting may well have taken place in Suffolk in recent years, but, as reeves remain well hidden when nesting, this has yet to be proved. Breeding probably occurred in 1988 when two males and a female were present at a coastal locality from 29th May, and a male and a juvenile were seen on 10th July. During the 1970s and 1980s, there was a significant increase in suitable habitat at coastal localities, which was specifically managed for breeding waders. Hopefully, nesting will soon occur regularly.

Groups of up to 25 are common at coastal localities from late March to early May and occasionally flocks of 70 or more are reported. Such gatherings are restricted to a few coastal sites, with Southwold, Walberswick, Minsmere, Aldeburgh and Trimley Marshes being the most favoured areas in recent times. These sites figured prominently during an exceptional spring passage in 1994 when 228 were at Minsmere on 2nd May. This was the largest concentration since the 'Great Fall' of 3rd-5th September 1965, when substantial gatherings included 350 at Walberswick, 150 at Minsmere, 120 on the Blyth and 100 on Havergate Island. Inland lakes and gravel pits, such as those at Bramford, Lackford and Livermere, occasionally host ones and twos, most often during autumn passage, although groups of six or more are rare.

Although Ticehurst mentioned a record of two at Great Yarmouth, Norfolk in January 1913, the county's first winter records did not occur until 1956 when singles were noted at Blythburgh on 2nd January and on the Alde on 25th February. There was only one further winter record for the 1950s, but since then singles or small flocks were reported almost annually and, nowadays, Ruffs are regular at a number of coastal sites. Occasionally, there are quite substantial gatherings, but these are most often in association with harsh weather, perhaps indicating displacement from the continent. The largest winter counts are of 19 at Minsmere on 16th December 1979, 30 at Minsmere in February 1980, 41 at Orfordness on 17th February 1991 and 16 on Trimley Marshes on 31st January 2000. Ruff winter in single-sex flocks and, although most records remain unsexed, there is no specific reference to a reeve during this season.

Jack Snipe *Lymnocryptes minimus*

A fairly common winter visitor and passage migrant

Reedbed stubbles, saltings, flooded meadows and boggy fringes to lakes and streams provide a winter refuge for this unobtrusive little wader. Jack Snipe normally occur singly or in small groups, feeding in muddy pools in thick stands of short vegetation. They are extremely selective in their choice of feeding habitat, so much so that favoured areas can be accurately pinpointed to within a few square metres year after year. For example, the Deben and Orwell estuaries host small numbers annually, but birds are almost exclusively confined to very small patches at Martlesham Creek, Levington Creek and Bourne Park Water Meadows. These birds are normally found only by flushing, but feeding or roosting birds can be located by careful searching from the shelter of hides such as those at Minsmere and Lackford. The county's wintering population is likely to be less than 100 in most years.

The secretive nature of the species has always made estimating numbers difficult and previous authors gave little indication of population levels. Ticehurst thought that the wader was "common enough" and Tuck (1891) listed it as a "winter migrant, sometimes abundant". However, Payn's assessment of it being "found in small numbers in winter in practically all bogs and marshes in which common snipe occurs" appears to vastly overstate its recent status. Large winter gatherings have been reported in January, including 40 at Shotley Marshes in 1978 and 16 at Martlesham Creek in 1993. In 1990, 21 were trapped for ringing at sites in south-east Suffolk.

Passage birds are regularly reported in March and April, and occasionally up to early May. There are two records later in that month and midsummer records include singles at Breydon Water on 21st July 1826, West Stow on 16th July 1958 and Minsmere on 15th June 1978. The first returning birds are usually noted in September, but more occur in October. Significant autumn gatherings have been noted in October near Oulton Broad with 30 in 1982, and at Minsmere with 13 in both 1984 and 1988. The spring exodus can also be conspicuous and double-figure concentrations have been noted at Levington in April 1992 and Martlesham in March 1993. The wader is occasionally reported at migration watch-points such as Landguard Point where it has been found on the open shingle beach.

During harsh-weather periods, Jack Snipe are sometimes forced to forage in atypical areas such as garden lawns and roadside verges.

Snipe (Common Snipe) *Gallinago gallinago*

An uncommon resident, common winter visitor and passage migrant

The Snipe is found at suitable wetland sites throughout the county, but mostly in winter and during passage periods. A few breeding pairs remain, mostly at coastal sites, with Minsmere and Walberswick being the most favoured localities.

The distinctive *tick-a, tick-a* call and drumming flight-display was once a familiar feature of a marshland spring, but the wader decreased steadily during the 20th century and nesting sites are now few and far between. Diminishing numbers were noted in the 1880s (Babington 1884-1886), although there was an apparent increase 50 years later when breeding localities were thought too numerous to list (Ticehurst 1932). Payn lamented the loss of nesting birds in West Suffolk, particularly those within a mile of his home village of Hartest, where 7-8 pairs formerly bred. He also listed losses in the Glem and Lark Valleys, around Lakenheath, Lowestoft, Sudbourne, Dunwich, Leiston, Minsmere and Flatford. The drainage of wet meadows, the dredging of rivers and the destruction of other boggy habitats were undoubtedly the principal reasons for the decline, with many meadows drying up completely in recent springs. A survey of breeding waders and other waterfowl on the coastal marshes and saltings in 1988 and 1989, revealed 39 pairs, with 86% frequenting the Blyth estuary (Holzer *et al.* 1993). 25% of the total grassland of the estuaries studied occurred on the Blyth and the lack of soft penetrable ground was a significant factor in the absence of the species at other sites. Reports from elsewhere in Suffolk add little to breeding numbers and it is likely that the county's breeding population is less than 60 pairs, with inland nesting largely confined to the Lark, Little Ouse and Waveney Valleys.

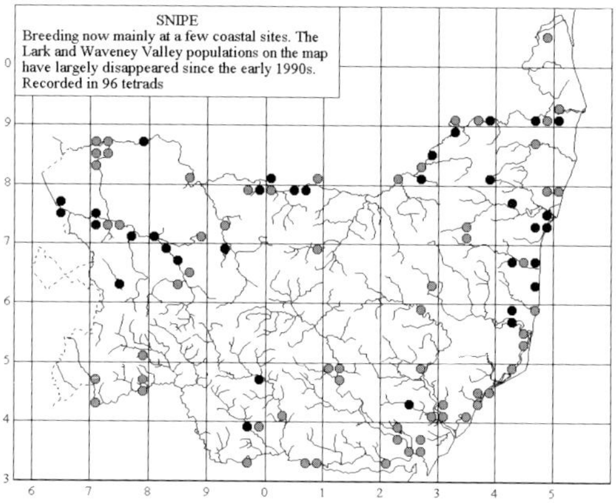

Autumn immigration begins in late July and peaks in October/November. Small groups of up to ten birds are often noted amongst flocks of Dunlin moving south offshore in autumn and during harsh-weather periods. Coastal marshland and damp meadows along river valleys are the favoured habitat of passage and wintering birds, and concentrations are regularly reported at Walberswick, Minsmere, Trimley and Shotley in December and January. Counts of 200-400 have been noted on ten occasions at coastal localities between 1978 and 1991 with 500 at Shotley on 30th December 1981, the largest recorded gathering. Ringing recoveries show that the origins of the wintering population lie in northern Europe and Scandinavia. Up to the end of 1998, Snipe from Sweden (5), Denmark, Czechoslovakia, Germany, Belgium and the Netherlands (2) have been collected by Suffolk shooting parties and Suffolk-ringed individuals have been recovered in Norway, Sweden, Denmark, France (3) and Morocco.

The Snipe suffers greatly during severe weather periods and there is often an exodus to warmer climes. The bulk of the county's wintering population departs in late March.

Great Snipe *Gallinago media*

Accidental: formerly a rare passage migrant – c.40 records involving 70 individuals

1906	Aldringham-cum-Thorpe: Thorpe Fen, singles shot 19th September and 1st October
1935	Snape: shot August
1958	East Bergholt: Flatford, August
1972	Benacre: Benacre Ness, 14th September

There have been only five 20th century records for Great Snipe. However, during the latter half of the 19th century, the Great Snipe was recorded regularly, mostly in August and September and, in some years, in reasonable numbers. The extreme dates are 21st August and 18th November. There were three spring occurrences. North-east Suffolk was the most productive area where 12-13 and nine were recorded in 1842 and 1880 respectively. These birds were all shot.

Although a number of records remain under consideration by the BBRC, the influx into Britain in 2002 may well prove to be the biggest of recent years. At least two were found in Suffolk, at Trimley Marshes Nature Reserve and at Corton – unfortunately relatively few observers saw them.

The Great Snipe breeds in north-east Europe and north-west Asia, and it winters in Africa. The European range has retracted eastwards and northwards during the 19th and early 20th centuries (Cramp *et al.* 1974-1994) and this was paralleled by a sharp decline in occurrences in Suffolk.

Up to the end of 2000, the Great Snipe had been recorded in the British Isles on 291 occasions of which 111 were since 1957 (BBRC).

Long-billed Dowitcher *Limnodromus scolopaceus*

A very rare passage migrant: nine records

1840	Breydon Water: male killed early October*
1963	Orford: Havergate Island, 13th October to 20th December*
1964	Orford: Havergate Island, f.s.p. 1st June
1969	Benacre: 22nd September *
1977/8	Orford: Havergate Island, two 22nd October to April
1979	Minsmere: 28th September 28th to 10th October
1980	Orford: Havergate Island, 22nd September
1985	Alton Water: first-winter, 20th October to 14th December
	Minsmere: juv. moulting to first-winter, 30th October

Separating the Long-billed Dowitcher in the field from its close relative, the Short-billed Dowitcher, *L. griseus*, is extremely difficult. Therefore, it is not surprising that the first four records (marked with asterisks) involved six that were not specifically assigned. There has been only one positive record of Short-billed Dowitcher for Britain and Ireland, so those listed probably all relate to Long-billeds. Nationally, there were 225 records up to the end of 2000 of which only nine were prior to 1958 (BBRC).

The Long-billed Dowitcher breeds in Alaska and north-east Siberia and winters mainly in Central America. It is an annual visitor to Britain and Ireland and, unlike most other American waders, is found frequently on Britain's east coast. Nationally, the bulk of the occurrences are in late September and through October, and most Suffolk records conform to this trend. However, Long-billed Dowitchers are traditionally long-stayers, as shown by two birds lingering into December and two overwintering on Havergate Island.

Woodcock (Eurasian Woodcock) *Scolopax rusticola*

A fairly common resident, winter visitor and passage migrant

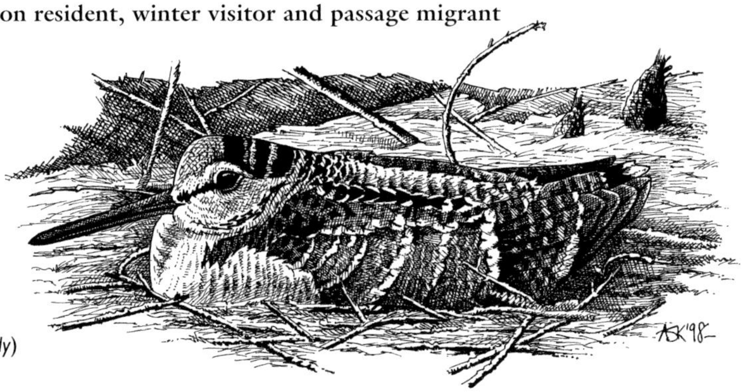

Woodcock
(Adam Kennedy)

Woodcocks silhouetted over coastal and Breckland forests, as they perform their roding display at twilight, are indeed a magnificent sight. Views are often limited to frantic flapping as a flushed Woodcock disappears through or over the trees, but the species is confident of its camouflage and its true beauty can be examined at close quarters if one is found hiding on the woodland floor. Nationally, there has been a progressive decline in breeding numbers since the late 1960s, which has accelerated during the 1980s (Marchant *et al.* 1990). The species is widely distributed during winter and is found in most woods and copses. However, wintering Woodcock are more common in coastal woodlands, probably due to autumn influxes that are sometimes quite substantial.

The Woodcock was formerly a very rare nesting species and, apart from a nest at Brettenham in 1801, there were no other confirmed breeding records during that century. However, the breeding population increased significantly during the first quarter of the 20th century when nesting was recorded at several localities in West Suffolk, as well as a few in the north and central coastal areas. Large-scale afforestation of the sandlings and Breckland, in the 1930s, undoubtedly accelerated this colonisation. Male Woodcocks are polygamous with the pair bond lasting only till egg laying. Probable or confirmed breeding was recorded in 23 of the 10-km squares in the *1968-72 Atlas* and possible breeding in a further eight. An average of 10-25 'pairs' per 10-km square was used tentatively to assess the national population at that time, which would give 230-575 'pairs' for Suffolk. The *New Atlas* showed a national decline in occupied 10-km squares of 36.9%, although there was no overall retraction in range. This reduction was paralleled in Suffolk where the species was lost from five 10-km squares, but was found in one additional square and, using the same criteria, produces a reduced population of 190-475 'pairs' in Suffolk. The Woodcock is an early nester, with roding often reported in February and egg-laying taking place in late March.

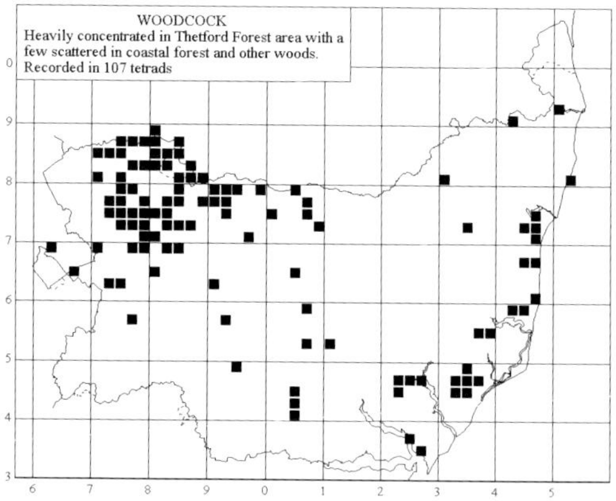

WOODCOCK
Heavily concentrated in Thetford Forest area with a few scattered in coastal forest and other woods.
Recorded in 107 tetrads

The Woodcock is more numerous during winter and is common in woodlands and copses on the coast and breck. However, it is relatively scarce in the south-western and central cereal-growing areas. This secretive wader normally lays low in the dense woodland cover during daylight, but leaves its hideaways soon after dusk when it moves to feeding areas (Lack 1986). Shooting parties frequently disturb birds and, as it is a quarry species, many are bagged. A small copse holding ten or more is not unusual, but 70, flushed by a Shotley shooting party during very cold weather on 31st December 1981, is exceptional. Shooting returns from large, well-keepered estates give an indication of population levels and these can be quite substantial during harsh winters. The largest reported bags include 343 at Somerleyton in 1961/2 and 121 at Euston in 1976/7. Woodcock suffer greatly during freezing conditions and starving birds are often forced to search for food in new areas. A large fall was reported during Christmas week in 1961, particularly in the Southwold and Minsmere areas, where 100 were present daily. Site fidelity during winter has been proved (Lack 1986) and, in consequence, the Woodcock may take several years to recover from the effects of severe weather as reported in the winters subsequent to 1962/3.

Autumn immigration is often evident at coastal localities, although most birds arrive during the hours of darkness. Arrivals are normally noted in late October and November, usually coinciding with stormy weather. Birds often pitch into thick cover on the immediate coastline where they may remain for several hours before venturing further inland. Thousands of Woodcock were said to have drowned off the Lowestoft and Yarmouth coast following a severe storm in the autumn of 1928 with one fishing boat collecting 470 (Wernham *et al.* 2002). Passage is much less obvious in spring than in autumn. Suffolk has an excellent collection of ringing returns, all as a result of shooting. One ringed in Northumberland in 1894 and shot in Suffolk three years later is the first recovery and pre-dates the national ringing scheme. Woodcocks ringed in the Netherlands (5), Denmark (2), Germany and Estonia have been shot in Suffolk in the depths of winter and ringing dates suggest cold-weather influxes. One ringed at Kesgrave on 18th January 1964 was shot in Denmark two springs later and another on passage at Landguard Point in October 1988 was shot in France the following month.

Black-tailed Godwit *Limosa limosa*

A common winter visitor and passage migrant – a few oversummer

This handsome wader is found at coastal estuaries and marshes in all months of the year. The Black-tailed Godwit is an extremely rare breeding bird in Britain, with a range of 33-66 pairs for the period 1989-1999 (Ogilvie *et al.* 2001). One to three pairs regularly nest on grazing meadows at sites in Suffolk's central coastal zone and flocks of several hundred occur on passage. The wintering population has increased significantly in recent years with feeding flocks of 200 or more being commonplace on selected estuarine mudflats, and roost counts frequently reach four figures on the Stour.

The Black-tailed Godwit was formerly considered a delicay and was shot and snared to extinction on its East Anglian breeding grounds. In the late 18th century, fattened godwits fetched 2s. 6d (12p) to 5s (25p) each (Ticehurst 1932). The Norfolk breeding population declined rapidly in the early 19th century, the last nest being found at Horsey Mere in 1829 (Ticehurst 1932). In the Cambridgeshire fens, it lingered on till 1847. Previous authors are confident that the fenlands around Lakenheath were a stronghold for the godwit, but it was lost to Suffolk as a breeding species early in the 19th century. There were only sporadic nesting attempts in Britain during the first half of the 20th century, but a single breeding pair on the Ouse Washes in 1952, heralded colonisation of that area, where numbers peaked at 65 pairs in 1972 (Bircham 1989). Following frequent oversummering by potential breeders throughout the 1950s and 1960s and the strong suspicion of nesting on the Alde in 1968 and 1970 (Banks 1971), the wader returned to Suffolk to nest at three coastal meadows in 1972. Breeding continued through to 1990, with a maximum of six pairs at four localities in 1986. Thereafter, nesting has been limited to a solitary pair at a single site.

The species was formerly very rare during winter and Ticehurst listed only four records. However, its status changed dramatically over the next 50 years and, nowadays, Suffolk estuaries play host to substantial winter flocks. A concentration of 500 on the Orwell in October 1953 was exceptional for that era, as was c.540 on the Stour in October 1958. The wintering population increased steadily during the 1960s and 1970s and the Stour is currently Britain's principal estuary for Black-tailed Godwits, with roost counts of 1,000+ being logged throughout the winter. This site is of international importance for the species, with a five-year average maximum count of 1,859 (Cranswick *et al.* 1995). A total of 2,077 was noted on the Orwell in November 1989 and 2,372 were on the Stour during October of the following year.

Following its extinction as a breeding species in Britain, the godwit became extremely scarce on passage, so much so that from 1851 to 1866 there were a mere ten records for Suffolk and Norfolk combined. Even up to the 1930s, the largest flock size reported was only 13 (Ticehurst 1932). The species is now common on both spring and autumn passage, and flocks of up to 800 occur on the estuaries and 30-150 at other coastal wetlands. Counts of birds on spring passage begin to build up at the beginning of March, occasionally as early as mid-February, being most noticeable on the Blyth, the Alde complex and the Deben where there are no substantial wintering populations. Three-figure flocks are noted on all three estuaries during March and April, and counts on the Blyth of 800 on 12th April 1969 and 862 on 11th April 1992 are particularly high for that estuary.

From mid-July, those returning from northern breeding grounds normally join oversummering flocks of non-breeding birds and autumn passage usually reaches a peak in August. The migration of the Black-tailed Godwit is similar to that of the Redshank in that the Icelandic populations winter in Britain and western Europe whilst those from central and eastern Europe migrate to Africa (Alerstam 1982). Studies in the Netherlands were unable to provide methods of separating Icelandic birds, *L. l. islandica*, from the nominate, *L. l. limosa*, in the field (Roselaer & Gerritsen 1991).

Six ringing recoveries, all involving birds caught at Butley Creek, included one found on its Icelandic breeding grounds and one each in the Netherlands and France. Birds colour-ringed in Germany have been noted during autumn passage and an Icelandic bird was found wintering on the Stour. Offshore movements are rarely encountered, which is surprising bearing in mind the large wintering population, and 35 moving north off Landguard Point on 9th May 1985 is exceptional.

Despite the nucleus of Britain's small breeding population being centred just over the county border in Cambridgeshire, inland records for Suffolk are scarce. Ticehurst listed one at Brandon on 9th January 1886 as the only inland occurrence and, from 1950 to 1975, there were a mere three spring (April/May) and six autumn (July/August) records (Last 1976). The species began to show more regularly in the

1980s and, since 1991, it has been noted annually in north-west Suffolk. It is seen mostly during passage periods, usually from late March to mid-June and mid-July to early October, and singles at Livermere on 24th-29th January 1987, Lackford on 19th February 1994 and flying east over Great Waldingfield on 26th December 1994 are the only winter records for the 20th century. Numbers are normally limited to ones and twos and occasionally small flocks, but groups of 15-20 have been noted at Lackford, Livermere, Cavenham and Lakenheath between 1991 and 1998 – all during the spring and summer months.

Bar-tailed Godwit *Limosa lapponica*

A fairly common passage migrant and uncommon winter visitor

Distinctive brick-red male Bar-tailed Godwits amongst migrating flocks that rest and feed at coastal wetlands are one of the most spectacular sights of the spring. Groups of 30 or more are common during passage periods and Minsmere, Walberswick and the Blyth estuary are favoured localities. Migration watch-points log offshore movements, principally in May and August/September, and these often reach three figures. The enhancement of wildlife habitats in the Lark Valley, during the 1980s, has led to regular visitations to West Suffolk, chiefly on spring passage. Small wintering flocks occur annually at estuarine localities.

The Bar-tailed Godwit winters on the coasts of the British Isles and the Wadden Sea, and along the west coast of Africa to South Africa (Cramp *et al.* 1974-1994). Britain's wintering population was estimated to be around 60,000 in the mid-1970s (Lack 1986), but a decline of about 20% was noted in the next decade and was greater than for any other wader species (Cranswick *et al.* 1992). Bar-tailed Godwits have shown a preference for the sandier parts of the larger estuaries (Prater 1981) and this may explain its scarcity in Suffolk during winter. A count of 110 on the Orwell in February 1955 was by far the highest for that period. The BoEE (now WeBS) produced an uninspiring series of counts throughout the 1980s, but increased numbers in the early 1990s, including 131 on the Alde complex in January 1992 and 133 on the Stour in February 1992 are perhaps encouraging signs for the future. The former estuary regularly holds small wintering flocks and is Suffolk's best winter site for this species.

Bar-tailed Godwits leave their wintering grounds in February and spring passage peaks during the last few days of April and the first two weeks of May. Breydon fowlers considered 12th May as 'Godwit Day' (Payn 1978). Spring gatherings of 100-200 were noted on five occasions from 1947 to 1995 and larger concentrations include 462 at Breydon Water on 28th April 1984, with 351 at Havergate and 170 at Minsmere the next day. Stragglers continue to be recorded until early June and there have been a few instances of oversummering. The first of the autumn begin to appear in late June and migration continues through to early November. In August, large moulting flocks congregate on the North Sea coasts, principally on the Wash and the Wadden Sea, but these quickly disperse to wintering grounds elsewhere in Britain and North Africa. The wader readily associates with wildfowl and other wader species in offshore movements, and easterly gales in August and early September sometimes force migrating flocks close inshore. Substantial movements include more than 500 along the shore at Minsmere on 18th August 1958, 406 flying south off Landguard Point on 1st September 1988, and 720 south off Southwold and 1,824 off Landguard Point on 30th August 1992. The latter movement was associated with gales and the timing of the counts suggests that at least 3,000 passed through. In addition, flocks were found sheltering from the weather at Benacre Broad (450), Havergate Island (575) and Minsmere (295). Gatherings of c.300 on Havergate Island on 17th August 1979 and 200 at Benacre on 5th September 1982 are the only other autumn counts of 200 or more.

There are only two ringing recoveries affecting Suffolk – birds ringed in Norway and Sweden being recovered at Breydon Water and on the Deben respectively.

This godwit was once an extreme rarity at inland localities with only four records up to 1962, including 120 flying ENE over Risby on 29th April 1962. A flock of 25 was at Livermere on 7th May 1982 and a strong passage was noted in Breckland two springs later. Since 1987, the species has been recorded annually in West Suffolk, principally during April and May. Singles at Lackford on 17th January 1988, and 13th and 27th February 1993 are the only inland winter records.

Eskimo Curlew *Numenius borealis*

Accidental: one record involving two individuals

1852 nr Woodbridge: two shot November

The two birds shot at Woodbridge were the first of seven British records of Eskimo Curlew. Details of one shot on the Alde sometime prior to 1870 are rather vague and therefore previous authors did not accept the record.

The Eskimo Curlew bred abundantly in western Canada in the 1860s and post-breeding flocks flew a narrow migration path down the coast of Labrador to South America. Following extensive trapping and shooting in the 19th century, the species was decimated, and may well now be completely extinct.

Whimbrel *Numenius phaeopus*

A common passage migrant

The seven-note whistle of migrating Whimbrel is a familiar sound on the coast during spring and autumn, by night as well as by day. The wader is common in both passage periods, although larger numbers are noted during spring when many congregate on coastal grasslands. Whimbrels feed on mudflats, pastures and arable fields. Winter reports are rare in Suffolk.

Passage normally starts in late April and peaks in mid-May, with a few stragglers still moving through in early June. Return migration is less marked and normally gets underway in late June, peaks in August and continues through to mid-September. A few laggards remain until October and there are three November records. Spring passage is invariably more obvious and, in good years, a continuous northward drift is reported at coastal localities. For example, 499 Whimbrel flew north-east over Breydon Water on 7th-9th May 1991. The Alde/Ore estuary complex regularly attracts large concentrations, with Havergate Island being a favoured high-tide retreat. Substantial counts from this site include 104 in May 1951, 117 on 11th May 1961, 150+ on 10th May 1985 and 148 on 1st August 1985. Significant gatherings elsewhere are 150, which landed at Minsmere on 3rd September 1965 as part of the 'Great Fall', a roost of 142 at Iken Marshes on 1st May 1994 and a peak of 224 on the Beccles/Worlingham Marshes on 29th April 1996. However, these totals are dwarfed by the massive spring roosts recorded elsewhere in Britain and Europe. For example, there are counts of 1,500-2,000 in Somerset, while up to 30,000 in Holland, Belgium and Germany are frequent (Prater 1981). One ringed at Boyton on 3rd May 1992 was shot at Loon Plage, France on 28th July 1993.

The species was formerly extremely rare in West Suffolk and up to the 1960s, there were only five records. Nowadays, Whimbrels regularly pass through inland sites and are particularly evident along the Gipping and Lark Valleys. The vast majority of records refer to singles, mainly in flight, although occasionally in groups of up to seven. There are normally around 5-6 inland records each year and there is a slight bias towards spring passage. It is likely that the increase in reports is due to observer awareness rather than a change in the species' migratory habits.

There are only ten records for the period November to mid-March, all involving single-day observations on the coast and estuaries, although some of these could relate to early spring or late autumn migrants. Single-day observations of singles for the midwinter months were from Havergate Island on 1st December 1962, Minsmere on 12th February 1979, the Stour on 9th December 1980, the Blyth on 17th January 1981 and Butley Creek on 2nd January 1992.

Curlew (Eurasian Curlew) *Numenius arquata*

A common winter visitor and passage migrant – a few oversummer

The Curlew frequents a variety of open, coastal habitats during the winter months, usually close to estuaries, feeding on open intertidal areas, meadows and arable fields often several miles from saline waters. Groups of 50-100 are common and WeBS counts regularly produce four-figure roosts on the larger estuaries. A small breeding population exists in Breckland and non-breeding birds oversummer on estuaries.

Although a small breeding population existed in north-west Norfolk in the early part of the 20th century (Ticehurst 1932), colonisation of Breckland did not occur until 1947, following extensive flooding (Robertson 1954). Four pairs nested on Lakenheath Warren in 1948 and breeding on Breckland's heather-bracken type heaths increased quickly to 12 pairs in the early 1950s. A stable population of 12-15 pairs currently exists in the Suffolk Breckland. Curlews are seen widely on the county's estuaries throughout the summer months, but as yet there has been no nesting activity reported. The only breeding record from the coastal belt involved a pair that occupied afforested land at Fritton from 1955 to 1959 (Payn 1978). Nesting birds return to their territories as early as February and leave soon after their young have fledged. The Curlew is a common and familiar wintering wader, occurring in good numbers on all estuaries. A high-tide roost of several hundred regularly forms at Clamphouse Marshes on the Orwell, but the Stour holds the largest concentrations, the highest counts being 2,395 in March 1985 and 1,896 on 20th August 1989. The above counts show that the highest numbers are noted during passage periods and this is also noticeable on the Blyth where the average count for March was 81 for the period 1990-1995 compared with 35 for February. The March count is normally the highest of the year for the larger estuaries.

The Curlew is one of the earliest returning waders, being noted annually at migration watch-points from the second week of June until October. Day totals rarely reach three figures and a brief continental cold spell, during an otherwise mild winter, was thought responsible for a southerly movement involving 840 off Landguard Point on 11th February 1989. This species is largely a nocturnal migrant and during some nights their contact call can be heard as birds pass overhead. Many move overland as demonstrated by a report of 'many' which landed on a school playing field in Bury St Edmunds at dusk on 9th September 1986. Emigration is regularly noted off Landguard Point during March and April.

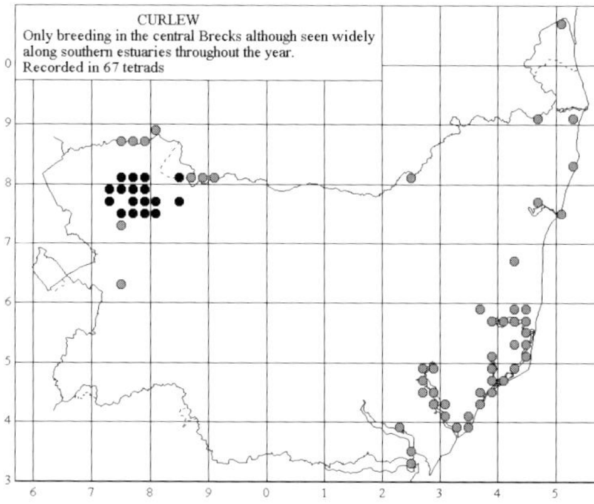

CURLEW
Only breeding in the central Brecks although seen widely along southern estuaries throughout the year.
Recorded in 67 tetrads

Ringing recoveries have shown that the species is faithful to its wintering site (Lack 1986), but severe weather often results in a southerly exodus to warmer climes. For example, two Suffolk-ringed Curlews, shot during harsh weather in France within a day of each other in February 1991, were undoubtedly attempting to avoid the fate of other shorebirds that remained on the estuaries during that month (see also Grey Plover and Redshank). A Felixstowe-ringed bird, shot within 100km of Moscow, eight years after ringing, demonstrates the vast distances that the Curlew can travel. The latter recovery is only the fourth British-ringed Curlew to be found in Russia. Birds ringed in Finland (3), Sweden, Germany and the Netherlands have also been recovered in Suffolk. Six Suffolk-ringed Curlews have been shot in France, one in Denmark and two others were found dead in Finland.

Upland Sandpiper *Bartramia longicauda*

Accidental: one record

1964 Minsmere: 24th September

The above individual was viewed and heard briefly by five observers as it flew over Minsmere's Scrape and nearby fields.

The Upland Sandpiper breeds in North America and winters in South America from southern Brazil to northern Argentina. The Minsmere bird is one of 36 that were recorded in the British Isles between 1958 and 2000 (BBRC). The date is typical and it constitutes the sole East Anglian record.

Spotted Redshank *Tringa erythropus*

A fairly common passage migrant – a few overwinter

Migrating flocks of Spotted Redshanks pass through coastal sites in spring and autumn and Minsmere is easily the most favoured locality. It is also a regular visitor to the Alde and Blyth estuaries, but is scarce on the Deben, Orwell and Stour. A small, but regular, wintering population frequents the central coastal area. It is only an occasional visitor to inland sites.

In the late 19th and early 20th centuries, this species was a scarce passage migrant, although more common during the autumn. The largest gathering noted by Ticehurst was of only six on Breydon Water on 9th July 1883 and there was little change in its status up to the 1950s. The development of coastal nature reserves provided an increase in shallow, saline lagoons, which were much favoured. Flock sizes steadily increased throughout the 1960s and 1970s and, by the 1980s, autumn parties of 70-85 were recorded annually at Minsmere, where, on 21st July 1991, Suffolk's only three-figure concentration of 112, was noted. Other sizeable gatherings include 70 at Walberswick on 18th August 1965 and 70 at Havergate on 13th September 1993. Birds in full breeding plumage in mid-June were generally assumed to be oversummering (Payn 1978), but a better understanding of the wader's migration habits has revealed its true status. Spring passage birds are seen from late March, with the last of them disappearing in mid-May. These are quickly followed by the first returning adults (usually females in full summer plumage), appearing from about 10th June. Spring numbers are normally small with flock sizes rarely exceeding 20. By the end of June, gatherings of 50 or more are regular at Minsmere, but peak passage normally occurs in August, when juveniles join adults, and passage continues through to October. Feeding flocks normally linger for several weeks and there is some interchange between sites. One ringed at Chew Valley Lake, Somerset, on 25th August 1966 was controlled on the Butley River exactly one month later.

The Spotted Redshank was formerly extremely rare during winter and singles in December at Breydon Water (1876) and Orwell (1903), and another in January at Breydon Water (1913), were the only records for those months prior to 1932 and were thought to have involved 'pricked' birds (Ticehurst 1932). Wintering on a regular basis did not take place until 1949-1950, when up to seven were found in the Walberswick-Blythburgh area. The wintering population for Britain and Ireland stood at between 80 and 200 in the early 1980s (Lack 1986), with most occurring on the siltier estuaries. The Blyth and Deben estuaries, along with the Walberswick shore pools, are most favoured by the species, although flock sizes rarely reach double figures. Spotted Redshanks are increasingly reported on the upper reaches of the Alde and Orwell. The stony parts of the southern estuaries appear unsuitable and, therefore, are avoided. There is often a swift exodus of wintering birds at the onset of severe weather.

Up to 1953, there were only five inland records, but, nowadays, one or two are logged annually at Breckland lakes and gravel pits, almost exclusively during passage periods. One at Lackford on 2nd December 1995 is the only exception. Up to the end of 1995, there had been over 40 inland occurrences, the largest inland party being four at Lackford on 2nd May 1990.

Redshank (Common Redshank) *Tringa totanus*

A common resident, winter visitor and passage migrant – decreasing as a breeding species

The Redshank is one of the most common of the county's waders with territorial pairs summering at coastal and inland localities, although significant decreases in breeding numbers have been noted. Redshanks are territorial feeders during winter, although many large areas of exposed mudflats hold 100 or more and four-figure roosts gather at high tide. It is almost exclusively coastal in winter, where immigrants from further north supplement numbers. A substantial wintering population occurs on river estuaries.

The British breeding population has fluctuated greatly over the past 200 years. A decline and range contraction during the early 19th century, when the species became virtually restricted to eastern coastal counties, was followed by a recovery from 1865 (Marchant *et al.* 1990). The Redshank bred widely throughout Suffolk in the 1930s and Ticehurst believed that it was increasing. The piping display call could be heard in most river valleys and it also nested on heathland at Martlesham and Sutton, and in cornfields at Herringfleet (Payn 1978). The draining and ploughing of wet meadows resulted in substantial reductions in the breeding population and now only small pockets exist away from the coast and estuaries.

A survey in 1988 and 1989 found 533 breeding pairs on the coast, with the Blyth, Alde complex and Deben holding the bulk of the birds (Holzer *et al.* 1993). There was a clear preference for cattle-grazed or ungrazed marshes (34% and 21% respectively) and ungrazed saltings (24%). A few isolated pairs remain on the upper reaches of the Stour, Deben and Waveney and, in West Suffolk, one or two pairs hold territory along the Lark Valley and at Livermere. The total county breeding population is probably less than 600 pairs.

The British breeding population is of the race *T. t. totanus* and is fairly sedentary. Local birds leave their breeding areas and move to the estuaries almost immediately after the young have fledged. This normally takes place at the end of June, although numbers build up in July and rapidly increase in August. The wintering population is supplemented by birds of the Icelandic population *T. t. robusta*. The presence of both races was confirmed by biometrics taken of birds wintering on the Orwell during 'Operation Redshank', a study to demonstrate the importance of the estuary in the light of the expansion of the Port of Felixstowe. The combined September WeBS counts, for all Suffolk estuaries, regularly exceed 5,000, but the highest totals are normally noted in midwinter when 7,000 or more are usually present. Ringed Redshanks from the Suffolk coast have travelled to or from Iceland (7), Sweden, Denmark, Germany, the Netherlands (7), France (13), and Portugal. The movements either to or from France and one to Portugal may well involve local breeding birds, although one of the French birds, ringed on autumn passage at Boyton and controlled in May on the Mediterranean island of Corsica, was presumably of continental origin. Local breeders return to the nesting territories in mid-April and Icelandic birds move north towards the end of that month.

The Alde complex is of international importance for the species in winter with five-year average maximum counts of 1,713, for the period 1989-1994 (Cranswick *et al.* 1995). The Orwell and Stour estuaries were formerly of this status, although both have shown massive decreases with respective averages down from 2,409 and 2,025, in 1970-1975 (Wright 1989) to 1,376 and 1,305, in 1989-1994. This represents respective losses of 57% and 64%, although both estuaries remain nationally important. The loss of essential feeding areas, mainly to port expansion and to marina developments, is the principal reason for this decline and the alarming downward trend is typified by peak counts on the Stour: 4,755 in 1970-1975, 3,831 in 1975-1980, 2,100 in 1985-1990, and 1,478 in 1990-1995. Displaced birds may well have moved to the Deben where numbers have increased substantially, although the ability of this estuary to sustain such a large population is questionable.

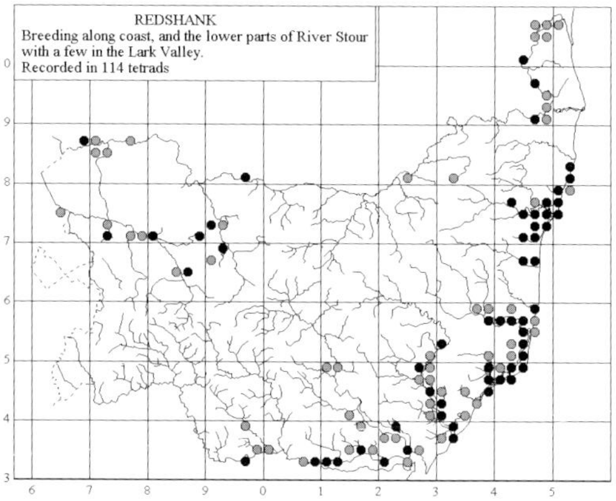

The species is particularly susceptible to severe weather periods and, during the cold spell in February 1991, no fewer than 448 corpses were found on the Deben, which represented a loss of 42% of the estuaries' normal wintering population.

Coastal movements are regularly logged during passage periods, although day-totals rarely exceed 20. It is during the onset of harsh-weather periods that more substantial numbers are noted and an exceptional southerly movement of 2,300, off Minsmere on 21st December 1969, is the largest reported.

The Redshank is a regular visitor to inland waters during the winter months, most often occurring in ones and twos with double-figure counts rare. Snow and ice soon force the birds back to saline waters.

Marsh Sandpiper *Tringa stagnatilis*

Accidental: five records involving seven individuals

1947	Southwold: Buss Creek, three 5th-6th May
1977	Benacre: 14th September
1981	Minsmere: 14th-23rd July
1998	Felixstowe: Landguard Point, S 19th September
1999	Trimley St Mary/Martin: Trimley Marshes, 31st August

The 1947 Marsh Sandpipers in Buss Creek occurred at a time when this gully was tidal and a local hotspot for migrant waders.

The Marsh Sandpiper breeds in Bulgaria and Romania eastwards to eastern Asia and is an annual visitor to Britain. There were 47 records for Britain and Ireland between 1958 and 1985 and, as Kent and Norfolk accounted for 34% of these – the Suffolk share is rather meagre. Up to the end of 2000, the species had been noted in Britain and Ireland on 116 occasions (BBRC).

Greenshank (Common Greenshank) *Tringa nebularia*

A common passage migrant – occasionally overwinters

The Greenshank is a vociferous wader and is often heard well before it is seen as it passes along the coast during spring and autumn migration. It prefers the gullies and creeks on the river estuaries, but is also found by the edges of lakes, on flooded meadows and in sedge beds. It is frequently attracted to inland waters, and new sites in the Lark Valley are particularly favoured. One to three wintering birds were noted annually in the late 1970s and throughout the 1980s, but occurrences have since become scarce.

Spring migration normally commences in early April and peak numbers normally occur in early May. Groups of ten or more are regular at coastal localities and a total of 45 on Breydon Water on 3rd May 1990 is the largest spring gathering. Greenshanks are more numerous in autumn and return is usually noted from late June, with numbers building up in July and peaking in August or September. Over 40 often gather on each of the river estuaries with Breydon Water, the Alde complex, Deben and Stour attracting the largest numbers. Autumn concentrations occur in August and September, and Havergate Island is a preferred gathering area, where high counts include 84 on 7th August 1951, c.100 on 7th August 1979 and 51 on 17th August 1985. Minsmere is also a favoured feeding area with high counts of 60 on 3rd September 1965 and 55 on 30th July 1980.

The bulk of Britain and Ireland's wintering population is confined to the west coast and Ireland, with very few frequenting eastern counties (Lack 1986). Ticehurst listed one at Thorpe Meare on 14th December 1888 as the sole winter record, and the next was at Benacre on 29th January and 6th February 1950. There were a further eight records up to 1977, and thereafter it was noted in 14 consecutive winters. Numbers are normally limited to singles, although three were noted on the Stour on 20th January 1985. What was presumed to have been the same individual frequented the Orwell and Stour in consecutive winters from 1977 to 1987. There are no winter records away from the coast.

One ringed at Levington in autumn 1987 was found at the same site four years later, showing that traditional stopover sites are used on passage. Another ringed at this site in August 1987 was recovered in France in July 1989.

Greater Yellowlegs *Tringa melanoleuca*

Accidental: three records

1975	Breydon Water: 8th-13th September
1985	Walberswick/Minsmere: 4th July to 14th August
1995	Southwold: 14th May
	Burgh Castle: 15th-25th May

This American wader has occurred almost on cue in the middle of each of the last three decades. The 1975 Breydon Water bird frequented the northern shore of the estuary, but was also observed on the Suffolk side on the last date. The records from Southwold and Burgh Castle in May 1995 undoubtedly refer to the same well-travelled individual that previously visited Holliwell Point, Essex. There are 25 records for Britain and Ireland for the period 1958-2000 (BBRC), the bulk of which were noted during the autumn.

Lesser Yellowlegs *Tringa flavipes*

Accidental: seven records

1938	Waldringfield: River Deben, shot 1st September
1950	Minsmere: 26th-28th August
1958	Orford: Havergate Island, 25th September
1978	Minsmere: 29th May 29th to 5th June
1982	Minsmere: 8th-14th October
1995	Minsmere/North Warren: 6th-11th May
2001	Cattawade: River Stour, 10th-12th October

This Nearctic wader had been recorded in Britain and Ireland on 300 occasions up to the end of 2000 (BBRC). Occurrences show a clear westerly bias with the bulk of the reports from southern Ireland and south-west England. The six Suffolk records are all from the coast and estuaries.

Suffolk's first record involved a Lesser Yellowlegs shot at Waldringfield. This was documented in *The Transactions of the SNS*, but was omitted by Payn.

Green Sandpiper *Tringa ochropus*

An uncommon winter visitor and common passage migrant

Farm ponds, gravel pits, muddy dykes, streams, flooded meadows and the smallest of pools are all favoured habitats of this unobtrusive wader. Although it favours the saline limits of the larger estuaries, for example just upstream from Wilford Bridge on the Deben and Bourne Bridge on the Orwell, extensive mudflats are generally avoided. However, Green Sandpipers are occasionally forced there when freshwater habitats become frozen. This wader can be seen in every month of the year, but is rare in May. The species normally occurs in ones and twos but, occasionally, in flocks of 10-15. Green Sandpipers are locally common at inland localities during passage and winter periods.

The wintering population has probably been understated in recent SBRs, which report 25-39 birds at 18-24 sites for the period 1988-1992. Alton Water Reservoir and the freshwater borrow-dykes, adjacent to the Alde/Ore and Deben estuaries, normally attract small numbers, and Lackford and Bramford are the best inland sites. The wader is most susceptible to harsh weather as witnessed in February 1991, when several were found dead. Green Sandpipers are very site-faithful and therefore the wintering population would have taken a few seasons to recover from the mortality witnessed in 1991. Numbers were well down in the subsequent winters of 1991/2 to 1994/5.

Small numbers occur on spring passage from March to mid-April, with a few stragglers remaining until the first few days of May. The species is one of the earliest autumn migrants with returning birds often noted in the first week of June. Green Sandpipers are more numerous during autumn passage, although concentrations of 20 or more are rare. Large gatherings include 45 and 30 at West Stow Sewage Farm on 9th and 24th August 1955 respectively, 30 at Minsmere in August 1963 and 25 at Bramford Water Park on 26th August 1988.

Ringing data demonstrate the site fidelity of many birds, which return to the same wintering area year after year. One ringed at Shingle Street on 13th August 1967 was recovered at Maine-et-Loire, France, on 28th August the following year.

Wood Sandpiper *Tringa glareola*

An uncommon passage migrant

Freshwater marshes, meadows and small pools provide this sandpiper with a feeding refuge during passage periods. The species is normally seen in groups of 1-3 and, exceptionally, six or more. It is scarce in spring, but is normally more evident during the autumn. The bulk of the reports are from coastal sites, with managed wetlands such as Walberswick NNR, Minsmere and Trimley Marshes hosting the larger numbers. It is not uncommon at inland sites and is regularly noted at Lackford and Livermere.

The first spring arrivals are usually noted during the second week of May, but singles in late April are not unusual. The earliest occurrence involved one at Minsmere on 15th April 1968 and there is a cluster of records around 16th-18th. Oversummering individuals were recorded at Minsmere in 1965 and at Buss Creek, Southwold, in 1975.

Returning birds normally occur from early or mid-July, with peak migration recorded in early August. There was a remarkable influx into Britain during the autumn of 1952 (Nisbet 1957), when as many as 60 were noted along the Suffolk coast, a total which included a concentration of at least 26 at Reydon on 4th August. Two further birds were reported at inland sites. Most birds pass through by the end of September and, very occasionally, a few linger into October. There are only two November records: a rather tame bird at Boyton on 13th November 1966 and one at Havergate Island on 9th November 1975.

Terek Sandpiper — *Xenus cinereus*

Accidental: 11 records

1951	Southwold: Buss Creek, 2nd-5th June
1972	Minsmere: 19th-22nd May
1975	Breydon Water: 1st June
1978	Breydon Water: 5th July
1981	Minsmere: The Scrape, 1st August
1990	Breydon Water: 29th-31st May
1992	Southwold: Boating Lake, 27th May
1995	Minsmere: The Scrape, 14th June
	Burgh Castle: 15th June
1998	Walberswick: 6th September
1999	Minsmere: The Scrape, 27th-28th May

There were 59 records for Britain and Ireland up to the end of 2000 (BBRC) and the Suffolk records compare well with the national trend that shows a clear bias towards May and June. As with Marsh Sandpiper, most British records have been noted in the south-eastern counties (Dymond *et al.* 1989).

The 1951 individual occurred just a few days after one in Sussex that constituted the first British record. The BBRC considered the 1995 records involved different individuals.

The Terek Sandpiper breeds in Finland through to eastern Siberia, and winters in southern Africa, and south Asia to Australia.

Common Sandpiper — *Actitis hypoleucos*

A common passage migrant – a few overwinter

Migrating flocks of Common Sandpiper stop off at wetland sites throughout the county, favouring the margins of lakes, ponds and streams, coastal lagoons, estuaries and flooded meadows. This species occasionally frequents seaweed-clad jetties, groynes and rocky shores. A few birds overwinter annually. The Common Sandpiper breeds beside upland lochs, reservoirs and rivers in northern and western Britain although the population has been in slow decline since the mid-1980s.

Although breeding has been confirmed in Norfolk (Taylor *et al.* 2000), it is doubtful whether the species has ever nested in Suffolk. Ticehurst gave some detailed accounts, but he concluded that breeding had not been "satisfactorily determined". Payn was more positive and listed a report of a nest found with eggs at Icklingham on the River Lark on 1st June 1929. Very occasionally, displaying pairs have been found in midsummer and a pair was seen copulating at Weybread Pits on 16th May 1994. Most reports refer to birds frequenting faster-flowing rivers such as the Little Ouse, Lark and upper Stour and, although the habitat appears suitable, future colonisation is most unlikely.

Common Sandpipers pass through the county in good numbers during most years. The first of the spring arrive in early April and peak migration normally occurs in late April or early May, with a few lingering until the first few days of June. Return migration gets underway in mid-July with numbers

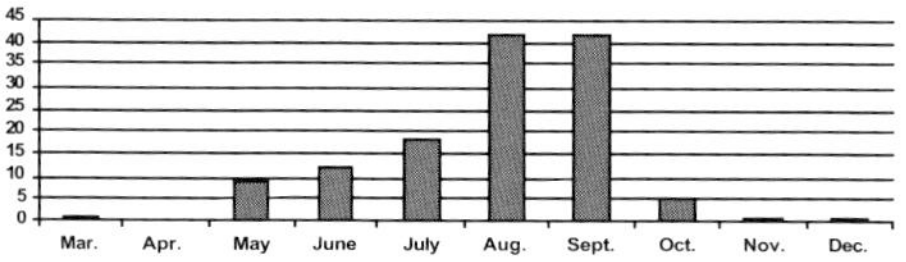

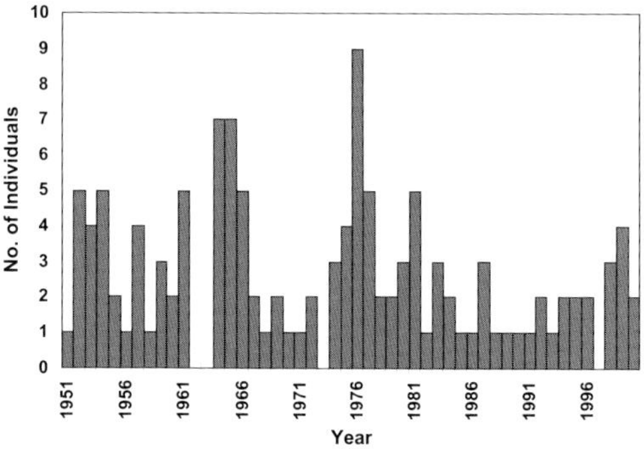

Above: The seasonal occurrence of the Red-necked Phalarope from 1951-2000

Right: The annual totals of the Red-necked Phalarope from 1951-2000

singles at Livermere on 5th September 1983 and 21st August 1999. The 19th century records are more remarkable owing to the lateness of the occurrences.

The Red-necked Phalarope is a late spring migrant, rarely showing before the end of May or, more often, the beginning of June. It is more plentiful in autumn, with returning birds being noted as early as mid-July (usually adult females) and peak passage occurs in August and September. There have been four October, three November and one December reports. Records of these tardy individuals, as well as an early bird at Havergate on 28th March 1977, fall well outside the species' normal migration periods and must be viewed with some suspicion. The winter quarters of the North Atlantic population is still unknown, the nearest recognised wintering area to Britain being the Arabian Sea (Cramp *et al.* 1974-1994). It is possible that birds occasionally occur in winter, but there is also some question over the possibility of misidentification. A photograph published in the 1970 SBR, entitled 'Red-necked Phalarope, Boyton, October 26th 1970', aptly illustrated such pitfalls, as it was subsequently correctly identified as a Grey Phalarope.

Grey Phalarope *Phalaropus fulicarius*

A rare winter visitor and passage migrant

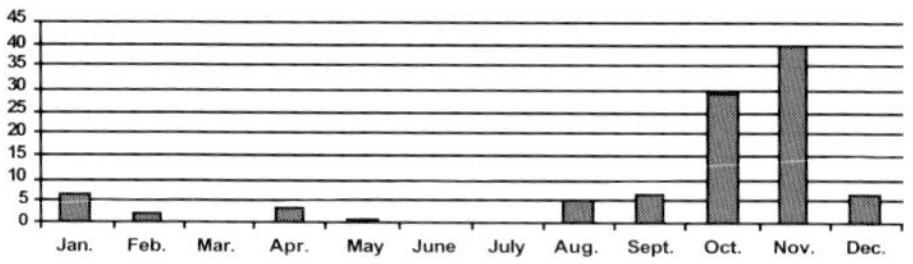

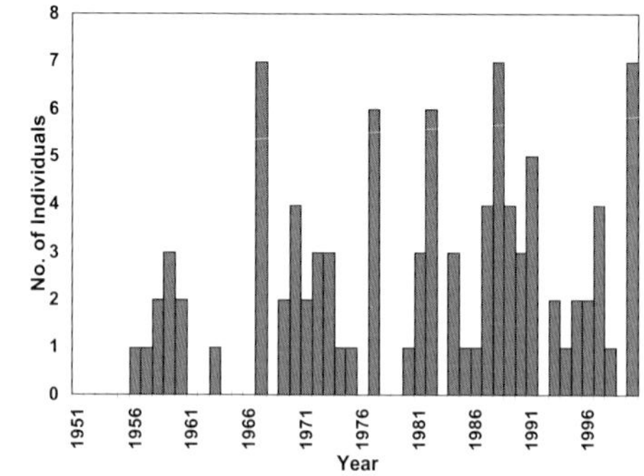

Above: The seasonal occurrences of the Grey Phalarope from 1951-2000

Right: The annual totals of the Grey Phalarope from 1951-2000

The Grey Phalarope is reported at coastal sites in late autumn in most years, usually during or just after storms. It is more pelagic in its habits than the Red-necked Phalarope and is rarely seen inland. It is very rarely reported during spring.

The vast majority of reports are received in late October and through November, with a few occurrences in December and January. The majority refer to individuals either flying or feeding just offshore, although occasionally one will take up residence and stay for several weeks. One well-watched individual was present in Lowestoft Harbour from 12th December 1993 until 12th March 1994. One on the sea and three flying south off Lowestoft on 9th November 1988 is the largest number recorded in a single day.

There are only two records for May: one long-staying individual arrived at Minsmere on 11th April 1977 and stayed until 3rd May, and another on 2nd May 1969 had attained full summer plumage. One off Lowestoft on 9th August 1991 is the earliest autumn migrant.

There are five inland records: one shot on the River Gipping at Great Blakenham, sometime prior to 1886, one that hit telegraph wires at Lakenheath on 20th September 1886, one shot at Denston on 22nd November 1904, one at Bury St Edmunds B.F. ponds on 19th August 1970 and one at Thorington Street Reservoir on 29th October 1986.

Pomarine Skua *Stercorarius pomarinus*

An uncommon passage migrant, mostly in autumn. Occasionally overwinters

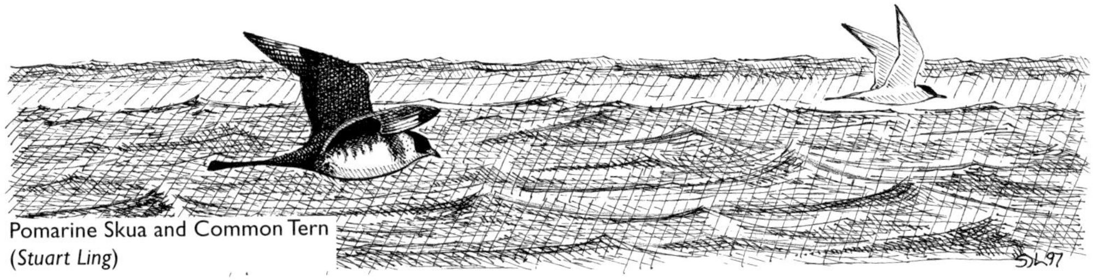

Pomarine Skua and Common Tern
(*Stuart Ling*)

The Pomarine Skua is recorded annually offshore, usually singly or in groups of up to ten and principally during the late autumn months. The species is reported irregularly on spring passage and, in recent years, a few immatures have overwintered off north-east Suffolk.

The status of the Pomarine Skua was formerly described as "an autumnal migrant twenty to forty miles out in the North Sea" (Ticehurst 1932) and arrivals coincided with the herring and sprat shoals. All records then related to the months of September to December. Fishermen were offered a bounty for a good specimen and a great many were collected and brought into Great Yarmouth and Lowestoft. However, as taxidermy became unfashionable, records dried up and there were no reports from 1925-1959. There was an increase in occurrences during the 1960s, but observers lacked confidence over identification and many were reported as "probables". An improvement in optical aids and a better understanding of the species' migration habits and plumage characteristics have resulted in the species being logged annually since the 1970s. An upsurge in seawatching activities in the mid-1980s saw a huge increase in reports, particularly during the autumn. The skua rarely occurs in groups larger than three and a group of ten moving north on 25th September 1988, off Covehithe, is the largest recorded.

Between 1961 and 1984, up to eight were reported annually with the exception of 1963 when 15 were recorded. Suffolk's share of an unprecedented influx to east coast counties in November 1985 was about 50, with 15-20 reported in December, including nine moving south in a half an hour off Lowestoft, 26th December. A substantial number of wintering birds and an even spread of autumn occurrences led to the highest year total of 92 in 1994. The area of sea between Benacre and Southwold has been the most favoured in recent times, although small numbers are regularly reported off Ness Point, Lowestoft, Dunwich-Minsmere and Landguard Point.

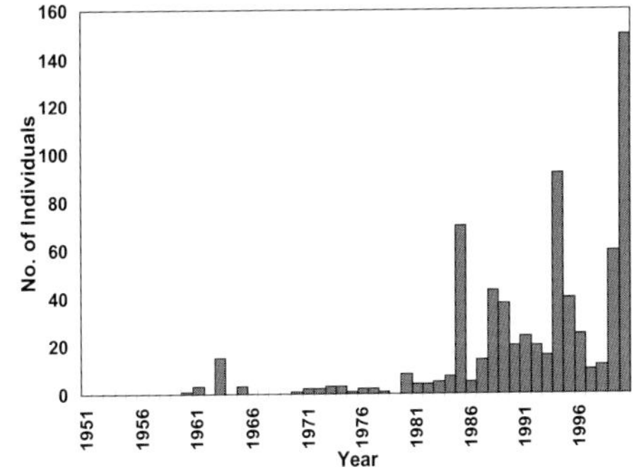

The annual totals of the Pomarine Skua from 1951-2000

The skua is surprisingly scarce during spring and, in recent years, records have been complicated by the presence of wintering birds. There is a regular easterly passage through the English Channel and North Sea over 90% of which occurs between 30th April and 14th May and probably involves Baltic breeding birds (Cramp *et al.* 1974-1994). Generally, birds on spring passage are adults returning to their breeding quarters and most display the characteristic 'spoons' (elongated, broad-ended central tail feathers). Northward migration probably passes too far offshore to be seen by birdwatchers which may explain the paucity of spring records. Up to 1993, there were a mere eight spring occurrences involving 12 individuals noted between the dates of 3rd May and 2nd June. In 1994, however, up to seven immatures, possibly wintering elsewhere in the North Sea, lingered offshore until the end of April. An immature on 7th May and two on 14th May may also have been wintering birds.

The Pomarine Skua was formerly rare during winter. Ticehurst listed only one record and there were just six reports between 1963-1986. However, since 1990 wintering birds have been noted almost annually, the highest concentrations being ten between Covehithe and Minsmere from January to mid-April 1995 and 23 in Sole Bay in early January 2000. The northeast coastal zone is the most favoured area, where this species often harass Kittiwake flocks and, more occasionally, larger gulls. The vast majority of wintering Pomarine Skuas are immatures.

Although the Pomarine Skuas is capable of swift pursuit to steal fish from gulls and terns, it is not as agile as the Arctic Skua, so the lengthy acrobatic manoeuvres associated with the latter species are rarely practised. However, larger gulls are occasionally seized on the wing as witnessed off Ness Point, Lowestoft, on 2nd September 1990, when one was seen to grab a flying Herring Gull by its wing and bring it down into the sea where it was drowned. The skua then stood on the carcass and fed from it as it drifted south with the tide (SBR).

Occasionally, Pomarine Skuas venture up the river estuaries and have been reported upstream on the Waveney as far as Beccles, and on the Orwell to Ipswich. Inland records, however, are extremely rare and occur only after severe gales. Singles shot at Elveden, 30th October 1848, Lakenheath Fen, November 1850 and November 1903 and Hardwick, September 1883, together with sightings at Alton Water, 1st September 1980 and Hadleigh on 18th September 1995 are the only records. The last individual was observed following a plough.

Arctic Skua *Stercorarius parasiticus*

A common passage migrant. Occasionally overwinters

The Arctic Skua is the commonest of the four Palearctic skua species, being noted regularly offshore each autumn and sometimes in good numbers. The species is never plentiful in spring and there are few winter records. It is an extreme rarity away from the immediate coastline.

The Scottish breeding population numbered around 3,350 pairs in 1985-1987 (Lloyd *et al.* 1991) and the bulk of these, as well as those nesting further north and passing through Britain, winter in the South Atlantic. Only a small proportion is seen off Suffolk, where annual totals have averaged 200-300 during the period 1987-1995. Northerly gales in late August/early September may force birds closer to our shores and southerly movements of 50 or more in a day have been logged in the Benacre-Southwold area as follows – 88 on 28th August 1987, 71 on 14th September 1988 and 76 on 27th August 1989. These figures were eclipsed on 29th August 1996 by a mainly southerly movement, involving at least 300 birds. Numbers logged off Felixstowe are consistently lower than those of north-east Suffolk. A total of 46 flying south, off Landguard Point on 14th September 1994, is the largest day total.

Arctic Skuas are rare in spring, being most evident in late April and early May, although normally there are less than ten sightings each year. Six adults off Minsmere on 13th March 1994 were particularly early.

Arctic Skuas have been reported between 6th June and 3rd July on 14 occasions, but return passage rarely gets underway until mid-July and normally peaks in September. Midsummer appearances presumably relate to non-breeders or failed breeders, as successful pairs remain within the southern colonies (Shetland) until early August, and two weeks later at higher latitudes (Furness 1987). Autumn migration continues through to October and a few laggards are occasionally reported up to early December. A flock of 14 moving north off Minsmere on 2nd December 1987 is unusual.

Wintering individuals were formerly extremely rare with only three records up to 1985. Thereafter, one or two have been noted in most years usually between Kessingland and Sizewell with regular observations confirming that individuals stay throughout the winter.

Arctic Skuas are rarely noted up the estuaries and have only been reported in West Suffolk on five occasions, all records relating to storm-driven individuals. Ticehurst listed one on the Stour on 16th June 1922 and three inland records for the 19th century, including one at Exning in January. Singles at Herringswell on 27th September 1982 and at Lakenheath Warren on 29th May 1984 are the only inland records since then.

Long-tailed Skua *Stercorarius longicaudus*

A scarce passage migrant (c.125 records)

Formerly an extreme rarity, this species is now recorded annually in small numbers, usually towards the end of August or at the beginning of September. It is still much the scarcest of the four Palearctic skuas and extremely rare on spring passage.

Long-tailed Skuas breed in the subarctic and winter in the southern hemisphere (Cramp *et al.* 1974-1994). The species migrates to its breeding grounds via the northwestern Atlantic and only a small proportion pass in close proximity to the British coastline. In autumn, a few move south through the English Channel, but, in spring, the species tends to take a more westerly route, hence there are just two Suffolk records: an adult flying south over Minsmere, 21st May 1992, and another over Landguard Point, 30th May 1996. Although the skua is now reported annually during autumn, numbers rarely reach double figures. The one notable exception occurred in 1991, when an influx involving 3,250 individuals was reported off the east coast (Cawston 1993). Suffolk's share was 37 and included a flock of 12 juveniles and an adult which passed south off Bawdsey on 7th September, with similar numbers, probably the same birds, logged off Southwold earlier the same day. Extreme autumn dates are 16th July 1989 and mid-November 1891.

The species was formerly rarely reported in British waters and up to 1979 all records were considered by BBRC. Payn mentioned six occurrences for the 19th century and only four more up to 1974. A better understanding of the species' habits and plumage characteristics, together with more powerful optical aids and a growing interest in sea-watching have led to more being positively identified. From 1980-1986, an average of 200 was reported annually in Britain (Dymond *et al.* 1989), although the species remains a rarity off Suffolk. It is likely that many are overlooked.

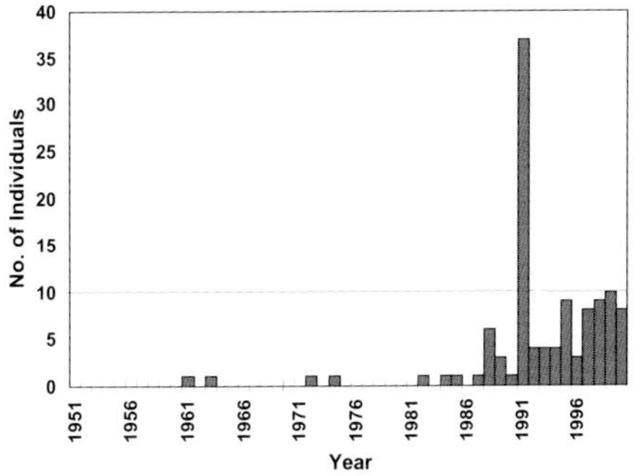

The annual totals of the Long-tailed Skua from 1951-2000

Two specimens were found to have consumed earthworms (Ticehurst 1932, Hele 1870), which at the time were thought to have been "thrown up" by Black-headed Gulls. It is possible, however, that the worms were gathered by the skuas themselves, perhaps from behind the plough.

One found at Newmarket in mid-November 1891 is the only inland record.

Great Skua *Catharacta skua*

An uncommon passage migrant. Occasionally noted in winter

This skua is reported annually in variable numbers at offshore localities, principally between late August and November, and is scarce in spring. In some years, one or two opportunists may loaf around offshore for a few weeks principally in northeast Suffolk, but sightings increase dramatically during strong northerly winds. It is rare in southeast Suffolk occurring almost exclusively during severe onshore gales.

Great Skuas breed in scattered colonies in northern Scotland, Iceland, the Faroes, Spitzbergen, Bear Island, Hopen and North Norway (Furness 1987). A few pass off Suffolk during the autumn months most often singly. Groups of four or more are rare and day-totals rarely reach double figures. The highest totals include ten off Minsmere on 10th October 1987, 11 off Covehithe, 11th August 1989 and ten off Corton, 4th October 1992. The species is only occasionally recorded on spring passage, but poor visibility and strong north-easterly winds produced a northerly movement of ten on April 20th 1990, which is exceptional for that season. There are no records for June.

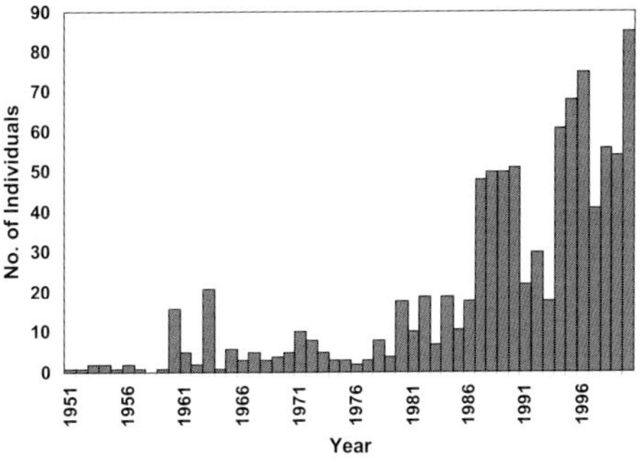

The annual totals of the Great Skua from 1951-2000

Ticehurst believed that the Great Skua was not uncommon on the herring grounds during September and October and referred to about 30 records involving 50 individuals for the period 1832-1932. It was considered to be a scarce passage migrant in the late 1970s with an average of about three records each year (Payn 1978). Along with the recent upsurge of interest in sea-watching, there has been a ten-fold increase in records and, during the period 1985-1994, there was an average of 36 records per annum. In reality, the skua is probably no more common today than it was during the 19th century. The first of the autumn is occasionally noted in mid-July with peak numbers normally between late August and mid-September.

Winter records are not as regular as those for Arctic and Pomarine Skuas, but, nevertheless, there were about 20 during the 20th century. The bulk of the records refer to single day observations of birds offshore often following winter storms.

Five ringed birds found dead in Suffolk, all ringed as chicks in Shetland, give some indication of the origins of the county's passage birds.

There have been only eight reports away from the immediate coastline and, quite remarkably, three during the winter months. Ticehurst listed three records, all from 1914-1926, but there were no further reports until 1968, when one was reported at Ipswich Docks on 12th November. Great Skuas were noted in 1980 at Livermere on 14th July and Alton Water on 31st August, where one was seen to kill and partially devour three Coots, and a ringed bird was found at Groton in 1983. One was seen to rise from a roadside rabbit carcass at Hadleigh on 31st January 1986 and another was at Ixworth on 29th August of that year.

Mediterranean Gull *Larus melanocephalus*

A fairly common winter visitor and passage migrant. A few pairs oversummer

The Mediterranean Gull is most often seen in the company of Black-headed Gulls chiefly at coastal localities, but is increasingly being noted at inland gravel pits, especially those in the vicinity of landfill sites. There has been a huge increase in occurrences, in all seasons over the past 20 years, and one or two pairs now breed annually. Between 10 and 20 regularly overwinter and there are distinct spring movements in some years.

Up to the 1950s, the gull was an extremely rare vagrant. Occurrences at Breydon in 1886 and 1909 were the only records in Suffolk prior to 1954, but, thereafter, the species began to show annually, with 1963 being the only blank year. Mediterranean Gulls are extremely site-faithful and often return to the same feeding site year after year. Many of the early records involve regular winterers including one that frequented the Covehithe area in successive winters from 1964-1980 causing an annual pilgrimage to the area by year listers. The yearly totals ranged from 2-7 during the 1970s, rising to 25 by the end of the 1980s and between 30 and 160 in the 1990s. Ten together at Landguard Point on 6th March 1998 is the county's largest gathering to date.

There is a notable increase in records between late April and June, which possibly involves birds passing through to Baltic nesting grounds. Many are in first-summer plumage and, although the increase is noted at many coastal sites, it is best illustrated by the 26 which passed through Breydon between 29th April and 25th June 1983. Proof of interchange between Suffolk and Baltic breeding colonies lies with a bird ringed at Rostock, Germany, which frequented Felixstowe's promenade in consecutive years from 1987-1990. The latter record further demonstrates the site fidelity of this species. A colour-ringed bird at Minsmere in spring 1996, had been ringed in either Hungary or Slovenia.

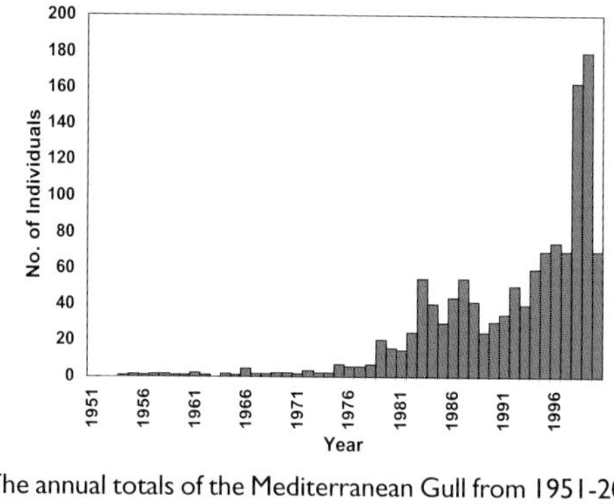

The annual totals of the Mediterranean Gull from 1951-2000

Following Britain's first breeding record in Hampshire in 1968, the national population increased steadily to between 54 and 60-79 pairs by 1999 (Ogilvie *et al.* 2001). The increase coincided with range expansion and a general increase in the world population and colonies were building on the other side of the North Sea with 125 pairs in the Netherlands in 1990. In Suffolk, displaying adults have been reported during most summers since 1977 and potential breeding pairs have defended territories at suitable breeding sites since 1980. Over-summering was noted annually during the early 1980s and a pair attempted to nest at Havergate Island in 1986 before being driven away by Black-headed Gulls. Nesting again took place at Havergate in 1993 and almost annually thereafter with a peak of four and three nesting pairs noted in 1999 and 2000 respectively producing a total of four young. Since 1995, up to three pairs nested amongst Black-headed Gulls on saltings on the River Blyth, although most attempts were thwarted by spring tides that flooded the nest sites. Two young fledged in 1999 and, in addition, two juveniles seen nearby in August 2000 is perhaps further indication of successful breeding. One or two pairs regularly hold territories at Minsmere, although egg-laying has yet to be confirmed.

Mediterranean Gulls regularly venture up river estuaries and are frequently reported on Oulton Broad, in Ipswich Docks and at Alton Water reservoir. Occasionally, the species will mingle with Black-headed Gulls behind the plough. The first inland record involved one in first-winter plumage at Lakenheath on 29th March 1984, but, since 1987, the gull has been an annual visitor to inland waters, with Lackford Wildfowl Reserve and Bramford being the principal sites. The gull has been regularly located amongst a pre-roost bathing flock at the latter site and an adult and three first-winters, present throughout November 1994, constitute the largest inland gathering.

Laughing Gull *Larus atricilla*

Accidental: one record

1995 Minsmere-Sizewell: first summer 5th-7th & 9th-11th July
Lowestoft: Ness Point, 8th July

The above individual joined a pre-roost gathering of Lesser Black-backed Gulls on Minsmere's Scrape. Despite a protracted stay, the bird was quite elusive as it commuted between Minsmere and several other sites. It was regularly seen at Sizewell, where it fed amongst a throng of gulls and terns around the offshore rigs and roosted with flocks on the beach. It made at least one visit to the roof of the Birds Eye Foods factory at Ness Point, although sightings there were brief.

A report of a Laughing Gull at Wherstead and Landguard Point in November-December 1977 was originally accepted by BBRC, but following a review the record is now considered not to be fully substantiated.

The Laughing Gull breeds in North America and on the Caribbean islands and winters in the USA and South America. It is a rare vagrant in the British Isles, being reported on 106 occasions up to the end of 2000 and only twice prior to 1958 (BBRC).

Franklin's Gull *Larus pipixcan*

Accidental: two records

1977/8 Lowestoft: second-year 13th November-23rd March
1991 Burgh Castle: Breydon Water, ad. 30th June

Suffolk's first record involved a long-staying and well-watched individual, which associated with other gulls in the Lowestoft area for most of that winter. It developed a pattern of staying in the Ness Point-Harbour area for about an hour after dawn before flying off inland, except during wintry weather when it remained around the harbour for most of the day (Brown 1979). The gull scavenged from waste-food bins at Birds Eye Foods factory and was also observed following the plough at Barnby, North Cove and Mutford.

Suffolk's second Franklin's Gull was found on the Norfolk side of Breydon Water, but spent the late afternoon and evening on mudflats with Black-headed Gulls at Burgh Castle (Cawston 1993).

The Franklin's Gull breeds in North America and winters on the western coast of Central and South America from Guatemala to Chile. It is an extremely rare vagrant to British Isles being noted on 42 occasions up to the end of 2000 (BBRC).

Little Gull *Larus minutus*

A fairly common passage migrant and scarce summer and winter visitor

This graceful gull is an annual visitor to Suffolk, being noted in both passage periods, usually in singles or small flocks. A few, mainly immatures, oversummer in most years and 1-2 are found each winter. Visits to inland waters are now regular in spring often coinciding with the passage of Black Terns.

One at Grundisburgh in 1834 was Suffolk's first documented record and it was noted as a rare coastal visitor for the remainder of that century. In the first third of the 20th century, the Little Gull occurred primarily as a scarce autumn and winter visitor. Ticehurst thought that it missed our coast altogether during spring and listed only four records for the months of April, May and June. There is now a regular spring passage, which has become more prominent at inland localities since the 1970s. Occasionally birds linger into the summer months and in June 1966 one built a nest on Minsmere's Scrape (Hutchinson & Neath 1978). Breeding took place on the Ouse Washes, Cambridgeshire, in 1975 and, in recent years, the number of oversummering immatures has increased significantly on the Suffolk coast. Display has been noted on several occasions and in 1991 up to 13 (including seven adults) frequented Trimley Marshes throughout the summer.

Little Gulls
(*Adam Kennedy*)

Although there are a few inland records prior to the 1960s, the first record in West Suffolk involved one at Livermere as recently as July 1967. Nowadays, passage birds occur regularly, principally during spring, with Livermere and Lackford W.R. being the most favoured sites. A count of 59, mainly adults, at the latter locality on 11th April 1992, is the highest recorded inland gathering, with an overall total of 65-70 passing through the site from 8th-23rd April of that year.

Offshore movements occur annually, principally between September and early November and, in some years, these are quite substantial. There were 14 three-figure counts up to the end of 2001 and those of 150 or more include 170 between Minsmere and Sizewell on 25th October 1976, 267 moving south off Southwold on 13th September 1993, 250 flying north off Kessingland on 7th November 1999, a record 506 north off Thorpeness also on 7th November 1999, 239 south of Minsmere on 7th November 2000 and 214 south off Sizewell in just a few hours later and 222 (219 south and three north) off Thorpeness on 21st October 2001. Little Gulls often roost in the company of Black-headed Gulls and terns, although they will gather into single-species flocks when there are good numbers present offshore. For example, up to 60 roosted on Lowestoft's Oval from 6th August-21st September 1987 and 62 were on the nearby Denes Camp Site on 15th August 1996.

The gull is reported in ones and twos each winter, but easterly gales sometimes force flocks of 50 or more close to our shore. The species was fairly common all along the Norfolk and Suffolk coast following severe gales in February 1870 and, more recently, the highest concentrations have all been in the Lowestoft-Great Yarmouth area. These include 55 on 9th December 1959, 102 flying south on 6th December 1978 and 43 flying north on 23rd January 1984.

Sabine's Gull *Larus sabini*

A rare passage migrant – c.50 records

The Sabine's Gull is a rare autumn transient mainly to Britain's west coast, with Atlantic storms normally being responsible for forcing birds close inshore. The breeding range extends through North America and northeast Siberia and it winters in the south Atlantic off Namibia and western South Africa. It is one of the more common Nearctic visitors to Britain and Ireland, with no fewer than 1,869 being recorded during the period 1957-1985 (Dymond *et al.* 1989). As with other pelagic winterers, the records are biased towards Ireland and south-west Britain. For example, Suffolk's share for the same period was a mere 1% (19 records) of the national figure.

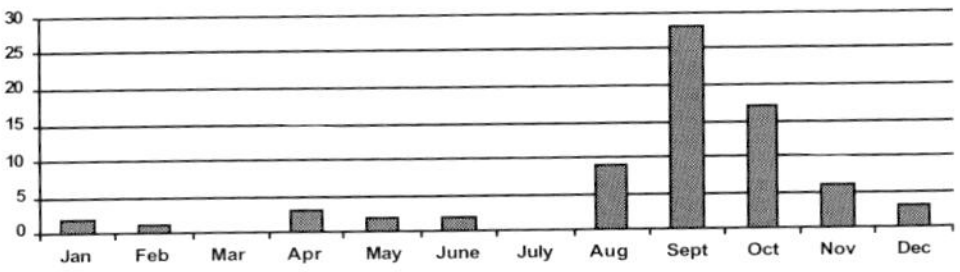

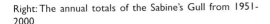

Above: The seasonal distribution of the Sabine's Gull (1881-2000)

Right: The annual totals of the Sabine's Gull from 1951-2000

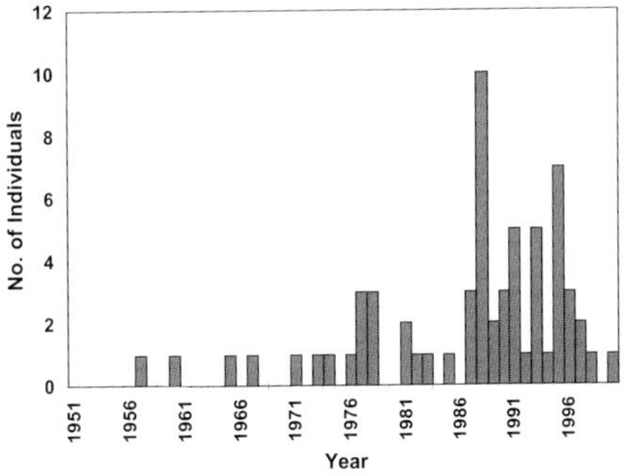

Although the gull is reported annually offshore, usually in movements with other seabirds, records are limited to around three per year. The vast majority of records have occurred north of Aldeburgh, with one on Havergate in 1967, three off Landguard Point following the 'Great Storm' of October 1987 and singles there during the autumns of 1991 and 1996, being the only records for south-east Suffolk. Although most records relate to birds passing through, one or two have occasionally lingered around the harbours in north-east Suffolk and the sewage outfall off Ness Point, Lowestoft, has been a favoured feeding spot in recent years.

The bulk of the records relate to birds in first-winter plumage and fall between August and November, but there are seven winter reports: three in December; three in January and one in February. These records do not conform to the species' normal migration pattern and the authenticity of winter occurrences in general has been questioned in the past (Dunn 1983). However, the Suffolk records were noted by some of the county's most experienced and reliable recorders and the SORC are convinced that the birds were correctly identified.

There is only one record for West Suffolk, involving a juvenile which joined the gull roost at Livermere Lake on 11th-12th September 1995.

Black-headed Gull *Larus ridibundus*

An abundant resident, winter visitor and passage migrant

This is Suffolk's most numerous gull with large congregations occurring wherever there is a sustainable food source. There is a huge immigration during the autumn and the county holds a substantial winter population. Flocks of 10-100 can be found along the length of the Suffolk coast, but larger concentrations occur around estuaries, harbours and docks, sewage farms and outfalls, pig-fields and refuse tips. Flocks frequently follow the plough and birds are attracted to scraps put out in urban gardens throughout the year. The gull breeds in large colonies mainly at estuarine localities, but also inland. Control measures are employed at some managed nature reserves to limit predation to breeding waders and terns.

The only known nesting colony up to the 1850s was at Wangford Warren in West Suffolk. Isolated breeding attempts followed at Covehithe, Thorpe Fen and at Euston Park during the late 19th and early 20th centuries, but there was mounting concern that the gull was facing extinction as a breeding species in Britain. However, in 1927 a colony became established in Blythburgh Fen and, by 1931, 24 pairs were present, rising to 50 by 1938. In 1958, breeding numbers peaked at 5,070 pairs, at five colonies, with the bulk of these on Havergate Island. Thereafter, the nesting population has ranged between 2,153 and 3,221 pairs (Wright & Waters 1991). The majority of colonies have been established on estuarine saltings or by coastal lagoons, but floods at Lakenheath Fen in 1947 created the ideal habitat for c.700 pairs to form Suffolk's largest recorded inland colony. There was no further mention of this colony, so presumably it was a one-off occurrence. The settling lagoons at Bury St Edmunds B.F. created a more permanent habitat and a colony, founded in 1933 and peaking at 100 pairs in 1972, is now the largest in West Suffolk with around 30-40 pairs nesting annually. Although most birds here breed amongst vegetation on dried up ponds, others build nests in dead trees protruding from the water's surface at a height of up to 2.5 metres. Similarly, a colony which became established on an island at Livermere Lake in 1997 also contained many tree nests, some more than four metres above ground level. Apart from the well-established Bury St

or movements have been reported either at offshore localities or on the lower reaches of river estuaries. These include 3,000 at Breydon in January 1983, 2,000 at Minsmere, February 1985; a southerly movement totalling 5,100 off Landguard Point over five dates in early January 1986, c.5,000 off Landguard 20th December 1991, a remarkable 12,000 between Sizewell and Thorpeness on 7th January 1996 and 12,000 feeding in Sole Bay on 4th-5th February 1999, 3,500 off Landguard on 16th January 2000 and 7,500 off Thorpeness on 22nd February 2001. The 1996 and 1999 totals coincided with massive concentrations of gulls along the length of the coast which were thought to have been attracted by sprat shoals close inshore.

Smaller numbers congregate at freshwater localities, although Alton Water regularly attracts three-figure totals. Common Gulls were scarce in north-west Suffolk early in the 20th century, with most authors listing every record in local accounts (e.g. Clarke 1897 and Caton 1931). However, although Ticehurst described its status in West Suffolk as occasional, he stated that there was hardly any suitable district that did not receive visits from time to time. The species was considered to be an occasional summer visitor, passage migrant and winter visitor to Breckland in the early 1950s (Vine 1951), although it has since increased significantly. Gravel workings along the Lark and Gipping valleys now attract the largest concentrations with counts exceeding 500 being noted at Lackford as follows – 580 on 25th January 1992, 700-800 January-March 1995 5,000 on 16th January 1997, 1,500 on 28th December 1998, 1,000 in January and 1,500 in December 2000. A count of 534 was logged at Bramford on 2nd February 1997.

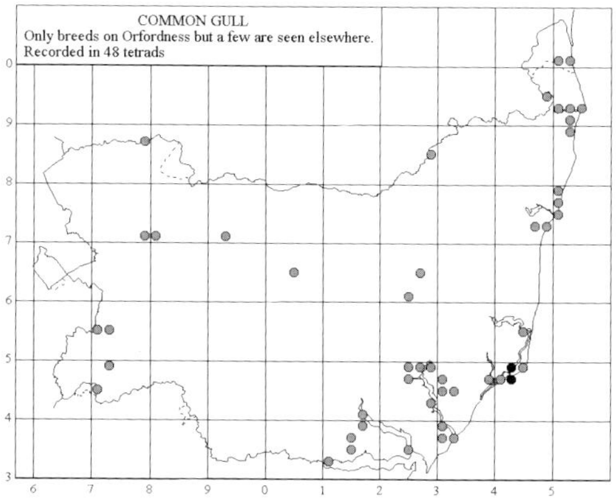

Ringing recoveries show that the origins of wintering birds lie in Scandinavia, the Baltic States, Russia, Germany and the Low Countries. A high percentage are from Norway (13 out of 29 foreign-ringed birds for the period 1979-1995).

The predatory instincts of the species were demonstrated at Ipswich Wet Dock on 13th January 1987 when one was seen to capture and eat a Yellowhammer during bitterly cold weather (Waters 1990).

Lesser Black-backed Gull *Larus fuscus*

A common summer visitor and passage migrant. Increasing numbers overwinter

Britain's largest lowland breeding colony has become established on Orfordness. This gull is principally a summer visitor being present from February through to October, although, in recent years, a significant number have become concentrated at inland feeding areas during winter and a few remain on the coast. Lesser Black-backed Gulls frequent refuse tips, pig fields and urban environments both the length of the coastal strip and at inland localities.

Three chicks hatched from a single nest on Havergate Island in 1957 was the first confirmed breeding record. Two pairs bred there during the following summer, but, thereafter, nesting was discouraged for the sake of the Avocets (Wright & Waters 1991). In 1968, a mixed colony of Lesser Black-backed and Herring Gulls was discovered on Orfordness. Numbers of Lesser Black-backed Gulls increased steadily from 100 pairs in 1968 to 1,000 by 1980, 5,000 by 1984, 9,043 by 1993 and 19,700 by 1998. Nesting elsewhere involved sporadic breeding attempts often mixed with Black-headed Gulls. For example in 1993, an overspill from Orfordness resulted in seven pairs attempting to breed again on Havergate Island, two pairs nested amongst Black-headed Gulls on the Blyth and a pair bred at Trimley Marshes. Roof-top nesting has became a feature of coastal industrial areas since 1996, when gulleries became established on the roofs of a workshop at Lowestoft and warehouses in Ipswich. In 1997, warehouse roofs, silos and sheds at the Port of Felixstowe were occupied and numbers quickly built to around 200 pairs by 2000. The population of roof-nesting birds in Lowestoft increased dramatically from 15 pairs in 1999 to 750 in 2001 and a few pairs spread to nearby residential areas where they nested on chimney tops. By 2002, over 100 pairs were nesting at four industrial sites in Ipswich.The Lesser Black-backed Gull is a notorious predator and has been associated, on several occasions, with failures in fledging success of Havergate's wader and tern colonies. Although Orfordness is one of the few large colonies in Britain which is not culled, there are attempts to restrict its southward spread and nests opposite Havergate Island are often raked.

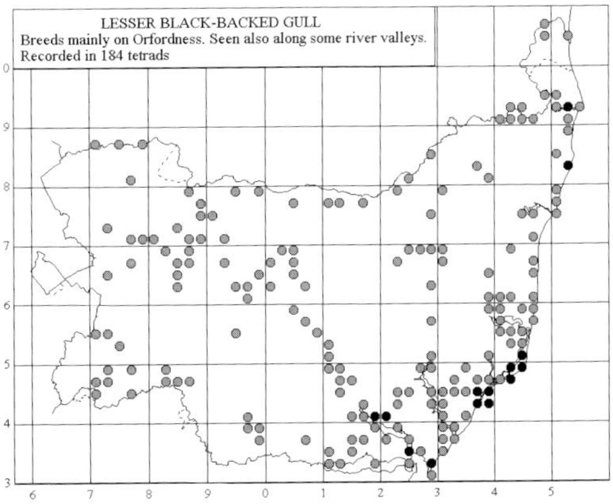

British breeding Lesser Black-backed Gulls are of the race *L. f. graellsii*, although there are many dark-mantled individuals present in the Orfordness colony and it is likely that some are intergrades between *L. f. graellsii* and *L. f. intermedius*. Interchange between the Orfordness colony and colonies in the Rotterdam area of the Netherlands has been confirmed by ringing returns.

Considerable offshore movements occur during passage periods, but the actual timing of migration is clouded by the gulls moving to and from the Orfordness colony. An account detailing migration in 1950 (Barnes 1953) stated that passage was observed from 5th April with a maximum of 30 on Havergate 15th April and a few remained throughout May. The first autumn bird was at Southwold on 9th July and "considerable numbers" passed through in August, with a peak of 80-100 on Benacre Ness, 30th August. The Lesser Black-backed Gull is one of the earliest summer visitors to Britain, with new arrivals noted from mid-February. Breeding birds re-establish their nesting territories soon after their return as shown by a count of c.2,000 present on Orfordness on 22nd February 1998. The Alde-Ore, the estuarine complex closest to Orfordness, provides feeding and bathing opportunities for breeding birds in spring and summer and therefore regularly attracts the largest numbers. A count of 2,000 was logged for Benacre Broad on 21st August 1995. A constant stream of birds is noted moving south off Suffolk each autumn (August to October) – the largest count being c.2,500 off Landguard on 8th October 1983.

There were few records for West Suffolk for the 19th century and singles shot at Brettenham in December 1881 and Livermere on 26th March 1886 are the only Breckland records for that century. Ticehurst referred to a Lesser Black-backed Gull flying over Tostock and there were a few records from Sudbury. Nowadays, there are large inland gatherings, most often in the vicinity of landfill sites and coinciding with the general exodus from breeding colonies in July. Flooded gravel pits are favoured sites for bathing and preening. Concentrations of 250+ are all post-1987 and are limited to only three sites: Long Melford; Livermere and Lackford. Numbers joining a pre-roost bathing party at Lackford have increased steadily in recent years with 7,500 present on 17th October 2000. Evidence of young still being dependent on parents, away from the nuptial area, was seen at Lackford, on 26th July 1991, when a beleaguered adult was seen to regurgitate food to two full-grown juveniles.

Lesser Black-backed Gulls were formerly rare during winter, with Babington listing only two records and Ticehurst a further three. A hard-weather movement off Minsmere, involving 80 adults and immatures on 9th January 1968, was exceptional for that period. Nowadays, the gull is widely reported and, during the 1993 Winter Gull Roost Census, no fewer than 265 were located, with 220 of these at inland localities (Bimpson 1994). Lackford is by far the most favoured winter roost site (82% of the county total), the nearby landfill site being a significant influence on this population.

Ringing recoveries show that most of Suffolk's breeding birds winter in Iberia and northwest Africa (Askins *et al.* 1997) and, from 1979-1995, birds ringed in Finland, Norway (11) and the Netherlands (5) have been found in Suffolk.

'Baltic' Gull *L. f. fuscus*

Accidental: one possible record

Payn was of the opinion that birds of the nominate form *L. f. fuscus*, which breed mainly on the northern Baltic coasts, regularly passed through Suffolk and that single birds occurred in "mixed parties of gulls". He referred to a flock of 60 adults at Benacre in late August 1949, which were considered to have been of this race. However, the observers (B. W. Tucker and J. A. Barnes) were less definite about the identification and although there was an inference that the birds were "typical of *L. f. fuscus*" they concluded only that "none was of British origin" (Barnes 1953). These birds were almost certainly *L. f. intermedius*.

A four-year old bird found dead "off" Orfordness on 24th October 1981 had been ringed as a pullus within the breeding range of *L. f. fuscus* in Finland in 1978, which should have provided the necessary confirmation that the 'Baltic' Gull had occurred in Suffolk. However, the finding information is scant and there are only four similar ringing recoveries elsewhere in Britain (Jonsson 1998), which points to occurrences being very rare indeed. An adult identified in the field at Blythburgh on 10th-11th November 2000 is Suffolk's strongest claim to date with identification based on size, plumage characteristics and a very late moult pattern. However, even this bird could not be fully substantiated.

The 'Baltic' Gull breeds in loose colonies in the northern Baltic, overwinters in East Africa, and tends to take a more direct, overland migration route. This, together with plumage characteristics, points to darker-mantled adults seen moving off Suffolk being of the race *L. f. intermedius*, which breeds in southern Norway, western Sweden and Denmark.

Herring Gull *Larus argentatus*

A common resident, winter visitor and passage migrant

There have been few groups whose taxonomy has been under more scrutiny in recent years than the larger gulls. The Yellow-legged Gull *L. [a.] michahellis* and the Caspian Gull *L. [a.] cachinnans* are regarded as a separate species by some authorities, but not yet by the BOURC. British breeding Herring Gulls are assigned to the race *L. a. argenteus* and the winter population is supplemented by immigrants of the larger, darker race *L. a. argentatus* from elsewhere in northern Europe, Scandinavia, the Baltic States and Siberia.

Herring Gulls show a preference for more maritime habitats and large numbers congregate around the fishing towns and hamlets of Lowestoft, Southwold, Dunwich, Aldeburgh and Felixstowe Ferry. Refuse tips are also a great attraction and wanderers are seen widely in inland Suffolk. Small flocks are present throughout the year, both on the coast and inland.

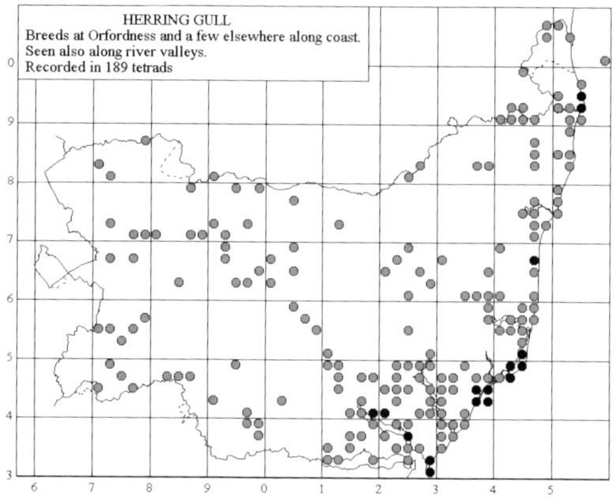

Suffolk's first breeding record involved two pairs which nested successfully on Havergate Island in 1958. Nesting again took place at that site the following year and these early pioneering birds heralded the founding of the nearby Orfordness breeding colony, which was to develop dramatically from three pairs in 1963 to 40 in 1968 and to 1,250 in 1973. The mixed (with Lesser Black-backed) colony continued to flourish throughout the 1970s and 1980s and, by 1998, 4,750 pairs of Herring Gulls were present. Dutch-ringed birds have been recovered on Orfordness, but only one from the latter locality has been found in colonies in the Netherlands. Only small numbers nested elsewhere, including 1-3 pairs at Minsmere from 1968-1981 and a single pair at Havergate in 1968. Control measures at the latter two sites may well have curtailed expansion. In 1993, a small colony became established on roofs beside Lowestoft Harbour had built up to 39 pairs by 1998 and 250 by 2001. A lone pair, nesting at Landguard Point in 1996, was the pioneer of a substantial breeding colony within the neighbouring Port of Felixstowe. Here nests were built on warehouse roofs, sheds and silos and numbers increased to around 200 pairs by the summer of 2000 despite continuous control measures taking place. Small colonies also became established on warehouse roofs in east and central Ipswich where c.75 pairs were nesting at four sites in 2001.

The 1993 Winter Gull Roost Census found 2,095 in Suffolk, with most frequenting the coast and estuaries (Bimpson 1994). The warm waters around the Sizewell Rigs attracted the bulk of the population – 1,150 on 24th January. The species' reluctance to roost at Lowestoft Harbour, where large concentrations scavenge for fish offal throughout the day, is possibly due to nocturnal occupation by the more aggressive Great Black-backed Gulls. Pre-breeding gatherings of up to 5,000 are reported annually in the Aldeburgh area during the second half of February.

The Herring Gull was rare in Breckland at the beginning of the 20th century with just a few isolated records. It was particularly scarce around Thetford – typified by an account from Euston where the species was noted only twice between 1893 and 1931 (Caton 1931). Fluctuating wintering numbers were noted at Breckland localities in the late 1940s/early 1950s. Less than 50 wintered in 1947/8, up to 1,000 in 1948/9 and a peak of c.3,000 was reported in 1949/50 (Vine 1951). Nowadays, such high totals are rare in West Suffolk, probably due to the decrease in livestock rearing. Feeding flocks are now concentrated around landfill sites, where numbers can range from 200-1,000. These figures are only partially reflected in roost counts, with comparatively small numbers arriving at Lackford each evening to bathe and preen. Only 254 were located as part of the 1993 Winter Gull Roost Census, but 600 were present on 15th February, a total which probably included passage birds. Most inland Herring Gulls feed on heaths, fields and refuse tips during the day and fly to the coast each evening to roost on the estuaries or the open sea, often reaching their destination after dark. Overland movements can be seen at dusk over most of the county.

Yellow-legged Gull (Western Yellow-legged Gull) *L. [a.] michahellis*

An uncommon passage migrant and winter visitor

Birds showing characteristics of the race *L. [a.] michahellis*, colloquially known as Yellow-legged Gulls, are increasingly reported at coastal localities. Although the race is noted in every month of the year, there is a noticeable peak in occurrences in early autumn. For example, from around 85 individuals noted in 2000, the respective monthly peaks for August and September were 38 and 37. At the turn of the 20th-21st century, the pig-fields close to the Blyth estuary provided ideal viewing opportunities and other favourite sites were Southwold Harbour, Minsmere, Lackford and Livermere Lake. Fields drilled with chicken offal at Wetherden were exploited by thousands of large gulls in the late 1990s and ten Yellow-legged Gulls were noted amongst the flocks from 6th September to 29th November 1997, with six present on 17th October and four on 2nd November.

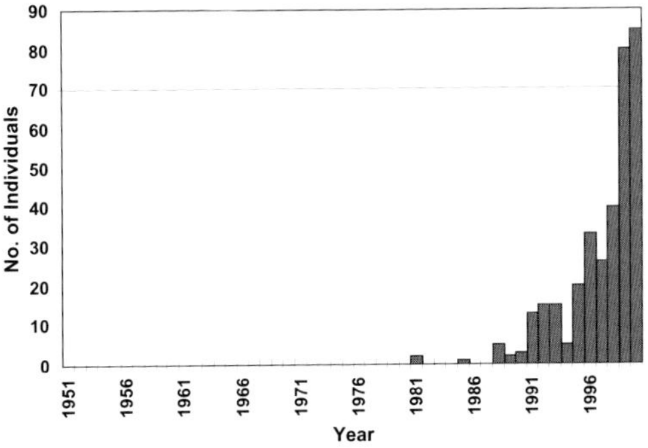

The annual totals of the Western Yellow-legged Gull from 1951-2000

Males have held territories in the mixed breeding colony on Orfordness. Two apparently paired with Lesser Black-backed Gulls in consecutive years from 1998-2000 and, although eggs were laid during two of these years, these failed to hatch. Hybridisation is a regular feature at colonies in the Europort/Rotterdam areas in the Netherlands (Askins *et al.* 1995).

Yellow-legged Gulls breed around the Mediterranean and along the Atlantic coasts of France and the Iberian Peninsula. A few colonies have become established in central Europe.

Caspian Gull *L. [a.] cachinnans*

Status uncertain – probably an uncommon passage migrant and rare winter visitor

A first-winter Caspian Gull, observed feeding on discarded chicken offal at Wetherden, from 6th September 1997, was the first county record of this 'race' of Herring Gull. This individual along with a second were seen intermittently at the site until 29th November. Thereafter, careful scrutiny of gull flocks on the coast has revealed that it is an annual visitor with numbers increasing through the late summer/early autumn period and peaking in winter/early spring. Caspian Gulls have been noted throughout the winter months and up to mid-April, and five together at Carlton Colville on 2nd January 2001, when display was observed, is the largest winter gathering. The departure of the Yellow-legged Gull coincides with that of the Lesser Black-backed Gull, but the arrival of the Caspian Gull from the continent reflects its own post-breeding dispersal and wintering pattern (B. Small, pers. comm.). There has yet to be a record for May or June with the earliest returning birds usually noted from mid-July.

Caspian Gulls are most often observed feeding with other gulls on pig-fields, particularly those close to the River Blyth, as well as on refuse tips or bathing on estuaries. During the autumn and winter of 1999/2000, it was estimated that as many as seven occurred in the Blythburgh/Southwold area alone. A juvenile at Southwold Harbour on 24th August 1999, another at Walberswick on 8th September 2000 and two together at Southwold Harbour on 18th August 2001 constitute the first British records of birds in this plumage stage (B. Small, pers. comm.). Caspian Gulls were frequently noted inland between 1998 and 2001 with Lackford and Livermere Lake being the most favoured localities.

American Herring Gull *L. a. smithsonianus*

Accidental: one record

1999 Southwold: Town Marshes, first-winter 23rd April

Along with a number of records for Great Britain, the above well-documented report remains under consideration of the BBRC. Up to the end of 2000, there were 37 accepted records for Britain and Ireland (BBRC), the vast majority of which were noted in southern Ireland.

Iceland Gull *Larus glaucoides*

A scarce winter visitor

Iceland Gulls are reported annually, principally on the immediate coastline and normally in the company of other large gulls. The species breeds on the east and west coasts of Greenland and is often faithful to a particular wintering site to which it will return in consecutive years. It rarely ventures up river estuaries and is scarce at inland localities.

The Lowestoft area is by far the most favoured site, where 1-2 are reported during most winters. Two adults and a second-winter bird, present at Ness Point in January and February 1984, constitute the largest group reported. Iceland Gulls formerly lingered at Lowestoft throughout the winter, being attracted to the fish quays and waste food bins sited in the grounds of the Bird's Eye food processing factory and the sewage outfall. Since the mid-1980s, there has been a severe decline in the fishing industry and modern methods result in much fish processing being done on board ship. This, together with the removal of the food bins, has resulted in Lowestoft being far less attractive than it was during the 1970s and early 1980s. Sightings there are now limited to a few single-day observations. Iceland Gulls are occasionally found in the gull roost at Minsmere, particularly during passage periods.

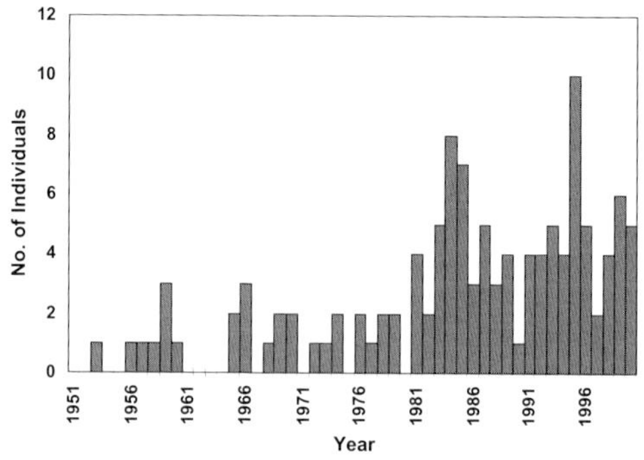

The annual totals of the Iceland Gull from 1950-2000

The site fidelity of the species was demonstrated at Felixstowe, where one, which appeared on 18th January 1984, in immature plumage, returned in successive years and was last observed during the 1991/2 winter.

Regular winterers return in mid-October, but most others arrive in December and January. Normal departure occurs in late March or April, but lingerers have been noted in May on six occasions and one at Easton Bavents on 22nd June 1956 is the sole record for that month.

Iceland Gulls have joined other gulls to scavenge at refuse tips on at least two occasions: a second-winter at Foxhall Tip on 22nd December 1991 and an adult at inland Wetherden Landfill site from 8th-17th January 1995. A first-winter bird joined an evening pre-roost at Redgrave Lake in early March 2002. The paucity of records at such sites is undoubtedly due to a lack of regular observations. Five additional West Suffolk occurrences were all noted at the Lackford roost: a third-winter from 14th-21st February 1993 and joined by a second-winter on the 20th, a first-winter and an adult on 29th January and 18th March 1995 respectively and a second-winter on 14th February 1997.

Kumlien's Gull *L. g. kumlieni*

Accidental: two records

1996 Minsmere: 7th January & 28th December.

These records probably relate to the same adult returning in consecutive winters.

The BBRC has accepted records of individuals showing characters of the western race of Iceland Gull, *L. g. kumlieni*, colloquially known as the Kumlien's Gull. Up to the end of 1998, there were 78 such records for Britain and Ireland (BBRC), although subsequent records were no longer considered, for reasons mainly of taxonomic difficulties.

Glaucous Gull *Larus hyperboreus*

A scarce winter visitor

Small numbers of Glaucous Gulls winter annually, principally in north-east Suffolk with the fishing harbour, food processing factories, refuse tips and sewage outfall, in and around Lowestoft, forming the main attractions. A few linger with other gulls during some winters, but many records refer to single-day observations. Glaucous Gulls are rare at inland localities, although visits have become increasingly frequent in recent years.

Glaucous Gulls are normally reported singly in midwinter, most often in association with other large gull species. Assessing numbers can be difficult as the species is wide-ranging and may visit a number of sites over several kilometres of coast. Numbers can often be determined by comparing plumage and age characteristics. In some years, however, gulls will remain faithful to a single locality when population levels can be more accurately determined. For example, in mid-November 1939 seven were counted in Lowestoft Harbour and in January and February 1978 no fewer than eight (two adults and six immatures) were present in the Lowestoft area. Long-staying Glaucous Gulls are no longer frequent in the Lowestoft area for much the same reasons as Iceland Gulls.

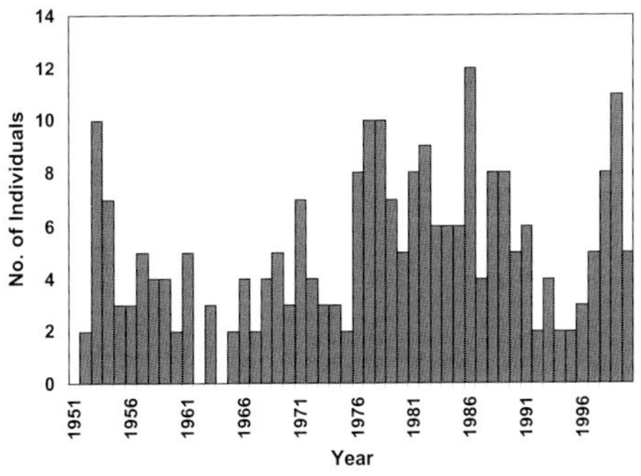

The annual totals of the Glaucous Gull from 1951-2000

Site fidelity was demonstrated by an individual that wintered in the Felixstowe area in consecutive years from late 1985 to early 1990. A bird in first-winter plumage was noted in November 1985 and stayed to at least 24th July 1986. It reappeared in March 1987, staying right through the summer until 10th April 1988, then again from 11th September 1988 until 27th March 1989 and finally 30th August 1989 until 21st April 1990. During the last year of its stay, a smudge of oil was noticed on its breast and this may well have led to its demise.

The majority leave in late March, but there are also many April records and 11 for May. Birds lingering through the summer months include: the above Felixstowe bird; an injured immature at Breydon until mid-August 1968 and an immature there on 3rd June and 30th July 1988. One at Ness Point, 19th July 1975, was probably an early returning bird and there are two August arrivals. Most birds arrive in late October or early November.

The gull will occasionally venture into river estuaries to be seen as far upstream as Woolverstone on the Orwell and Oulton Broad, but there were no occurrences away from the coast and estuaries prior to 1991. Thereafter, there have been four occurrences equally divided between Bramford Water Park and Lackford. All have been noted in January or February, most often joining other large gulls to bathe before going to roost.

Great Black-backed Gull *Larus marinus*

A common winter visitor and passage migrant. A few oversummer

This gull is widely reported at coastal and estuarine localities during winter, and, in recent times, a few are attracted to inland refuse tips. Small numbers of mostly immatures are seen during the summer.

Ticehurst described the gull as a common winter visitor to our coastline and increasing to such an extent that he considered it almost commoner that the Herring Gull. Babington said that it was seldom seen any distance from the coast and lists only three non-coastal records. In the early 1950s, Breckland farmers indicated that the species was only an occasional winter visitor to their region for "as long as they could remember" (Vine 1951). However, a Breckland census, for the period 1946-1950, revealed a relatively large, but fluctuating wintering population, ranging from under 50-450 with the meres forming roosting sites.

A total of 523 individuals was located during the 1993 Winter Gull Roost Census with 75% of these in Lowestoft Harbour (Bimpson 1994). The gulls feed offshore and around the harbour during the day and groups often rest for long periods on quayside roofs. Although the estuaries were less important as roosting sites, they are important feeding sites and significant numbers are noted during WeBS counts. For example, the annual peak on the Alde-Ore complex ranged between 150-500, during the period 1985-1994, and gatherings of 200 or more were noted on the Orwell and Stour during the late 1980s. Numbers increase dramatically during severe-weather periods such as seen on 14th January 1987, when 1,500 gathered on Minsmere's Scrape.

The gulls begin to arrive in late September with the main concentrations noted in mid-winter. Most departed from March to mid-April and, as with other gull species, landfill sites are the most favoured feeding localities. The largest concentrations have been noted as follows: c.200 at Foxhall, 2nd January 1978, 300 at Lackford (flighting in from the nearby Hall Heath tip), December 1989 and 310 at Bramford, 26th December 1990 and c.500 there on 5th January 1991.

Ticehurst reported a flock of 200 which spent the summer on Orfordness, but this record must be suspect in view of the spit's subsequent colonisation by Lesser Black-backed Gulls. One or two birds have over-summered on Havergate Island and on Orfordness since the 1960s, but suggestions of breeding (Payn 1978, Wright & Waters 1991) were largely based on circumstantial evidence and there was no conclusive proof of nesting until 1999. In that year, two pairs established territories amongst the gull colony on Orfordness and a full clutch was subsequently predated, a fate which fell upon a replacement clutch. A total of five pairs held territory during the following summer and, from the four nests that were found, at least one chick fledged. The latter was colour-ringed and was subsequently seen at two sites in Northern France. Warehouse roofs within the confines of the Port of Felixstowe also played host to one or two nesting pairs in 2001 and 2002.

The Fennoscandia breeding population is entirely migratory and ringing recoveries show that a significant proportion of those wintering in Suffolk originate in that region. Some were reared at colonies either near or on the Great Ainov Islands close to the Russian-Norwegian border.

Kittiwake (Black-legged Kittiwake) *Rissa tridactyla*

Kittiwakes
(*Stuart Ling*)

A locally common resident, winter visitor and passage migrant. Breeds at two sites

Kittiwakes occur at offshore localities, particularly during the winter, and sometimes in abundance. Huge movements are logged in autumn and winter following severe northerly gales. Breeding colonies have become established on man-made structures at Lowestoft and Sizewell. The gull is seldom seen away from coastal waters and is very much a rarity in West Suffolk.

The Kittiwake has been known in Suffolk since before 1333, being then sufficiently abundant around the "now erosed" St Leonard, at Dunwich, for a parcel of land embracing a quay to be accorded the local name of this species (Moreley 1949). Whether nesting took place there around that time is open to speculation. It was rather rare in the Great Yarmouth area (Pagets 1834), not very common around Aldeburgh (Hele 1870) and generally not very common on the coast (Babington). Babington recorded it as solely a winter visitor, but Ticehurst said that it followed the herring shoals and was very common off the coast in autumn and winter.

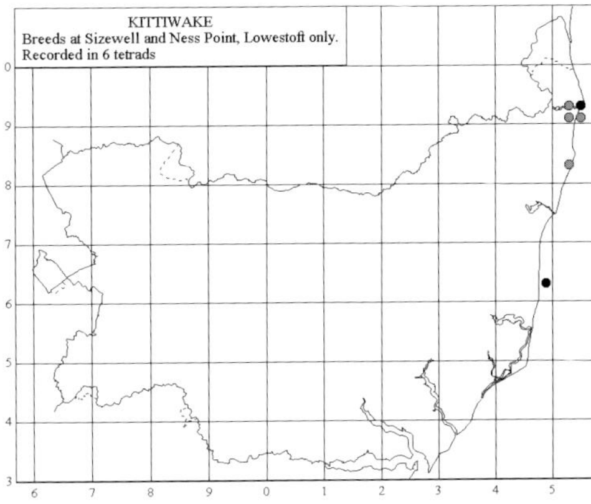

A significant increase in numbers became apparent in the Lowestoft area around 1946 with birds mainly present from May to October or November (Brown 1986). This increase continued through the 1950s and, in 1958, two pairs nested on Lowestoft's South Pier Pavilion. The progress of this colony has been extensively monitored (Brown 1986, Brown 1990). Numbers increased steadily and, by 1970, 32 pairs were present. During the 1970s, the colony spread onto buildings surrounding the harbour area and, by 1979, the breeding population had reached 86 pairs. Many of the favoured buildings were then demolished and birds were dissuaded from nesting on others by means of cementing ledges and the erection of netting. This caused fluctuation in numbers from year to year. The greatest threat to this colony came in the late 1980s when plans were drawn up to demolish the South Pier Pavilion as this was the only remaining nest site. However, the birds had become quite an attraction for holiday-makers and locals alike and when Associated British Ports offered to construct a purpose-built wall, at a cost of £10,000, to which the gulls would hopefully transfer, this was eagerly accepted. The final year of breeding on the South Pier was 1988 when there were 107 nests, but the birds soon became accustomed to their new home and have flourished ever since. A peak of 259 nests (202 of these successful) produced 303 young in 1995. More than 3,000 young have fledged in Lowestoft's harbour area and fledging success is high, with an average of around 1.5 young flying from each nest. More northerly British colonies suffer greatly from predation, with Great Skuas and Great Black-backed Gulls being frequent culprits. Unusual nesting sites at Lowestoft include tyre fenders, oil rig window frames and mooring posts. Breeding attempts away from Lowestoft have largely been met with failure, but, since 1994, colonies have become established on Sizewell rigs building in number to 22 pairs in 1995, 84 in 1997, 92 in 1998, 140 in 1999, 180 in 2000 and 219 in 2001. The Suffolk colonies are the only ones between Yorkshire and Kent.

Offshore movements are reported annually and sometimes these are quite substantial. The vast majority remain well out to sea during winter but flocks of up to 200 will follow incoming boats. The largest movements have occurred between September and February and high counts (3,000+) include: 4,000 moving south off Covehithe and Minsmere, 24th November 1963; 3,000-4,000 off Lowestoft, 2nd November 1986; 6,000 south, in two hours, off Southwold, 10th January 1993 and c.5,000 north off Southwold, 4th November 1995. Occasionally, weather conditions will force thousands to inshore waters. There was an amazing influx in early 1996 including 20,000 feeding in the surf, between Sizewell and Thorpeness, on 7th January. Counts of 6,000 moving south off Thorpeness the following day was undoubtedly part of this influx. Large numbers were also reported in Sole Bay in early 1999 when flocks of 7,000 occurred on 15th January and 12-15,000 from 4th-5th February.

There are only 22 inland occurrences up to the end of 1998 with the vast majority being logged at Lackford, involving dead or moribund individuals or birds disorientated after severe storms. Most inland occurrences are between November and March.

There is a good selection of ringing recoveries, five of which concern birds reared on the Farne Islands, one from Denmark and another ringed as a juvenile on Kharlov Island, Murmansk, Russia.

Ivory Gull *Pagophila eburnea*

Accidental: one record

1999 Aldeburgh: 5th-31st December.

This confiding individual spent most of its daylight hours scavenging along Aldeburgh beach, although it was also seen at Orfordness, Walberswick and Southwold. On one occasion, it was released unharmed after becoming entangled in a fisherman's line. Fireworks, ignited as part of the celebrations for the new Millennium, were thought responsible for finally scaring the bird away.

A gull seen to fly out on to "the lumps" on the Suffolk side of Breydon Water channel, on 15th May 1938, was listed by Payn as an Ivory Gull. The record was poorly documented but accepted on the strength of correspondence between Ticehurst and the finder, Fred Cook, with the identity of the bird as an Ivory Gull being determined largely by a process of elimination. The record, re-assessed by the SORC in 1998, was considered not fully substantiated and has been deleted from the files.

This gull breeds in the high Arctic and has visited the British Isles on 123 occasions up to the end of 2000 (BBRC). The records are biased towards the northern North Sea coasts with most occurring between November and early January (Dymond *et al.* 1989).

Gull-billed Tern *Sterna nilotica*

A very rare visitor: 17 records involving 23 individuals

1925 Breydon: four 17th May
1959 Covehithe: 19th June
1967 Dunwich: 3rd September
1971 Covehithe: 23rd May
1976 Aldeburgh: 28th May
1977 Breydon: 6th June
1980 Walberswick: 5th May
1987 Benacre: ad. N 24th June
1991 Felixstowe: Landguard Point, N 28th May
1997 Felixstowe: Landguard Point, two 1st May

There have only been ten Suffolk occurrences since 1925 (see above). All Suffolk records refer to brief visits, mostly by single birds to coastal localities between 14th April and 1st September. Two together were at Breydon in September 1894 and 8th May 1878 and four were there on 17th May 1925. Breydon monopolised occurrences from 1849-1925 when a total of 13 individuals was recorded. The tern has since been recorded far less often, no doubt reflecting its marked decline as a breeding species in northern Europe. For example, c.650 pairs nesting in Denmark, during the period 1865-1900, compared with only 10-15 pairs in 1995 (Cramp *et al.* 1974-1994). Extreme dates are 14th April and 3rd September.

The main Eurasian population is now restricted to the Mediterranean coast and inland Spain and Turkey, discontinuously through to southeast China. Breeding is erratic elsewhere in Europe and includes one record of a lone pair at Abberton Res., Essex, in 1949, followed by an unsuccessful breeding attempt the following year (Cox 1984). It is an annual visitor to the British Isles being noted on 271 occasions up to the end of 2000 (BBRC).

Caspian Tern *Sterna caspia*

A very rare visitor: 43 records

The tern breeds on the Baltic and Black Sea coasts and small numbers occur in Britain annually, normally during the summer months. All bar one of the county's records have occurred between 5th April and 23rd August, with July being the favoured month. An immature shot at Breydon on 4th October 1825, was the exception and was Britain's first. The estuary has since hosted the bulk of the early visitations.

The species was not recorded between 1910 and 1960. One visited Benacre Pits, on 21st July 1960 and since then Caspian Terns have visited almost annually from 1960-1967 with 12 records shared amongst Minsmere, Havergate Island and Benacre, including six individuals which visited Minsmere between 9th July and 6th August 1967. One at Livermere on 8th August 1982 was the first record for West Suffolk, but the species has since visited Lackford Wildfowl Reserve on four occasions.

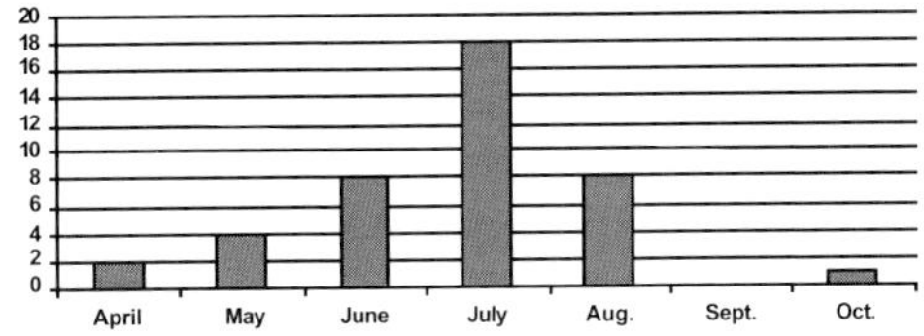

The seasonal occurrences of the Caspian Tern (all dated records 1825-2001)

The Caspian Tern is an annual visitor to Britain and Ireland, being recorded on 266 occasions up to the end of 2000 (BBRC).

Lesser Crested Tern *Sterna bengalensis*

Accidental: two records

1991 Benacre: Broad, ad. 25th August
1992 Minsmere: ad. 4th-6th August

The above records almost certainly refer to the female, which nested amongst Sandwich Terns and paired with one of them on the Farne Islands, Northumberland, from 1984 until at least 1997. The above visitations were brief, although the Minsmere bird did return on consecutive evenings to roost amongst other terns.

The Lesser Crested Tern breeds in North and East Africa, east to Australia and is an extremely rare visitor to the British Isles, occurring on only seven occasions to the end of 2000 (BBRC).

Sandwich Tern *Sterna sandvicensis*

A fairly common summer visitor and passage migrant

This tern frequents coastal waters throughout the summer months and forms evening roosts at Minsmere and Havergate Island, sometimes in considerable numbers. Colonies have been established at both sites with varying degrees of breeding success. Coastal movements are regularly logged during passage periods.

There was only a scattering of records on the Suffolk coast prior to 1890 (Ticehurst 1932) but, thereafter, the species occurred more frequently, being reported as an annual visitor in spring and autumn. A few pairs possibly bred in the 19th century, but evidence is rather flimsy. Four pairs certainly bred in 1923, but there followed a gap of 28 years before nesting was reported again. Colonisation of Havergate Island began in 1951 when 30 pairs bred and a decade later this colony had grown to c.350 pairs, rising to a peak of c.800 pairs in 1962. Thereafter, there were marked fluctuations in numbers, with the species deserting the island altogether during some summers. Nesting was not recorded at Minsmere until 1965 when 110 pairs bred and it was believed that these birds had shifted from Havergate (Wright & Waters 1991). Breeding ceased at Minsmere in 1978, but the Havergate colony is still flourishing with up to 300 pairs breeding annually.

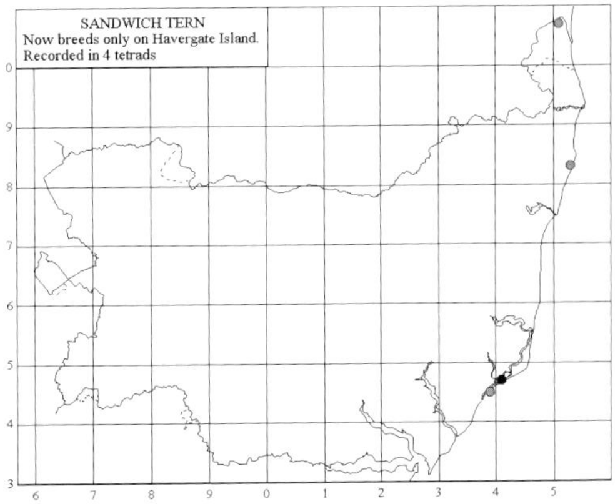

Sandwich Terns are amongst the earliest returning migrants, with the first of the year normally reported in mid-March, one at Minsmere on 6th March 1969 being the earliest. Numbers build swiftly through

April and reach a peak in early May, when four-figure gatherings are occasionally reported. A total of 175 at Havergate on 31st March 1996 is an exceptionally high count so early in the year.

Sandwich Terns winter off the West and South African coasts and the exodus from Suffolk begins in early July. Peak passage occurs in August with a few lingerers still present in October. There are six records for early November, the latest being one noted preening on top of a post on Wherstead Strand on 7th November 1997, and one for December at Lake Lothing on 13th December 2000. One off Aldeburgh beach on 6th January 2000 is the only winter record.

Ringing data show that autumn gatherings include terns raised in both British and continental colonies, with birds from Norfolk, Scotland, Germany and the Netherlands being reported. Chicks ringed at Minsmere have been found in France (2), Portugal, Spain, Ghana (4), Liberia, the Ivory Coast (2) and Sierra Leone and the dates of recovery indicate that some Suffolk-reared birds winter and spend their first summer in West Africa.

Offshore movements are regularly reported in May, August and September, the largest being 450 south off Southwold on 1st September 1982. Breeding gulls and terns at Minsmere and Havergate attract passage birds to roost. Minsmere's highest counts include c.1,000 on 7th-8th July 1966; 2,000 on 2nd-3rd May 1968 and 1,000 during April and May 1978, whereas Havergate's peaks include: 2,500 at roost in April 1976; 1,000 on 27th April 1981 and 1,900 on 3rd May 1996.

Sandwich Terns are rarely seen on the estuaries and are scarce at inland localities with singles or single flocks being noted once or twice each year mostly during May, August and September. The flooded gravel workings in the Gipping and Lark Valleys have been the most favoured sites in recent years.

Roseate Tern *Sterna dougallii*

A scarce passage migrant

The Roseate Tern is almost annual in occurrence being noted at coastal localities, usually during passage periods and in association with flocks of other gulls and terns. Roseate Terns have an almost cosmopolitan distribution although the range is highly fragmented. In Europe, it breeds principally on islets with other tern species in Britain, Ireland, Brittany and the Azores. It is declining in north-west Europe and is considered to be in danger of extinction as a British breeding species (Batten *et al.* 1990).

Occurrences are normally limited to about five per year, although the tern was much commoner during the 1960s, when numbers reached double figures on four occasions, including 23 in 1966. The latter total includes a group of seven at Minsmere on 14th August. The British breeding population crashed by about 75% between 1969 and 1987 (Lloyd *et al.* 1991), which undoubtedly explains the paucity of records in Suffolk in recent years.

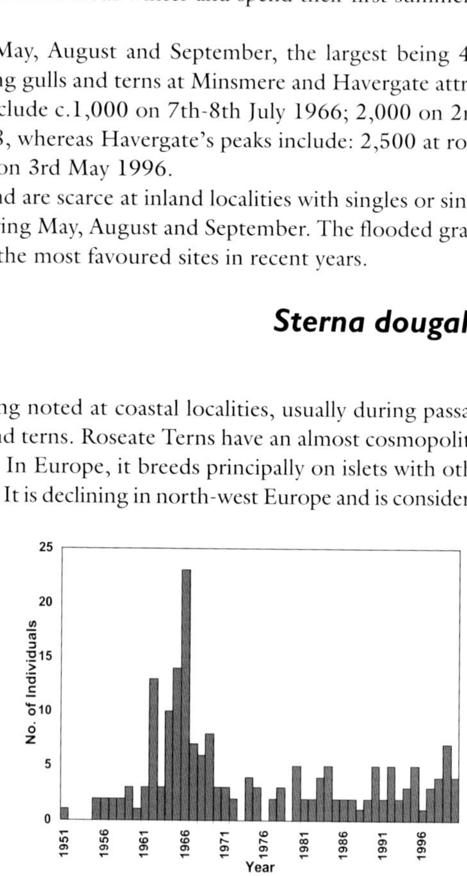

The annual totals of the Roseate Tern from 1951-2000

Babington and Ticehurst lacked any confidence in reports during their era, although the latter author did cite 19th century claims of sightings from Orford, Breydon and Landguard Point. Ticehurst said that "it would not be too surprising to find that a pair occasionally breed, as it does so annually in Norfolk". One at Havergate Island on 15th August 1951 is the first fully-documented record for the county.

Roseate Terns are reported most often in May and June, but there are six April records with one at Havergate on 14th (1960) the earliest. Non-breeding pairs occasionally frequent coastal localities throughout the summer months , although the only breeding behaviour observed involved two copulating and nest scraping during their stay at Minsmere from 16th-26th June 1994. The tern is regularly recorded in August, but there are only five September records and a juvenile at Southwold on 6th October 1989 is the latest. An adult with Common Terns at Alton Water, 2nd August 1990, is the only record away from the immediate coastline.

Common Tern *Sterna hirundo*

A common summer visitor and passage migrant

This is the most familiar British tern, being present throughout the summer months at both coastal and inland waters. Breeding numbers have declined substantially since the early years of the 20th century, with most beach colonies deserted as a result of human disturbance. Colonies are now dispersed along the coast and estuaries, where numbers fluctuate greatly. In recent years, breeding has been reported at inland gravel workings in the Gipping and Waveney valleys and on tern-rafts at Alton Water Reservoir. The species is common during passage periods and sizeable concentrations feed at the Sizewell Rigs. Southerly movements are regularly logged at migration watch-points during August and early September.

The relatively inaccessible beaches of Orfordness have long played host to the largest breeding concentrations. Between 1867 and 1930, 1,000-1,500 pairs bred on Lighthouse Beach (Ticehurst 1932) and, in 1943, over 200 pairs were at Shingle Street (Vulliamy 1943). A few pairs had nested previously at the latter site but, in the late 1940s, the colony crossed the Alde to North Weir Point at the tip of the shingle spit. A peak of 200-250 pairs was noted in 1951 and the colony continued to flourish until the early 1960s. Breeding no longer occurs on Orfordness, although an offshoot from this site probably resulted in the colonisation of Havergate Island, where nesting first took place in 1953. A small ternery became established on Corporation Marshes, Dunwich, in 1948 and breeding commenced on the Blyth and at Minsmere in 1962. Breeding has taken place intermittently at various sites between Southwold and Kessingland since the 1930s. Minsmere and Havergate Island have been the only sites to consistently host colonies since the 1960s and, although the former site has witnessed a dramatic decrease, there has been a slight increase at Havergate. Overall, Suffolk has suffered a 65% decline in breeding numbers from 1969-1987, compared with 20% nationally (Wright & Waters 1991). Common Terns were found breeding on a shipyard roof, on Lake Lothing, Lowestoft, in 1993, although the colony had probably been in existence since at least 1986 (Easton 1994). Initially, only three pairs were found, but numbers progressively increased to reach a peak of eight pairs in 1995. Roof nesting was recorded in Finland in 1971, but this is the only instance of this behaviour in Britain. Up to 28 nests were found on the Alton Water tern-rafts in 1999.

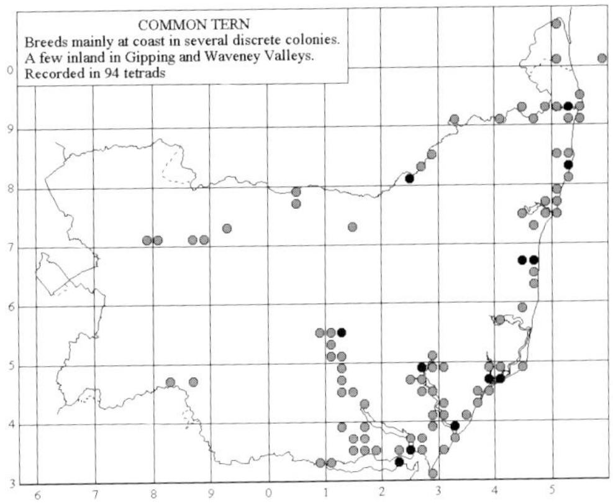

The tern was formerly very much a rarity at inland localities – so much so that all sightings were listed in SBRs up to the early 1980s. Common Terns are now regularly reported at inland waters during passage periods and 1-2 pairs remain throughout the summer months. A pair nested at Sudbury in 1971 and, since 1993, successful breeding has been noted annually at Sharmford Mere, Coddenham, and at Weybread Pits. An easterly movement involving 125 at Lackford on 3rd May 1990 shows that Common Terns occasionally pass through inland gravel pits in significant numbers.

Common Terns normally arrive in mid-April, although singles have been noted in March on six occasions with one at Sizewell on 26th March 1980 being the earliest. Return migration is normally underway in late July and peaks in late August. From 19th-29th August 1949, four-figure flocks roosted with Sandwich Terns on Walberswick Marsh, peaking at 3,000 on 23rd (LFC) and, on 29th August 1961, a southerly movement involving 2,000 was noted off Minsmere. Other large movements south include 442 off Southwold on 19th August 1982 and 839 off Landguard on 20th August 1987. Migration continues through September and a few are still present in early October. There are two winter records: one found dead at Thetford Warren in January 1906 and another feeding with gulls around Sizewell Rigs from November 1974 through to 26th February 1975. This overwintering individual was also frequently observed at Minsmere. There are 14 other November records with one at Lowestoft on 16th (1977) being the latest. Two terns seen with gulls off Minsmere on 13th December 1964 were listed as 'Commics'.

Whiskered Tern *Chlidonias hybrida*

Accidental: five records

1910	Hollesley: Shingle Street, ad. with Common Terns, 16th-17th September
1987	R. Yare: river mouth, 27th June
1988	Minsmere: ad. 26th May
1995	Felixstowe: Landguard Point, 12th June
	Breydon: 15th June

The tern has been recorded in Britain and Ireland on 129 occasions up to the end of 2000 (BBRC) and there is a clear southerly bias to the records.

The breeding range extends from southwest Europe through to Manchuria and south to southern Africa and Australasia. The European population winters in Africa.

Black Tern *Chlidonias niger*

A fairly common passage migrant

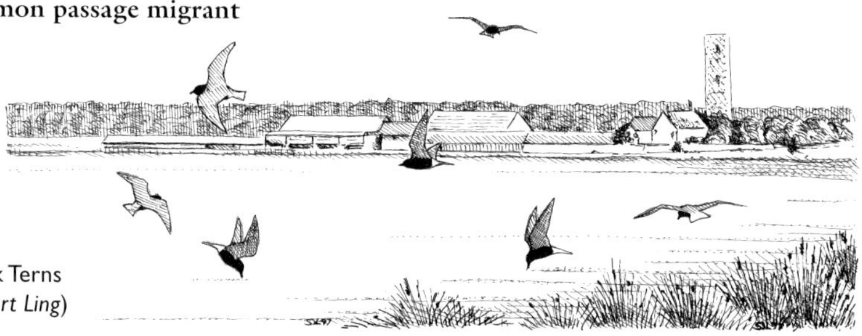

Black Terns
(*Stuart Ling*)

Black Terns pass through both coastal and inland sites normally in small numbers, although south-easterly winds in spring are ideal conditions for large movements. Coastal waters such as Benacre Broad, Minsmere, Trimley Marshes and Alton Water are favoured stop-off points and the species often accompanies other terns at Sizewell Rigs, particularly during the autumn. Lackford, Livermere, Weybread and Redgrave have been the most favoured inland sites in recent years.

East Anglia was formerly the stronghold of the British breeding population and Babington was in no doubt that the tern bred in the fens around Brandon and Mildenhall. Following extensive drainage early in the 19th century, the tern became extinct as a breeding species in Britain and there have since been only sporadic breeding attempts – none of which have been in Suffolk.

Birds on spring passage have been noted as early as 8th April 1967 and 11th April 1993. However, the tern is rarely seen before late April and the main migration is in May, with a few stragglers to early June. Failed breeding birds, making an early return, probably account for the midsummer occurrences, which have been noted fairly frequently in recent years. The species begins to show in numbers from the end of July, when adults are joined by juveniles, and peak passage occurs in September. There are few October records and singles at Havergate on 6th November 1962; Minsmere, 9th and 12th November 1984 and East Lane, 3rd November 1995 are the only records for that month. One flying south off Sizewell on 3rd December 2000 is the lateset record for Suffolk.

The creation of large areas of standing water in the Lark, Gipping and Waveney valleys by the flooding of redundant gravel workings has resulted in a huge increase in records from inland localities. Overland migration is more evident in spring and, with inland sites being more intensively watched, their importance has only recently been realised. Prior to 1990, the largest inland gathering was 40 at Livermere in 1979 but, thereafter, counts between 40 and 150 have become quite regular. A record movement was logged at Lackford between 2nd-4th May 1990 and involved an amazing 328. The terns arrived from the west soon after dawn with numbers building throughout the day to peak during late afternoon and early evening. The breakdown was 126 on 2nd May, 149 on 3rd and 53 on 4th. Other high counts include: 112 at Lackford and 45 at Weybread on 11th September 1992, 85 at Lackford and up to 42 at Weybread on 11th-12th May 1993 and 89 at Livermere Lake on 3rd May 1997.

Coastal gatherings and movements are also sometimes substantial. During the 'Great Fall' 150 gathered at Minsmere on 3rd September 1965, 100 moved south off Southwold and 70 were off Minsmere, 30th August 1992 and 70 moved south off Landguard, 1st September 1994.

White-winged Black Tern *Chlidonias leucopterus*

A rare passage migrant: 27 records involving 45 individuals

Visitations to Britain and Ireland increased dramatically in the second half of the 20th century from only 50, prior to 1958, to 792 up to the end of 2000 (BBRC). Records show a clear bias to south-east England and overall the tern is more common on autumn passage. Suffolk records, however, are mainly in spring and fall between 22nd April (eight at Breydon 1901) and 18th September (immature at Sizewell and Minsmere 1979).

Breydon monopolised records from 1871-1901, with singles or small flocks totalling 19 individuals many of which were shot. Four were shot from five present at Breydon on 26th May 1871, three were present towards the end of May 1873 and eight were noted on 22nd April 1901. Two at Shingle Street in 1906 were followed by a 44 year gap before one visited Minsmere on 21st May 1952. Two were at Reydon and Minsmere in June 1960 and August 1969 respectively and a flurry of records in late 1970s, involving eight individuals, was followed by five in the 1980s and a further seven from 1990-2001. The only West Suffolk record involved one at Lakenheath on 5th June 1994.

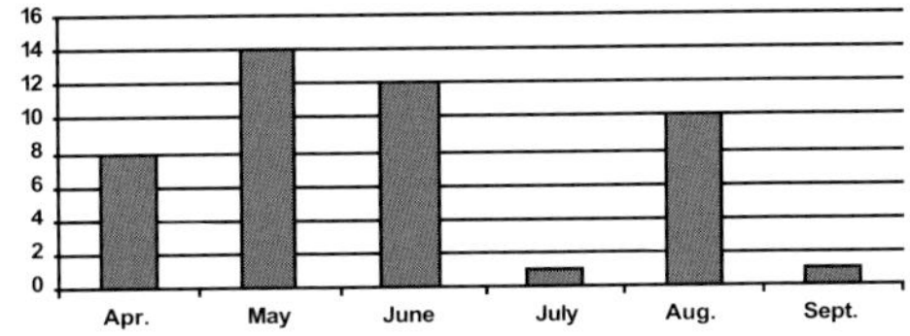

The seasonal occurrences of the White-winged Black Tern (all dated records 1871-2001)

Guillemot (Common Guillemot) *Uria aalge*

A common winter visitor and passage migrant

Guillemots nest in huge colonies around Britain, although they are absent as a breeding species in south-east England, between Flamborough Head and the Isle of Wight. However, it disperses widely during winter and occurs off the Suffolk coast and, occasionally, on the river estuaries. The wintering population has increased greatly in recent years and Sole Bay now holds regular concentrations. A general increase in wintering numbers in the southern North Sea has been attributed to a southerly shift of sprats (Camphuysen 1989). The species is often prominent in large seabird movements, but distance, weather and light conditions sometimes prevents specific identification and, in consequence, many birds are logged as 'auk species'. Oil-spills occur annually and their devastating effect can be seen by the hundreds of dead and moribund auks, mainly Guillemots, either beached or lying close inshore. Both southern and northern races occur along with a few of the 'bridled' form.

Wintering birds are well spread over large areas of sea and are normally not viewable from land. However, flocks become more obvious when the sprat shoals venture into inshore waters. High counts include: 300 in the Kessingland/Benacre area from 30th January-26th February 1993, 550 off Minsmere on 8th January 1994 and 216 off Covehithe the following month. The species was particularly abundant at inshore localities during those two winters and counts can be attributed to wintering flocks rather than coastal movements. Persistent northerly winds often force thousands of emaciated individuals close to our shores and the results can often be seen on the tideline, where the number of corpses grows daily. The massive seabird 'wreck' of February 1983 provides no better example, the Beached Bird Survey locating 428 Guillemot corpses (see also Razorbill).

Coastal movements are regularly reported most often involving singles or small groups amongst other seabirds, but occasionally numbers can be quite substantial. Passage birds are noted from April with peak spring numbers normally occurring in mid-May and a few stragglers until early June. Return passage normally gets underway in late July or early August and the largest autumn numbers occur in October. Many of the auks passing by are not specifically identified although a large Guillemot contingent is normally apparent. Some of the highest daily counts have been noted in the Covehithe-Southwold area and include: 272 on 2nd December 1987; 353 on 13th February, 280 on 3rd March, 345 on 29th October and 230 on

30th October 1988, 210 on 8th October 1989 and 724 (in two hours) on 16th December 1991. Almost all the birds involved in these movements were flying north. All previous counts were dwarfed by huge northerly movements from the end of January to mid-March 1999 – the highest being 3,771 north (in three and a half hours) on 12th February and 2,020 (in two and a half hours) on 11th March. It was believed that these birds were feeding on sprats offshore and were moving between feeding areas. Huge numbers were also present during the next three winters and Suffolk's record movement was noted on 3rd December 2000 when 3,942 moved south in the morning and 387 north in the afternoon.

There are only five inland records and all but one occurred during the 19th century. One hit telephone wires at Bury St Edmunds in April 1915, following terrific storms which saw "thousands" moving north off Lowestoft on 6th April. One on Alton Water, 20th February 1989, is the sole record for the reservoir and the only freshwater occurrence in recent years.

There are no real surprises amongst the ringing returns with birds originating from Wales, Scotland (mostly Shetland) (21), Ireland and the Farne Islands (5).

Razorbill *Alca torda*

An uncommon winter visitor and passage migrant

This auk is reported regularly each winter, but in smaller numbers than the Guillemot. Specific identification is again not always possible in seabird movements and, although the auk appears to be less abundant than Guillemots, it is probably more numerous in inshore movements than the number of specifically identified birds suggest. Many specific reports refer to sick and dying individuals found on the tide-line following oil spills. The species is strictly marine and there are no inland records.

Oil slicks and the stress of weather often force large numbers close inshore. Oil leaking from a ship wreck off Aldeburgh in June 1946 resulted in hundreds being beached, with the clean up operation hampered by uncleared minefields. The Razorbill was the dominant species involved in the seabird 'wreck' of February 1983, when no fewer than 17,986 corpses were washed on to Britain's shores (Lack 1986). Totals of 706 Razorbills, 428 Guillemots, 36 Puffins and 19 Little Auks were found in Suffolk. The Razorbill is undoubtedly involved in the movements of unidentified auks, mentioned under Guillemot, although the extent is unknown. A day-total of 35 north off Benacre, 13th October 1963 is the largest of the few counts of specifically-identified birds to reach double-figures.

The records are usually confined to the winter months although there are occasional summer records. Young Razorbills leave their colonies when only half grown at around 2-3 weeks old and accompany their parents till mid-August when adults moult into winter plumage. All Razorbills become flightless during this period and normally avoid inshore waters. Ticehurst referred to flightless youngsters that he had handled from Lowestoft in early August which were no larger than Little Auks and two juveniles, still in down, were killed off Aldeburgh during August or September sometime prior to 1870 (Hele 1870). Adults accompanied by young were noted in northeast Suffolk on 13th July 1950 and 5th July 1952 (Payn 1978).

Razorbills ringed in Scotland (14), Skokholm and Skomer Islands and on the Calf of Man have been found in Suffolk.

Black Guillemot *Cepphus grylle*

Accidental: six records

1863	Aldeburgh: "young bird" obtained 9th November
1875	Lowestoft: found dead on beach
1912	Lowestoft: "young one, taken in herring-nets" 23rd October
1980	Dunwich: Shore Pools, 9th-13th January
1983	Easton Bavents: flying north 29th October
1991	Southwold: on sea, first-winter 21st October

Of the four records in the 20th century, only one was present for more than a day. This involved a well-watched individual which fished on one of the shore-pools at Dunwich in January 1980. The 1983 occurrence coincided with a large movement of Little Auks.

Little Auk *Alle alle*

A scarce winter visitor and passage migrant. Subject to occasional influxes

Prolonged northerly gales in late October and November often force Little Auks to move south close inshore and then to re-orientate north when winds drop or change direction. 'Wrecked' individuals are regularly found at inland localities. Reports between December and March are much scarcer and most refer to tideline corpses. In the absence of northerly winds, the auk is an extreme rarity and in some years it is not reported at all. Normally, sightings are limited to ones and twos or small flocks, but, occasionally, substantial movements are logged at migration watch-points. Little Auks making landfall with immigrant thrushes and starlings have been reported on about ten occasions since 1970.

Ticehurst stated that "though hardly a year passes but that odd ones come ashore, some years stand out with exceptional visitations". He cited October 1841, December 1848, November 1861, January and February 1895 and 1912, February and March 1900 and November 1917 as exceptional months. Nowadays, Little Auk movements are restricted almost exclusively to the period from late October through to mid-December with only a few individuals noted from January to early March. Groups of up to 15 were logged between Lowestoft and Minsmere during the seabird wreck of February 1983 and are the largest early-year counts of recent years. A summer-plumaged bird was found dead at Aldeburgh on 9th April 1982, but there have been no spring movements.

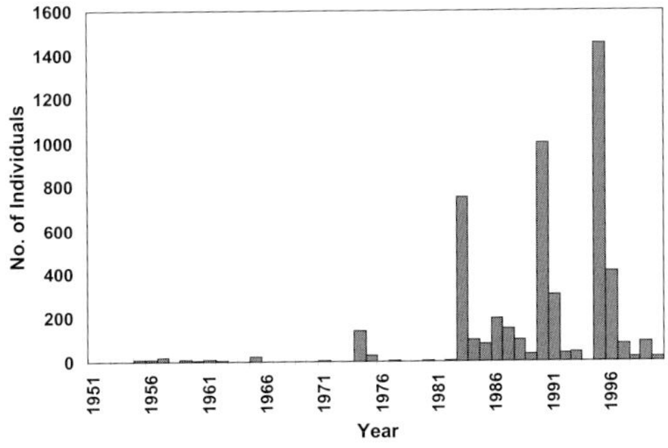

The annual totals of the Little Auk 1951-2000

Movements involving 20 or more are not uncommon and some birds will linger close inshore, on coastal broads or in harbours. A marked northerly passage involving an estimated 300 birds was noted off Benacre on 29th October 1983, which was then the largest ever recorded, but this was eclipsed by northerly movements of 301, in two and a half hours, off Southwold on 28th December 1990; 576, in six and half hours, off Southwold, on 13th December 1990 and 641 off Covehithe on 2nd November 1995. Movements involving well over 200 were logged at several sites, between Lowestoft and Felixstowe, on 20th October 1991, with the highest numbers again off north-east Suffolk. During periods of movements, the species regularly ventures up river estuaries where it has been found in borrow-dykes and amongst moored boats in yachting marinas. Five flew inland with Starlings at Bawdsey on 20th October 1991, where one of the auks was taken by a Great Black-backed Gull and swallowed whole (SBR).

Severe gales will scatter birds to inland localities, where they are often found in unusual circumstances. A chicken-run provided shelter for a wrecked bird at Sudbourne, on 11th November 1957, another flew "within four feet" of a motorist's windscreen on the Newmarket bypass, on 29th October 1983 and one was found under a wood-pile at Swefling on 21st November 1984. Similar incidents have been noted in 16 years (28 records) from 1950-1995 and almost annually throughout the 1980s. Most involve birds found in gardens, but others have occurred in woodland and on inland rivers and lakes. Storm-driven birds were found regularly in west Suffolk during the 19th century and 40 were picked up in Newmarket during the arctic winter of 1894/5.

Puffin (Atlantic Puffin) *Fratercula arctica*

A scarce passage migrant and winter visitor

The Puffin is the rarest of the four regularly occurring auks with sightings often limited to the occasional record amongst seabird movements. Late September and early October appear to the most favoured period for passage birds, although the species is occasionally noted in winter, particularly during harsh weather periods. There have been no significant movements, with five north off Covehithe, on 28th September 1989, and another five north off Southwold, on 12th October 1992, being the largest day counts.

The vast majority of Suffolk records refer to tideline corpses, occurring most often as a consequence of oil spills or adverse weather conditions. Prolonged north-easterly gales at the end of March 1900, caused one of the largest-ever 'wrecks' of this species, when Puffins and Little Auks were washed up all along the Norfolk and Suffolk coast (Ticehurst 1932) and no less than 20 were found in the Great Yarmouth area from 2nd-3rd April. The biggest natural wreck of recent times occurred in mid-February 1983, following persistent northerly winds and choppy seas which drove hundreds south in search of food. Starving birds were forced close inshore and, although only two were reported alive, no fewer than 36 corpses were cast ashore, including one ringed at Sule Skerry, Orkney, the previous summer. Five additional ringed birds have originated from the Farne Islands (3), Fair Isle and the Isle of May. Britain is at the southern limit of the Puffin's breeding range and ringing data have shown that east-coast breeders remain in the North Sea throughout the year (Cramp *et al.* 1974-1994). Southern colonies are occupied from late March and it is likely that the above late-winter incidents are a result of pre-breeding concentrations moving south due to impossible feeding conditions further north. Puffins were often caught in sprat and herring nets and cast overboard (Ticehurst 1932) and the general decline in reports of tide-line corpses is perhaps indicative of the demise of the East Anglian fishing industry.

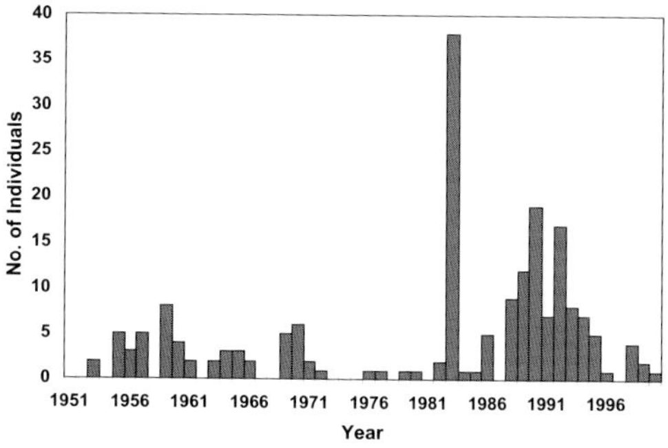

The annual totals of the Puffin from 1951-2000

At least 14 individuals have been found wrecked in West Suffolk of which the following five are post-1950: an immature captured alive at Bury St Edmunds on 24th November 1953; singles on Higham Pool and at Long Melford 25th October and 1st November 1955 respectively, Newmarket, 27th September 1957 and a dead bird at Mildenhall, 23rd June 1964.

Pallas's Sandgrouse *Syrrhaptes paradoxus*

Accidental: batches of records from three 19th century irruptions

This sandgrouse is a partial migrant, breeding on the Asiatic steppes and is subject to occasional irruptions. The species is an extremely rare visitor to Britain, with only five records (six birds) from 1958-1985 but, occasionally in the past, there were huge invasions. The last of these took place in 1863 and 1888 when Suffolk received its fair share of the records.

About 200 were present at coastal localities between 28th May and 22nd November 1863. Seven flying in from the sea at Thorpeness heralded the arrival of several flocks of up to 50 in number at Breydon Water, Kessingland, Walberswick, Sizewell, Thorpe, Aldeburgh, Tangham, Alderton and Sutton. Inland, a few were found on heathland around Thetford – one was captured alive at Elveden and sent to the London Zoological Gardens, three were killed at Santon Downham and another at Wangford Warren. The birds were well sought after by gunners and, as there was no close season, many were shot. Ticehurst estimated that at least 30 were killed.

A larger irruption occurred from May 1888, involving perhaps as many as 500, with the bulk of these frequenting Breckland. The first was noted at Mildenhall at the end of May and others subsequently at Newmarket, Greatt Welnetham, Bradfield St George, Clare, Great Ashfield, Thetford, Wangford, Elveden and Barnham. An August flock of 200-300 passing over Eriswell was the largest group recorded. Otherwise, a flock of 11 frequented Herringfleet on 27th May followed by singles or small flocks at Lowestoft, Southwold, Sizewell, Aldringham, Breydon Water and Woodbridge. The last locality recorded the largest coastal flock when 80-100 flew over in August. Most departed that autumn, but a few remained till the summer of 1889.

Groups of nine and five were noted at Lowestoft from 9th-10th May and 14 at Aldeburgh on 15th May 1890 were the final Suffolk records.

The flat, featureless landscapes of Breckland that existed at that time closely resemble the species' natural breeding haunts and, therefore, with such huge influxes, it is not surprising that nesting took place. Breeding was noted near Newmarket and Barnham in 1888, and "possibly" at Eriswell in 1889 (Ticehurst 1932).

Rock Dove (Rock/Feral Pigeon) *Columba livia*

An abundant resident from feral stock

Feral Pigeons are direct descendants of the Rock Dove, but have been treated with contempt by the county's ornithologists. They are virtually ignored despite appeals to the contrary in SBRs. Feral Pigeons breed extensively in urban areas, nesting in derelict buildings, church towers and on any suitable ledge on a variety of structures. Large flocks congregate around granaries and feed on fields in rural areas and are plentiful near dockland wharves or warehouses. Feral Pigeons are largely regarded as environmental pests, mainly due to fouling, and extraordinary measures have been employed to rid town centre buildings of roosting and nesting birds, including the provision of dummy owls and an array of nets, wires and spikes. Culling has also depleted local populations, although numbers quickly recover if this practice is not maintained.

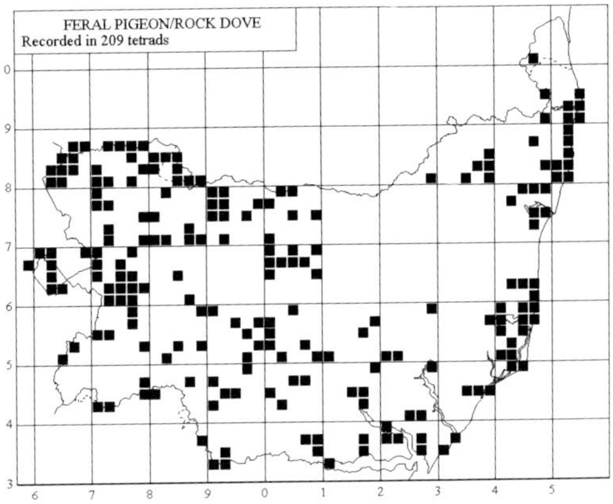
FERAL PIGEON/ROCK DOVE
Recorded in 209 tetrads
0
9
8
7
6
5
4
3
6
7
8
9
0
1
2
3
4
5

The species has undoubtedly decreased since Victorian times, when the keeping of dovecotes, racing and homing pigeons was more fashionable. This decline has been attributed to the rise in fortunes of the Stock Dove during the early 1900s.

The map shows breeding concentrations in town centres such as Ipswich, Newmarket and Lowestoft and the species appears to be more numerous in West Suffolk. However, it is likely to have been under-recorded in many areas.

As the Feral Pigeon is largely sedentary, winter concentrations occur especially in high density breeding areas. The largest reported flocks were all from industrial areas adjacent to Ipswich Docks, where peak counts ranged between 1,000 and 1,800 from 1992-2000, their presence attracting the attentions of Peregrines, one or two of which were resident in winter around the Orwell Bridge throughout the 1990s.

Stock Dove *Columba oenas*

A common resident and passage migrant

Parkland, mixed areas of farmland and woodland edge are the favoured haunts of this species, although it is extremely adaptable and will at times exploit other habitats such as heathland and even the treeless wastes of Orfordness. Small flocks of 10-50 appear on cultivated areas outside the breeding season, with three-figure congregations occasionally noted on winter stubbles. Coastal movements are regularly reported during late autumn, although these are rarely substantial.

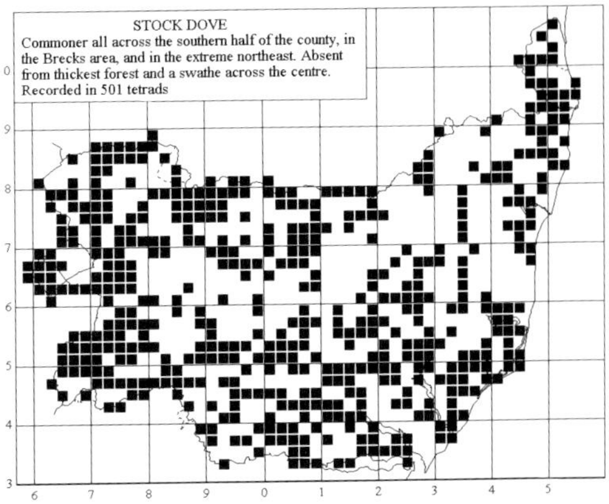
STOCK DOVE
Commoner all across the southern half of the county, in the Brecks area, and in the extreme northeast. Absent from thickest forest and a swathe across the centre.
Recorded in 501 tetrads
0
9
8
7
6
5
4
3
6
7
8
9
0
1
2
3
4
5

Assessing the status of this species has long been a problem, as its presence is seldom reported. SBRs make scant reference and, in some years, it is not mentioned at all. Ticehurst considered the species to be "exceedingly common throughout the County" and that it had increased from 1880 to 1930. This conforms to the national trend and coincides with a marked northward and westward expansion of range. However, the introduction of cyclodiene-based seed dressings, along with the intensification of arable farming in the 1950s, caused a steep decline in numbers, especially in eastern England (Sharrock 1976). CBC results show that the population has since partially recovered and is now stabilising (Marchant *et al.* 1990), and, although there are indications that farmland is a less favoured habitat than in pre-war years (O'Connor & Mead 1984), record levels were reached in 1995 (Marchant & Wilson 1996).

Reydon Grove Farm, near Southwold held 2-6 pairs from 1964 to 1971 (Benson & Williamson 1972), but there were none in 1997 (Pearson 1998). Local declines were noted in the Felixstowe area from 1985 to 1996 (R. B. Warren *in litt.*).

The Stock Dove breeds widely but is scattered rather thinly throughout the county and it is decidedly scarce in the principal cereal growing areas of central Suffolk. Large hollow trees are most favoured as nesting sites, although derelict buildings, church towers, holes in cliff faces and owl boxes are also used. Rabbit burrows are now only occasionally used by nesting Stock Doves whereas around 1780, "multitudes bred in the warren districts round Brandon" (Ticehurst 1932). Eggs were often laid in deserted burrows and in tunnels through rabbit-cropped gorse and, after allowing parents to feed their chicks through a grill of sticks placed at the burrow entrance, the offspring were gathered by warreners for the table (Sheppard & Whitear 1924-1925). The relatively unspoilt shingle spit from Sudbourne south to Alderton has long provided feeding opportunities for the species. Ticehurst stated that flocks came across from Sudbourne Woods to feed on various seeds and the sea-pea, and Banks (1971) thought the latter plant was sought by the species at Shingle Street and Alderton, where he noted a gathering of over 500 on 25th December 1966. During the 1980s, around 40 pairs nested in abandoned military buildings on Orfordness, as well as in rabbit burrows, underground chambers and bunkers. In 1947, chicks were found on a platform seven metres below ground level in a pit excavated by the army on Berner's Heath (Butt & Vine 1947).

Winter gatherings of 100-300 are reported in most years, but flocks of 700 at Elveden in December 1970, 600 on Breydon Water's South Wall Marshes on 17th January 1980 and over 500 noted above were exceptionally large.

Ringing returns show that Stock Doves in Britain are extremely sedentary, with only a quarter of nestlings travelling more than eight km from their natal area (Murton 1966). There have been only two recoveries from 46 birds ringed on Orfordness during the period 1984-1998, both found within 10km of the ringing site. However, coastal movements are occasionally substantial and reports of birds arriving from the sea indicate that there could be some immigration from the continent. Migrating flocks are most often noted in late October and November, and normally occur in association with movements of Woodpigeons. Several hundred Stock Doves visiting Havergate Island in December 1952 were considered to be passage birds (Payn 1978) and a remarkable movement involving 2,000 was noted at Minsmere from 13th-23rd November 1959. Southerly passage is regularly logged at Landguard Point during late autumn, the highest count being 2,787 from 23rd October to 18th November 1994, which included 465 on 1st November and 430 the next day. There were four other day-counts that exceeded 200 that autumn. About 400 flew south over Southwold on 26th October 1998.

Woodpigeon (Common Wood Pigeon) *Columba palumbus*

An abundant resident, winter visitor and passage migrant

The Woodpigeon breeds widely throughout the county in all habitat types, although woodland, both deciduous and coniferous particularly in farming areas, is the most favoured. Hedgerows, gardens and buildings are also used in urban and suburban environments. It gathers into large feeding flocks in late autumn and is discouraged from damaging crops by shooting and various bird scaring devices.

The map shows that the species is widely spread throughout the county with gaps probably reflecting lack of coverage rather than a genuine absence in some areas. Nationally, there has been some decline during the 1970s, although a partial recovery has occurred since then (Marchant *et al.* 1990). The Reydon Grove Farm study recorded an estimated 50 pairs annually during the period 1964-1971 (Benson & Williamson 1972) but there were only 12 pairs in 1997 (Pearson 1998).

Although arable crops are the principal food source, natural foods such as beech mast, ivy and other berries, and various grasses and clovers are also eaten. A population of around 30 is resident at Landguard Point, where it feeds on holm-oak acorns and sea kale seeds during the autumn. About 40 pairs breed successfully on Orfordness, where eggs are laid on bare shingle most often amongst stands of rosebay willowherb and sea-purslane. Breeding pairs utilise old buildings and nest low in the few bushes that exist around the old RAF Station, some nests are constructed entirely of wire strands from the remnants of the abandoned Cobra Mist early-warning radar station on Lantern Marsh.

Outside the breeding season, the species may occur in substantial feeding flocks, these favouring large open fields containing crops of peas, beans, young cereals and oil-seed rape. Three-figure flocks are common enough throughout the county and concentrations of 1,000 or more are recorded in most years. Gatherings of 3,000 or more have included 3,000 at Nacton on 20th November 1982, 4,000 at Higham on 2nd March 1983, 3,000 at Blythburgh on 13th January 1988 and c.4,000 at Lakenheath on 23rd February 1997. A huge roost at Gipping Great Wood was logged regularly during the late 1990s, the highest counts included 3,000 on 21st November 1997, 5,500 on 16th November 1998, 4,300 on 27th January 1999 and 4,200 on 9th December 1999.

There are no significant spring movements and passage often goes unnoticed. Numbers logged at Landguard Point rarely reach three figures and 154 flying south on 24th March 1995 is exceptional for that period. Spring passage is noted from early March till the end of May, although movements could be attributed to coasting rather than active migration.

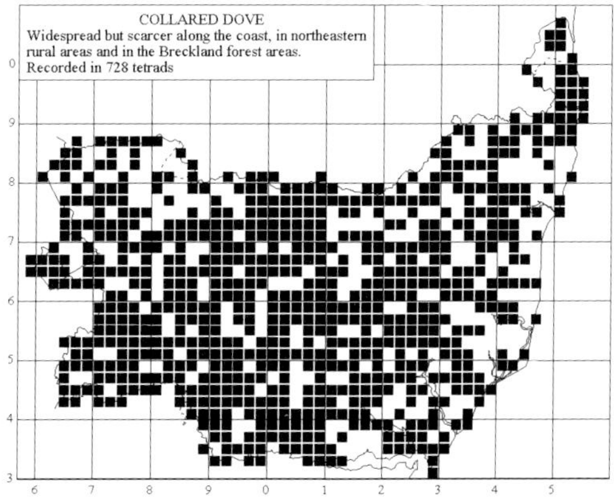

There has been much debate as to whether the huge flocks moving offshore, noted in most autumns, are of continental origin or are British-bred birds coasting southwards. *BWP* referred to autumnal movements of Fennoscandian and eastern European populations to wintering grounds, mainly in south-west France and Iberia. Autumn occurrences of continental birds, mainly in eastern Britain, were considered to be drift movements in overcast conditions over the North Sea. Occasionally, offshore movements are enormous. For example, parties of 500 arrived from the north-east at Gorleston on 28th-30th November 1959, which "perhaps" totalled 25,000 birds (Allard 1990) and southerly movements over Landguard Point include c.13,500 on 20th October 1983, 23,215 on 4th-12th November 1991, a remarkable 86,109 from 9th October to 13th November 1994 (including 30,610 on 2nd November) and 61,534 from 10th October to 11th November 1998 (including 37,722 on 29th October). Observations at LBO have revealed that the largest movements occur in early morning and during periods of clear skies, which perhaps indicate direct passage from Scandinavia to Iberia. This theory is reinforced by the lack of huge wintering flocks in inland Suffolk following periods of heavy passage. However, ringing evidence is rather meagre considering the numbers shot, with only a single recovery involving a bird from abroad – ringed on a lightship off Texel, the Netherlands in December 1959 and recovered at Oulton Broad the following winter. From the thousands of birds shot each year in Suffolk, only 97 were reported with rings up to the end of 1995. From these, 38 had moved less than 10km, 58 between 10km and 100km. and only one over 100km. The last bird had been ringed in Buckinghamshire. A total of 40 Suffolk-ringed birds was recovered in the same period and of these 28 had moved less than 10km, 11 between 10km and 100km, and only one over 100km. The long-distance recovery involved one ringed at Alton Water in July 1992 that was shot in Lincolnshire in September 1993. Not included in these statistics are two birds ringed at Landguard Point in 1994 and 1996, and both shot in France.

Collared Dove (Eurasian Collared Dove) *Streptopelia decaocto*

A common resident

The Collared Dove's colonisation of Britain is one of the most spectacular ornithological events of the 20th century. This dove now breeds widely throughout the county, although surprisingly it is thinly distributed on the coast, except around the towns of Ipswich and Lowestoft. It is also relatively scarce in rural Breckland and the north-east. The species is most common in urban environments, especially around parks and gardens, where it favours ornamental evergreens, such as holm oak and yew, as a nesting site. Winter flocks congregate around poultry units, livestock buildings, and dockside wharves and granaries in Ipswich and Lowestoft, but in lesser numbers than formerly. Pest control measures and a reduction in grain processing are thought responsible for this local decline.

Britain's first nesting pair was found in Norfolk in 1955. The first to be seen in Suffolk was one at Lakenheath the following year, where breeding took first took place in 1959. A colony of over 100 became established at Felixstowe in 1961 – a year when breeding was also reported at Gorleston and Kessingland. Ipswich and the coastal towns of Lowestoft, Southwold and Aldeburgh were soon colonised, but the spread into rural areas was relatively slow. A small population built up at Ixworth in the mid-1960s and breeding continued at Lakenheath. It soon became well-established in the Stour Valley where nesting took place as far upstream as Haverhill (Hudson 1972). Increasing numbers were noted in central Suffolk including the towns of Bury St Edmunds and Stowmarket. Numbers increased rapidly during the 1970s and, although the highest concentrations were in urban areas, hardly any parish in Suffolk was without a nesting pair. It nested profusely in town centre parks, churchyards and larger gardens, and the Lowestoft population reached a peak of 2,000-3,000 pairs in the late 1970s. A decline, first noted in Ipswich in 1983, was paralleled nationally (Marchant *et al.* 1990) and continued through to the mid-1990s.

The species has one of the most protracted breeding seasons of all British birds and this has undoubtedly aided its success. Incubation has been reported in every month of the year with fledglings frequently reported in January, and the species is capable of producing 4-6 broods annually.

In the late 1970s, substantial flocks congregated on the roofs of the granaries and warehouses alongside Ipswich Docks, to such an extent that they were considered a health hazard. This encouraged food manufacturers to employ pest controllers and within a few years this population had been virtually wiped out. The doves fed on grain spillage during the day and roosted in nearby Holywells Park each evening. A winter flock of 250 in 1975 progressively increased to peak at c.700 on 23rd November 1979. The only other sites to host gatherings of 300 or more were Acton Airfield (445 'winter' 1975) and Commercial Road, Lowestoft (300-500 from 1984 to 1992). The Lowestoft flocks fed around the dockside grain silo by day and moved to roost at Leathes Ham in late afternoon.

Numbers increase at coastal localities during passage periods and small movements are logged annually at Landguard Point. Southerly passage totalling 162 was noted at this site in October 1984. A group of 12 was seen to arrive from offshore at Pakefield on 25th November 1969, in an exhausted condition, and one from the flock was seen to fall into the sea. One ringed at Eyke on 21st January 1973 was recovered in Co. Antrim, Northern Ireland the following year and another ringed as a nestling at Landguard Point in May 1987 was found at Cleethorpes, Lincolnshire in August the following year.

Turtle Dove (European Turtle Dove) *Streptopelia turtur*

A summer visitor and passage migrant

The Turtle Dove is widely distributed throughout the county, although higher densities occur on the coast and in Breckland. Large pre-migration flocks congregate at coastal sites in August and, occasionally, overwintering individuals are found, most often amongst Collared Dove roosts.

Ticehurst reported that the species had "probably much increased" in the 50 years up to 1932 and this was paralleled nationally. It was thought that a northward expansion of range was responsible for increased numbers. Turtle Doves remained plentiful throughout the 1940s but, by the late 1950s, local declines were noted, particularly in the south-west of the county. The uprooting of tall hedgerows and thickets was thought to be responsible for declines in that area (Payn 1978). Early SBRs gave few indications as to any change in status, but, from 1963 to 1979, CBC data showed a gradual increase nationally and, thereafter, a fall of around 60% (Marchant *et al.* 1990). A decline in weed seeds, as a result of chemical treatment to arable crops and grassland, is thought to be the principal reason for the decrease and the *New Atlas* highlights similarities in range contraction for this species and Grey Partridge. The Reydon Grove Farm study revealed a range of 7-10 pairs from 1964 to

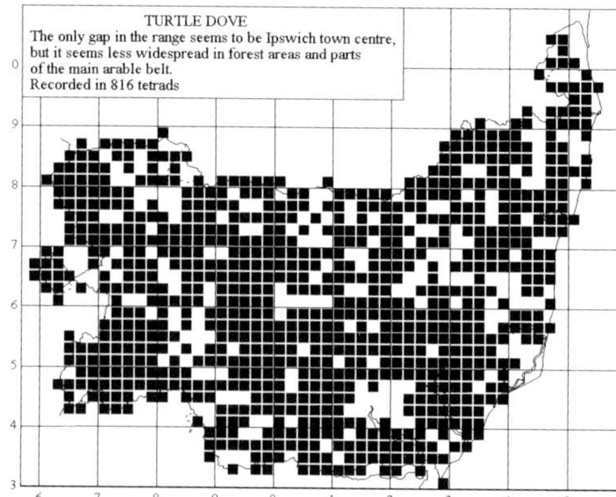

1971 (Benson & Williamson 1972) compared with only one from 1997 to 1998 (Pearson 1998).

The Turtle Dove is a rather late spring arrival with the first rush of birds normally noted in early May. A few are seen in late April each year, but singles at Flatford on 2nd April 1955 and at Haverhill on 4th April 1989 were exceptionally early. Although Suffolk's largest gatherings traditionally occur just prior to autumn passage, the largest count involved 500 at Staverton Park on the unusual date of 31st May 1968. The largest autumn concentrations were 300 at Framlingham in August 1958 and c.360 at Levington in August 1975. Most depart in early September, but a few linger to October and occasionally into November. There are 11 winter records and, although most relate to single-day observations, overwintering has been confirmed on three occasions: Ipswich Docks from January to April 1975 and in January 1977, and Lowestoft in 1991/2.

Five Suffolk-ringed birds have been recovered on the Iberian Peninsula.

Ring-necked Parakeet (Rose-ringed Parakeet) *Psittacula krameri*

A scarce visitor – has bred

Ornithologists showed little interest in this species prior to it being placed in Category C of the British list in 1983. Feral birds have since been reported annually, being noted singly or in pairs and, although a lone pair nested annually at one site in the late 1970s and early 1980s, no family or roosting flocks have been reported. In addition, there are a few records of birds visiting bird tables, a habit regularly noted in its suburban strongholds such as those around London (Lack 1986). There are usually less than ten records each year, and 13 in 1990 is the best year to date. Confusion with other large green parakeet species probably occurs from time to time.

Suffolk's sole breeding records relate to a pair which nested annually in a hole in the masonry of Aldham Church in the years 1977-1986, but success was limited to just one juvenile in 1986. The male disappeared in 1987 and the female was found dead in February four years later. One, probably two, entered a chimney in central Ipswich in April 1990, but nesting was not suspected.

An interesting record involved one that appeared to arrive from offshore at Ness Point, Lowestoft, on 23rd October 1990.

Great Spotted Cuckoo *Clamator glandarius*

Accidental: one record

1992 Aldeburgh: juv. moulting to first-winter from 29th October to 12th November

This well-watched individual was initially discovered at Slaughden Quay, but was surprisingly elusive and remained undetected in the area until 5th November, when it was relocated on nearby marshes. It was last seen on 12th November, which is the latest recorded date for this species in Britain.

The Great Spotted Cuckoo occurs in Britain and Ireland as a vagrant from southern Europe and had been noted on 42 occasions up to the end of 2000 (BBRC). There is a clear easterly bias to British records (from Sussex north to Orkney) and most occur in autumn (Dymond *et al.* 1989).

Cuckoo (Common Cuckoo) *Cuculus canorus*

A common summer visitor and passage migrant

The familiar call of the Cuckoo is one of the most eagerly awaited and most welcome signs of spring, with the first of the year most often being reported by readers of local newspapers rather than by birdwatchers. However, most of the exceptionally early reports are probably due to confusion with the *coo-coo* call of the Collared Dove. Cuckoos are found widely throughout the county, occurring in most habitat types, although reedbeds, open woodlands and heathland are most favoured. Numbers have declined markedly in recent years.

Spring arrivals are rarely noted before mid-April. There are only six March records, with one at Wickhambrook on 14th being the earliest of three mid-March records for 1990, a year that proved exceptional for early migrants. The main arrival takes place in May with early concentrations occurring at coastal localities. There is a time-lapse between arrival and the first call, and migrant birds are notoriously silent (Wyllie 1981). It is often difficult to determine whether non-singing males refer to birds returning to their territories or to passage birds. The reedbeds of Walberswick and Minsmere host high densities and are one of the best sites to observe the species. A gathering of 35 at Minsmere on 30th May 1962 was thought to have included migrants. The poplar plantations that formerly existed around Lakenheath were particularly favoured by the species and concentrations of up to 30 were noted annually from 1977 to 1985. The species was attracted by the abundance of warblers, which nested amongst the undergrowth, along with frequent infestations of caterpillars on the poplars. Seven were observed feeding on an abundance of caterpillars on saltings at Felixstowe Ferry in late June and early July 1988.

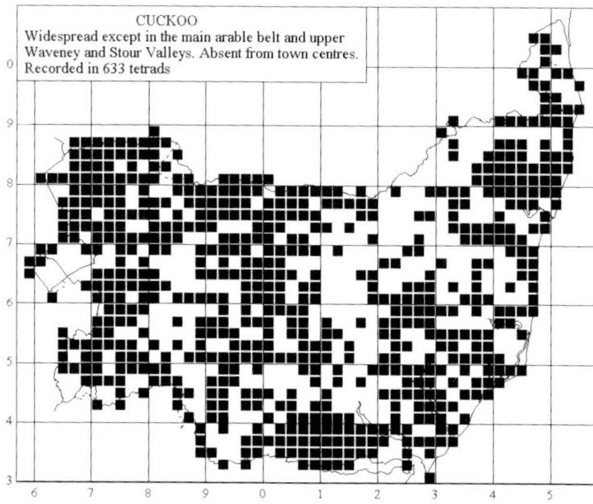

CUCKOO
Widespread except in the main arable belt and upper Waveney and Stour Valleys. Absent from town centres.
Recorded in 633 tetrads

More than 50 species have fostered young cuckoos in Suffolk (Payn 1978) – the host species depending greatly on habitat type. For example, Reed Buntings, and Reed and Sedge Warblers are most favoured in reedbeds and Meadow Pipits on heathlands. Dunnocks and Pied Wagtails are regularly parasitised in farming areas, the former being the most popular host. More unusual hosts have included: Song Thrush (on at least three occasions), Skylark, Swallow, Wheatear, Bullfinch and House Sparrow.

SBRs consistently reported a decrease, throughout the 1960s and 1970s, but this was not reflected in national CBC data that have shown a relatively stable population (Marchant *et al.* 1990). However, it should be stressed that important habitats frequented by the species were not covered as part of this census. Payn suggested that the widespread use of pesticides and the destruction of the nesting habitat of its host species are the principal reasons for this decline.

Censusing this species can be a difficult task as males may roam and cross the territories of others. The SOG conducted surveys on 27th May in both 1973 and 1978 that received considerable media attention. A minimum of 250 and 124 calling males respectively were located, but poor weather may well have hampered fieldwork in the latter year (Paine 1978). It remains plentiful in Breckland and along the coastal strip, but is very scarce in arable areas of central and north Suffolk, and is thinly distributed along the Waveney and upper Stour Valleys. Urban areas are avoided and the larger towns of Ipswich, Felixstowe, Lowestoft, Bury St Edmunds, Haverhill and Newmarket show as gaps on the map.

Territorial males continue calling through May and June, but rarely into July. One calling at Haverhill on 3rd July 1971 is the latest reported, although the bubbling call of the female was frequently recorded in the first week of July at Lakenheath in several years. A female calling on 24th August 1952 is exceptional. Cuckoos are one of the first summer migrants to leave, with males departing first at the end of June and females following soon after. There are a number of instances where birds have arrived from offshore in late July and these may relate to Scandinavian birds on passage. Only three out of the 23 trapped at Landguard Point on autumn passage were adults and 65% of the juveniles occurred between 28th July and 11th August. Juveniles often remain dependent on foster parents well into August, although a newly-hatched chick in a Reed Warbler's nest on 22nd July 1953 is exceptionally late. Lingering birds depend greatly on the availability of a sustainable food supply. There were nine October records up to the end of 2001, the latest involving one that frequented Sizewell Dunes until 16th October 1979 and fed on an abundance of larvae of the grass eggar moth.

Ringing recoveries indicate the migration route. Singles ringed at Walberswick and Capel St Andrew, in July 1955 and 1960 respectively were recovered in France later in the autumn and another ringed in 1962 at Benacre, on the late date of 30th September, was found the following autumn in Spain. A female ringed at Landguard Point on 19th May 1985 flew into a window at Littlebourne, Kent on 13th June 1987 and laid an egg prior to release.

Yellow-billed Cuckoo *Coccyzus americanus*

Accidental: two records

1971 Reydon: 18th-19th October
1989 Felixstowe: Landguard Point, first-winter, trapped, 25th October

The Reydon individual was picked up from the roadside and died the next day. Its skin was on display at Southwold Museum, but on the museum's closure this specimen, along with many others, was transferred to Hertfordshire Museum. The Landguard Point bird delighted hundreds of observers during its single-day visit.

This Nearctic vagrant is a regular visitor to Britain, mainly to the south-west. It is very rare in east coast counties. There were 64 records for Britain and Ireland up to the end of 2000 (BBRC).

Barn Owl *Tyto alba*

A fairly common resident in the east, scarce in the west

The Barn Owl is one of the most loved of all British birds. Following the national trend, the population in Suffolk has declined markedly and the owl is now virtually restricted to the eastern half of the county, with only a few reported elsewhere.

In the early years of the 20th century, the Barn Owl was generally well distributed throughout the county and was the commonest of the owls (Ticehurst 1932). Up to 1945, the Barn Owl was a familiar sight on most Suffolk farms, but thereafter, numbers fell sharply. This decline has continued through to the end of the 20th century and the owl is now almost extinct in West Suffolk, with just a few pairs hanging on in the Little Ouse and Kennett Valleys. Changes in agricultural techniques are the principal reason for the decline, which has resulted in a shortage of feeding opportunities and nest sites, but an increased frequency of severe winters since the 1940s have also taken their toll. Dutch elm disease resulted in the loss of many large hollow trees, which were favoured for nesting and roosting, and the demolition or renovation of farm buildings traditionally used as nesting sites have also had a detrimental effect. Modern farming practices, such as the replacement of the horse by the tractor, the use of combine harvesters, the elimination of marginal grass strips, the widespread use of pesticides and chemical seed-dressings, the grubbing out of hedgerows and the ploughing of meadows and grazing marshes, are all unsympathetic to voles and other rodents, the principal prey of the Barn Owl.

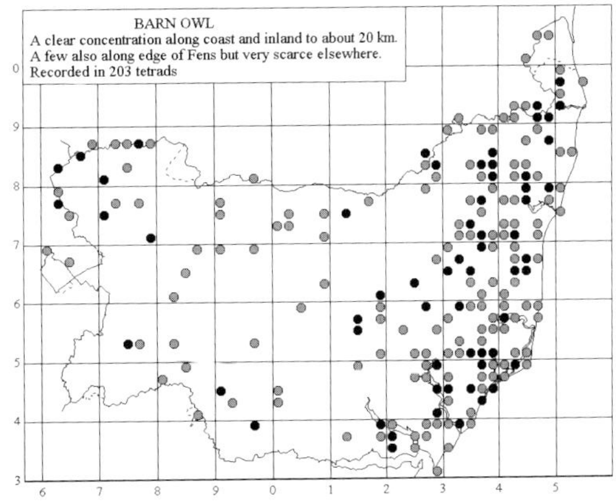

The effects of severe winter weather were demonstrated in 1987/8 when 19 Barn Owls were found either moribund or dead. Initial reports suggested that the birds had died as a result of warfarin poisoning and this story made the national press. However, those examined were emaciated and there were no traces of chemical ingestion (Martin 1988). The owl's habit of hunting roadside verges has often led to the bird's demise and double-figure casualties are reported annually. The provision of nest boxes has been successful in areas of good feeding habitat and may be the key to future recolonisation of old haunts.

Despite widespread losses, eastern Suffolk still holds some of the highest densities in Britain, with more than five pairs in each 10-km square (Shawyer 1987). There is a clear concentration in areas within about 20km of the coast with the northern part holding the most. A few pairs remain along the edge of the fens but there are now only scattered records from elsewhere. The number of deliberate releases of, so-called, rehabilitated birds complicates the Barn Owl's current status. Many have been liberated into old haunts that no longer hold a sustainable food supply and ringing recoveries have shown that most of these die of starvation within a few days of release. Five breeding pairs per occupied 10-km square gives a breeding population of 100-125 pairs, although Wright (2001) gives 51-90 pairs for the period 1995-1998.

Second broods are rare in Britain and are only triggered by an abundance of prey (Bunn *et al.* 1982). The only Suffolk example involved a pair feeding young on 4th June 1953 and a second brood being fed there up to a week before Christmas.

The Barn Owl is extremely sedentary, often remaining faithful to the same roost or nest site throughout its adult life (Bunn *et al.* 1982). However, juveniles must move away from the natal area, even if only a few kilometres, and such post-fledging movements may account for Barn Owls seen flying south during the autumn. Migrants or, more likely, local wanderers are occasionally logged at Landguard Point between August and November, and one flying towards the coastline was observed about three kilometres off Shingle Street on 15th October 1984. A nestling ringed in Warwickshire on 5th August 1976 was found dead at Stowmarket (beside the A14) two years later and represents one of the longest known movements of a British-reared Barn Owl. However, it is possible that this bird was a road casualty nearer to its natal area and, after becoming lodged on the vehicle, was inadvertently transported to Suffolk. Barn Owls ringed as nestlings in Surrey (two), Buckinghamshire and Norfolk have been found in Suffolk. One ringed at Landguard Point on 28th September 1986 was found dead at Tendring, Essex, on 9th February 1987, during a winter of particularly high mortality.

The dark-breasted continental race, *T. a. guttata*, has been recorded in Suffolk on eight occasions of which five were at the end of the 19th century: Lowestoft on 24th February 1898 and 10th November 1900, off Lowestoft on 23rd September 1886, at sea off Suffolk in October 1880 and near Yarmouth on 2nd September 1878. The only reports for the 20th century involved singles at Minsmere on 3rd April 1953, at Shotley in September 1984 and one trapped at Landguard Point on 11th June 1997.

Scops Owl *Otus scops*

Accidental: four 19th-century records

pre-1886	Burgh Castle: "taken"
pre-1886	Fritton: "taken"
1865	Haughley: Haughley Bushes, "taken"
1873	Rougham: "shot"

This tiny owl is an extremely rare visitor to Britain from southern Europe with only 28 records during the period 1958-2000 (BBRC), compared with 64 previously.

All Suffolk records relate to birds killed in the 19th century, with the two Lothingland specimens formerly in the collection at Somerleyton Hall.

Snowy Owl *Nyctea scandiaca*

Accidental: seven records

1847	Icketshall St Andrew: imm. female shot 19th February
1878	St Olaves: Fritton Lake, Herringfleet Decoy, November
1885	Felixstowe: Landguard Point, shot near lighthouse 9th February
1957	Walberswick/Westleton: male 1st-2nd November
1958	Sibton: 8th February
1964	Hollesley: Shingle Street, mid-January
2001	Felixstowe: Landguard Point/Port of Felixstowe, imm. male from 24th October to 5th December
	Waldringfield: same 7th-8th December

All Suffolk records refer to late autumn or winter visitations and, despite being this species being very conspicuous, sightings have been limited mostly to single-day observations. The long-staying 2001 individual was a notable exception and a ship sailing from Canada to Europe undoubtedly aided its arrival. It was reported that no less than 50 Snowy Owls sought refuge on the vessel after being caught in a severe storm off Quebec. Most birds left the ship as it sailed across the Atlantic but a few stayed on until it reached port. Those that reached Belgium and the Netherlands were in an emaciated condition and were soon captured and taken into care. The Suffolk individual, however, was able to capture its own prey and was watched by thousands of birdwatchers as it roosted on the landfill area adjacent to the Port of Felixstowe.

In addition to the above records, a first-winter female at Weston on 6th-7th October 1999 caused much interest until a man claiming to be its owner pursued it across a field.

The Snowy Owl breeds in the high Arctic, but disperses southwards during winter. A single pair bred on Fetlar, Shetland between 1967 and 1975.

Little Owl *Athene noctua*

A fairly common resident

This owl favours open countryside with an abundance of hedgerows containing old trees, and traditional farm buildings. Although Little Owls are sometimes disturbed during daylight, it is at dusk that they become more obvious when more exposed perches are chosen.

Ticehurst listed five records for the period 1840-1877, one of which involved a bird captured alive offshore, which he considered to be a genuine immigrant from the continent. These occurred before Lord Lilford's extensive and successful introduction of Little Owls to Northamptonshire during 1888-1890. Lilford obtained chicks from London markets where they were sold as house pets (Holloway 1996). Releases were also made in Kent, and by the end of the 19th century a feral population had become established in these two counties, along with Bedfordshire and Rutland. Expansion was rapid and Little Owls reached West Suffolk in the early 1900s and by 1911 they had spread to the coast. Nesting soon followed at Sudbourne, Halesworth, Aldeburgh, Beccles and Lowestoft. A population explosion occurred from 1910 to 1930, resulting in the species rivalling the Barn Owl as Suffolk's most common owl. The species' liking for beetles and earthworms is well-known, but as the owl was seen to take Pheasant chicks, it was considered as a pest by gamekeepers and, in consequence, hundreds were killed. On one large estate on the Norfolk/Suffolk border, 151 were killed in 1926 and 77 in 1928 (Ticehurst 1932). Holes in trees are the most favoured nesting sites, but rabbit burrows have also been used.

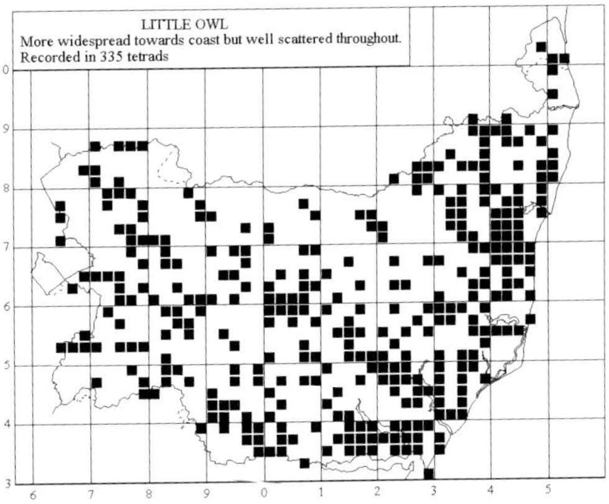
LITTLE OWL
More widespread towards coast but well scattered throughout.
Recorded in 335 tetrads

The species has decreased greatly since its peak in the 1940s, when it was the most common and widespread owl in the county (Payn 1978). SBRs reported a decline as early as 1950 and this continued through to the mid-1960s. A series of cold winters together with organochlorine pesticide poisoning was thought responsible. A slow recovery became evident in the early 1970s, which accelerated in the 1980s. The map shows that the Little Owl is widely spread throughout the county, although more so in the eastern half. It is scarce in central Suffolk and around Lowestoft. A conservative figure of 5-10 pairs per occupied 10-km square was used to determine a national population of 6,000-12,000 pairs (Gibbons *et al.* 1993), the same criteria give a population of 870-1,740 pairs for Suffolk. However, Wright (2001) estimated 470-670, for the period 1995-1998, based on the results from the survey of breeding raptors and owls.

Little Owls are largely sedentary as evidenced by ringing returns that show that 71% of 322 recoveries were within a 10km radius of the ringing site (Lack 1986). It is, however, reported annually at Landguard Point, particularly during the autumn but, as yet, there is no proof of immigration.

Little Owls following the plough have been noted in Suffolk on two occasions.

Tawny Owl *Strix aluco*

A common resident

The Tawny Owl is currently Suffolk's commonest owl, being widely recorded throughout the county, with one or two pairs in most woods. The population is relatively stable and is less prone to the severity of harsh winters than most other residents. The species is becoming more common in suburban and urban areas.

Numbers declined in the 19th century mainly as a result of over-zealous gamekeeping (Marchant *et al.* 1990). This was obvious from a noticeable recovery in numbers during the First World War. Babington considered the species to be much less common than the Barn Owl and Hele thought it rare around Aldeburgh. The owl was thinly distributed in Ticehurst's day, being "a fairly constant inhabitant of old forest and parkland", but was almost absent in younger woods and treeless districts.

Holes in hollow trees are the most favoured nesting sites, but Ticehurst referred to a pair that nested regularly in Tostock church tower and to another, near Harleston, which incubated on the ground at the foot of a fir tree. Robertson (1954) also found a nest containing two owlets under a Corsican pine in Thetford Forest.

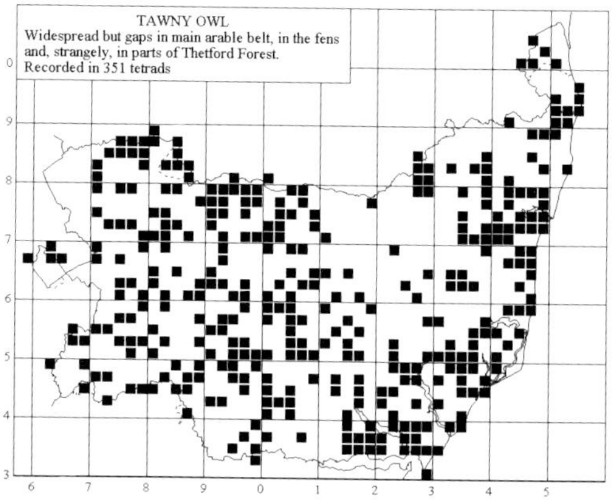

TAWNY OWL
Widespread but gaps in main arable belt, in the fens and, strangely, in parts of Thetford Forest.
Recorded in 351 tetrads

Tawny Owls are strictly nocturnal and therefore many pairs are likely to have been overlooked during atlas fieldwork. Knowledge of overall population trends and breeding numbers is rather limited. Wright (2001) estimated the population to be stable at around 650 pairs based on the results of the survey of breeding raptors and owls in Suffolk from 1995 to 1998. The map shows the species to be widespread, although scarcer, in the arable belt especially nearer the River Waveney. It is surprisingly scarce in parts of the Breck and is absent in the Mildenhall fens. Nationally, there has been a steady decline since the mid-1970s, and the CBC index fell by 50% between 1975 and 1995 (Marchant & Wilson 1996).

The species' diet is varied, with an assortment of birds and mammals being taken. Unlike other owls, its liking for the former makes it less susceptible to vole fluctuations and, therefore, creating a higher degree of stability in the population. Tawny Owls frequenting Landguard Point and Felixstowe Docks feed almost entirely on birds at roost, captured under the port's floodlights.

Tawny Owls regularly nest in Christchurch Park, in the centre of Ipswich, and are frequently seen and heard in other parts of the town.

There are few more sedentary species and only two of the 17 Tawny Owls recovered after being ringed in Suffolk have been found further than ten km from their ringing sites.

Long-eared Owl *Asio otus*

A fairly common winter visitor and passage migrant and a scarce resident

Although a few pairs breed in conifer belts in Breckland and the coastal strip, this owl is better known as a winter migrant, with most arriving in late October and early November, and departing in March. Communal roosts are regularly reported during the winter months, but these rarely reach double figures.

The Long-eared Owl was described as being common near Beccles, Elveden and Lowestoft early in the 19th century and, towards the end of that century, was reported nesting at eight coastal and two West Suffolk sites (Babington 1884-1886). It was considered to be the most plentiful species of owl around Thetford, with few plantations of any size not holding a pair (Clarke 1897). In the late 1930s, Long-eared Owls remained common in Breckland conifer plantations and also bred in mixed woodland in south-west Suffolk (Payn 1978). Nests are most often found in old crows' nests, but, very occasionally, in hollow cavities in oaks and on the ground (Glue 1977). There was a distinct lack of breeding records in the early 1950s, with SBRs reporting just a single pair on the coast every year or so. By the end of that decade, the coastal population was reported to be in the region of 4-8 pairs, but details from its Breckland stronghold were sketchy. By the mid-1960s, the county's population was estimated at ten pairs, seven of which were in Breckland, and ten years later the owl was reported nesting at eight coastal and four West Suffolk sites. This species is extremely unobtrusive and nesting is often only confirmed once the young begin to fledge and the 'squeaky-gate' food begging call is heard. In consequence, population levels in SBRs are likely to be underestimates. Nesting was found in 13 and ten 10-km squares in Suffolk respectively during fieldwork for the *1968-72 Atlas* and *New Atlas*, and 15 during the Breeding Raptors and Owls Survey (Wright 2001). Similar criteria to that used to assess the national population, gave a county breeding population of 39-130, 30-100 and 45-150 pairs respectively. Although Wright (2001) gave a much more conservative estimate of 10-15 pairs with numbers remaining reasonably constant. The actual population is likely to lie closer to the first set of figures as Breckland densities are amongst the highest in Britain (Sharrock 1976).

Long-eared Owls are regular autumn immigrants and their arrival is often quite visible, as they are seen way offshore before struggling to make landfall. Many hitch rides on passing container ships and have even been observed hunting amongst the cargo. Although new arrivals can be found anywhere along the coastal strip, they are logged annually at Landguard Point. An exceptional total of 20 visited this site on 15th November 1986 and was part of a national influx. One or two spring migrants are noted at Landguard Point during most years. Long-eared Owls ringed in the Netherlands and Sweden have visited Suffolk and three immigrants ringed at Landguard Point in October and November have been recovered elsewhere in southern Britain.

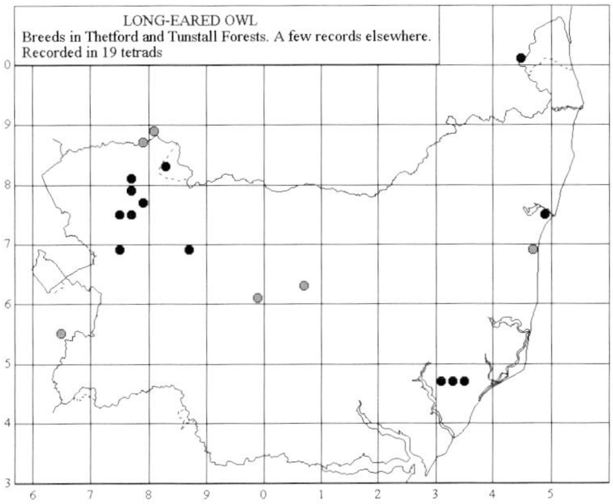

The owl roosts communally during winter, most often inside dense clumps of blackthorn. Ticehurst described flushing 8-10 from a small carr in Lowestoft marshes and 8-12 were in thorn trees near Sudbury in 1975. During severe weather in February 1979, four roosts totalling 28 birds were located. Winter gatherings of 6-8 have been noted regularly at widely scattered localities on the coast and in central Suffolk since 1979. Examples of sites used have included a blackthorn hedge at Aldham, thickets adjacent to the Lavenham railway line, a hedgerow near Groton Wood and a group of sallows and hawthorns at Leathes Ham, Lowestoft.

Short-eared Owl *Asio flammeus*

A fairly common winter visitor and passage migrant, and scarce resident

Short-eared Owls are much more conspicuous than Long-eared Owls as they usually hunt diurnally in open countryside, especially on heaths, grazing marshes, saltings and along river-walls. The Short-eared Owl is a regular autumn immigrant, arriving at coastal localities from early October onwards.

Nesting occurs irregularly in coastal areas and very occasionally in the Breck, but numbers depend greatly on the availability of prey. Breeding does not occur at all during poor vole years. For example, in 1972, no fewer than 17 pairs bred, including nine in the Breck, but there was just a single instance of breeding between 1988 and 2002. During good vole years, breeding can be prolific as seen at Havergate Island in 1968 when six pairs raised c.20 young. The open grasslands of Orfordness have proved one of the most favoured areas and, at times, up to seven pairs have nested.

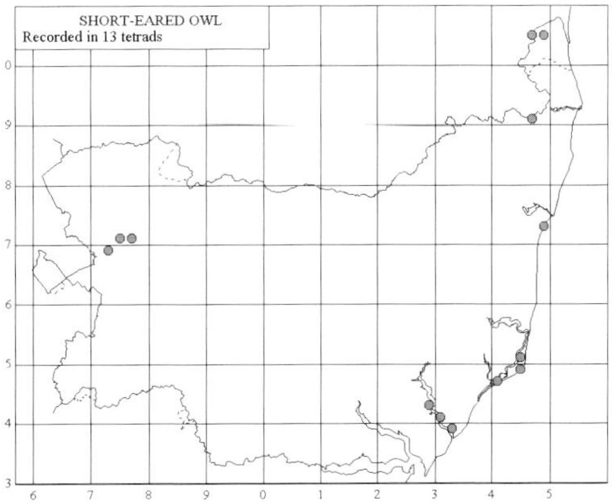

The owl is best known as a winter visitor and passage migrant arriving in October and departing in March. Short-eared Owls, in common with Long-eared Owls, are regularly seen in autumn labouring against the elements as they make their way inshore, often being harassed by passing gulls. They also roost communally, usually on the ground amongst long grass. Gatherings are normally in single figures, but occasionally they can be much higher. In 1907, 30 were on Orfordness in November and 50-100 were flushed by a shooting party on marshes at Alderton on 20th December 1958. A winter count of 25 was logged at Herringfleet in 1970 and 36 were in the air together at Trimley Marshes on 4th November 1974. Huge concentrations were reported nationally in 1972, including 116 roosting at Breydon Water and Halvergate levels, just over the county boundary in Norfolk (Allard) but, unfortunately, wintering numbers were ignored in the SBR for that year.

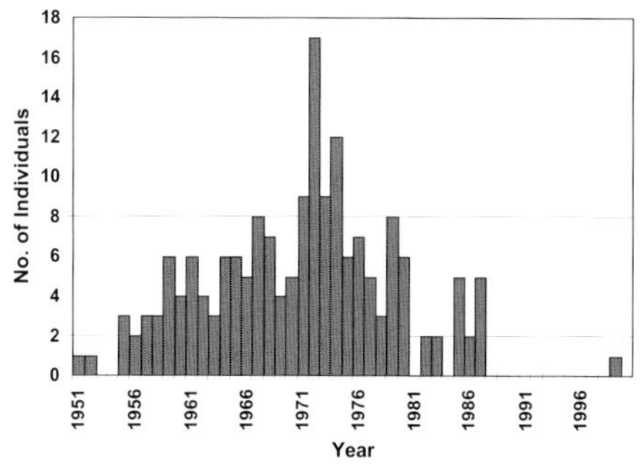

Numbers of summering pairs of Short-eared Owl from 1951-2000

One ringed at Vaasa, Finland, in June 1961 and recovered at Brandon on 31st January 1965, is Suffolk's only foreign ringing recovery.

Tengmalm's Owl *Aegolius funereus*

Accidental: five records

1884	nr Newmarket: "caught in rat-trap" 20th November, another to 9th December
1889	Thorington: "caught in a pole-trap" 15th January
1901	Southwold: beach, "picked up exhausted" 30th October, Grand Hotel, another c.30th October

Babington listed two additional records: "one killed at Bradwell, some years before 1846" and another "from the sand district across Sutton Heath". However, the whereabouts of the specimens were unknown even in Ticehurst's day and there was no further documentation to back up the records. Reports involving one said to have been captured near Ipswich on 17th October 1891 and another seen sitting in a tree at the edge of a small copse at Ixworth on 21st October 1901 were also unacceptable (Payn 1978). The Newmarket bird was caught during the night in a rat trap, in a wood on the Suffolk/Cambridgeshire border. The specimen was examined by Babington who noted that another was seen there soon afterwards, which was believed to be still present on 9th December 1884.

There was a small influx of Tengmalm's Owls to Britain in 1901 and two were found alive in Southwold. Others occurred in Norfolk, Yorkshire and Shetland (Ticehurst 1932).

This owl has a circumpolar holarctic distribution, breeding in boreal climatic zones and mountains (Mikkola 1983). The origins of the visitors to Britain probably lie in the Eurasian taiga, although possibly in the forest belt of North America. Northern populations are occasionally eruptive and Suffolk's dated records are all from the period 1884-1901. October 1901 must have been an amazing month with three records in Suffolk alone. The species is now an extremely rare vagrant to the British Isles, having occurred on only seven occasions from 1958 to the end of 2000 (BBRC).

Nightjar (European Nightjar) *Caprimulgus europaeus*

A locally common summer visitor and passage migrant

Nightjars churring over heath and breck are one of the delights of a summer evening. The species is now restricted to forestry plantations and heathland habitats, and breeds in good numbers in Breckland and on the sandlings. Passage birds are regularly reported on the immediate coastline.

The Nightjar was formerly widespread throughout the county and, although heathland has always been most favoured, more diverse habitats were at one time chosen, including broadleaved woodland and

Nightjars
(*Adam Kennedy*)

open beach at the back of the tideline. Nightjars nested in coppiced woodland, either in clearings or in short coppice, with eggs often found on heaps of bark shavings (Ticehurst 1932). In the 19th century, the Nightjar was a common feature of the whole of Breckland and of the heaths and commons on the coastal strip. Nesting was also noted in the southern parishes of Bures, Cavendish, Sudbury, Polstead, Bentley and Freston, in the central areas of Rattlesden, Felsham, Tostock, Thurston, Norton, Rougham, Ickworth and Saxham, and in the Waveney Valley at Oakley, Wortwell, Mendham, Homersfield and Herringfleet. The neglect of coppice woodlands, together with the application of pesticides and disturbance on the immediate coast, resulted in the loss of the species in all habitats except heathland. In addition, the fragmentation of heath and scrub, by afforestation and agricultural reclamation, may have further reduced the population (Marchant *et al.* 1990).

During the 1950s, a thriving population existed in north-east Suffolk, where breeding was reported at Herringfleet, St Olaves and Fritton. In the same period, Nightjars frequented the heaths around Ipswich, nesting on Fox's Heath, Purdis Heath and from Foxhall to Waldringfield Heath. However, the mass destruction of heathland, together with urbanisation, took its toll and, by the late 1960s, the species was lost from all parishes north of Blythburgh and just a few pairs lingered on around Ipswich. However, the nucleus of the population hung on in its heathland strongholds in the central coastal zone and in the Breck, and it was from here that it spread to forestry areas soon after young plantations replaced mature pinewoods.

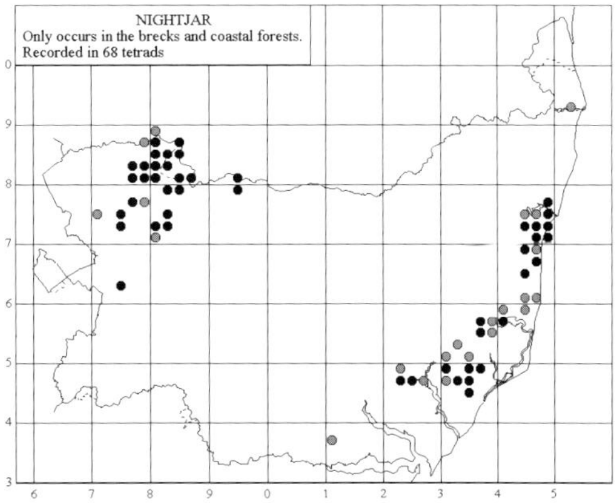

A national census in 1981 revealed that the Suffolk population was much higher than anticipated, with 123 churring males occupying suitable habitats on the coast and Breck. Numbers increased steadily on the coast, with birds exploiting clear-fell forestry areas. On 16th October 1987, there was a sudden and dramatic increase in suitable habitat when a ferocious storm swept through the coastal zone. Overnight, almost the entire forestry areas of Tunstall and Rendlesham were razed, and subsequent clearing and replanting created suitable habitat that the species was quick to occupy. Ravenscroft (1989) and Bowden (1990) examined the species' optimum habitat requirements, focusing on the age-structure of the vegetation of heathland and forest clearings. Their findings showed that Nightjars were becoming increasingly dependent on forest habitats, with a high proportion using plantations up to ten years old. A survey in 1992 located an unprecedented 317 territories, divided between the coast (167) and the Breck (150).

Careful manipulation of heathland habitats can result in a dramatic increase in numbers. For example, at Minsmere, the removal of invading birch and Scots pines to create small glades with bare patches resulted in an increase from five pairs in 1982 to 40 in 1989 (Burgess *et al.* 1990).

The first of the spring are normally noted in the second half of May and males begin singing almost immediately. A study at Minsmere revealed that females arrive on average 11 days later (Berry & Bibby 1981). There are only five April records, the earliest being birds at Blaxhall on 16th April 1865 and 8th April 1876. One at Cavenham on 25th April 1993 was the earliest occurrence in the 20th century. Churring continues throughout May, June and July, but song is rarely reported after mid-August. A singing bird at Blythburgh on 2nd September 1961 is exceptionally late, but another, still incubating a clutch of eggs in the King's Forest in early September, is unprecedented. There are nine October records including one on 30th October 1956, but the latest was at Worlingham on 1st November 1957. One was found resting on a compost heap at a Felixstowe allotment on 8th October 1995.

Migrants are occasionally found at migration watch-points in spring and autumn, most often resting amongst coastal scrub. Occasionally, Nightjars are found in strange circumstances in the middle of the breeding season. For example, singles taken at sea off Lowestoft in June 1913 and trapped at Landguard Point on 8th June 8th 1990 were probably tardy spring migrants. One ringed on Wangford Warren in July 1988 was trapped at Safi, Morocco, in May 1990, and constitutes Britain's most distant recovery.

Swift (Common Swift) *Apus apus*

An abundant summer visitor and passage migrant

The skies above towns and villages are often filled with screaming Swifts as they plunder the air for food. Swifts breed widely throughout the county and sudden concentrations often occur over sizeable bodies of freshwater. Movements involving several thousands often coincide with weather fronts at the height of the breeding season.

The first arrivals are not normally encountered before the beginning of May, although a few early birds are occasionally noted in the latter half of April. Numbers build up rapidly during early May and most are back at their nesting sites by the middle of that month. One which clung to the side of a Beccles house, during poor weather on 16th-18th March 1983, was the earliest of four March records for the county.

The map shows that Swifts are widespread throughout Suffolk, although there are few squares showing confirmed breeding. Many records may relate to feeding flocks. The species appears to be scarce around the Alde estuary and inland to Tunstall and Rendlesham forests, and there are some notable gaps in West Suffolk and along the Waveney Valley.

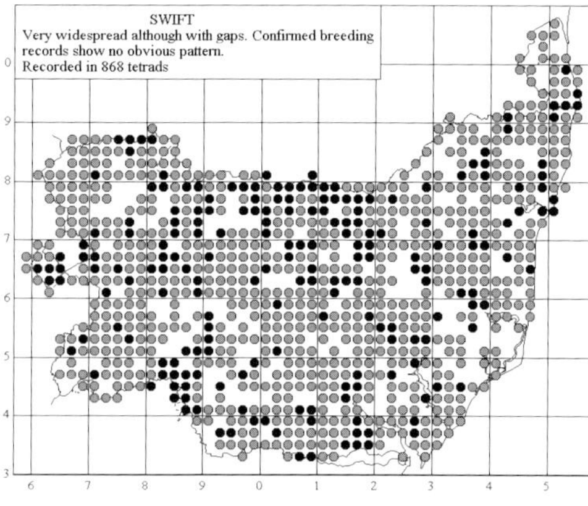

Swifts nest in roofs or in small cracks in old and new buildings alike, and particularly favour church towers. A nest containing one egg, positioned precariously in a hollowed-out branch of an elm tree, was found by the author in June 1971 at Greyfriars, East Bergholt, and represents the county's only reported instance of tree nesting. Summer gales, thunderstorms and prolonged periods of inclement weather will force thousands to feed in huge concentrations. Three-figure counts are regularly logged at larger lakes, during poor weather periods, where insects are collected just above the water's surface. Alton Water reservoir and the larger gravel pits in the Gipping, Lark and Waveney Valleys regularly attract good numbers. The county's largest movements have all occurred at coastal localities and include c.6,000 at Minsmere on 30th July 1980, 5,000 over Covehithe Broad on 5th August 1985, 6,000 moving south off Benacre on 9th July 1991, 5,000 over Minsmere on 14th July 1991 and 5,000 offshore at Thorpeness on 22nd July 1999. The species often associates with Swallows and martins and is a common prey item of the Hobby.

Departure in autumn is rapid and most birds have left by the end of August. Swifts become rare after mid-September and only a few pass through in October. There are 16 November records and one that lingered over Ipswich from 29th October to 9th December 1974 is the latest county record. Although one at Kirkley Cliff, Lowestoft, on 6th January 1966 probably involved a lingering bird that had gone undetected elsewhere.

One ringed at St Osyth, Essex, on 9th June 1955 was recovered in Newmarket 11 days later and another, caught at Alton Water on 8th June 1984, was found in Banc D'Arguin, France, on 17th May 1989.

Pallid Swift *Apus pallidus*

Accidental: three records involving two individuals

1999 Covehithe: 31st October
Southwold: St Edmund's Churchyard/Boating Lake, 31st October
Leiston-cum-Sizewell: Sizewell car park, 31st October

The Pallid Swift breeds in north-west Africa, and Iberia to southern Iran; it winters in Africa. It is a rare visitor to Britain having been noted on 27 occasions up to the end of 2000 (BBRC). The Suffolk records were part of the largest ever national influx of the species that involved at least 12 individuals.

The Sizewell bird tested the identification skills of hundreds of birdwatchers as it fed over the power station and car park throughout the afternoon.

Pacific Swift *Apus pacificus*

Accidental: one record

1981 Ellough/Shadingfield: 19th-20th June

This was the first record for the Western Palearctic and involved a bird that was captured on a gas rig off Bacton, Norfolk. It was transported ashore by helicopter to Ellough airfield where it was identified and released unharmed. It was seen associating with Swifts at nearby Shadingfield the following day.

There had been two further records of birds reaching Britain without known human assistance up to the end of 2000 (BBRC).

Alpine Swift *Apus melba*

A very rare vagrant: 22 records

Alpine Swifts are recorded in Suffolk two or three times each decade, almost exclusively at coastal localities. All records refer to single-day occurrences with the majority seen for just a few seconds. The species' breeding haunts lie in Iberia and north-west Africa, through southern Europe to India and in East and South Africa. The Western Palearctic population winters south of the Sahara. The species is noted annually in Britain and Ireland, with 490 records up to the end of 2000 (BBRC).

Suffolk's first record involved one shot at Angel Hill, Bury St Edmunds, about 1835, and was followed by four others that century, including the only other inland bird – killed at Wickhambrook in June 1881. None were reported from 1887 to 1958, but, thereafter, there was a steady stream of occurrences, with 2nd May and 13th September being the extreme dates. All 15 of the 20th century records are confined to the coastal strip, between Breydon Water and Aldeburgh, except for one that briefly flew over Woodbridge airfield on 4th July 1982 and another flying south off Landguard Point on 11th July 1991. One flying north at Landguard Point on 6th June 2002 was the fifth record for that month.

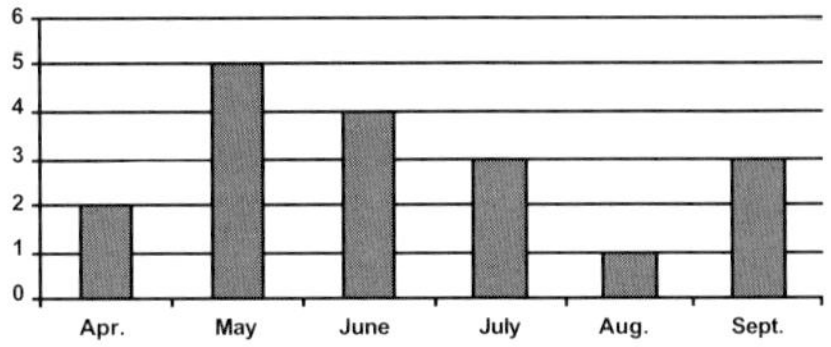

The seasonal distribution of the Alpine Swift (all dated records 1835-2001)

and woodland have shown a two-fold increase that has been attributed largely to the abundance of dead standing timber as a result of the outbreak of Dutch elm disease (Marchant *et al.* 1990). Lack (1986) predicted that the population would stabilise or fall once this disease had completed its cycle and, although the 25-year trend was still upward in 1996 (Wilson & Marchant 1997), it is still too early assess the impact of the loss of the dead trees. Numbers decreased slightly following the 'Great Storm' of October 1987, although SBRs in the mid-1990s show an upward trend. This storm caused little damage to old and decaying trees although in some areas woodsmen did take the opportunity to clear them as part of replacement planting regimes.

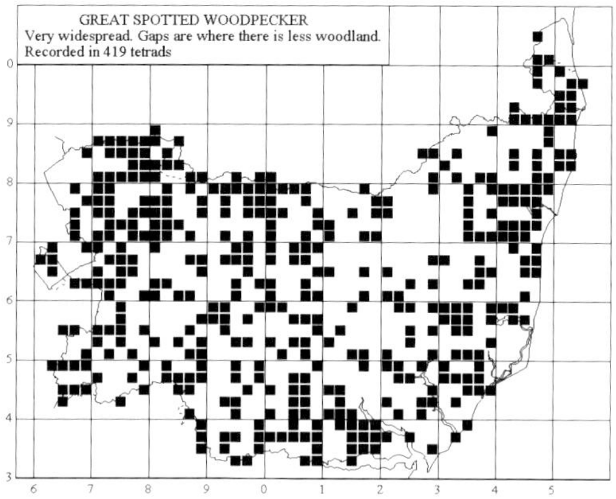

The map shows that the Great Spotted Woodpecker is widespread throughout the county with concentrations to the south and west of Ipswich, around the well-wooded areas near the Blyth and south to Minsmere, and also in north-west Suffolk. The population is sparsely distributed in the cereal dominated central areas, on the coastal marshes, along the Waveney Valley and in the south-west corner of the county.

A few are logged annually at LBO, with most records occurring during autumn passage and involving juveniles dispersing from their natal areas. There are only 13 ringing recoveries affecting Suffolk up to the end of 1995 and all except one were found within 10km of the ringing site. However, a juvenile male ringed at Garboldisham, Norfolk, on 2nd July 1995, was seen regularly at a peanut holder in an East Bergholt garden two summers later, a movement of 47km.

The larger, northern form *D. m. major* is probably a regular visitor to Suffolk, but, as it is identifiable only by biometrics, few are reported. Ticehurst examined five examples, all obtained in October, in the vicinity of Yarmouth between 1906 and 1911, and he referred to an invasion in 1861, when 20-30 were obtained on the Norfolk coast and one was found at Sizewell in November. There are four other records for the 1800s, including one captured on board a fishing boat in October 1898. The most recent reports involve singles trapped at Landguard Point on 21st May 1991 and 22nd September 1994.

Lesser Spotted Woodpecker — *Dendrocopos minor*

An uncommon resident

This is the rarest of the three resident woodpeckers, frequenting deciduous and mixed woodland, old orchards, parks and gardens, especially those in the river valleys or near streams or marshy areas. The species has always been scarce in Breckland. It can be extremely elusive, often detected only by its repetitive *kee-kee-kee* call. It is particularly attracted to alder carr. During the 1990s, the woodpecker has declined to such an extent that even the most ardent birdwatcher has often struggled to locate it during a whole year's observations.

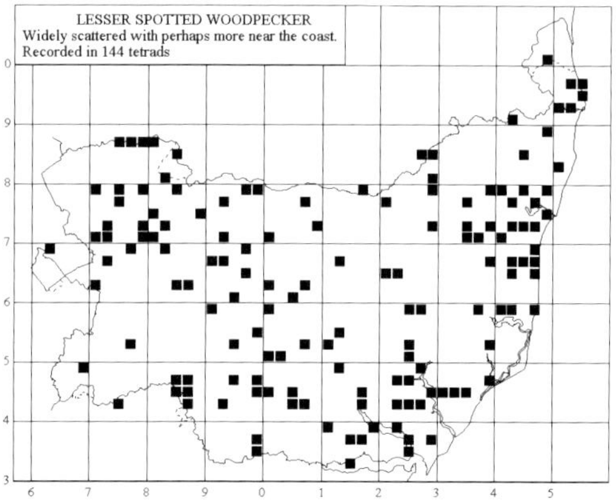

Sharrock (1976) showed confirmed breeding in 14 of Suffolk's 10-km squares and probable breeding in eight others, but, although there has since been no overall change in range, the woodpecker has become extremely local and is no longer common in any area. Small concentrations exist around the coastal nature reserves and in woodland close to the Deben estuary. The population increased strongly during the 1970s but fluctuated greatly in the next decade, when reports were received from around 85-89 sites. As with the Great Spotted, this woodpecker benefited greatly from an increase in available invertebrates caused by Dutch elm disease, although this proved to be only a short-term gain. Peak figures coincided with an abundance of standing dead timber but, following considerable clearance work that succeeded the 'Great Storm' of 16th October 1987, there was a dramatic decline. The species was reported from only 48 sites in 1992 and, three years later, had decreased to such an extent that it ceased to be monitored by the CBC (Marchant & Wilson 1996). The decline is further illustrated by a ten-year ringing summary which shows that 30 were ringed in the period 1986-1990, compared with only 11 in 1991-1995 (Marsh 1997) despite an increase in the amount of ringing effort. Lesser Spotted Woodpeckers are occasionally noted at Landguard Point, most often during autumn passage periods.

Drumming is heard especially early in the breeding season but one at Reydon on 12th January 1951 was particularly early. Generally, the species drums less often than Great Spotted Woodpecker. It occurs most often in woodland but is occasionally found feeding amongst hedgerows and will search roadside plants and even reedbeds for insects. Observations include one picking black flies and ants off broad beans in a Woodbridge garden in 1951 and another apparently feeding in a *Phragmites* reedbed at Livermere in 1978.

Short-toed Lark (Greater Short-toed Lark) *Calandrella brachydactyla*

A very rare passage migrant: 13 records

1889	Breydon Water: South Wall, shot 7th November
1951	Orford: Havergate Island, 24th June
1969	Minsmere: 10th-22nd May, another 5th September
1975	Walberswick: Shore Pools, 7th September
1982	Benacre: 11th September
1992	Felixstowe: Landguard Point, 23rd-25th September
1996	Felixstowe: Landguard Point, 21st-22nd May
	Benacre: Beach Farm, 31st May
1997	Southwold-Walberswick: 25th-30th May
	Felixstowe: Landguard Point, 29th June-1st July
2000	Southwold: 17th November
2001	Felixstowe: Landguard Point, 8th-10th May

The Short-toed Lark is a regular visitor to Britain, being noted mostly in the Shetland and Scilly Isles, but also in southern counties in May and from late September to mid-October. Visitations have become more frequent to the Suffolk coast with over half of the 13 records being noted from 1992-2001. Most of these individuals have shown characters of the more reddish, western races.

The breeding range extends from Iberia east to Manchuria, with the Sahel zone south of the Sahara forming the main wintering area for the western population.

Crested Lark *Galerida cristata*

Accidental: one record

1996	Felixstowe: Landguard Point, 2nd and 9th October

The above individual was very confiding, spending the afternoon feeding on rough ground and scampering across car parks, footpaths and on the Felixstowe promenade. Its presence attracted large crowds of birdwatchers, but eventually observer pressure forced the bird to seek a quieter locality to rest and feed. Its stay on its second visit to Landguard Point was limited to just a few minutes.

The species has been claimed in Suffolk on several occasions including a report of four on Dunwich Marshes, on 16th May 1946 (Payn 1978). Only the Felixstowe occurrence has been fully substantiated.

The Crested Lark breeds throughout continental Europe and across Asia to the Far East. It is an extremely rare visitor to Britain being reported on only 19 occasions up to the end of 2000 (BBRC) and the Landguard Point bird was the first in Britain since 1982.

Woodlark (Wood Lark) *Lullula arborea*

A locally common resident and scarce passage migrant

SL 97

Woodlark
(*Stuart Ling*)

This beautiful songster is a common inhabitant of heathland and forestry areas in the sandlings and Breckland. Woodland glades and open heath are the favoured habitats to which the Woodlark returns in February and leaves in September. The lark is occasionally noted at migration watch-points and, although winter flocks can be elusive, they have been located on stubbles or on recently tilled land near the coast.

Woodlarks were formerly restricted to heathland habitats on the coast and colonisation of Breckland is believed to have taken place during the 1840s. The coastal breeding range extended from Ipswich to the River Blyth in the 1930s and included 14 pairs at Foxhall (Ticehurst 1932, Payn 1978). Numbers were already increasing steadily in this period, undoubtedly benefiting from the availability of suitable habitat created during the early years of heathland afforestation. Lothingland was colonised for the first time in 1946, when at least four breeding pairs were equally divided between a mine-field at Gunton and a naval rifle range at Lowestoft's North Denes. At the same time, ten pairs were at Dunwich.

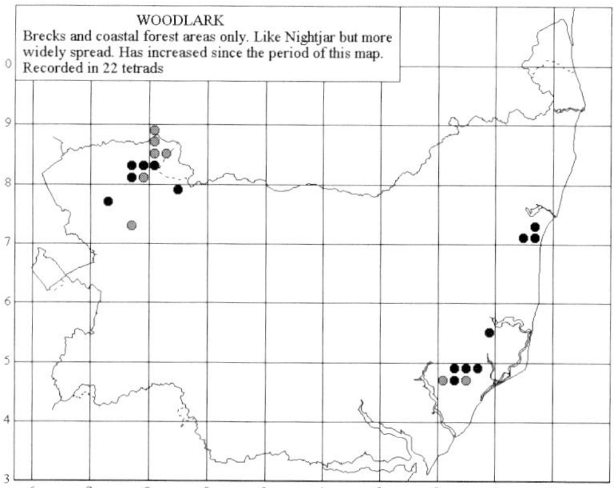
WOODLARK
Brecks and coastal forest areas only. Like Nightjar but more widely spread. Has increased since the period of this map.
Recorded in 22 tetrads
0
9
8
7
6
5
4
3
6
7
8
9
0
1
2
3
4
5

By the early 1950s, the Woodlark was widespread over a considerable area, ranging from Belton to Minsmere and nesting pairs were found well away from the coastal sandlings as far inland as Sotterley, Stoven, Walpole and Homersfield. A peak was reached in the early 1950s, but thereafter a sudden and rapid decrease took place. Initially, numbers appeared unchanged in Breckland, but a decline was very apparent at the species' coastal strongholds. The early 1960s saw numbers falling everywhere and, by the middle of that decade, the county held less than ten pairs. A partial recovery, which began in the late 1970s, accelerated in the mid-1980s, when there was an increase in the amount of forestry clear-fell areas. In 1986, the coastal population was 25-28 pairs (72% in forestry areas and the rest on heathland) and there were 50 pairs in Breckland (Waters 1987). The 'Great Storm' of 16th October 1987 created a massive amount of suitable habitat and the Woodlark was quick to colonise devastated areas. The population has risen quickly from 123 pairs in 1990 to 273 in 1994 and 459 in 1998. These figures show that Suffolk is now Britain's most important county holding more than a third of the national population in 1998 (Ogilvie *et al.* 2000). However, this increase is contrary to the national trend which shows little change in overall population levels but a marked contraction in range – in 1988-1991 the species was found to be absent in 62% of the 10-km squares occupied in 1968-1972 (Gibbons *et al.* 1993). Marchant *et al.* (1990) suggested that fluctuating populations "corresponded with climatic amelioration and its subsequent reversal", but the decline also correlates well with the demise of the rabbit through myxomatosis and the consequent regrowth of bracken and scrub. Clear-felled areas and plantations of up to three years old provide areas of bare ground and short vegetation which the Woodlark needs for foraging (Bowden & Hoblyn 1990).

Woodlarks remain on their breeding territories for most of the year with singing birds reported as early as 4th January (1991) and as late as 21st November (1989). During winter, Woodlarks are occasionally found on stubbles in single-species flocks, usually close to their nuptial areas. However, singles are sometimes found in Skylark flocks. Ticehurst considered winter records at Yarmouth and Lowestoft to be of occasional harsh-weather migrants of local origin that were shifted "off the bleak heathlands and breck to low-lying fields". He also noted the effect of the severe winter of 1916/7, which was thought responsible for the virtual extermination of the Woodlark in the Brandon district. There are only two records of wintering flocks on the coast prior to the early 1980s: seven at Thorpeness, on 8th January 1950 and six, which were flushed from the edge of a kale field at Campsea Ash, on 8th February 1957 (Payn 1978). Regular overwintering was discovered at Shottisham in successive winters from 1983/4 to 1986/7, when 20-30 were present. Other wintering flocks of 20 or more have been noted at Friston, 21 (30th December 1994), and at West Stow, 21 (25th January 1998). Numbers normally build up towards the end of the winter and 50 at Shottisham on 15th February 1985 is the largest concentration. Woodlarks vacate their Breckland strongholds during winter, but there are no known regular wintering sites. Payn mentioned flocks being put up from stubbles or bracken by beaters on winter shoots at Hengrave, Risby and the Fornhams and he detailed a flock of eight which spent several weeks around some stacks on Risby Heath. Although such flocks are surprisingly elusive, the lack of records of wintering flocks from West Suffolk in recent years is perhaps indicative of a change in habits.

Ringing recoveries confirm interchange between the coastal and Breckland breeding populations and East Anglian birds appear to be migratory (Bowden & Hoblyn 1990). Woodlarks ringed in Breckland have been recovered in Hampshire, Kent, Nottinghamshire, Lincolnshire and the Isles of Scilly. Woodlarks are rare at coastal watch-points, although one or two pass through during most years, usually from late September and mid-November and late February to mid-April.

Skylark (Sky Lark) *Alauda arvensis*

A common resident, winter visitor and passage migrant.

The Skylark is an early riser, delivering its delightful song from dawn until dusk in spring and summer. The species is common and widespread, but numbers have declined rapidly in the central cereal-growing areas and the population is much reduced throughout the county.

Suffolk's open countryside has long been favoured by this species and the map shows that it occurs almost throughout the county with most of the gaps likely to be due to under-recording. Skylarks breed amongst cereals and other arable crops with a clear preference for larger, more open fields. Mixed farmland with hedgerows, and young plantations are also suitable, but established woodland is avoided. Being such a common species, there are few references to it in SBRs, so assessing changes in status is difficult. However, CBC index levels demonstrate a long period of stability for the period 1966-1981, followed by sharp declines during the 1980s, to half their former level (Marchant *et al.* 1990). During the past 50 years, the loss of pastures and grassland leys has been considerable, on both sides of the county, and this would have contributed markedly towards the Skylark's decline. The Reydon Grove Farm study found between 9-25 pairs from 1964-1971 (Benson & Williamson 1972), compared to just a single pair in 1997 (Pearson 1998).

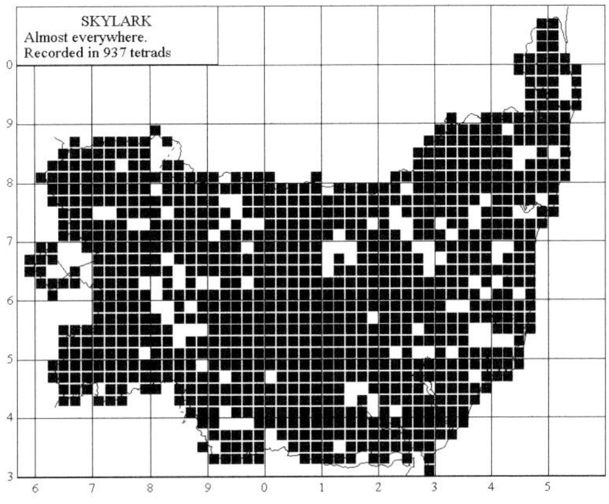

Single-figure groups are commonplace throughout the year and winter flocks of 50-100 are not uncommon. The species is susceptible to the effects of harsh weather, and may then become attracted to particular food-rich fields. Four-figure concentrations have been reported at Brantham, 1,500 on 21st December 1981, Great Welnetham 2,000 in January 1984 and the Alde estuary area, 1,000 on 9th February 1986.

Coastal passage is reported annually with several hundreds arriving from late September to early November, with the main movements in the last three weeks of this period. The species migrates diurnally and is frequently observed passing southwards or arriving from offshore. The LBO log demonstrates the variation in numbers from year to year. For example, October totals for 1990 were 2,335, including 853 on 13th, in 1991, 1,008 moved south, with a peak of 597 on 20th compared with 1992, when the autumn total reached only 657, including 119 on 8th November. An amazing 3,000 passed through Minsmere on 22nd October 1979. Movements can also be associated with the onset of harsh weather.

A Belgian-ringed Skylark found dead at Kenton, near Stowmarket, in 1990, confirmed immigration from the near Continent.

Shore Lark (Horned Lark) *Eremophila alpestris*

An uncommon winter visitor and passage migrant

Shore Larks
(Brian Small)

Shore Larks crouching amongst *Salicornia* on a saltmarsh, alongside coastal pools or on a shingle beach, are one of the joys of a birdwatcher's winter day. The wintering population is mostly restricted to north-east Suffolk with Benacre, Walberswick, Minsmere and Orfordness being the most favoured sites. Elsewhere along the coast, the species occurs solely as a passage migrant and is occasionally reported at Landguard Point.

Britain's first recorded Shore Lark occurred at Sheringham, Norfolk, in 1830 and one at Lowestoft Denes in November 1862 is Suffolk's first example, although birds shot in the Yarmouth area in 1850 and 1861 could have been taken in the county. Its presence in East Anglia ties in with its breeding range expansion into southern Scandinavia. It was unknown as a breeding species in the latter region till 1835 (Ticehurst 1932), but it has since flourished. Fluctuations in wintering numbers are closely related to the species' breeding success.

Flocks of up to a dozen birds are not uncommon at a few favoured sites, and very occasionally these have been more substantial. Gatherings of 57 were reported at Aldeburgh beach in 1966/7, between 60 and 80 at Minsmere in December 1972, 50 at Minsmere in January and early February 1975, 40 at Walberswick in November 1977 and 58 at Orfordness in January 1999. A flock of c.40 flying south at Benacre on 3rd February 1979 was part of a huge exodus of Skylarks at the onset of a period of severe weather. Wintering flocks are often faithful to a particular feeding site, sometimes frequenting the same area of shore throughout the winter. Interchange between sites is sometimes suspected and Britain's first ringing recovery of this species involved an adult male trapped at Walberswick on 1st November 1962 and recovered at Brightlingsea, Essex, at the end of that month.

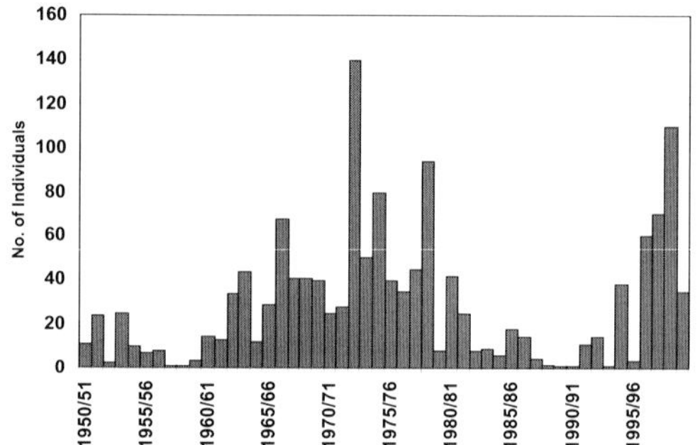

The annual winter totals of the Shore Lark from 1950/51 to 1999/2000

There are quite large fluctuations in wintering numbers. High numbers were recorded between the mid-1960s and the early 1980s, when the Walberswick shore pools and Minsmere's Scrape regularly hosted double-figure flocks. Numbers were particularly low during the mid-1980s and early 1990s.

Horned Larks normally return to their wintering areas in late October and stay until early April. Laggards have been reported in May on six occasions and twice in June, these being four on the saltings at Breydon Water on 16th (1956) and a single on a Lowestoft recreation ground on 4th (1987). One in worn, summer plumage at Ness Point, Lowestoft, on 19th-20th July 1991, was a remarkable occurrence and the only record for that month. There are no August records and two trapped and taken into captivity at Aldeburgh in September 1882 (Babington 1884-1886) and one on Minsmere's beach from 28th-30th September 1991 are the only reports for that month.

One killed at Bardwell in 1866 and singles at Alton Water from 8th-18th April 1979 and at Moulton from 20th-25th October 1994 are the only records away from the coast and estuaries.

Sand Martin *Riparia riparia*

A common summer visitor and passage migrant

Sand Martins breed in colonies on sea cliffs, river banks and sand and gravel pits. The population is subject to large fluctuations depending greatly on conditions in their wintering area in the Sahel region of West Africa. It is a common passage migrant, although it is not so obvious at migration watch-points as Swallows and House Martins.

The first of the year normally reach Suffolk in late March, the Sand Martin being one of Britain's earliest spring migrants. Numbers build quickly around lakes and reservoirs and flocks of 200-300 in early April are frequently reported. The largest spring gathering involved 1,500 at Lackford Wildfowl Reserve on 8th May 1992. Two at Bawdsey Cliffs on 21st February 1990 was remarkably early, but that particular spring was exceptional for early migrants. Sand Martins were reported before 15th March in nine other years all between 1977 and 2001.

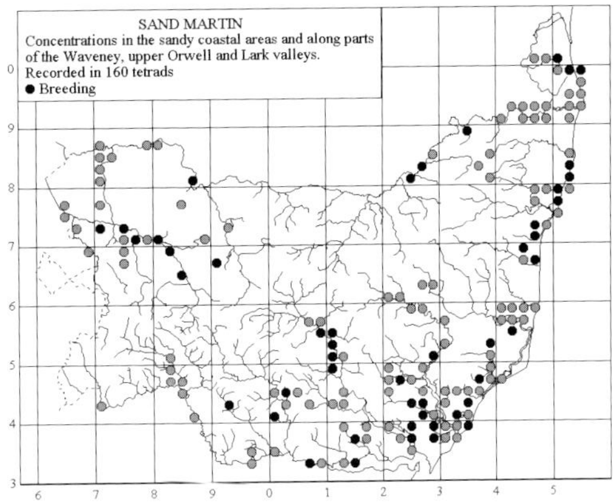
SAND MARTIN
Concentrations in the sandy coastal areas and along parts of the Waveney, upper Orwell and Lark valleys.
Recorded in 160 tetrads
● Breeding

The map shows that the breeding population is concentrated in the sandy areas towards the coast and along some river valleys – a pattern which is undoubtedly due to the availability of nest sites.

Up until 1968, there were large numbers of the species present in many areas. However, the population crashed between 1968 and 1969 due to drought in their wintering quarters, and numbers have not recovered since (Marchant *et al.* 1990). A census in 1991 revealed a county population of 2,500-3,000 pairs with the largest colonies being in sea-cliffs between Benacre and Dunwich (SBR), but the size of a breeding colony can vary enormously between the years – for example from 2-3 pairs to 1,000-2,000 pairs. Although sandstone cliff-faces are the favoured nesting sites, more unusual sites include sawdust heaps at Brandon and Wordwell, sand bunkers on Flempton golf-course, drainage holes in the riverside wall at Stratford St Mary, brick abutments of Temple Bridge, Cavenham, and sand piles amongst the sea-dredged aggregate-processing plant at Landguard Point.

Sand Martins are common on autumn passage, when juveniles and adults form reedbed roosts at coastal sites, occasionally gathering in massive numbers. For example, the Minsmere marshes hosted huge gatherings in 1981 with counts of 35,000, 20,000 and 4,000 being logged in July, August and September respectively. There are no other five-figure counts, although 5,000 were at Minsmere on 14th September 1977.

Return migration starts in early July and usually peaks in late August or early September, with most gone by the end of that month – slightly earlier than House Martin and Swallow. Sand Martins are often mixed with other hirudines, but occur in smaller numbers. The highest counts involved 1,000 south over Havergate Island on 9th September 1953 and 1,400 south off Covehithe on 11th September 1988. Most have left by early October, but there are a few November records. Two at Pakefield on 9th December 1951 and two at Sizewell on 2nd December 1982 are the only records for that month. Ringing recoveries show that the species' migration route is through France and Iberia to its West African wintering grounds.

Swallow (Barn Swallow) — *Hirundo rustica*

A common summer visitor and passage migrant

The arrival of the Swallow is eagerly awaited each spring and, being such a popular species, any change in its fortunes is readily reported. The species breeds widely throughout the county and sometimes gathers in huge numbers, especially during autumn, when evening roosts assemble at coastal reedbeds. Large numbers stream southwards during September and October.

Swallows generally arrive in early April, but, in favourable immigration conditions, a few are reported in March. Suffolk's earliest was noted on 6th March 1922 (Ticehurst 1932) and one over Minsmere's dunes on 12th March 2000 is the next date. In 1989, one at Haverhill on 24th March heralded an exceptional arrival, with 23 additional records from 17 other sites during that month.

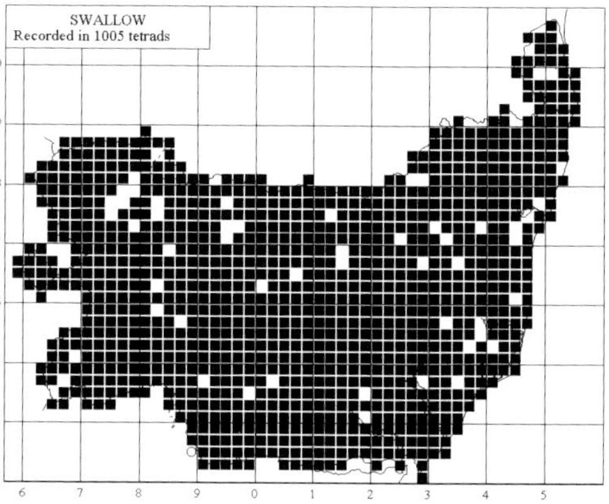

The map shows that there are few areas where Swallows are not present with the only significant gaps being in forestry areas of Breckland and along the coast.

Swallows nest in barns, out-buildings, Second World War pill-boxes and porches and are a familiar feature of the farmyard. Site fidelity was proved as early as 1846, when one returned to Gunton year after year, being identified by a piece of silk which was tied to its leg (Ticehurst 1932). There has been a considerable decline in numbers since 1980, which has been partially attributed to improved farm hygiene and the consequential reduction in flies, as well as a marked reduction in the availability of nest sites (Marchant *et al.* 1990). Rainfall in its winter quarters may also play a part. The Reydon Grove Farm study from 1964-1971 revealed an estimated 5-10 pairs (Benson & Williamson 1972), compared to just a single pair in 1997 (Pearson 1998). Barn Swallows also suffer greatly during sudden cold snaps as seen on 5th-6th June 1816, when hundreds could be collected in Ipswich as they sat on the grass "benumbed and starved" (Ticehurst 1932). Similar events occurred on 29th May 1869, Whitsun 1891 and May 1902.

Autumn migration starts in late July, but large gatherings rarely occur before the end of August. Peak passage occurs in September. Pre-migration gatherings are sometimes very large indeed. About half a million were reported to be roosting at Walberswick, from 1st-8th September 1966, the birds performing spectacular aerobatic flights before entering the reedbed. No other estimates come anywhere near this figure, but 10,000 or more were noted at Minsmere in September 1977 and August 1983. Coastal movements are also often considerable, with day counts ranging from 5,000-10,000 being logged at Landguard Point almost annually since 1981. Visible migration is far more evident in September, with a month count of c.65,000 being noted in 1981. The largest reported movement involved an estimated 30,000-50,000 birds at Shingle Street on 10th September 1958 (Payn 1978).

The bulk of the population has left by mid-October, but a few linger into November and there have been 19 December records. A tardy individual was noted at Nacton on 16th December 1956, but Suffolk's latest was at Bradfield St George on 24th. One at Bromeswell and Melton on 22nd January 1988 and again four days later at Melton Hill, Woodbridge, are remarkable records.

The Swallow has one of the longest migration flights of any passerine, the bulk of British breeding birds wintering in South Africa. Up to the end of 1995, 20 of the 231 recoveries of Suffolk-ringed birds have been found in African countries, 17 south of the Sahara and 13 in South Africa.

Red-rumped Swallow *Hirundo daurica*

A very rare passage migrant: 17 records involving 18 individuals

Visitations to Britain and Ireland have increased significantly during the past 40 years from only seven before 1958 to 357 from 1958-2000 (BBRC). The increase in vagrancy has been attributed to a northward expansion of breeding range from extreme southern Spain through to France (Dymond *et al.* 1989).

One at Eastbridge on 21st April 1987 was the first for the county, followed by five others that year, including one which lingered at Southwold on the late dates of 21st-25th November. Red-rumped Swallows have since been noted almost annually with 1988 and 1993 being the only blank years in the period 1987-97. Singles at Suffolk Water Park intermittently from 18th-23rd May 1995 and at Livermere from 8th-9th May 1997 are the only records away from the immediate coastline.

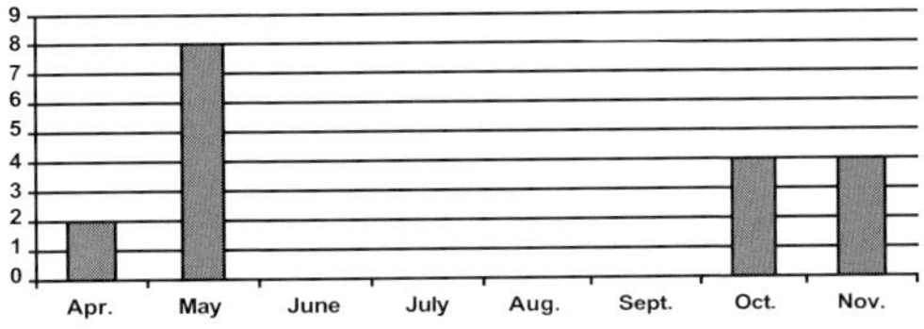

The seasonal occurrences of the Red-rumped Swalow (all records 1987-2001)

The Red-rumped Swallow breeds in Iberia, southern France, north-east Africa and the Balkans and winters south of the Sahara.

House Martin *Delichon urbica*

A common summer visitor and passage migrant

This species' characteristic globe-shaped nests of mud, clinging to the rectangular eaves of both new and old houses, are a common sight in both rural and urban areas. Unlike its close relatives, House Martins do not form large pre-migration roosts, but enormous coastal movements occur in September.

The House Martin is the last of the swallow family to reach Britain, normally arriving in numbers in late April and early May. There are 13 March records, including one at Woodbridge on 15th and, occasionally, early birds are in groups of up to five. Singles at Capel St Mary on 24th February 1990 and Southwold on 17th February 1998 are remarkably early.

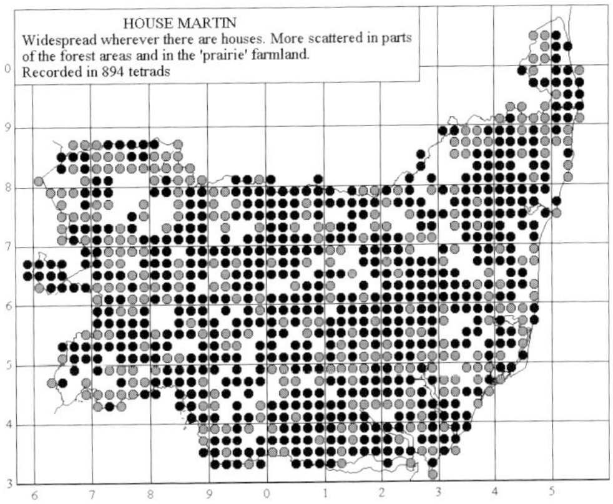

HOUSE MARTIN
Widespread wherever there are houses. More scattered in parts of the forest areas and in the 'prairie' farmland.
Recorded in 894 tetrads

The map shows that it is very widespread and the distribution matches that of houses. Most of the gaps shown are areas of dense forest (in Breckland and along the coast) or in 'prairie-like' arable farming areas in north and central Suffolk.

A comprehensive county-wide census of breeding numbers has never been undertaken and any rise or fall in the species' fortunes is largely judged on nest counts from favoured buildings. However, a survey undertaken in Bury St Edmunds in late June and early July 1975 yielded 247 nests (Last 1975). High counts from elsewhere include 80 at Glemsford in 1981, 69 on a Friston farmhouse and 43 on a factory at Long Melford in 1983, 88 on a cottage in Hadleigh in 1979 and 78 on Blythburgh water tower in 1988. Unusual nest sites include three with Swallows' nests in a cow shed at Wantisden in 1967, a colony of 57 under 12 street-lighting shades at Levington in 1978 and eight in the porch of Stoke-by-Nayland church in 1980.

House Martins rear up to three broods and, occasionally, young are tended at the nest as late as October. Sudden cold snaps greatly affect breeding success, but usurpation of nests by House Sparrows seems no longer to be the threat that it was formerly, due to the recent decline of the latter species. Thousands perished during severe weather from 24th-29th May 1869, including hundreds in Ipswich alone (Ticehurst 1932). House Martins are one of the few birds which return to their nest after fledging as seen by four individuals still visiting nests at Dunwich on 15th November 1981. In an exceptionally late breeding record, parents were still feeding young in a Wangford nest on 10th November 1985.

Autumn passage usually gets underway in late August and peaks in mid- to late September. Along the coast, large flocks stream southward close to the shoreline and four-figure day counts are regularly logged at Landguard Point. Passage is almost over by early October with a few trickling through to early November. The largest total was recorded at Southwold, when 45,000 passed south on 11th September 1988. In most years, a few linger to the third week of November, mainly around coastal towns and villages and there are numerous sightings if the weather remains mild. For example, between 1982 and 1987 numbers present varied from a low of seven to a high of 160. There are 20 December records, the latest being noted on 22nd at Gorleston-on-Sea in 1848.

There are few ringing recoveries, but one trapped at Boyton on 25th May 1968 was recovered in Vaala, Finland, three years later.

Richard's Pipit *Anthus novaeseelandiae*

A rare passage migrant: 43 records

Suffolk's records have been exclusively coastal with occurrences restricted to open grassland, marshes and cultivated areas. The first was noted on Havergate Island on 6th October 1968. It was followed by another at Minsmere on 24th November of that year. The bulk of the occurrences have occurred in October, with a peak towards the end of the month. Singles at Minsmere on 2nd May 1977 and North Warren from 5th-6th May 1997 are the only spring records. Nine records in 1994 constitutes Suffolk's best year and coincided with a large influx of various other eastern vagrant species. All records refer to singles except for two at Minsmere from 7th-8th October 1969 and up to three 1st-18th October 1970. Extreme dates for autumn occurrences are 13th September and 24th November.

The breeding range of the migratory race *A. n. richardi*, which occurs in western Europe, extends from western Siberia east to the Altai and Tarbagatai mountains and winters with local races from the Indian sub-continent to south-east Asia (Sharrock 1974). There has been an extraordinary upsurge in vagrancy to Britain from 140 records prior to 1958 to 1,245 from 1958-1985 (Dymond *et al.* 1989), which is probably due to a better understanding of plumage characteristics and an increase in the number of observers.

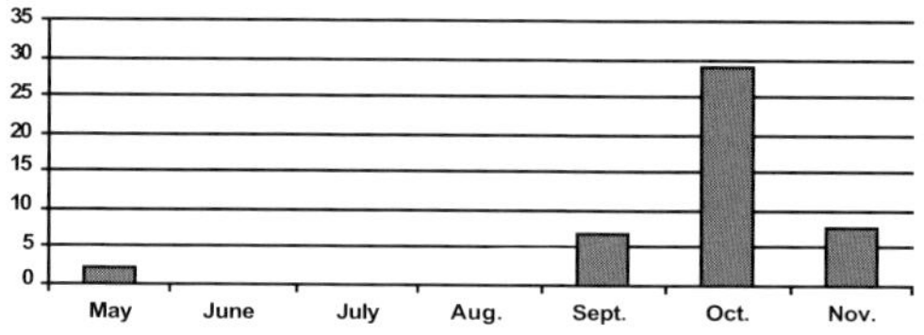

The seasonal occurrences of the Richard's Pipit (all records 1968-2000)

Blyth's Pipit *Anthus godlewskii*

Accidental: one record

1994 Felixstowe: Landguard Point, first-winter 4th-10th November

The above individual was originally identified as a Richard's Pipit, but careful examination both in the field and in the hand revealed its true identity (Odin & Marsh 1996). Unfortunately for the birdwatchers (and the bird itself) this individual fell prey to a local Kestrel.

The species is an extreme vagrant to Britain and the above individual is only the fifth from a total of nine authenticated records for Britain and Ireland up to the end of 2000 (BBRC), although there are a number of earlier claims still under consideration.

This pipit's breeding range extends from southern Siberia, China and north-eastern India and it winters in India, Sri Lanka and the Andaman Islands.

Tawny Pipit *Anthus campestris*

A rare passage migrant: 31 records

This species' choice of habitat differs slightly from Richard's Pipit – it favours shorter grassland. The increase in British records is not as marked as in the latter species, but again parallels the increase in observers. There were only 110 occurrences up to 1958 compared with 637 from 1958-1985 (Dymond *et al.* 1989).

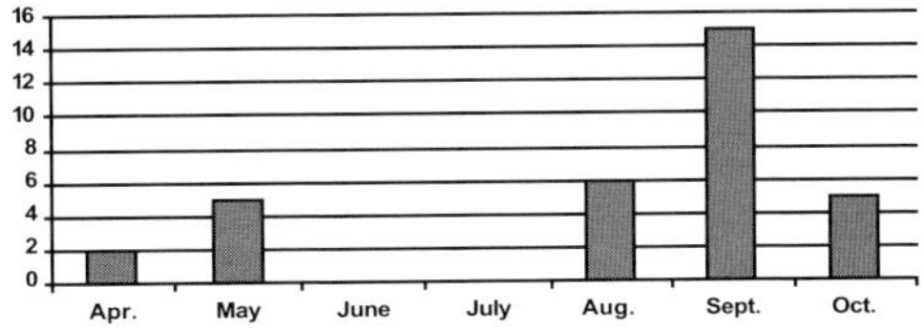

The seasonal occurrences of the Tawny Pipit (all records 1889-2001)

One caught near Lowestoft, on 2nd September 1889, is the county's first record, but a long period elapsed before there were further occurrences at Orford and Covehithe in autumn 1960. There were four other records for the 1960s including three, possibly five, at Sizewell during the 'Great Fall' from 5th-8th September 1965. Two at Minsmere on 9th September 1968 is the only other record involving more than one bird. There were only three records for the 1970s but, thereafter, visitations became almost annual with 1981, 1986, 1987 and 1990 being the only blank years. Most pass through quickly and few stay more than a few hours. One which fed on the cliffs at Easton Bavents from 27th October-3rd November 1991 was a long-stayer and the only record for November. A quarter of the occurrences have been in spring, which is slightly above the national trend (14% of records were in spring for the period 1958-1985) (Dymond *et al.* 1989). The extreme dates are 16th April to 28th May and 4th August to 3rd November.

The Tawny Pipit breeds in western Europe, but habitat changes have resulted in a marked retraction of its range during the 20th century. The Western Palearctic race *A. c. campestris* winters in the Sahel region south of the Sahara. Although formerly a nationally rare species, it now occurs annually principally on the English east and south coasts. Suffolk records are exclusively coastal.

Olive-backed Pipit *Anthus hodgsoni*

Accidental: one record

2000 Southwold: Constitution Hill/Golf Course, 12th-13th November

The above individual was located early in the morning in an elm hedge, but became extremely elusive later in the day when sightings were limited to an occasional flights views as it moved from one clump of gorse to another. It was seen intermittently the next day.

The Olive-backed Pipit breeds in north-east Russia to central and east Asia and winters in south-east Asia. It is a rare vagrant to Britain and Ireland, being recorded on 228 occasions up to the end of 2000, but only once prior to 1958 (BBRC).

Tree Pipit *Anthus trivialis*

A locally common summer visitor and passage migrant

The song-flight of the Tree Pipit is now observed mostly on heathland and young forestry plantations on the coast and in Breckland. The species is rarely reported away from these areas other than in passage periods.

The Tree Pipit was "somewhat scarce and distinctly local" in the early part of the 20th century (Ticehurst 1932) but, in the 1950s, nesting occurred widely in a variety of habitats throughout the county. Afforestation of heath and Breckland, during the 1930s, resulted in an increase in suitable habitat, which the species was quick to colonise. There were concentrations on heathland and marginal lands, from Ipswich north to Blythburgh, and in suitable places throughout Breckland. In the latter region, the range extended westwards to the fenland localities of Beck Row, Kennyhill and Sedge Fen and bounded by Knettishall, Livermere, Stanton, Rickinghall, Rougham and Depden in the east and south. Tree Pipits infrequently nested in central and southern areas, being recorded at Stowmarket, Stoke-by-Clare, Ousden, Haverhill and along the Waveney Valley as far upstream as Redgrave and Hoxne. A decline was noted throughout the 1950s and 1960s, attributed to the destruction of heathlands and the loss of other breeding areas through excessive growth of herbage and scrub, which followed the onset of myxomatosis. The county's breeding population then ranged from 50-100 pairs, with the bulk confined to heath and forest around Minsmere and Walberswick and in Breckland. In the 1970s and 1980s, a few pairs still nested in oak parkland at Staverton and in south Suffolk at Wherstead and Bentley. Forestry clearing in the early 1980s, resulted in an apparent increase

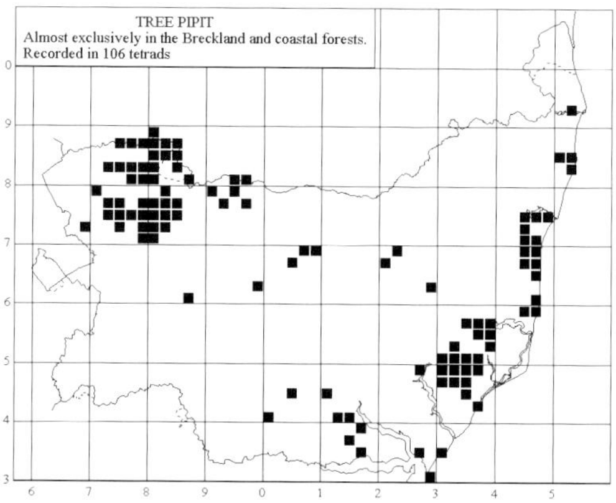

from only 45 pairs in 1981 to 150 in 1984. About 60% of this population was located in Breckland. The reported increase continued through to the 1990s, against the national trend, which has shown a downward drift since 1970 (Marchant *et al.* 1990). The map shows that the nucleus of the population still lies in Breckland with smaller concentrations on heathland at Minsmere and Walberswick and in Rendlesham Forest. Tree Pipits are surprisingly scarce in Tunstall Forest and are absent from heathland and woodland around North Warren and Thorpeness. One or two isolated pairs linger on in central and south Suffolk.

Tree Pipits are diurnal migrants and most return to their breeding grounds by mid-April. There are only seven March records with one at Walberswick on the 21st, in 1968, being the earliest. Spring passage is rarely obvious with the first of the year invariably being seen on the breeding grounds. A spring passage total of 22, at Landguard Point in 1986, is exceptionally high. Small movements pass along the coast each autumn, with peak passage occurring from mid-August to mid-September. Double-figure counts are rare, although during the 'Great Fall' of September 1965 an amazing 500 were at Walberswick, 150 at Minsmere and 25 at Lowestoft – totals which far exceed any other figures. About 25 at Havergate on September 3rd 1958 is also worthy of note. Fifty-two were logged at Landguard Point during autumn 1984, 23 in 1985 and 33 in 1986, but no other years scored more than ten. A few birds occasionally linger until early October and one at Fagbury Cliff on 24th October 1994 is the latest for the county.

An adult ringed at Walberswick in May 1968 was recovered in southern Spain the following autumn and a pullus ringed at Sutton Heath in June 1968 was found in Morocco in early spring 1969.

Pechora Pipit *Anthus gustavi*

Accidental: one record

1975 Minsmere: The Scrape, 27th April

The Pechora Pipit breeds in the scrub tundra and taiga forest zones of the subarctic extending from north-east Russia through Siberia to the Bering Strait. It winters in the Philippines, Borneo and Sulawesi and is a rare autumn vagrant to Britain, where it has been recorded on 67 occasions up to the end of 2000 (BBRC). The Minsmere occurrence was the first of only two spring records for Britain.

Meadow Pipit *Anthus pratensis*

A locally common resident, common passage migrant and winter visitor

The plaintive alarm call of the Meadow Pipit is often the first sign of the species' presence. It is still fairly well distributed on meadows, heaths and commons, during summer, although in far fewer numbers than formerly. The population is now mainly coastal, although there are small pockets in Breckland and in central and south-west Suffolk. It is far more common on passage and during winter.

The Meadow Pipit was well distributed throughout the county early in the 20th century and, although the loss of grassland has restricted its range, it remains common at coastal localities. However, the species is now more or less absent from the heavy clay areas of central and south Suffolk and is rare around Newmarket. In Breckland, the Meadow Pipit was "the most abundant bird of the heather" (Payn 1978), prior to afforestation, but only a few remain there today. There are also a few nesting pairs around Haverhill and along the Blyth and Waveney valleys. Breeding densities are demonstrated by data collected at the main breeding areas in 1993 which showed 21 territories in the Castle Marsh/North Cove area, 11 at Minsmere, 32 at Sizewell, 28 at North Warren, 30 at Havergate and four at Landguard Point.

Passage movements are occasionally considerable on the coastal strip, but probably in lesser numbers than formerly. Spring passage is usually light, occurring from mid-March to mid-April, the largest gatherings being 400 at Alton Water on 15th March 1981 and 200 on Cavenham Heath on 23rd March 1995. Ticehurst described numbers passing Lowestoft as "almost incredible", with autumnal increases noted from mid-August to November and peaking in October. Nowadays, peak migration occurs in late September when small flocks pass south from early till mid-morning or arrive from offshore. Day-counts occasionally reach four-figures, the highest being 1,378 at Landguard Point, 25th September 1988 and 1,200 (in one hour) at Minsmere on 17th September 1992.

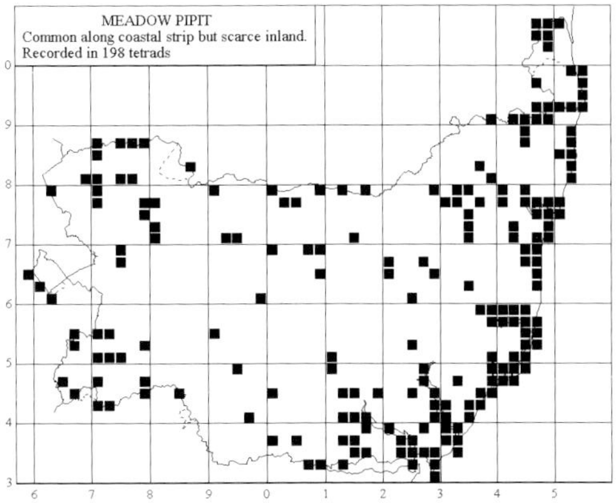

The overwintering population is more widespread, although the largest numbers frequent coastal localities, with saltings and sewage farms being favoured feeding sites. The pipit is most often noted in small flocks of 5-20, although three-figure flocks are not uncommon on coastal marshes, where birds feed on grassland as well as newly drilled fields. The largest wintering flocks include: 200-300 at Trimley Marshes, 31st December 1990; 200 at Aldringham, 7th February 1993 and 150 inland at Moulton, 22nd January 1994.

Most European Meadow Pipits move south in winter to Iberia and North Africa (Lack 1986) and this is demonstrated by ringing returns. For example, up to the end of 1995, Suffolk-ringed birds have been recovered in France (2), Spain (5), Portugal and Morocco (2). One found dead on Orfordness on 7th October 1998 had been ringed at Rogoland, Norway, on 3rd September 1995. The latter recovery coincided with a huge influx of passage migrants including record numbers of Ring Ouzels.

Red-throated Pipit *Anthus cervinus*

Accidental: three records

1982 Trimley St Martin: Loompit Lake, 15th May
1992 Bawdsey: Shingle Street, 11th October
2000 Bawdsey: Shingle Street, trapped 30th September

The Red-throated Pipit is an annual visitor to the British Isles, being noted on 425 occasions up to the end of 2000 (BBRC). There is a clear spring bias in eastern counties, but there are slightly more autumn records overall (Dymond *et al.* 1989). The three Suffolk individuals were each seen by only a handful of observers, the visits being all too brief. It is likely that the species regularly passes along the Suffolk coast during autumn passage and there have been a number of call-only claims which have not been fully substantiated.

This pipit's breeding range extends from Norway to north-east Siberia and it winters in Africa south of the Sahara.

Rock Pipit *Anthus petrosus*

A locally common winter visitor and passage migrant

The Rock Pipit is almost exclusively coastal, with singles or small groups frequenting estuarine localities during the winter months, as well as a few other selected sites on the immediate coastline. Numbers increase significantly during passage periods, particularly during the autumn, and it is most numerous around the Alde, Orwell and Stour estuaries.

Rock Pipits nest on rocky coastlines around the British Isles, but are absent, as a breeding species, between the Humber and the Thames. Ticehurst dismissed claims of regular breeding on the Felixstowe and Walton cliffs during the 19th century, on the grounds of lack of significant changes in habitat, together with its absence in the area over the period 1890-1930. Although there have been no records of birds holding territory, the pipit is occasionally seen during the summer months and one was in full song on a factory roof on the Norfolk side of Yarmouth Harbour, on 3rd July 1989 (Allard 1990). Single-day midsummer occurrences have been reported on five occasions: Minsmere, 15th July 1950; Burgh Castle, 19th July 1957; Minsmere, 27th July 1983; Lowestoft, 1st June 1991 and Landguard Point, 19th July 1993.

Most birds depart in late March and there are few April records, although small numbers are noted on spring passage with wintering birds slipping away almost unnoticed.

Return passage is normally noted from late September and there are a few August records, including three at Pakefield cliffs on 30th August 1978. The highest gatherings are most often noted later in the autumn and include: c.70 at Westwood Marsh, Walberswick on 19th October 1958; 40 on R Alde, 13th October 1985 and 54 on Orfordness, 13th November 1988.

It would appear that the bulk of the passage and wintering population consists of birds of the highly migratory Fennoscandian/north-west Russian race *A. p. littoralis.* The nominate British and Irish race *A. p. petrosus* is largely sedentary and rarely ventures away from its breeding area. There is no conclusive evidence of the British race ever occurring in Suffolk, although it has been reported by some observers. Three birds ringed in the Halland district of Sweden have been found wintering on the Suffolk coast, proving the presence of *A. p. littoralis.* One colour-ringed on the Isle of May, sometime between 1982 and 1986, frequented Benacre in 1991, but was not racially assigned .

Flocks of up to five regularly winter at about 12 coastal localities and the largest concentrations most often occur on the estuaries. These include: 32 on the north bank of the Stour, 16th January 1983; 33 at Slaughden, 25th December 1993 and 35 at Friston, on the Alde, 13th February 1994. None of these birds was racially assigned, although a group of 19 on Southwold Golf Course on 9th December 1992 was considered to be all of the race *A. p. littoralis.*

Rock Pipits will often feed in flooded meadows adjacent to river estuaries or by the coast and will occasionally mix with Meadow Pipits on sewage-works filter beds. The species regularly winters in the upper reaches of estuaries and on the Orwell as far up river as Ipswich Docks. However, it is seldom reported far from coastal environments, and there were only 26 inland records up to the end of 2000. The Lark and Gipping valleys have been the most favoured localities in recent years.

Water Pipit *Anthus spinoletta*

An uncommon visitor and passage migrant

The Water Pipit breeds in the high mountains of the Western Palearctic and is principally recorded in Britain as a passage migrant. A few overwinter on reed stubbles and beside coastal broads, but the species is more evident in spring, when summer-plumaged birds linger at wetland localities. Passage birds favour flooded meadows where they feed on insects at the water's edge. The pipit was formerly regarded as conspecific with Rock Pipit and the BOURC only recognised it as a distinct species in 1985. There is likely to have been some confusion between Water Pipits and Scandinavian Rock Pipits which would have probably influenced early records.

Two at Easton Broad on 3rd April 1937 constituted the first authentic record for the county, followed by a single at Benacre Pits on 22nd January 1951. Thereafter, the pipit was recorded regularly. There is usually a distinct influx from late March to mid-April and return passage is often noted in October. Water Pipits are normally reported singly or in groups of up to eight. Ones and twos are noted annually at a few favoured wintering sites, but groups of 26 on freshly-cut reed at Walberswick on 26th February 1976 and the same number at Minsmere in December 1994 are exceptional records.

Wintering birds sometimes linger to early April and are often joined by passage birds. The species is regularly noted at coastal sites in April and some birds attain summer plumage showing the characteristic pink flush to the underparts. There are three records for early May with 7th being the latest spring date. There are no summer records and one at Minsmere on 27th August 1989 was a particularly early autumn return. Water Pipits have yet to be noted in September and wintering birds begin to appear from mid-October.

There have been ten inland records and all bar two involve individuals in late March or April. The two exceptions are three at Lakenheath in February 1985 and two there on 28th January 1995. One in full summer plumage at Whitton, Ipswich, from 19th-26th April 1969 was the first inland occurrence and singles at Belstead in 1972 and 1973 were followed by one at Lackford in March 1975 – the first record for West Suffolk. Water Pipits have been regular noted at Lakenheath Fen and Washes since the mid-1990s.

Yellow Wagtail *Motacilla flava flavissima*

A locally common summer visitor and passage migrant

As a nesting species, the Yellow Wagtail is locally distributed mainly in the southern half of the county, although there are small concentrations along the Waveney Valley, at the coastal end of the Blyth and on the fenland ridge. Damp meadows and rough pastures are the most favoured nesting sites, but nearby arable crops, saltings and heathland are also chosen. Feeding concentrations are noted in early spring and evening roosts regularly gather in late August and September. The species is frequently recorded at migration watch-points and an increase in wetland nature reserves, gravel workings and reservoirs, over the past 50 years, has created ideal feeding and resting areas.

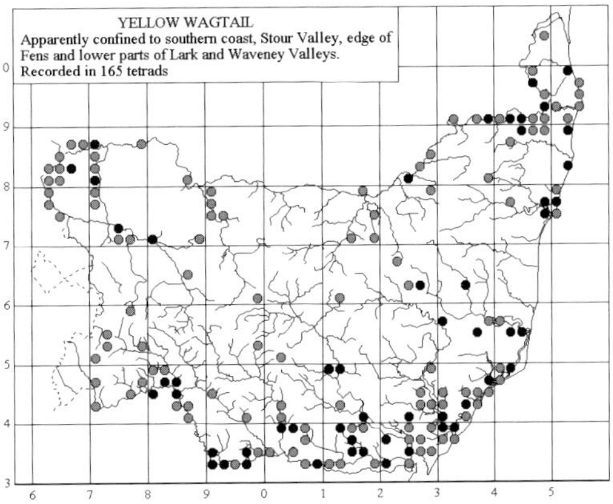

YELLOW WAGTAIL
Apparently confined to southern coast, Stour Valley, edge of Fens and lower parts of Lark and Waveney Valleys.
Recorded in 165 tetrads

The species' status has changed little over the past century, although the drainage of marshland habitats and the reduction in dairy herds along with the general intensification of agriculture has resulted in local declines and extinction is some areas. A noticeable shift of nesting birds from water meadows to heather was noted in Breckland in the early 1950s (Robertson 1954) and in 1965 a few pairs were still nesting on heathland on both sides of the county. The species was once plentiful on the immediate coastline, sometimes nesting on shingle towards the back of the beach. However, disturbance, most noticeable at Walberswick and Dunwich during the period 1960-1972, has resulted in desertion of this habitat (Pearson 1973). Ten pairs were breeding at Minsmere and a few lingered on in the Stour Valley at Sudbury in 1971 and one nested on heathland at Cavenham in 1991.

The main arrival occurs during the second week of April, although a few early birds are noted in late March in most years. One at Woodbridge on 27th February 1942 is exceptionally early and the only record for that month. Other early arrivals include one at Flempton on 8th March 1990 and another at Felixstowe Ferry, 14th March 1991. Yellow Wagtails sometimes gather in numbers at coastal meadows during spring passage, with Minsmere and Alton Water almost holding the monopoly of flocks of 50-100. April concentrations of that order were noted at Minsmere in 1951, 1953, 1979 and 1983, at Alton Water in 1983 and 1995 and Hopton-on-Sea in 1994.

Pre-migration gatherings occur in late summer and the wagtail was particularly abundant in 1989 and 1990. During the former year, a pre-roost flock of 200 was noted at Alton Water, on 23rd July and, in 1990, reedbed roost counts of 660, 750 and 800 were noted at Burgh Castle on 19th, 24th and 31st August respectively and 300 were at Holbrook Creek, from 26th-28th August. Autumn departure takes place from mid-August to late September and the species' distinctive call ensures that it is easily located at migration watch-points where visible passage is sometimes substantial. Monthly totals at LBO regularly reach three-figures in August and September, with the highest day-counts being 47 and 69 on August 22nd and 28th 1990 respectively. Few birds remain in October, although there are four November records and an Eastern Blue-headed Wagtail, which lingered at Minsmere from 16th November-8th December 1967, may well have been attempting to overwinter (see below). One which fed with Pied Wagtails at Holbrook Sewage Farm, between 27th December-4th January 1986/7, is the only suggestion of over-wintering. Ringing returns have shown that the wagtail migrates through Iberia and winters in tropical West Africa. A juvenile, ringed at Minsmere on 15th September 1963, was recovered the following spring in the Netherlands and another trapped at Benacre 9th September 1964 was found in the Algarve, Portugal, four autumns later.

The British and extreme north-west European population are of the race *M. f. flavissima*, although the Blue-headed Wagtail *M. f. flava* regularly passes through Suffolk. The Scandinavian and North Siberian Grey-headed Wagtail *M. f. thunbergi* occurs almost annually with the bulk logged in late April or May. Three other races have occurred as vagrants.

Blue-headed Wagtail *M. f. flava*

An uncommon passage migrant occasionally hybridising with Yellow Wagtails

This race nests in central and northern Europe and occurs in East Anglia as a regular passage migrant, being more obvious in spring when in breeding plumage. Like the other races, female Blue-headed Wagtails are not separable in the field from female Yellow Wagtails, so all records are of males.

One or two are noted annually on spring passage, usually feeding amongst flocks of Yellow Wagtails. Up to three or four sometimes travel with larger groups. Blue-headed Wagtails occasionally oversummer and breeding has been confirmed on a number of occasions, sometimes mated with female Yellow Wagtails.

Grey-headed Wagtail *M. f. thunbergi*

A scarce passage migrant – c.50 records

The Grey-headed Wagtail nests in Norway east to the Gydanski peninsula in northern Siberia and a few pass through Suffolk in most years.

One at Lowestoft on 9th May 1947 was the first for the county, but the sub-species had almost certainly been overlooked previously. The next was spotted amongst Yellow Wagtails at Thorpeness on 4th September 1955 and there then followed a 20-year gap before the next one at Lowestoft, 19th April 1975. There are only three autumn records, the last two involving males at Landguard Point, on 15th-16th September 1994, and 17th-18th September 1995. Four together, at Landguard on 30th May 1992, is the largest gathering. One at Alton Water on 7th April 1985 is the earliest occurrence and one at Lackford on 5th June 1992 is the latest spring record.

Ashy-headed Wagtail *M. f. cinereocapilla*

Accidental: two records

1977	Butley: male 7th May
	Alton Water: male 22nd May

The Ashy-headed Wagtail breeds in Italy, including Sicily and Sardinia, and north-west Yugoslavia and intergrades with the Spanish Wagtail *M. f. iberiae* in Corsica, Mediterranean France and North Africa. Ashy-headed Wagtails have previously been reported breeding in Kent and Northern Ireland.

Black-headed Wagtail *M. f. feldegg*

Accidental: one record

1985	Felixstowe: Landguard Point, first-summer male 30th June

The breeding range extends through the Balkans to southern Ukraine, Crimea, the western shores of the Caspian Sea, Iran, Afghanistan, Turkey, Levant and Iraq. It is recorded in Britain as an extreme vagrant, being noted on nine occasions up to the end of 2000 (BBRC).

Eastern Blue-headed Wagtail *M. f. simillima*

Accidental: one record

1967	Minsmere: 16th November – 8th December

This race has a breeding range restricted to the north-east coast of the Sea of Okhotsk, Kamchatka and northern Kuril Islands and is a straggler into Europe (Cramp *et al.* 1974-1994).

One trapped and examined soon after its arrival to Minsmere is Suffolk's only record. Other British records include specimens collected in Fair Isle in October 1909 and September 1912 (Snow 1971).

Yellow Wagtail sp. *M. flava*

There is often considerable variation in head-pattern and colour amongst males in large travelling parties of wagtails and, although flocks often contain a mixture of races, occasionally hybrids or mutants occur. Individuals showing characteristics of Sykes's Wagtail *M. f. beema* have been noted at Southwold from 28th-30th April 1979 and at Alton Water, where two males were noted on 8th May and a single 17th 1989, followed by another with a female and two juveniles on 9th June 1990. Despite the distinctive plumage characteristics, records of Syke's types almost certainly relate to hybrids between *M. f. flava* x *flavissima*. Birds with pure white heads, a characteristic of the White-headed Wagtail *M. f. leucocephala*, have been noted at Walberswick, 25th April 1978 and at Alton Water throughout the summer of 1980, but both birds were thought to be abberant forms.

Citrine Wagtail *Motacilla citreola*

Accidental: three records

1964 Minsmere: first-winter, photographed, 17th October-26th November
1967 Minsmere: 10th-11th October
1995 Minsmere: male 10th May

Although the first was photographed and filmed and seen by many observers, the latter two showed to very few. The wagtail has been noted in Britain and Ireland on 134 occasions up to the end of 2000 and the 1995 Minsmere occurrence is one of only five for May, all of which were noted during the 1990s (BBRC).

The wagtail's breeding range extends from central Asia through to Amurland and winters in India and the Far East.

Grey Wagtail *Motacilla cinerea*

A local resident, passage migrant and winter visitor

Rushing streams and river systems of upland districts are the more usual haunts of the species and Suffolk's slow-moving waters only become suitable where flows are restricted at locks, weirs, lake-overflows and water mills. Isolated pairs now breed on almost all of the county's rivers and, in good years, numbers seem to be restricted by nest sites available. The winter population is supplemented by birds from elsewhere in Britain and perhaps from abroad. It is regularly logged on passage, particularly during the autumn, most often recognised by its call as it passes high overhead.

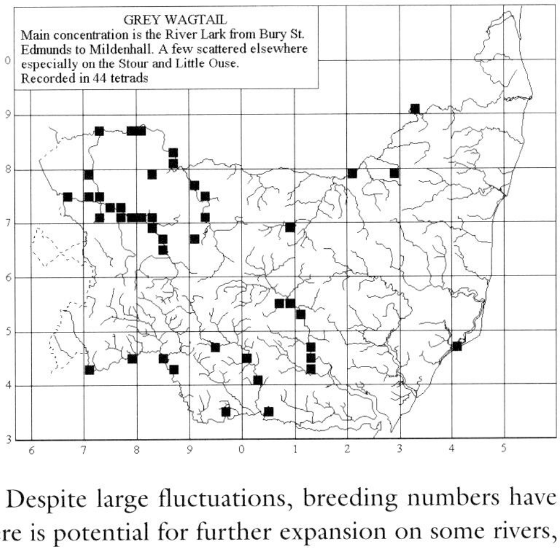

GREY WAGTAIL
Main concentration is the River Lark from Bury St. Edmunds to Mildenhall. A few scattered elsewhere especially on the Stour and Little Ouse.
Recorded in 44 tetrads

Few oversummering birds were found in Suffolk prior to 1950, with potential breeding pairs being located only at Mildenhall in 1865, Iken in 1888, Barsham and Blaxhall in 1911, Mettingham in 1921, River Lark in 1930s and Brandon in 1938. The species' spread into Suffolk, in the early 1950s, coincided with a general expansion into lowland counties, although colonisation by these early pioneers was dramatically halted by the two successive severe winters, 1961/2 and 1962/3, when the Grey Wagtail was lost as a breeding species in Suffolk for nine years. Its return in 1971, and subsequent recovery was aided by a succession of mild winters but again, noticeable dips in the breeding population followed the harsh winters of 1978/9, 1981/2 and 1984/5. Despite large fluctuations, breeding numbers have generally been on an upward trend, but although there is potential for further expansion on some rivers, the county maximum of 17 pairs in 1993 is unlikely to be exceeded greatly in the near future. The map shows that it is still mainly restricted to the River Lark downstream of Bury St Edmunds, but a few are noted on the upper reaches of the Stour and smaller streams in central Suffolk.

The population increase is paralleled by the numbers present throughout the county in all seasons. This is perhaps best illustrated by the number of sites where the species was recorded: 46 in 1986, 52 in 1988, 79 in 1990, 47 in 1992 and 75 in 1994.

On ledges or amongst ivy on a bridge or lock, generally above or close to flowing water, are favoured breeding sites. However, nests have been located amongst the workings of sluice gates and, in 1978, a pair incubated under the wheel-arch of an abandoned lorry at Lackford Quarry. One pair successfully fledged chicks from a nest on a building near Cornhill in the centre of Ipswich in 2001, their progress being monitored daily from the rooftop of an adjoining store.

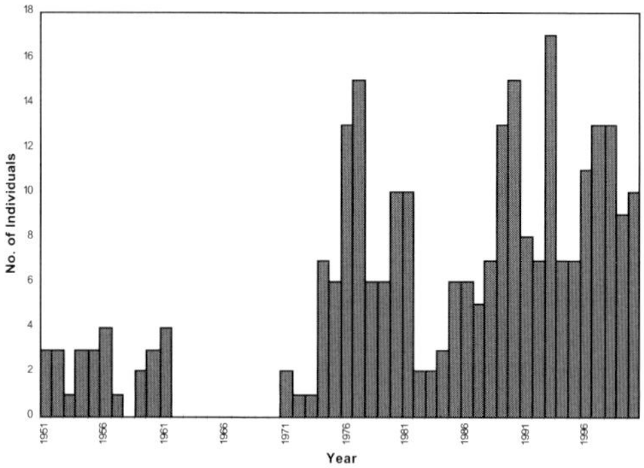

The number of breeding pairs of Grey Wagtail from 1951-2000

Most Scandinavian and many central European Grey Wagtails winter in Iberia and North Africa (Lack 1986) and this may account for the increase in the population during passage periods. The species is regularly recorded at migration watch-points and, occasionally, autumn movements are considerable. The largest ever recorded movement was in the autumn of 1993 when 110 were logged flying south at Minsmere, between 11th September and 31st October, with a maximum of 15 on 20th September and 64 were logged at Landguard Point between 12th September and 5th November. The largest movements normally follow successful breeding seasons. Many birds from northern Britain move south to south-west during autumn, but Berkshire to Witnesham is the furthest of three ringing recoveries involving Suffolk.

Some birds remain close to their breeding areas throughout the winter, but harsh weather may force them to migrate towards the coast. Wintering birds have traditional feeding sites often noted daily at the same estuarine stream, sewage works or slurry pit. Insects, attracted by the warmth of sewage filter beds, provide an important food source and there is hardly a sewage works in the county that does not host a wintering bird. One fed on insects with a Pied Wagtail under extensive night-time illumination at Sproughton B.F., 11th-18th January 1985.

Pied Wagtail *Motacilla alba yarrellii*

A common resident, passage migrant and summer visitor

The Pied Wagtail breeds widely throughout the county and is common in both rural and urban environments in all seasons. Post-breeding roosts occur at scattered localities in August and, building up during the autumn, are occupied throughout the winter. Small coastal movements are logged during passage periods.

The Pied Wagtail nests in most habitat types, being absent only from dense woodland and open heathland. Although the map shows it occurs throughout the county, it appears to be more prevalent in river valleys with more empty tetrads on the higher ground of central Suffolk and in the areas of dense woodland and forest. It breeds on farmland and readily nests in barns, outbuildings, crevices in trees and in old nests of other birds. Some rather unusual nest sites have been chosen, including an offshore rig at Sizewell outfall and an underground concrete chamber at Wherstead.

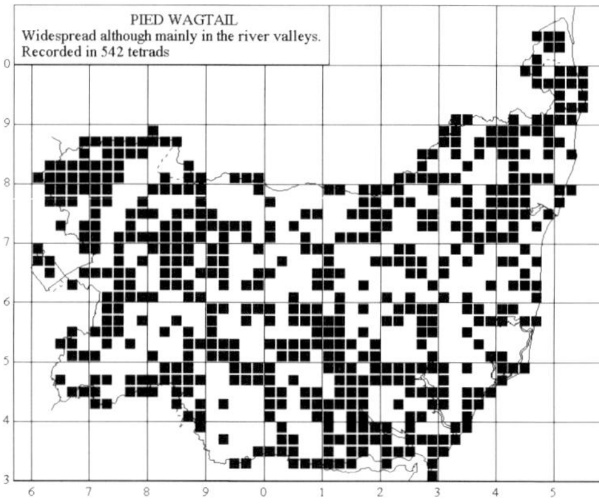

Wintering birds frequent both rural and urban environments. Many gather in flocks where food is abundant and filter beds at sewage works often attract feeding concentrations. Communal roosts most often occur in reedbeds, but factory roofs and even ornamental trees by busy car parks are also utilised. Roost sizes vary considerably from one site to another, some holding as few as 20-30 birds and others with 500 or more. Reedbed roosts of over 500 have been reported at Walberswick in October 1976 and at Redgrave in 1981. Tesco's car park at Copdock has attracted an evening roost since the early 1990s and 500 were present on 17th March 1993. Stowmarket Railway Station was favoured during the autumn of 1995 with up to 650 roosting between 16th October and 20th November. and two sites in Bury St Edmunds hosted roosts of 400 and 650 in January 1999. Like the Grey Wagtail, the species is seriously affected by severe weather, which was most noticeable following the arctic winters of 1961/2 and 1962/3. Ringing evidence suggests that the county's breeding population is largely sedentary, although harsh weather may encourage some to emigrate overseas. For example, three ringed at a Holbrook roost site, during early autumn between 1960 and 1962, were all recovered in Iberia, between late January and mid-March, in either 1962 or 1963, two of the most severe winters on record.

Local birds are joined by migrants during passage periods from March to early May and early September to early November. Visible migration is most evident at migration watch-points in the latter period when small numbers move south, usually singly or in loose flocks. Numbers peak in October when there is also an increase at communal roosts. The largest movement was logged at Landguard Point on 10th October 1999 when small groups totalling 71 birds flew south.

White Wagtail *M. a. alba*

A fairly common passage migrant

Birds of the nominate race, known as the White Wagtail, are common on spring passage, often coinciding with the immigration of Yellow Wagtails, during the second week of April. The main passage periods are late March to mid-April and early arrivals have been noted at Kessingland sewage works on 21st February 1992 and at Minsmere on 4th March the same year. Around 50-100 occur in good passage years, with coastal wetlands being the most favoured localities. Large concentrations include 45 at Minsmere on 24th March 1994. Small numbers of White Wagtails are reported in most autumns, most often in September with a few stragglers to mid-October, although the species is less easily identified from young Pied Wagtails during that season which may account for its apparent scarcity.

Waxwing (Bohemian Waxwing) *Bombycilla garrulus*

A rare winter visitor and passage migrant. Subject to influxes

Irruptions of Waxwing from remote taiga regions of Fennoscandia and western Siberia occur in some years, and these birds are one of the most exciting visitors to both rural and urban gardens. Most influxes are small and the species is absent altogether in some winters. However, arrivals are sometimes spectacular with three-figure flocks occasionally reported.

Small numbers occur in Suffolk in most winters, but during invasion years they are abundant. Recent 'Waxwing winters' were noted in 1949/50, 1957/8, 1965/6, 1970/1, 1990/1 and 1995/6. The timing of arrivals varies considerably from year to year. Influxes are rarely noted in Suffolk until after Christmas, even when there are earlier reports from elsewhere on Britain's east coast. Immigrants often arrive in waves and a flock of 100, arriving from offshore at Orfordness, on 27th January 1950, illustrates the lateness of the influxes in some years. Hele reported seeing two at Aldeburgh on 1st September 1888, but arrivals are rarely reported before late October. A claim of 150 in Dunwich Forest, on 12th October 1969, previously published by Payn, must be regarded as suspect as the birds were exceptionally early and there were few additional East Anglian records during the ensuing winter. A flock of 200-400 frequented a hawthorn hedge at Thorpeness in late October 1965 in a year when three-figure concentrations were noted at Aldeburgh, 200 on 11th November, Oulton Broad,

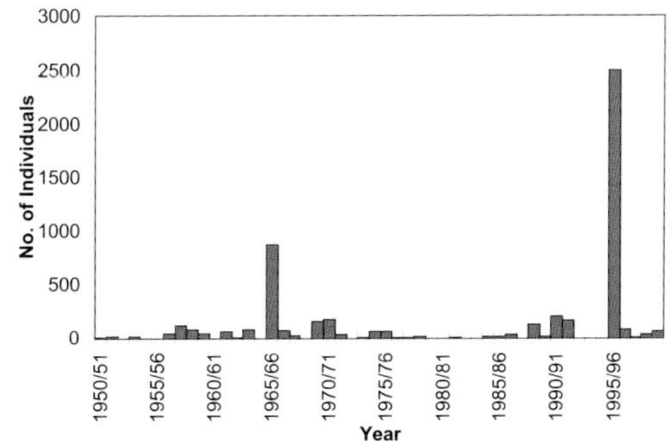

The numbers of Waxwings from 1950/51-1999/2000

c.100 on 15th November and Bury St Edmunds, c.150 during November and December. However, the events of early 1996 eclipsed all previous occurrences, when perhaps more than 2,500 were in the county and flocks of 50+ were widespread. Concentrations of 300 or more were noted around housing estates at Lowestoft, Woodbridge and Kesgrave, with a maximum of 453 at Kesgrave being the largest gathering ever recorded in Suffolk.

Most leave by mid-March, although occasionally a few linger into April. Two in Ipswich on 4th May 1971, two in Woodbridge on 5th May 1996, a single at Kelsale from 9th-15th May 1999 and another at Beccles on 9th May 2001 were the only May records.

A variety of berries, particularly rowan, cotoneaster, pyracantha and mallus form the favoured food source, but the species will also eat hips and haws and other fruits and will occasionally consume buds. The species has also been seen to eat snow, at Risby (Payn 1978) and Lowestoft (Crewe 1987), and insects. Birds rest on high vantage points such as television aerials and roofs before swooping down to strip shrubberies of fruits, but even large flocks can often be difficult to locate as they move to new feeding areas.

Birds bearing colour rings at Lowestoft in January and March 1989 had been trapped earlier that winter near Aberdeen, Scotland.

Dipper (White-throated Dipper) *Cinclus cinclus*

A very rare winter visitor and passage migrant

The Dipper has occurred in Suffolk on only 33 occasions, but has been present in 14 winters since 1946. The species often frequents the smallest of streams, in areas rarely covered by birdwatchers, and it is likely that many go unnoticed. Marine localities, such as Breydon Water and Minsmere, occasionally attract migrants moving through Suffolk in March and October.

The British race *C. c. gularis* and the Scandinavian Black-bellied Dipper *C. c. cinclus* are the two forms that have been found wintering in Suffolk. The majority of records have not been racially assigned and the remainder split fairly evenly between the two races.

The species is almost exclusively restricted to aquatic habitats favouring fast-flowing streams in the north and west of Britain. The British race is extremely sedentary, only moving away from moorland streams to more lowland areas at the onset of harsh weather (Lack 1986). It is sometimes difficult to confirm belly colour and it is possible that some of those assigned to the British race belong to the central European form *C. c. aquaticus*, although there is no documented evidence to confirm that this race has occurred in Britain. Three, one of which was shot, that frequented Icklingham Mill on the River Lark, in April and May 1927, were considered to have belonged to the British race. This is a remarkable record and one is tempted to suggest that they were pioneering a potential breeding habitat. The River Lark appears to be one of the most suitable localities for future colonisation.

Most birds arrive late in the autumn with records, almost without exception, falling between November and March. There are only two October records: two at Wiston Mill on the Stour in 1964 and another at Minsmere Sluice in 1972 and both refer to the Black-bellied race. Many records refer to single-day occurrences, although occasionally one will linger for several weeks.

A variety of sites are chosen as night-time roosts, but one entering a drainage pipe, under a concrete bridge over Belstead Brook, at Ipswich, at dusk is the only reference to a roosting site in Suffolk. This bird present from 7th November 1991 to 25th March 1992 was of the Black-bellied race and had been ringed at Burnham Market, Norfolk, the previous winter, indicating that Scandinavian birds may return to East Anglia in successive winters.

Wren (Winter Wren) *Troglodytes troglodytes*

An abundant resident and passage migrant

The Wren is one of Britain's most common residents, breeding in virtually all habitats with exposed coastal marshes and town centres being among the few places avoided. The population is adversely affected by severe winters, when numbers plummet. There are significant increases at coastal watch-points, during autumn and, in particular, October.

The species breeds widely throughout the county in woodland of all types, farmland, gardens, orchards, hedgerows, heathland and amongst sand-dunes on the immediate coast. The Reydon Grove study from 1964-1971 revealed that the species' preference to woodland, compared with hedgerows, was 60%-40% and that the Wren required twice as much space as the Robin (Benson & Williamson 1972). A range of 10-25 breeding pairs was found during this study, compared to 20 pairs in 1997 (Pearson 1998) showing numbers appear to be stable.

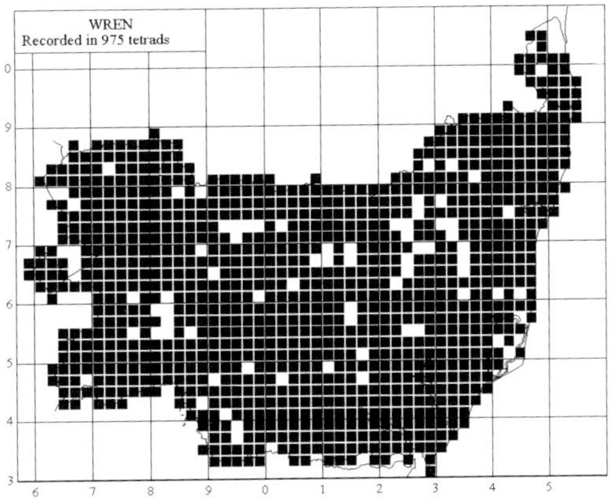

The Wren can survive the worst periods of the winter months by feeding and roosting under a blanket of snow. However, it is extremely vulnerable to prolonged periods of severe frost, when numbers are drastically reduced, although a swift recovery will follow a series of mild winters. For example, the Wren was almost wiped out in much of the county during the cold weather of 1962/3, although the coastal population fared better. Only 69 pairs bred at Minsmere, following the 'arctic' winter of 1978/9, but numbers quickly recovered with 130 pairs in 1980 and c.250 in 1981. The species is extremely territorial during winter and will frequent habitats not used for nesting, such as reedbeds. At Benacre, on 28th February 1952, 13 were counted amongst reeds, picking food from the water's surface. Another was observed swimming at a Bungay gravel-pit, on 18th December 1982, after making an unsuccessful attempt to land on a reed stem (Moore 1985). Competition for winter territories may begin in July and these are vigorously defended by use of an explosive alarm call and song (Lack 1986). However, large communal roosts are also formed and nests, specifically built for this purpose, are often used. A roost of 50 was found at Minsmere on 15th January 1985 and, two winters later, 14 were seen entering a nest-box at Kessingland and 15 roosted in a squirrel's drey at Minsmere.

Although the Wren is one of Britain's most sedentary species, there are obvious movements during spring and autumn. These are attributed to a small arrival and passage of continental birds (Lack 1986). Figures logged at Landguard Point show a distinct peak, most marked during late September and October, and to a lesser extent in April (Odin 1997a). There have been 38 recoveries of Suffolk-ringed birds up to the end of 1995 of which only eight have moved over ten km and four over 100km. The most distant ringing recoveries have all involved autumn-ringed birds. An adult ringed at Walberswick, on 26th October 1957, was found breeding near York two years later. A juvenile, again ringed at Walberswick on 25th September 1988, was controlled eight days later at Shoreham, Sussex, and one at Lackford on 29th September 1995 was found in Hampshire exactly one month later. One ringed at Foulness, Essex, in January 1959, was at Beccles in July and another at Anchor Plain, York, on 14th August 1983 was found dead at Erwarton on 9th February 1984.

Such an unobtrusive species should be spared persecution by man, but its reluctance to fly away from pursuers sometimes leaves it vulnerable. A popular 19th century 'sport' amongst groups of young men around Harleston (both sides of the River Waveney), was to kill birds by stoning. The bird was chased up and down a hedge till hit from one side or another (Candler 1888). This practice was known as 'stag-hunting' and was carried out before the days of compulsory education.

Unusual activity include one feeding on hibernating small tortoiseshell butterflies in a Walpole farmhouse in February 1985 and another feeding a juvenile Cuckoo at Minsmere on 23rd July 1989.

Dunnock (Hedge Accentor) *Prunella modularis*

An abundant resident and passage migrant

The Dunnock is widely spread throughout the county, being a common feature of town and country gardens, parks, hedgerows, farm yards, woodlands, marshland and coastal scrub. The species prefers to nest in dense undergrowth, but is most commonly found low in hedgerows. There is a significant increase in numbers during passage periods and, like many sedentary species, the Dunnock suffers greatly during severe weather periods.

There have been no dramatic fluctuations with local populations, although national statistics show a shallow but progressive decline since the mid-1970s (Marchant *et al.* 1990). It is clear from the map that it occurs almost everywhere, although there are a few gaps in the thicker parts of Thetford Forest and in the central arable belt. The latter may well be due to a lack of coverage. The Reydon Grove Farm study from 1964-1971 revealed a range of 32-49 pairs (Benson & Williamson 1972), compared to 19 pairs in 1997 (Pearson 1988). Males begin singing from mid-January and nesting normally begins in March. The species is frequently parasitised by Cuckoos. An unusual nest site was in a cauliflower plant on a Felixstowe allotment in 1990.

British-bred birds are probably sedentary, but they are joined by immigrants from the continent during passage periods (Lack 1986). Ticehurst noticed "passing migrants" on the coastline at Lowestoft and Orfordness in late September and October and, nowadays, Landguard Point's resident population increases dramatically during passage periods. Some are noted flying out of bushes, calling and towering upwards and then moving off south with other migrants, but often significant numbers remain in cover to rest and feed. Daily ringing returns from the latter site, show distinct autumn peaks in late September and October and a less pronounced spring peak in mid-March (Odin 1997a). A total of 36 was ringed from 100 present at Landguard Point on 1st October 1994, the county's largest ever concentration, and 60 there on 3rd April 1982 is high for the spring. Despite a significant number being ringed each year, there are relatively few recoveries and, as yet, no Suffolk-ringed birds have been found overseas. However, one ringed on Texel, Holland, in October 1965 was found near Leiston the following January.

The Dunnock is a regular visitor to garden feeding stations during winter and, although mainly solitary, foraging groups occasionally occur. A gathering of 30 feeding on snow, at The Grove, Felixstowe, on 22nd November 1993, is exceptional.

Alpine Accentor — *Prunella collaris*

Accidental: four records

1823	Oulton: Oulton Broad, n.d.
1894	Gorleston-on-Sea: Pier, 21st September
2000	Corton: 13th May
2002	Minsmere: Abbey Ruins, 16th-20th March

The first three records were from the Lothingland area, the first two birds observed at close quarters by eminent ornithologists of that time. There is some dispute as to the authenticity of the Gorleston individual, which was reported searching for food amongst wood-covered stones and piles under the pier (Ticehurst 1932). In consequence, the record is being reassessed by the BOURC (Taylor *et al.* 2000). The more-recent Corton and Minsmere individuals fed on arable fields and stone masonry of old buildings and attracted huge crowds of birdwatchers.

The species breeds in the mountains of Iberia, north-west Africa, central Europe east to Japan and has been recorded in the British Isles on only 42 occasions up to the end of 2000 (BBRC).

Robin (European Robin) — *Erithacus rubecula*

An abundant resident, passage migrant and winter visitor

An orange-red breast contrasting with the monotones of a snow-covered garden, together with a confiding nature, makes the Robin one of the most familiar and best-loved of all British birds. Although widely regarded as a common garden bird, the Robin breeds extensively in woodland, particularly where there is an abundance of undergrowth, but also in urban parks, farmyards and hedgerows.

The map shows the Robin to be widely distributed throughout the county, although there are gaps in the treeless areas adjacent to the Alde estuary, around the Lakenheath and Mildenhall Fens and in cereal-growing areas of central Suffolk. Coppiced woodland has greatly aided the expansion of the species' range.

The Robin is well known for its catholic choice of nest sites and will often raise broods in garden sheds and farmyard out-buildings. A pair, which nested in a disused iced drinks machine in Felixstowe in consecutive summers in 1990 and 1991, is unusual.

Marchant *et al.* (1990) suggested that the British population has remained "remarkably stable" over the last 100 years or so, apart from short-term variations following harsh winters. The CBC results show declines following the successive cold winters of 1961/2 and 1962/3 and again in 1978/9 and 1981/2. The Reydon Grove Farm study revealed a range of 24-44 pairs in 1964-1971 (Benson & Williamson 1972), compared to 17 pairs in 1997 (Pearson 1998).

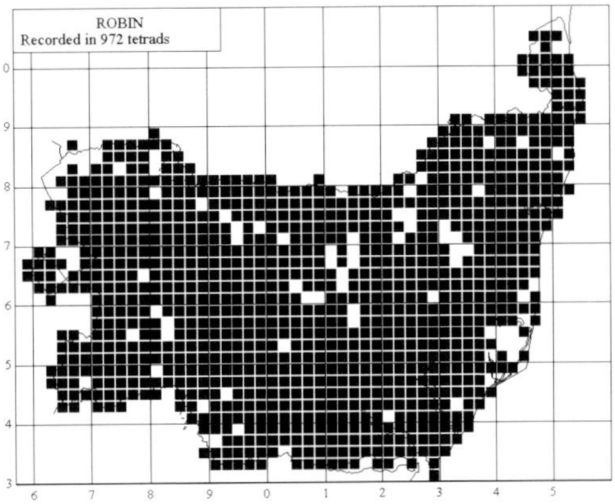

The Robin is a common passage migrant and it usually becomes evident at migration watch-points from mid-March till early May and again from late August till early November.

Ticehurst considered all coastal migrants as belonging to the continental race, *E. r. rubecula* but, although British-bred birds are relatively sedentary, a juvenile, ringed at Walberswick in early July 1965 and found in France the following January, proves that some move south during winter. Northern populations, however, are highly migratory and regularly pass through East Anglia during passage periods. The species is frequently associated with falls of other migrants and, on such occasions, gardens of coastal towns become alive with Robins, with 'ticking' birds occupying every bush. Three-figure concentrations are rare, but a spell of easterly winds, from 13th-20th October 1987, brought perhaps as many as 10,000 to the Felixstowe area. The latter fall is amongst the county's largest ever, with the 16th being the big day at Landguard Point, when 265 were ringed from an estimated 1,000 on site. Two of the above were recovered in France during the following winter. There have been numerous recoveries of Suffolk-ringed Robins migrating along Europe's western seaboard and some as far north as Finland.

Robins ringed on passage in Denmark and the Netherlands and found in Suffolk during winter, together with a Dutch-ringed bird which wintered at Landguard Point in 1996/7, shows that some that overwinter here are of continental origin.

Thrush Nightingale — *Luscinia luscinia*

Accidental: four records

1984 Felixstowe: Landguard Point, 13th-14th May (trapped 13th).
1995 Felixstowe: Landguard Point, 27th August-15th September (trapped 27th August)
1997 Hollesley: singing male 26th May-1st June
Felixstowe: Landguard Point, 28th-29th September

Thrush Nightingales usually remain hidden in deep cover when stopping off on migration, typified by the 1984 and 1997 occurrences at Landguard Point when birds were viewed with some difficulty. The long-staying 1995 individual, however, was uncharacteristically confiding and allowed several hundred birdwatchers the chance to observe the species at close range.

The Hollesley record involved a male which delivered its song from the heart of a damp osier bed reminiscent of its breeding habitat in eastern Europe. The song was recorded on tape.

The breeding range extends from Scandinavia and eastern Europe through to western Asia and winters in Africa. Although the Thrush Nightingale remains a rare visitor to Britain and Ireland, being recorded on only 139 occasions up to the end of 2000, occurrences have increased greatly compared with the mere two records prior to 1958 (BBRC). The increase in vagrancy coincides with a westward expansion of range since 1970 (Sharrock & Hilden 1983).

Nightingale (Common Nightingale) — *Luscinia megarhynchos*

A fairly common summer visitor and passage migrant

The Nightingale is locally distributed, mostly in the south and east of the county, with small pockets along the Little Ouse valley and in southern Breckland. It inhabits dense thickets, conifer plantations, ancient woodlands, particularly favouring those with a well-managed coppice under-storey, wetland scrub, such as that adjacent to reedbeds and gravel workings, parks and large gardens. There has been a marked decline since the early part of the 20th century. The skulking nature of this species means that it is often difficult to locate on passage, although small numbers are regularly logged at coastal watch-points.

Babington considered it "common everywhere" and Ticehurst "common throughout the County in suitable places". Climatic conditions may be the most important factor in influencing population levels between summers. In some years, many singing males will compete for territories in a relatively small area, whereas in others prime habitat is unused. Nationally, a contraction of range from northern localities became noticeable between 1910 and 1940 and declines were realised in western counties during the 1950s (Marchant *et al.* 1990). The Nightingale's change in status was discussed in 1967, when habitat losses, notably of thick hedgerows and small copses, were blamed for its disappearance from parts of Suffolk (Parslow 1967). The species has now been lost from many of its British haunts and Suffolk, along with Kent and Sussex, now holds the largest remaining concentrations (Gibbons *et al.* 1993). The county's share of the national total of 4,770 singing males, located during the 1980 BTO survey, was 367, 80% of which occupied the south and east of the county (Brown 1981). A total of 881 singing males was located in a repeat survey in 1999 – an increase of 140%. During the latter study, the highest densities were found in the central coastal zone, around the nature reserves of Minsmere and Walberswick, where 132 pairs (76 in 1980) were in residence. The parishes of Bentley and Hadleigh also held a significant population hosting 30 and 28 pairs respectively.

Nightingales are scarce at migration watch-points with ones and twos passing through in April and May and again in August and September. Most seem to return directly to their breeding territories with the first singing males being noted from mid- to late April. There are few records prior to 10th April, with one at Market Weston Fen on the 3rd, in 1991, being the earliest. Most Nightingales leave in August and October records are very rare. A lingering individual was noted at Bures on 12th November 1873 and one was found freshly dead on a Long Melford rubbish-tip on 20th December 1958. One ringed at Fagbury Cliff on 2nd May 1993 was still present on 19th November later that year.

Site fidelity and longevity has been demonstrated at Bawdsey Manor, where one was trapped many times between 1988 and 1996. This individual is currently the longest-lived Nightingale to be recorded in the British Isles. A nestling ringed at Playford on 10th June 1938 was recovered in Tourney-Charente, France, in December of that year.

Bluethroat *Luscinia svecica*

A scarce passage migrant

The Bluethroat occurs on passage almost annually, although its secretive nature suggests that many may go undetected. About 150 individuals were recorded in Suffolk during the period of 1951-2000 – the vast majority relating to migrants found on the immediate coastline.

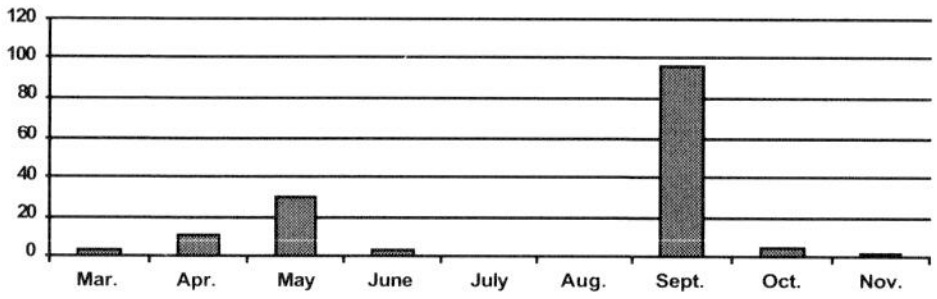

Above: The seasonal distribution of the Bluethroat from 1950-2000

Right: The annual totals of the Bluethroat from 1951-2000 (excluding those found during the 'Great Fall' of 1965)

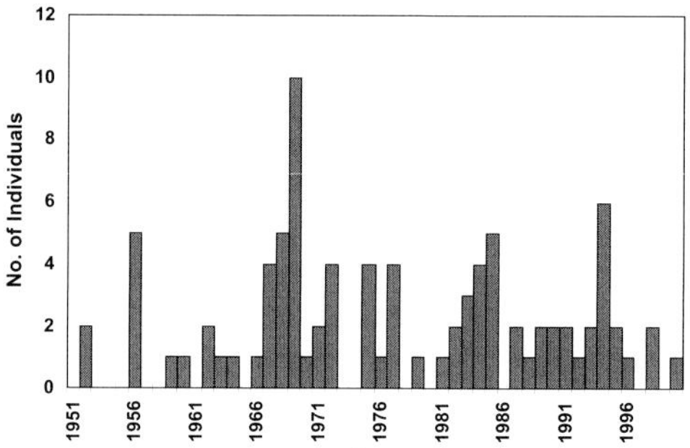

It was formerly more common on autumn passage when 1-2 could be expected in falls of other Scandinavian migrants, particularly those involving Redstarts and Pied Flycatchers (Ticehurst 1932). However, since the early 1970s, there has been a transformation, which is difficult to explain. An autumn total of 36 for the period 1950-1972 (plus 60 in the 'Great Fall' of 1965) compare with just five spring occurrences. Conversely, from 1976-1999, seven autumn occurrences compare with 37 for the spring. An increase in both the number of observers and ringing operations on the coast may explain the growth in spring records but, as coastal migration sites are searched more thoroughly during autumn, a recent change in migration pattern is likely to be responsible for autumn decreases. The vast majority of spring males are of the nominate red-spotted race *L. s. svecica*.

The species featured highly in the 1965 'Great Fall' when over 60 frequented the coastal strip between Lowestoft and Minsmere, during the period 3rd-7th September. Territorial behaviour was noted at Walberswick and Minsmere, where birds sought the damp corners of grass and reed, at the edges of pools, or along stretches of muddy tractor paths (Axell & Pearson 1966). A total of 25 birds was noted in 40ha. of marsh at the latter locality.

Red-spotted individuals are rarely reported before the second week of May, but occur regularly up to the end of that month. Suffolk's only June occurrences were in 1969 and involved males at Walberswick on 1st and at Havergate on 13th. One found entangled in fishing nets on Lowestoft Denes in July 1877 is the only record for that month. As most autumn occurrences involve juveniles, race is normally indeterminate. Bluethroats leave their north Scandinavian breeding grounds in late August (Cramp *et al.* 1974-1994) and, formerly, peak numbers passed through East Anglia in early September. There have been only five October records and one at Orford on 8th November 1962 is the latest.

White-spotted Bluethroat *L. s. cyanecula*

Accidental: 11 records

1960	Minsmere: 7th April
1972	Easton Bavents: 6th September
1977	Minsmere: 24th-25th April
1985	Barton Mills: 16th March
1987	Minsmere: 5th April
1996	Walberswick: 4th-6th April
1998	Felixstowe: Landguard Point, 2nd April
2000	Felixstowe: Landguard Point, 16th April
2001	Felixstowe: Landguard Point, trapped 17th-18th March
	Lowestoft: Ness Point, 24th March
2002	Orfordness: 16th March

White-spotted Bluethroats have a more southerly breeding distribution and, therefore, generally occur much earlier than Scandinavian red-spotted birds.

Bluethroats have been noted in March on six occasions: on the Shipwash light-vessel, 22nd-23rd (1909); at Aldeburgh on 21st (1969); at Barton Mills on 16th (1985); at Landguard Point on 17th-18th (2001); Ness Point, Lowestoft on 24th (2001) and Orfordness on 16th (2002). The last four birds were racially assigned to *L. s. cyanecula*, but the early dates suggest that the other two were of this race. The 11 records listed above all concern Bluethroats positively identified as belonging to the race *L. s. cyanecula*.

Red-flanked Bluetail *Tarsiger cyanurus*

Accidental: one record

1994 Felixstowe: Landguard Point, ad. male trapped 26th October

The above individual was present within the LBO compound all day, running the gauntlet of extremely territorial Robins on site.

The Red-flanked Bluetail is an extremely rare visitor to the British Isles being recorded on only 27 occasions up to the end of 2000 (BBRC). The species breeds in north-east Europe through Asia to Japan and winters in south-east Asia and is slowly advancing westwards. Breeding has been noted in Estonia since 1980 and it is believed that Norway will soon be colonised (Burton 1995).

Siberian Blue Robin *Erithacus indicus*

Accidental: one record

2000 Minsmere: 23rd October

The Sluice Bushes at Minsmere provided temporary refuge for this extremely rare migrant. It was discovered late in the afternoon by birdwatchers returning from observing the Sociable Plover and consequently was seen by relatively few observers.

The Siberian Blue Robin breeds in the Eastern Palearctic from Siberia to Indonesia. The above record constitutes the first record for Britain and Ireland.

Black Redstart *Phoenicurus ochruros*

An uncommon summer visitor and passage migrant. Occasionally overwinters

Black Redstart
(*Stuart Ling*)

Industrial wasteland, warehouse complexes, construction sites, docklands, old maltings and other buildings provide the Black Redstart with competition-free nesting areas. It is a rare British breeding bird with between 65 and 99 nesting pairs recorded from 1989-1999 (Ogilvie *et al.* 2001). During passage periods, the species is noted regularly at coastal watch-points and a few at inland sites. A small number overwinter in most years.

Singles at Darsham and Orford in November 1868 were the first county records of the species, although Hele had previously suspected its presence amongst timber in an Aldeburgh ship-yard. There were few records up to the end of the 19th century, but by 1932 passage birds were noted annually on the immediate coastline (Ticehurst 1932).

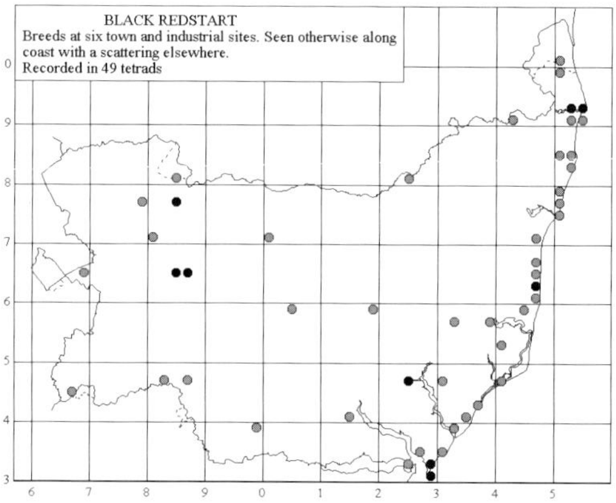

The Black Redstart began colonising southern counties of Britain in the 1920s, originally nesting in natural cliff sites and industrial areas. A report in the *East Anglian Daily Times*, of young Black Redstarts being tended in an Ipswich town centre garden in 1938 (Beecroft 1985), constituted the first documented breeding record for Suffolk. Nesting was also suspected at Lowestoft that year and it was here that the species formed a bridgehead before expanding further into the county. Bomb damage in southern England created new nesting opportunities and up to three pairs regularly bred in Lowestoft from 1943-1949. In the same period, isolated breeding attempts occurred at Aldeburgh, Gorleston-on-Sea (in an air-raid shelter), Brantham and Mildenhall (first in West Suffolk). As the redevelopment of bomb sites gathered pace in the 1950s, the British population declined and this was reflected in Suffolk where from 1952-1964 no more than two pairs bred annually. The only exception was in 1958, when favourable spring migration conditions encouraged 26 pairs to nest in Britain, of which seven were in Suffolk. Nesting took place for the first time at Sizewell Nuclear Power Station in 1963 and, although numbers continued to fluctuate, there was a general upward trend. The county's population surged in 1973, when 13 pairs were located and, three years later a possible 20 pairs (12 pairs plus eight singing males), from a national total of 104, were found. The population doubled over the decade with c.40 territory-holding males being in residence in 1985-1986. A special survey in the latter year revealed that a significant proportion of nesting pairs involved immature males, which were found to be less successful than their adult counterparts (Beecroft 1987). Disused gas works at Lowestoft and Ipswich have served the species well and old maltings at Snape and Ipswich are also favoured. The largest concentrations now exist in the vicinity of the Port of Felixstowe, but there is also a thriving population in Bury St Edmunds, mostly in the grounds of the Beet Factory. The British population was estimated to be around 80-120 territory-holding males during the late 1980s and early 1990s (Gibbons *et al.* 1993), and SBRs showed a fairly stable population of around 20 pairs in Suffolk. However, key areas, such as docklands at Felixstowe and Ipswich, were not checked thoroughly, so actual breeding pairs could have been up to twice the number of those found on a casual basis. The species was not found in Ipswich during fieldwork for the *New Atlas*, and thereafter it became scarce at its other former strongholds on the Felixstowe peninsula. In 1998, the Suffolk breeding population had declined to around five pairs.

Nests are most often located on a ledge or in a hole made by a missing brick, but more unusual sites include an allotment potting shed, lorry trailers, in an old Swallow nest and on an outside ledge of a beach-hut. In 1968, a pair nested in the superstructure of a mono-tower crane at a Lowestoft shipyard and raised five young despite the crane transversing 100 metres of track many times in the course of a working day.

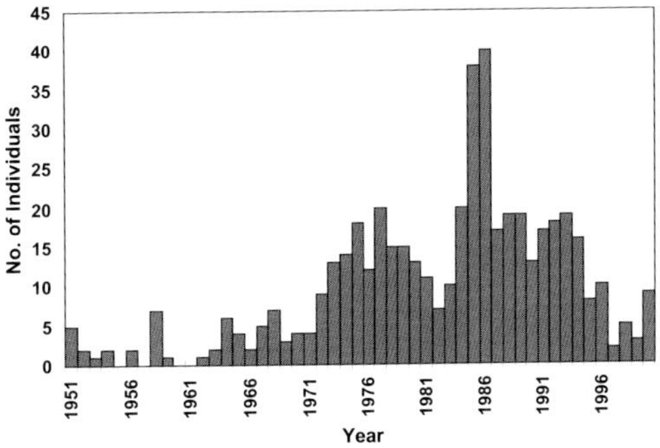

The number of territory-holding males/breeding pairs of Black Redstart from 1951-2000

Small numbers overwinter annually at coastal localities, most regularly at their breeding haunts at Lowestoft and Felixstowe.

The Black Redstart is one of the first summer migrants to reach Suffolk, although it is often impossible to distinguish passage birds from those overwintering. Small numbers normally arrive with Wheatears in mid-March and breeding birds are back at their territories by early April. Passage birds continue to be noted at migration watch-points until early May. The largest spring gatherings are 15 at Landguard Point on 7th April 1987 and 17 there on 31st March 1994. Autumn migration is noted from September to early November and peaking in mid-October. The species rarely figures highly in large falls of other migrants, although 17 were located amongst the thousands of Robins at Felixstowe, on 17th October 1988.

A Black Redstart ringed on Heligoland Island, Germany, on 8th April 1997 was controlled at Landguard Point on 6th June of that year and another ringed at Bristol, on 3rd February 1975, was shot at Kentwell on 20th October 1977.

Redstart (Common Redstart) *Phoenicurus phoenicurus*

A locally common summer visitor and passage migrant

The breeding population is now restricted to a few woods and copses, on or near heathland on the coastal strip, with a few pairs hanging on in Breckland. The species is common on the coast during passage periods and is usually associated with falls of other migrants.

The Redstart was formerly well-distributed throughout the county, but has declined alarmingly since the late 19th century. At that time, the species bred extensively on the sandling belt, from Fritton south to Ipswich and inland along the Waveney valley to Beccles, where it nested in town gardens. It was somewhat local in north-west Suffolk, but bred regularly round Brandon and along the Breckland fringe at Tostock,

Fakenham Magna, Euston, Stowlangtoft, Ickworth and Saxham. It was plentiful along the Stour valley from Bures to Nayland, where it nested in riverside pollards, and around Sudbury. No fewer than 14 nests were found in one evening at Long Melford (Ticehurst 1932). By 1920, the species was lost from many sites and decreased greatly at others, a decline which was witnessed throughout southern, eastern and central England (Alexander & Lack 1944). However, a partial recovery ensued in the early 1950s, when nesting birds were found on many Breckland heaths, at Mildenhall Warren, in and immediately west of Bury St Edmunds and parishes east and south of Ipswich. SBRs reported marked declines at Minsmere and elsewhere from 1969, which was paralleled nationally and attributed to severe drought conditions in the Sahel wintering area (Marchant *et al.* 1990). In the Walberswick area, the breeding population remained relatively stable from 1960-1969 at 14-20 pairs, but declined to only nine by 1972 (Pearson 1973). The county population continued to fall during the 1970s and a low point was reached in 1976-1977, when only 15-20 pairs remained on the coast and three in the breck. Numbers began to rise again in 1980 and, four years later, 40 pairs were distributed between seven coastal and two Breckland sites. A peak of 67 territories was noted in 1989. Walberswick, Minsmere, Staverton, Hollesley and Sutton heaths on the coast and Thetford Forest and Knettishall Heath in Breckland are now the only sites where nesting regularly takes place.

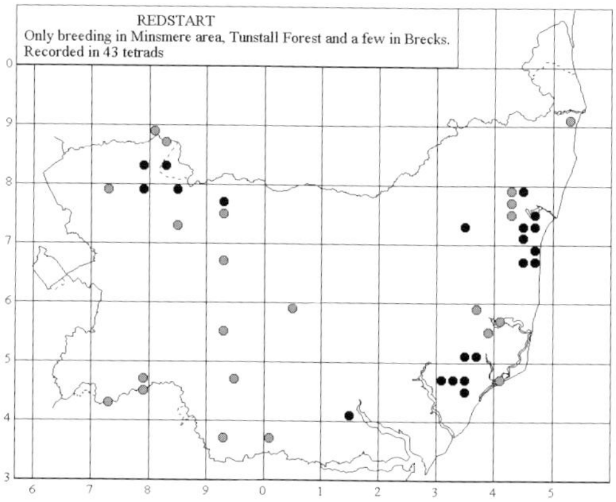

Heathland edges, ancient parkland, conifer plantations and old forest growth are the species' preferred habitat and holes in trees, nest-boxes and ivy walls are favourite nest sites. In Breckland, beams and rafters in farmyard sheds, outhouses and barns are more frequently used. For example, one cluster of farm buildings held four pairs and a fifth nested in a hole in the ground below a fence post (Robertson 1954). More unusual sites include a pile of firewood, a pipe-net hung on a rail, a sea-kale pot and under bracken.

The first spring migrants normally arrive in the second week of April, most returning immediately to their breeding territories. A male singing at Staverton Thicks on 21st March 1966 was remarkably early, beaten only by a passage bird at Pakefield on 19th in 1956. Up to 2000, there were 22 March records in total and all bar one were from the coastal strip, the exception being one at Akenham on 22nd March 1973. Passage migrants continue to appear at coastal localities until mid-May with occasional stragglers still passing through in early June. Return passage commences in August and peaks in mid-September. The Redstart was one of the principal species involved in the 1965 'Great Fall', when an estimated 250,000 were grounded between Lowestoft and Minsmere. Generally, groups of 20 or more are rare with 4-5 amongst other migrants being nearer the norm. Passage birds are regularly reported up to mid-October and a few linger to the end of the month. One at Bawdsey on 23rd November 1966 is exceptionally late and there have been 11 other records for that month. Ringing recoveries show that most passage birds are moving from Scandinavia to North Africa. From over 500 ringed following the 'Great Fall', there were six foreign recoveries: four from Spain, one from Portugal and one the following spring in Norway. Suffolk-ringed birds have also been found in France, the Channel Isles and Morocco. A nestling from Yorkshire passed through Landguard Point two springs later and another, ringed at Dungeness, Kent, was found at Kesgrave.

A male showing characters of the eastern race *P. p. samamisicus* was noted at St Edmund's Churchyard, Southwold, from 28th-30th September 1991.

Whinchat *Saxicola rubetra*

A common passage migrant. A few pairs breed

The species has a very tenuous foothold as a breeding species in the county with probably less than ten pairs remaining on the fens and Breckland heaths with an occasional pair on the coast. Whinchats are common during passage periods and may appear almost anywhere.

Early in the 20th century, the Whinchat was sparsely distributed on heaths, gorse commons and on rough grassland adjacent to marshes and low meadows, on the coast, in Breckland and on the fens. The nucleus of the coastal breeding population was then around Thorpeness extending to heathland east of Ipswich. Concern over decreasing numbers resulted in the species being targeted for a special study in 1938, but, although 11 nests were found beside the main Melton to Hollesley road and a further two at Martlesham, the results were woefully incomplete. Around 30-40 pairs nested in the early 1950s, between Blythburgh and Aldeburgh, and 27 pairs bred in the Walberswick-Minsmere area in 1959, including 15 pairs at the latter site where some nests were predated by Red-backed Shrikes. The species declined markedly during the 1960s and, in 1963, only 15 pairs were found along the whole of the coast. By the mid-1970s, the Whinchat was lost as a coastal breeding species and numbers in north-west Suffolk were down to a mere 11 pairs. The latter population has since fluctuated greatly from a single breeding pair to a maximum of 20 pairs in good years. There have been only isolated breeding attempts on the coast in recent years.

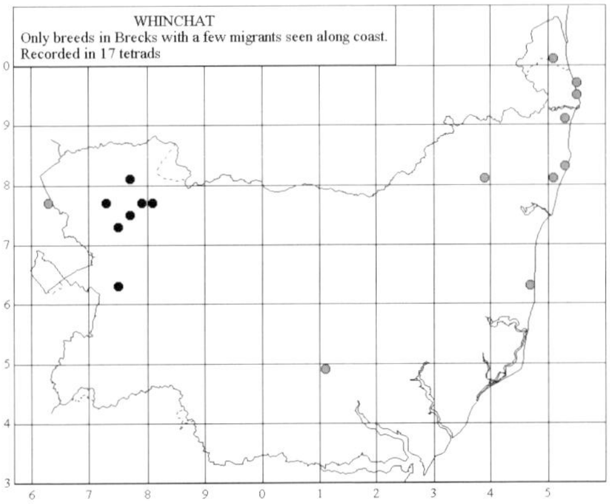

The Whinchat is regularly logged at migration watch-points, most often singly or in groups of up to five or six. Passage birds are also noted inland. The species rarely arrives before late April and the highest spring numbers occur in early May, with c.40 at Landguard Point on 8th May 1980 being the largest spring gathering. One at Gedgrave, 20th March 1964, is the earliest of only three March records. Returning birds are occasionally noted in July, but passage does not normally get underway until mid-August with peak numbers during the first half of September. Few are noted after mid-October but laggards include one at Felixstowe Ferry from 23rd November-8th December 1979 and another at Alton Water from 9th-24th December 1984. Landguard Point has received the largest concentrations in recent years, the highest being 37 on 25th September 1977 and 29 on 2nd September 1979. However, these figures are eclipsed by the huge numbers involved in the 1965 'Great Fall', when an estimated 3,000 were present in north-east Suffolk.

A nestling ringed on Westleton Heath in 1959 was recovered in Golega, Portugal, more than four years later.

Stonechat (European Stonechat) *Saxicola torquata*

A locally common resident, winter visitor and passage migrant

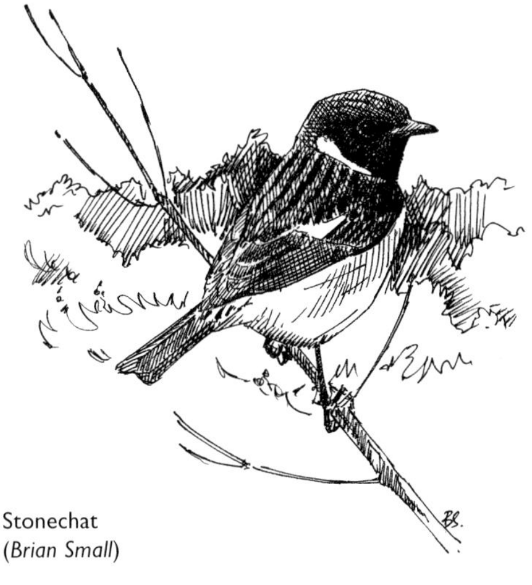

Stonechat
(Brian Small)

The breeding population is now restricted to pockets of heath and coastal scrub between Woodbridge and the River Blyth. Although the Stonechat is basically sedentary, juveniles disperse in autumn and wintering birds are found at scattered localities throughout the county.

The scolding *chack* of the Stonechat perched high on a gorse bush was once a familiar sound on coastal heaths and commons, from Ipswich through to Lowestoft Denes, along the Waveney as far as Diss Common, and throughout Breckland.

Prolonged freezing conditions have a devastating effect on the breeding population and speed of recovery depends much on the mildness of subsequent winters. The Stonechat suffered greatly during the harsh weather in 1916/7 and was almost extinct after the effects of four severe winters over

A pair at Aldeburgh on 1st July 1961 and a single at Minsmere on 3rd July 1982 are the only other records for that month.

Return passage commences in mid-September and continues through to early November, although there are a few records in late August. There were only five late November records prior to the winter of 1995-1996, but there then came an unprecedented number of either extremely late passage or overwintering birds, which coincided with one of the largest influxes of thrushes ever witnessed in Suffolk. Ring Ouzels were noted at Lowestoft, Southwold, Thorpeness and Landguard Point between 26th November and 4th January – at least six individuals were involved. One at Southwold from 23rd December – 1st January was the longest stayer. Other winter records involve singles at Lawshall on 21st January 2001 and another at Westleton on 6th December of that year.

The species usually occurs singly, although groups of three to five are not uncommon. Gatherings of 20 or more are occasionally reported, the highest counts being: c.100 at Boyton, 9th October 1966; 50 at Walberswick on 16th September 1968; c.100 at Southwold Sewage Works; 6th October 1998 and 102 at Aldringham Walks; 9th October 1998. The Walberswick concentration included a single flock of 44, part of an influx to Britain's east coast. A 19th century record of 20, in a Rattlesden bean field, represents the largest inland gathering.

Suffolk-ringed birds have been recovered in France on two occasions. A spring migrant at Walberswick was found near Cambon, Herault, on 1st November and another ringed at Landguard Point during the October 1988 fall was a road casualty at Sanquinet on 23rd December of that year. It is likely that both birds were still on passage when found in France, as their normal wintering range is Spain and north-west Africa (Cramp *et al.* 1974-1994).

Blackbird (Common Blackbird) *Turdus merula*

An abundant resident, passage migrant and winter visitor

The Blackbird is one of the most familiar and widespread of British birds. It nests in most habitat types, and is a common inhabitant of parks and gardens in urban areas. The large resident population is joined by immigrants from the continent during winter and the species is sometimes abundant during passage periods.

Blackbirds are less susceptible to the effects of harsh weather than other thrushes and this, together with its ability to thrive in towns and villages, is responsible for a national population increase since the early 1900s. However, the species suffers badly in open country and, during the hard winter of 1776, Blackbirds and thrushes were said to have been "mostly destroyed" (Norman 1994). During the first half of the 20th century, the Blackbird displaced the Song Thrush as the dominant thrush of the Suffolk countryside. The CBC index showed a further major increase during the 1970s, followed by a shallow decline (Marchant *et al.* 1990). The Reydon Grove Farm study from 1964-1971 revealed a range of 21-46 breeding pairs (Benson & Williamson 1972), compared to 16 pairs in 1997 (Pearson 1998).

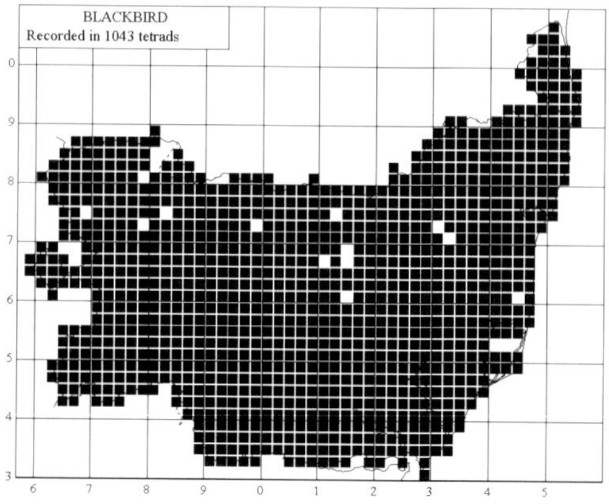

The Blackbird is one of the earliest of our birds to nest, with pairs incubating by mid-March. Particularly early records include a nest with five eggs on 4th January 1951, one observed feeding young at Ipswich on 26th February 1980 and another with a recently-fledged juvenile at Bawdsey on 23rd February 1992.

Although Suffolk's breeding Blackbirds are largely sedentary, some from more northerly counties are migratory. An analysis of data collected at Landguard Point (Odin 1991) shows spring passage starts in late February and peaks in the first half of March. There birds are largely moving east to north-east from Britain to countries east of the Netherlands. The main autumn arrival occurs around late September, often with a second wave from mid-October to early November. Passage is largely over by mid-November, although there are occasional influxes during hard-weather periods. Immigrants normally arrive in darkness, often intermingled with other thrushes. However, diurnal migrants can frequently be seen making landfall, either falling from the sky or flying in from offshore. LBO's best trapping day occurred on 23rd October 1991 when 207 were ringed. The timing of the trapping shows that few birds were present at dawn, but arrivals were spread throughout the day.

The largest concentrations are normally noted during passage periods and include 500 at Walberswick on 18th October 1958, 3,000 at Minsmere on November 5th 1961, 500 at Landguard Point on both 6th October 1984 and 3rd November 1986, and c.700 at Bawdsey on 26th October 1999. The origins of these birds lie in Scandinavia and elsewhere in northern Europe. Blackbirds ringed in the Low Countries, Denmark, Germany, the former USSR, Sweden and Finland have been recovered in Suffolk. The largest spring concentration is 100 at Landguard Point on 7th March 1989. Wintering birds from Suffolk have been found back at their country of origin in most of the countries listed above and also Estonia and France.

No fewer than 5,217 Blackbirds had been ringed at Landguard Point up to the end of 1991, from which there have been 114 recoveries. Of these, 105 were found dead – 20 road casualties, nine killed by hitting glass, 15 taken by cats, seven taken by avian predators and two shot. The other 52 birds recovered dead were categorised as 'cause unknown', although a small number were found dead in ponds or caught up in human artefacts (Odin 1991).

Fieldfare *Turdus pilaris*

A common winter visitor in varying numbers and common passage migrant

Although the Fieldfare is scarce in some years, it is normally a regular feature of a Suffolk winter, frequenting hedgerows, orchards, pastures and arable land, sometimes in abundance. The species is a regular visitor to parks and garden feeding-stations, particularly during periods of harsh weather. Immigrants can frequently be seen arriving from offshore during October and November and passage often continues through to late afternoon. Heavy snow-falls or prolonged frost normally result in hard-weather movements, and can cause a mass exodus from inland to the coast.

The breeding range extends from central and northern Europe through to Siberia, but there has been a gradual westerly expansion and colonisation of Britain which began in the 1960s. The Fieldfare has nested in south-eastern England, but breeding has yet to be confirmed in Suffolk.

Return emigration of wintering birds commences in February and continues into March and April, although laggards are often noted in May and occasionally during the summer months. The county's first instance of probable oversummering occurred in 1963 when five were noted at Lakenheath in mid-June and another there on 21st July. Thereafter, there have been regular midsummer reports, mostly concentrated into the period 1967-1982, although most relate to single-day observations.

Early immigrants are occasionally reported in late August, but the main arrival does not occur until mid-October, continuing through to late November. Groups of 25-50 are regularly encountered and three-figure flocks are not unusual. Four-figure gatherings have been noted on nine occasions and 3,500 flying east over the King's Forest, on 20th October 1992, is the highest-ever count. It would appear that birds arriving in October and November pass straight through with wintering birds appearing in late December. During periods of harsh weather, Fieldfares gather in apple orchards and concentrations of 500 are not uncommon. However, a flock of 3,000, which fed on apples in a Hadleigh orchard, on 14th January 1990, is exceptional. There was a particularly heavy immigration during the winter of 1995/6, when large flocks were reported from many sites and included 3,000 flying west over Minsmere on 1st November, a gathering of 1,400 at North Warren on 17th December and 4,000 at Westleton on 28th December 2000.

Scandinavian-ringed birds have been recovered in Suffolk on two occasions and three wintering in the county were subsequently found in Sweden or Finland in spring or summer.

Song Thrush *Turdus philomelos*

A common resident, passage migrant and winter visitor

The Song Thrush is a common feature of parks and gardens, but also inhabits heathland, woodland edges, farms and hedgerows. The species is far more migratory than the Blackbird with a significant proportion of the local population moving south during winter. Nationally, a decline of 52% in the breeding population, detected in the mid-1990s, resulted in the species being added to the 'red list' of Birds of Conservation Concern.

The map shows that the Song Thrush is widespread throughout the county, although its patchy distribution in the forestry areas of Breckland and around the Alde estuary running north-west to the Waveney is probably due to a lack of suitable breeding habitat.

Song Thrushes formerly outnumbered Blackbirds in all lowland habitats by a considerable margin, with the ratio gradually changing during the 1920s and 1930s. Blackbirds had become the commoner by the 1940s (Marchant *et al.* 1990). The Song Thrush's change in fortunes has been attributed to a series of cold winters. A distinct lack of thrushes in Ipswich and Copdock followed the severe winter of 1939/40, although Blackbirds remained plentiful (Elliston 1940). This was the first of three successive cold winters, closely followed by another in 1947, which resulted in a steep decline in the population. Harsh weather again took its toll in 1961/2 and 1962/3, and in 1978/9 and 1981/2. The Reydon Grove Farm study from 1964-1971 revealed a range of 8-19 pairs (Benson & Williamson 1972), compared to only two pairs in 1997 (Pearson 1998). Nest predation from an increased Magpie population, a reduction in the area of spring tillage, loss of hedgerows and pastures and an increase in the use of molluscicides and insecticides have also been considered as possible reasons for the species' failure to recover. However, influences on population change by the Magpie and other corvids have now been ruled out due to an apparent increase in Song Thrush nesting success since the 1960s (Gibbons *et al.* 1993).

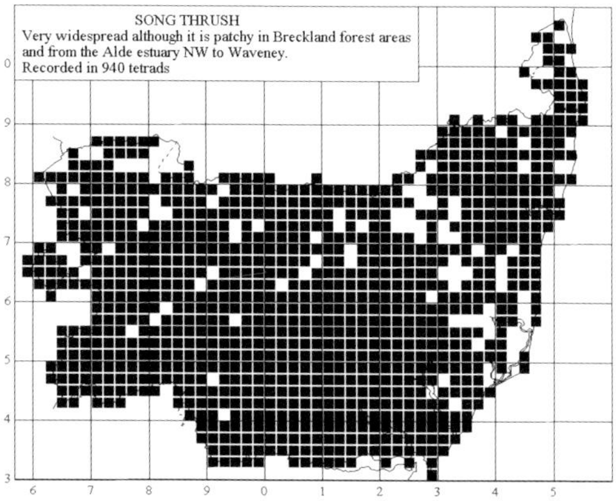

Like the Blackbird, the Song Thrush is an early nester with incubation normally commencing in early March. A pair incubating a full clutch, at Worlington on 27th February 1964, was exceptionally early.

Although the species regularly passes through migration watch-points, it rarely occurs in large numbers. Spring passage begins in mid-March and lasts until the end of that month, and a second wave (whose members usually show characteristics of the continental race *T. p. philomelos*) passes through during the second half of April. Return migration normally occurs from mid-September to early November with a peak during late September or early October. A considerable number of passerines were grounded during strong gales (attributed to the remnants of Hurricane Hortense) on 6th October 1984, and thousands of Song Thrushes sought refuge at coastal sites between Lowestoft and Felixstowe. The latter site saw a spectacular southerly movement of an estimated 10,000 birds and those closely examined were thought to be *T. p. philomelos.* The Song Thrush rarely accompanies other thrushes during diurnal movements.

Six foreign-ringed birds have been found in Suffolk: three from the Netherlands and one each from the Channel Islands, Germany and Sweden. Thirty-seven Suffolk-ringed Song Thrushes have been recovered abroad. These birds were either on passage or wintering in the Low Countries, France and Iberia, with a significant proportion falling to hunters.

Redwing *Turdus iliacus*

A common winter visitor and passage migrant

The Redwing is a familiar winter visitor in variable numbers frequenting berry-bearing hedgerows, woodlands, open pastures and gardens, often in the company of other thrushes and Starlings. The high pitched contact calls heard overhead on cool autumn nights signifies the arrival of the Redwing to its winter quarters.

Wintering Redwings are most often noted in feeding flocks of 20-50, but these regularly reach three figures. They are most conspicuous on open pastures where they forage for earthworms, often in association with Fieldfares, or as they strip roadside hedgerow haws during autumn and early winter. Smaller numbers frequent areas of mowed grassland in urban parks, playing fields and larger gardens and during colder weather will search leaf litter on woodland floors.

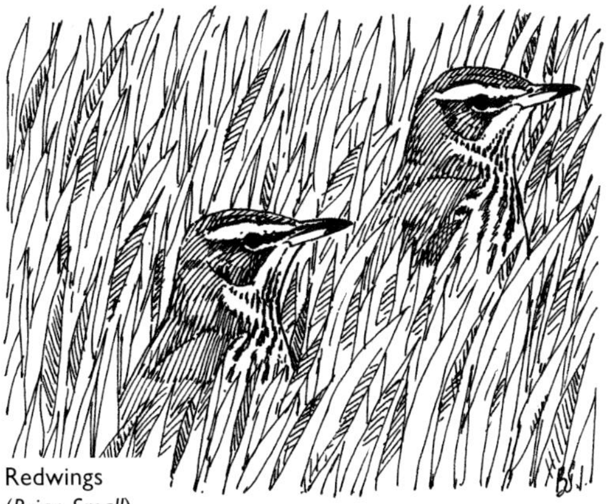

Redwings
(*Brian Small*)

Immigrants begin to arrive in late September, with peak passage being noted in late October and early November, and most flocks pass straight through the county. The species is most susceptible to freak weather conditions during immigration periods. For example, in 1960 when a 'wreck' was witnessed all along the east coast, 621 Redwings were cast ashore on a short stretch of beach, between Lowestoft and Gorleston-on-Sea, following autumn gales. It was estimated that well over 4,000 corpses were beached in that area (Payn 1978). The Redwing is usually the principal species in hard-weather movements of thrushes and there is occasionally a mass exodus during the course of the winter. The largest counts, however, mostly relate to passage movements and include 2,000 at Lowestoft on 21st October 1955, 2,000 north over Beccles on 27th February 1957, 5,000 at Landguard Point on 6th October 1984, 2,000 at Fakenham Magna on 6th October 1984, thousands at Lowestoft on 6th October 1984, 4,400 at Landguard Point on 31st March 1985 and 5,000 at Minsmere on 12th October 1997. Spring migration normally starts in late February and continues to April with a few still passing through in early May.

Ringing returns show that the origins of the wintering population lie in Scandinavia. Redwings ringed in Finland and Norway have been found here, whereas Suffolk-ringed birds have been recovered in Finland, Norway, Belgium and France.

The song of the Redwing is occasionally delivered from suitable breeding habitat in the county, such as dense oak and birch woods, from mid- to late May and sometimes in June and raises speculation that nesting may take place. The Redwing has bred sporadically in Britain since 1925, mostly in Scotland, but has also nested in a few English counties, the most notable being 1-5 pairs in Kent (Gibbons *et al.* 1993). There are five single-day records for June or July and two were at Henham on 12th June 1999, but nesting has yet to be confirmed. A flock of 13 at Playford on 3rd August 1953 were early passage migrants.

Mistle Thrush *Turdus viscivorus*

A common resident, passage migrant and winter visitor

Parks, large gardens and woodland edges provide this species with nesting habitat. Post-breeding gatherings are regularly noted on areas of short turf such as heathland and playing fields. The Mistle Thrush is widely distributed throughout the county, although the population is denser in the north-west and south-east. The species is an occasional passage migrant but records of flocks arriving from offshore are considered suspect.

Nationally, the species' status changed markedly between 1800 and 1850 when, after being restricted to southern Britain, it increased spectacularly and spread as far as Scotland and Ireland (Marchant *et al.* 1990). This expansion apparently continued at a slower pace into the 20th century, although there is no evidence to suggest that numbers increased in Suffolk – it was as common throughout the county in the 1880s (Babington 1884-1886) as it was 50 years later (Ticehurst 1932). The Mistle Thrush is susceptible to cold winters and numbers dropped significantly during 1961/2 and 1962/3, although recovery was swift. CBC index values show the population to be in steep decline in the 1980s after being relatively stable throughout the 1970s (Marchant *et al.* 1990).

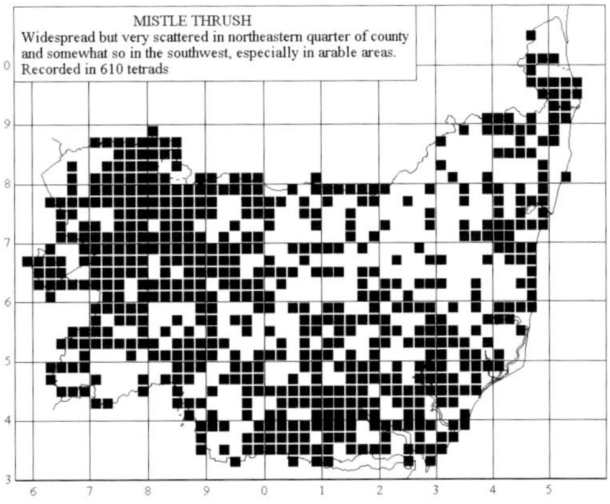
MISTLE THRUSH
Widespread but very scattered in northeastern quarter of county and somewhat so in the southwest, especially in arable areas.
Recorded in 610 tetrads
0
9
8
7
6
5
4
3
6
7
8
9
0
1
2
3
4
5

Although the map shows the species to be widely spread throughout the county, it is much commoner in north-west and south-east Suffolk with small concentrations around Lowestoft, Minsmere and Walberswick. It is only sparsely distributed along the Waveney and upper Stour Valleys and is absent from some of the central cereal-growing areas.

The Mistle Thrush has one of the most protracted breeding seasons of any British species with first clutches laid in February and second broods at the end of June. A pair was seen nest building near Beccles on 20th January 1949 and another accompanied two nearly-fledged young at Martlesham Heath on 5th February 1990. One had just completed a clutch of four eggs in Reydon Wood, on the exceptionally late date of 23rd November 1920.

Late-summer flocks of 20-30 regularly frequent grassland sites and orchards. Gatherings of 50-100 have been reported on eight occasions and there have been five flocks in three-figures. Flocks totalling 300 were attracted to fallen apples at Bradfield Combust on 25th-26th August 1984 and 268 were in the King's Forest on 2nd August 1992.

Small parties, usually of ten or fewer birds, are regularly logged at Landguard Point during passage periods and two arriving from offshore there on 29th October 1983 show that immigration does occur. Adults in southern counties are mainly sedentary, but northern birds move south in autumn and may reach France (Lack 1986). It is likely that those logged at Landguard Point relate to passage birds. A single Dutch-ringed bird was found dead at Rendlesham during the harsh winter of 1947, although generally ringing evidence does not suggest there is a significant influx of immigrants from the continent during winter. Records for the early 1950s suggest that the species formerly arrived in significant numbers. For example, Mistle Thrushes were said to have been steadily making a landfall at Hopton-on-Sea and Corton on 14th October 1950 with immigration continuing throughout the afternoon and into the evening. The following year, 50 were seen heading inland from the shore at Kessingland on 4th October and 31 came in from the sea at Walberswick on 1st November. The timing and large number of immigrants arriving in north-east Suffolk suggest misidentification and that the birds were actually Fieldfares.

American Robin *Turdus migratorius*

Accidental: one record

1994 Felixstowe: Docks, first-winter male freshly dead, 1st November

The above individual was found freshly dead on top of a container being loaded onto a ship in the dock basin. The container had previously been stored on Trinity Terminal, which is adjacent to Fagbury Cliff. The specimen is now at the Ipswich Museum.

The American Robin breeds in North America up to the Arctic Circle and winters in the southern states of the U.S.A. south to Guatemala. It is a rare vagrant to Britain, being noted on only 32 occasions up to the end of 2000 (BBRC). There is a predominance of records for the period November-February.

Cetti's Warbler *Cettia cetti*

A scarce resident and very rare passage migrant

The explosive song of the Cetti's Warbler, often delivered from a low perch in dense marshland scrub, is quite unmistakable. It can be heard in all months although it is less vociferous during winter. However, its skulking nature means that clear views are often difficult to obtain. The warbler has only colonised Britain in the past 30 years or so and now breeds in several southern counties, but although there is an abundance of suitable breeding habitat, the species has struggled to survive the effects of harsh winters.

One at Minsmere, from 29th March to 18th June 1971, was the first county record, an occurrence which warranted a note in *British Birds* with regard to its continuous nocturnal singing (Burton 1979). Singing males, present at Minsmere during the subsequent two summers, indicate that nesting probably took place and, in 1976, territorial birds were noted at four sites. Breeding was confirmed at two sites the following summer. Numbers varied from 3-5 pairs up to 1980 and, thereafter, the population spectacularly increased to a peak of 31 territories at seven coastal sites in 1984, including seven at each of Carlton Marshes and Minsmere and 11 at Walberswick. The latter coincided with a national high of 316 males

The species has been recorded in Britain and Ireland on only 43 occasions up to the end of 2000 (BBRC), but identification is tricky and, in consequence, occurrences could be more frequent than records suggest. The Suffolk birds were both trapped at Fagbury Cliff in a period when hundreds of *Acrocephalus* warblers were present on site and during an exceptional autumn for eastern vagrants (Piotrowski 1994).

Marsh Warbler *Acrocephalus palustris*

A rare passage migrant: c.35 records – all since 1986

The Marsh Warbler breeds annually in southern England and, following a decline at its Worcestershire stronghold, the population is now centred in Kent. The British breeding population ranged between 22 and 58 pairs for the period 1989-1999 (Olgivie 2001). Although there is no conclusive proof that nesting has ever taken place in Suffolk, singing males have occupied suitable breeding habitat. The species occurs predominantly as a spring passage migrant with the majority of records occurring from late May to mid-June.

It seems quite remarkable that the first for the county did not occur until 1986 (Lancaster 1987), especially as the species has been recorded almost annually ever since. It is possible that birds had been overlooked in the past, but as most recent sightings involve singing males, this explanation seems unlikely. Although the Marsh Warbler has declined markedly as a British breeding species since the 1970s, the European population has expanded northward and eastwards (Gibbons *et al.* 1993) and it is likely that there has been a genuine increase in birds on passage.

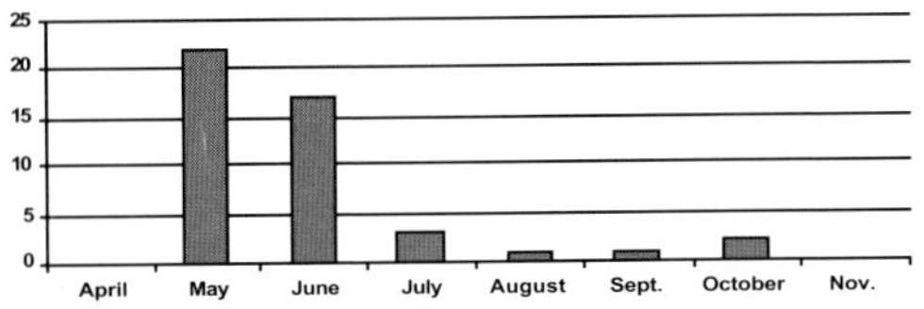

Above: The seasonal distribution of the Marsh Warbler from 1986-2000

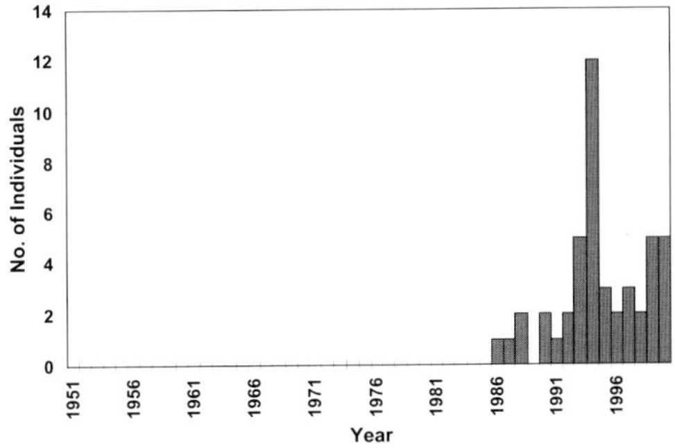

Right: The annual totals of the Marsh Warbler from 1951-2000

The Marsh Warbler is one of the latest summer migrants to reach Britain and this is confirmed in the records. A male singing in a pub car park at Somerleyton on 15th May 1996 is the earliest occurrence. A significant proportion of the records are from migration watch-points, although singing males are increasingly found frequenting suitable nesting habitat. Singing males noted at Boxford in 1994, Stowmarket in 1994 and 1997 and at Timworth in 1995 constitute the only inland records. The Boxford and Stowmarket individuals were present in suitable nesting habitat which is perhaps an indication that breeding will soon take place in the county.

Departure is also normally early and, from the four autumn records, two conform to migration patterns: Landguard Point on 28th July 1990 and Fagbury Cliff on 15th August 1993, but the others at Fagbury Cliff from 20th-23rd October 1990 and on Southwold Golf Course on 11th October are well outside the normal date range.

Reed Warbler (Eurasian Reed Warbler) *Acrocephalus scirpaceus*

An abundant summer visitor and passage migrant

Extensive reedbeds, *Phragmites*-fringed rivers, lakes, gravel workings, ponds, dykes and even small streams with a few reeds provide this species with a nesting and feeding habitat. The coastal marshes and river valleys hold large populations, although the species is difficult to census and, in consequence, few sites are surveyed regularly. Reed Warblers are numerous during autumn passage.

Reed Warblers arrive late in the season with few present before early May. Singles at Walberswick and Minsmere on 5th April in 1980 and 1989 respectively are exceptionally early arrivals. Reed Warblers frequent reedbeds during passage periods but will also associate with other migrants along hedgerows, in town centre parks, around farmyard ponds and amongst coastal scrub. The species normally occurs singly or in groups of up to ten, but coastal floodlights have proved to attract substantial numbers. For example, c.100 were attracted to young broadleaf plantations at Fagbury Cliff on 26th May 1994, which is by far the highest spring count. Spring passage continues well into June.

Return passage normally commences in late July, when some pairs are still tending young. It peaks from mid- to late August and continues through September. The species is scarce in the second half of October and there are eight records in November up to 22nd. One trapped at Landguard Point on 2nd December 1994 was exceptionally late. Concentrations at Fagbury Cliff include 200 on 15th August 1993, 100 on 16th August 1993 and 100 on 14th August 1994. One ringed at Parkeston, Essex, in July 1992 was controlled at Fagbury the following May and again at Fagbury on 11th November 1994. The longevity of the species was demonstrated by one ringed as a juvenile at South Lopham Fen, Norfolk, on 29th July 1988 and controlled at Lackford eight years later.

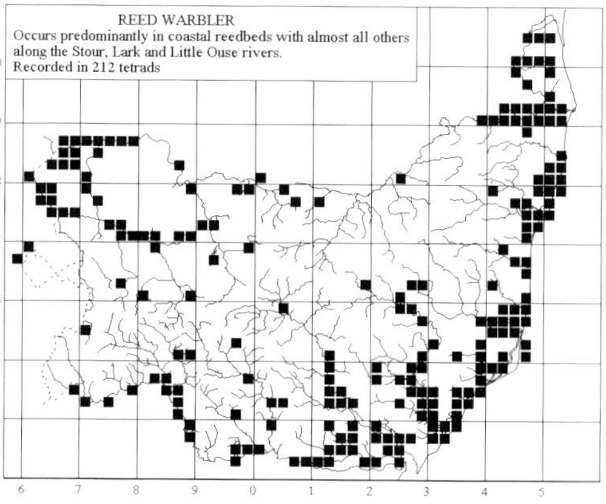

REED WARBLER
Occurs predominantly in coastal reedbeds with almost all others along the Stour, Lark and Little Ouse rivers.
Recorded in 212 tetrads

There has been an inexplicable shift in the area of recovery of Suffolk-ringed Reed Warblers. From 1960-1967, there were 12 recoveries in Portugal – the species' fattening area prior to the trans-Saharan journey to its wintering grounds – but there has since been only one recovery in Portugal. Recent recoveries have come from the Channel Islands, France, Spain, Morocco and Senegal. Reed Warblers ringed in Sweden, Denmark, Belgium, the Netherlands, France, Spain and Senegal have been found in Suffolk.

Great Reed Warbler *Acrocephalus arundinaceus*

Accidental: 11 records

1958 Minsmere: 28th June
1961 Aldeburgh: North Warren, singing 18th May, joined by a second bird 18th June, both stayed to 2nd July
1964 Minsmere: singing male 26th May
1965 Walberswick: Westwood Marsh, 5th September
1966 Minsmere: 7th July
1976 Aldeburgh: North Warren, 13th June
1990 Iken: Picnic Site, singing 14th June
1992 Aldeburgh: Halfway House, singing 31st May
1993 Minsmere: singing 28th-29th May
1998 Levington: trapped 16th May

Records of Europe's largest and noisiest warbler occur periodically, with ten out of the 11 records falling in the period of mid-May to early July and most often singing from bushy areas close to water. The oversummering birds at North Warren in 1961 led to much speculation as to whether breeding had taken place. The 1964 record involved a male which sang near Minsmere's reception hut for an hour, in the territory of a pair of Red-backed Shrikes, which eventually chased it away.

The Great Reed Warbler breeds over most of Europe, in north-west Africa, southern Sweden east through Asia to Japan and has been noted in Britain and Ireland on 209 occasions up to the end of 2000 (BBRC).

A description of a long-staying, singing male which frequented a nettle-bed at Wrentham from 21st June to 2nd May 1977 was never submitted for consideration by BBRC and, despite its song being recorded and the record included by Payn, it has been deleted from the files.

Eastern Olivaceous Warbler *Hippolais pallida*

Accidental: one record

1995 Benacre: Beach Farm, 12th-13th August

The above was a surprise addition to the Suffolk list. It was found in a hedgerow some 200 metres from the shore. This is the earliest autumn report from 14 British records up to the end of 2000 (BBRC), with the majority of occurrences being between mid-September and late October.

The Eastern Olivaceous Warbler breeds in the Balkans and eastwards to Kazakhstan. It winters in Africa south of the Sahara.

Booted Warbler *Hippolais caligata*

Accidental: one record

1996 Gorleston-on-Sea: 3rd-4th September

The Booted Warbler breeds in north-west Russia east to Mongolia and south to Iran and winters in India. It was once an extreme vagrant in Britain and Ireland being reported only once prior to 1958 and then on 21 occasions between 1958-1985 (Dymond *et al.* 1989). It is now an annual visitor with 89 records in all up to the end of 2000 (BBRC).

This long-awaited addition to the Suffolk list was found feeding along the foot of weed-covered cliffs. The record conforms to a national trend which has seen an increase in records from eastern and southern counties.

Icterine Warbler *Hippolais icterina*

An uncommon passage migrant: c.130 records – mostly in autumn

Five or six occur annually at coastal localities mostly during autumn passage, although occasionally in spring. The species often favours tall broad-leafed trees, where it forages for insects high in the canopy, but it will also feed in low scrub, such as tamarisk clumps at coastal resorts.

The bird was not recorded in Suffolk until one was trapped at Minsmere on 12th August 1961. Five were reported in 1965 and then, except for 1990, the species has been recorded in every year from 1969-1995. Increased ringing activities at migration watch-points have undoubtedly led to an upsurge in records as demonstrated in 1993, when nine were trapped from a county record year-total of 14. Landguard Point and, for a brief period, Fagbury Cliff have been the most productive sites, although Icterine Warblers are frequently located in Minsmere's Sluice Bushes, in high trees at the Sparrow's Nest and Belle Vue gardens and in Warrenhouse Wood at Lowestoft and in St Edmund's churchyard, Southwold. Singles at Beccles on 30th August 1970 and at Bury St Edmunds on 21st September 1971 are the only inland records.

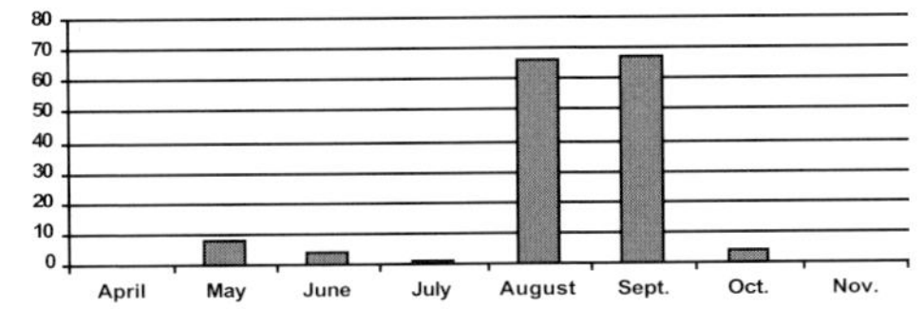

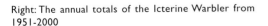

Above: The seasonal distribution of the Icterine Warbler from 1961-2000

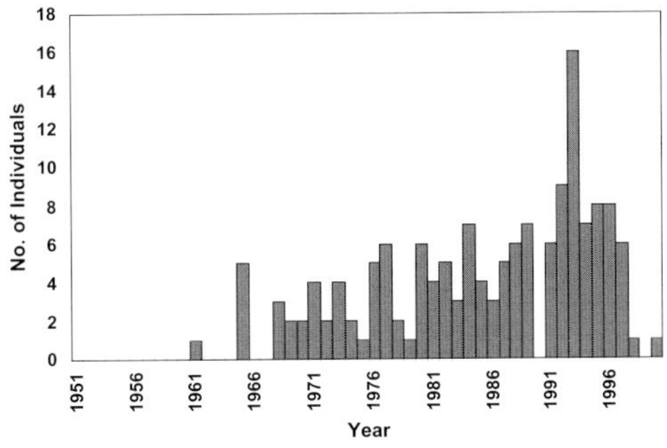

Right: The annual totals of the Icterine Warbler from 1951-2000

There are 11 spring records with a singing male at Walberswick on 14th May 1980 being the earliest. Other singing males have been noted at Minsmere, Landguard Point and Fagbury Cliff, but none have lingered more than two days. The only midsummer occurrences were two singing males: one at Minsmere on 24th June 1986 and another at Landguard Point on 3rd July 1994. The first of the autumn is normally noted in mid-August, with an adult trapped at Landguard Point, on 6th August 1996, being the earliest. Migrants continue to pass through to early October and a tardy individual was noted at Lighthouse Score, Lowestoft, 10th October 1989. Icterine Warblers often feed high in the canopy during autumn migration as seen at Fagbury Cliff, where a long-staying individual picked aphids from the underside of sycamore leaves, from 12th September-8th October 1992. When trapped on 29th September the bird weighed an amazing 23 grams, which is nearly twice the species' normal arrival weight.

An interesting record involved one flying in from offshore and briefly landing on the South Pier at Gorleston-on-Sea, 24th August 1974 (Allard 1990).

Melodious Warbler *Hippolais polyglotta*

A very rare passage migrant: 14 records

1970	Minsmere: 14th-15th August
1971	Aldeburgh: Slaughden Quay, 29th August and presumably the same 4th September
1982	Orford: Havergate Island, 29th August
1983	Felixstowe: Landguard Point, singing male 7th-13th May (trapped 7th)
1989	Lakenheath: Sedge Fen, singing male 28th June
	Felixstowe: Sewage Works, 12th-13th September
1994	Trimley St Mary: Fagbury Cliff, trapped 9th June
1995	Felixstowe: Landguard Point, singing male trapped 31st May
1996	Felixstowe: Landguard Point, trapped 30th May
1997	Felixstowe: Landguard Point, singing male 14th June
1998	Felixstowe: Landguard Point, male trapped 17th June
2000	West Stow: Country Park, singing male 18th May
	Felixstowe: Landguard Point, ad. male trapped 27th July
2001	Felixstowe: Landguard Point, ad. male trapped 1st July

Melodious Warblers breed in south-west and central Europe and north-west Africa and winter south of the Sahara.

The more technical aspects used to separate *Hippolais* warblers in the field were unknown until comparatively recently and therefore the pre-1983 records must be considered as suspect. Identification was then mostly based on the brightness of plumage and leg colour rather than head shape and wing characteristics such as primary projection. The recording of wing biometrics by ringers has greatly aided fieldcraft and it is significant that from the subsequent 11 records eight were trapped between the dates of 7th May to 27th July. Of these, nine occurred on the Felixstowe peninsula – the exceptions being singing males in a poplar plantation at Lakenheath and at West Stow Country Park. The latter individual could have been in the area for at least three days.

Marmora's Warbler *Sylvia sarda*

Accidental: one record

2001	Leiston-cum-Sizewell: Sizewell Dunes, singing male 29th May

The scrubby banks in front of Sizewell Nuclear Power Station provided refuge for this spectacular little warbler. Although the bird was hidden from view for long periods, it regularly sang from the tops of bushes to the delight of its admirers. However, over-eagerness by some birdwatchers late in the afternoon may well have led to its premature departure.

The Marmora's Warbler breeds on islands in the western Mediterranean and sparsely on the Spanish coast. It is a partial migrant to Algeria and Tunisia. The above individual is the fourth record for Britain and Ireland (BBRC).

Dartford Warbler *Sylvia undata*

A very rare resident and passage migrant

Dartford Warbler and Stonechat (*Adam Kennedy*)

After an absence of about 60 years, one or two pairs have returned to breed on coastal sandlings. This small, dark, long-tailed warbler is surprisingly elusive, mostly keeping well hidden amongst gorse or tall stands of heather. It is often heard well before it is seen – its distinctive contact call revealing its presence. Records from habitats unsuitable for breeding relate to wanderers searching for new areas to pioneer.

Suffolk's association with the species lasted from at least 1830-1939. Specimens confirmed its presence in 1830 and nesting subsequently occurred on a number of gorse-clad heathland areas between Ipswich and Lowestoft. However, there is no evidence to suggest that Dartford Warblers ever frequented Breckland. Heathland around Aldeburgh, Leiston and Sizewell was particularly favoured and it bred "in numbers" up to the end of the 19th century (Ticehurst 1932). A contraction of range occurred early in the 20th century and the species disappeared from Suffolk altogether in the 1930s. The last of that era was at Walberswick in about 1939 (Payn 1978). Severe winters of 1860/1, 1880/1, 1916/7 and, perhaps, 1939/40 were the principal cause of the decline, although the fragmentation of heathland, by grubbing and burning, made the species vulnerable to natural disasters.

A juvenile at Felixstowe Ferry on 29th-30th November 1987 came as a big surprise to local birdwatchers, but this individual appeared to be very weak and almost certainly died on the second day. This occurrence heralded the return of the species after being absent for more than half a century. The following year, one was noted in Minsmere's Sluice Bushes, on 3rd December, and then a singing male frequented Dunwich Heath from 6th November 1992-20th July 1993. By 1995, Dartford Warblers were holding territories at three sites and breeding was confirmed the following year, when two juveniles were reared at one of them. Thereafter, the breeding population expanded rapidly from three pairs in 1997 to 12 in 1998, 20 in 1999, 33 in 2000 and 61 in 2002 (P. Etheridge *in litt.*). Despite these promising signs, the Dartford Warbler is unlikely to return to its former abundance having found a different Suffolk to the one from which it departed. The sandling belt then stretched without interruption from Ipswich to Lowestoft and there was much fringe habitat.

The association between Dartford Warblers and Stonechats has been well documented (Moore 1975), but in one remarkable case a warbler on Dunwich Heath in 1993 actually assisted a pair of Stonechats in their parental duties, taking food to the young birds.

One trapped at Landguard Point on 16th May 1995 was a surprise addition to the LBO list.

Spectacled Warbler *Sylvia conspicillata*

Accidental: one record

1997 Felixstowe: Landguard Point, male 26th April-2nd May (trapped 26th)

The above individual was initially located in a mist net and subsequently delighted thousands of observers as it showed intermittently in nettles and low bushes around Landguard Fort.

The Spectacled Warbler breeds in the Mediterranean basin, North Africa and on the islands off West Africa and winters in desert regions north of the Sahara. It is an extremely rare visitor to the British Isles, the above individual being one of four recorded in the British Isles up to the end of 2000 (BBRC).

Subalpine Warbler *Sylvia cantillans*

A very rare passage migrant: 11 records involving 12 individuals

1986	Felixstowe: Landguard Point, male 26th September-2nd October (trapped 27th)
1987	Felixstowe: Landguard Point, 8th-10th June (trapped 8th)
1988	Felixstowe: Landguard Point, 23rd-24th April (trapped 23rd)
1989	Felixstowe: Landguard Point, trapped 30th May
	Dunwich: Greyfriars, first-summer trapped 4th June
1993	Weybread: singing male 24th-25th April
	Trimley St Mary: Fagbury Cliff, first-summer male 16th-22nd May, trapped 16th, singing 20th-22nd
	Felixstowe: Landguard Point, two females trapped 28th May
1994	Minsmere: Sluice Bushes, singing male 24th-25th May
1995	Trimley St Mary: Fagbury Cliff, trapped 31st May
2000	Leiston-cum-Sizewell: Sizewell, freshly dead 11th November

From 1986-1995, this small *Sylvia* warbler was an almost annual visitor to Suffolk. Sites close to Felixstowe Docks dominated the records and its fast, chattering song has been heard at Minsmere, Weybread (the only record away from the immediate coastline) and Fagbury Cliff.

The two autumn records, compared to nine for spring, conforms to the national trend which show a predominance of spring occurrences with most noted during May.

The Subalpine Warbler breeds in south Europe, north-west Africa and west Turkey and winters in the Sahel region, south of the Sahara. It is a regular visitor to Britain and Ireland being noted on 475 occasions up to the end of 2000 (BBRC).

Sardinian Warbler *Sylvia melanocephala*

Accidental: one record

1994 Felixstowe: Landguard Point, male trapped 20th May

The Sardinian Warbler breeds around the Mediterranean eastwards to Afghanistan and is a resident or partial migrant to south of the Sahara. There are 58 records for Britain and Ireland, up to the end of 2000 (BBRC), of which only one was prior to 1958.

The above individual became extremely elusive following its release, although the harsh scolding chatter was occasionally heard from the thick canopy of the holm oaks, at the front of the Observatory, throughout the morning. Late in the afternoon, it gave excellent views to the assembled birdwatchers (Marsh 1995).

Barred Warbler *Sylvia nisoria*

An uncommon passage migrant: c.100 records

Barred Warblers breed in Europe from Germany, north Italy and south Sweden eastwards throughout Asia and are annual visitors to Britain, predominantly to the east coast. In Suffolk, the species occurs singly with other warblers although occasionally two or three are present at one site. On migration, Barred Warblers invariably frequent dense clumps of coastal scrub, where there is an abundance of bramble, intermixed with tamarisk, hawthorn and blackthorn and its skulking nature means many may well go unnoticed.

The species was not identified in Suffolk until 28th August 1912 when, following north-easterly winds, one was found at Lowestoft. The same conditions brought an influx of Wrynecks, which often arrive simultaneously with Barred Warblers. The latter site also hosted the next on 16th September 1931 and then one visited Walberswick on 18th September 1950. Since 1955, Barred Warblers have been found during most autumns and there have been only seven blank years. Groups of three have been noted at Minsmere on two occasions: 8th September 1966 and 2nd September 1973.

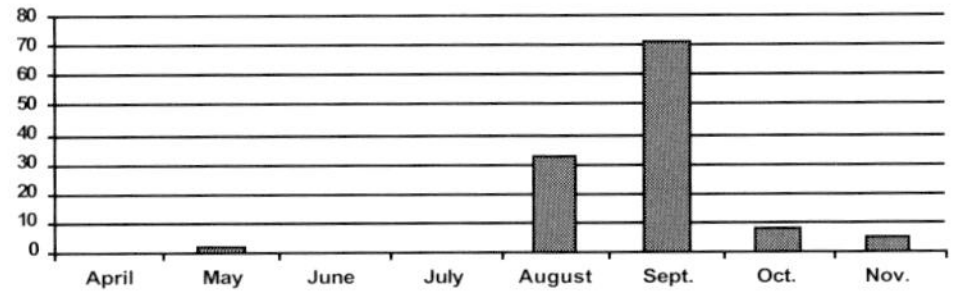

Above: The seasonal distribution of the Barred Warbler from 1912-2000

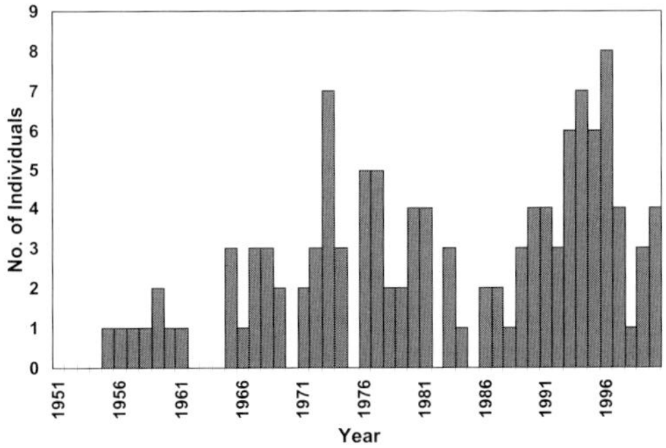

Right: The annual totals of the Barred Warbler from 1951-2000

Although there has been an increase in records, there has also been a corresponding increase in observers, ringing activities and overall coverage.

There were only seven spring records for Britain and Ireland during the period 1958-1985 (Dymond *et al.* 1989) and, therefore, singing males at Minsmere on 22nd May 1960 and at Landguard Point from 30th May to 1st June 1987, are significant from a national perspective. Barred Warblers mostly arrive during the last few days of August or early September, although laggards are occasionally noted in October and November. One at Minsmere on 9th August 1968 is the earliest autumn occurrence and all six November records are for the period 1991-2000, with one, which frequented an old railway cutting at Lowestoft from 26th November-6th December 2000, being the latest.

One at Brandon on 18th August 1983 is a remarkable inland record.

Lesser Whitethroat *Sylvia curruca*

A common summer visitor and passage migrant

The repetitive, rattling song of the Lesser Whitethroat can be heard in many parts of Suffolk during spring and summer. This little warbler is widely but thinly spread throughout the county, although there are strongholds around the nature reserves in the central coastal zone, south Ipswich, the Shotley peninsula and in the extreme south-west of the county . It favours fairly open habitats such as heathland and gorse-covered commons, but will also nest in tall, thick hedgerows and gardens. During passage periods, the species is a regular visitor to migration watch-points.

Lesser Whitethroats rarely arrive before mid-April with the bulk of the males defending territories by the first week of May. Nesting takes place almost immediately, usually in thick cover, on heath and Breckland, in tall hedgerows, young plantations, overgrown railway embankments and, occasionally, industrial areas. The nest site is usually situated much higher than other warblers and nests have been found on a lateral branch of a fir tree, over three metres from the ground, and nearly nine metres up a thorn tree (Payn 1978).

A population decrease was noted during the 1950s. Numbers were down in the Southwold area and generally throughout west Suffolk, although 15 pairs remained at Minsmere. The grubbing out of high hedges and the loss of scrub habitats were thought to be responsible for population declines of Lesser Whitethroats and other warbler species. The coastal strip, between Aldeburgh and Southwold, currently holds the highest densities and, although there are marked fluctuations between sites, numbers are generally increasing. This conforms to the national trend which shows an overall increase of 16.2% between the 'atlas' periods, largely as a result of increased densities on farmland (Gibbons *et al.* 1993).

Autumn migration normally commences in mid-August and continues to early October. There are four November records with one at Bradwell on 12th being the latest. A remarkable record involved an overwintering bird which fed in some Ipswich gardens from 17th-25th January 2001.

Groups of up to ten are not uncommon during passage periods and more significant gatherings are occasionally noted. A total of 40 was logged at Minsmere on 29th September 1991, but the largest concentrations involve birds drawn to flood-lighting around Felixstowe Docks. The largest day-counts were achieved at Fagbury Cliff and included 50 on 20th September 1992, 60 on 2nd May 1993 and an amazing 150 on 12th September 1993. Relatively few were affected by the conditions which led to the 'Great Fall' of September 1965, perhaps due to the south-easterly migration route taken by the species. Lesser Whitethroats pass through the eastern Mediterranean to winter in Ethiopia and Sudan. The migration route is confirmed by Suffolk-ringed birds being recovered in Italy in 1963, the Lebanon in 1973 and Egypt in 1994. All were trapped in Suffolk in late August of those years and relocated whilst still on passage.

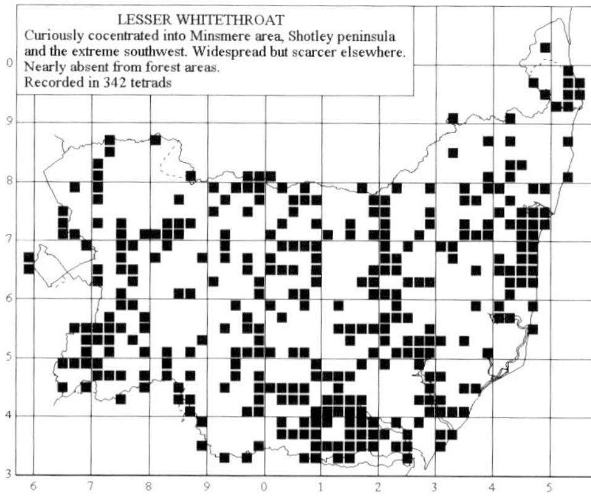
LESSER WHITETHROAT
Curiously cocentrated into Minsmere area, Shotley peninsula and the extreme southwest. Widespread but scarcer elsewhere. Nearly absent from forest areas.
Recorded in 342 tetrads

Individuals showing characters of the eastern race *S. c. blythi*, formerly known as Siberian Lesser Whitethroat, were trapped at Minsmere, 30th October 1964 and Landguard Point, 17th October 1987, 13th October 1989, 5th-6th October 1992 and 21st September-20th October 1994. An individual showing characters of the race *S. c. halimodendri*, was discovered at Fagbury Cliff on 26th October 1994 and lingered until 6th November. The latter race breeds in the Russian steppes from the Volga to Altai, although it is not recognised by some authorities, being considered as an intergrade between *S. c. blythi* and *S. c. althaea*.

Whitethroat (Common Whitethroat) *Sylvia communis*

A common summer visitor and passage migrant

The Whitethroat breeds in a variety of habitats, although it tends to avoid dense woodland and reedbeds. The warbler is well distributed throughout the county, although it is decidedly less common on parts of Breckland, around Bury St Edmunds and Newmarket and the cereal-growing areas of north Suffolk. Its scratchy chatter is a familiar sound along country lanes, weedy thickets, allotments, scrubby areas, ditches and wooded pastures. The species regularly passes through migration watch-points, occasionally in abundance.

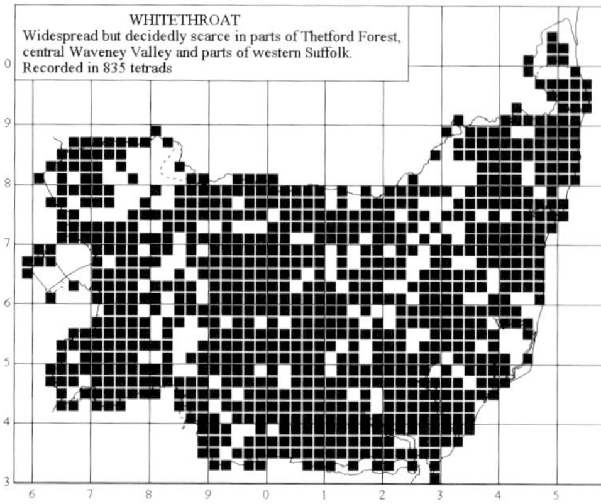
WHITETHROAT
Widespread but decidedly scarce in parts of Thetford Forest, central Waveney Valley and parts of western Suffolk.
Recorded in 835 tetrads

The Whitethroat was formerly Suffolk's most common warbler, but the population is subject to fluctuations, depending on the rainfall levels in the species' Sahel wintering grounds. It suffered greatly when rains failed in 1968 and 1969, resulting in an alarming crash in the numbers returning to Britain to breed. In the latter year, around 77% of the previous year's breeding stock failed to return (Sharrock 1976) – a decline which was noticeable throughout the county. The Reydon Grove study from 1964-1971 revealed a range of 6-27 breeding pairs (Benson & Williamson 1972), compared with 21 in 1997 (Pearson 1998).

Few return to their breeding territories before the third week of April and of the 13 pre-10th April records, seven were in the years prior to the 1969 crash. One on 1st April 1959 is the earliest. Most have departed by mid-October, but there are nine November records. One at Herringfleet on 25th November and another which lingered at Benacre Denes from 7th November-7th December 1991 are the latest. Suffolk-ringed birds have been recovered in France, Portugal and Morocco indicating a south-westerly migration to their African wintering area. During passage periods, concentrations can occur almost anywhere, although sites close to the Port of Felixstowe have hosted the largest numbers in recent years. For example, spring gatherings of 100 or more were present at Fagbury Cliff on 16th May 1993 and again on 29th April, 1st and 5th May 1994 and, in autumn, 150 were present from 29th-31st August 1992. During the 1965 'Great Fall', 200 and 150 were recorded at Minsmere and Lowestoft respectively, on 3rd September.

Garden Warbler *Sylvia borin*

A fairly common summer visitor and passage migrant

The Garden Warbler favours mature deciduous woodland with a tangle of undergrowth or well-grown coppice, although it will also frequent woodland edge, osier beds and, occasionally, hedgerows. The highest concentrations are found around the coastal reserves between Aldeburgh and Southwold and inland to the A12, between the Deben and Alde estuaries and on the Shotley peninsula. It is rare in the north central areas. The species is common at coastal localities during passage periods.

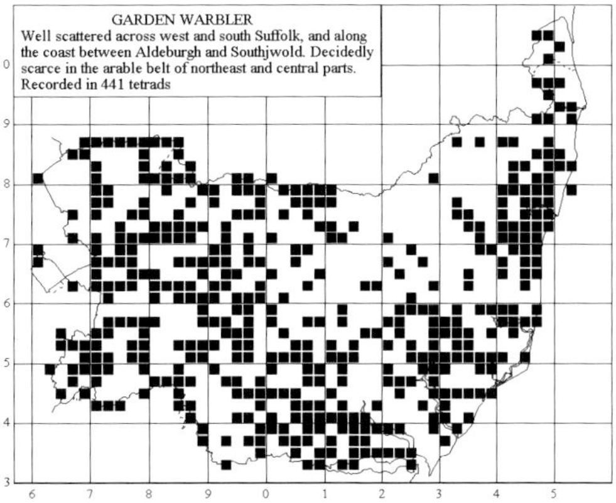

The first of the year are most often heard before seen with new arrivals singing in dense scrub or high in developing canopy, vigorously proclaiming a nesting territory. Most arrive during the last week of April or early May. There are only three early-April records involving singles at Walsham-le-Willows on 4th April 1974, Ufford on 7th April 1988 and Ashbocking on 8th April 1998.

The breeding population has remained relatively stable at well-monitored sites, although densities are slightly lower than Blackcap. The Reydon Grove Farm study from 1964-1971 revealed a range of 3-6 breeding pairs (Benson & Williamson 1972), compared with three pairs in 1997 (Pearson 1998). During the 1970s and early 1980s, the poplar plantations around Lakenheath abounded with songs of Garden Warblers holding the county's largest concentration of around 50-100 pairs, but most of this woodland has since been felled and only a few pairs remain.

Autumn migration gets underway in late July and peaks in mid-September. Few are noted after mid-October, although there have been 12 November records, singles at Lowestoft and Minsmere, on 13th November 1988 and 2000 respectively, being the latest.

The warbler figured prominently in the 1965 'Great Fall', when an amazing 2,000 were estimated at Minsmere on 4th September, although almost the entire arrival had moved on by the next day, unlike most other species which lingered on for some time. Small numbers are reported regularly at many sites during passage periods and occasionally in gatherings of up to 20. A spring concentration of 50 at Fagbury Cliff on 8th May 1994 is exceptional.

Birds ringed in Germany and Belgium were found on passage at Minsmere and Landguard Point respectively and Suffolk-ringed birds found in the Channel Islands and Morocco indicate a south-westerly migration route.

Blackcap *Sylvia atricapilla*

An common summer visitor and passage migrant. A few overwinter

The Blackcap is now Suffolk's commonest *Sylvia* warbler, breeding in wooded habitats throughout the county. The species is frequently associated with large falls of migrants, particularly during autumn passage, and a small wintering population has increased in number in recent years.

The highest breeding densities are found in the central coastal zone north of Sizewell and in woodland on the Shotley peninsula. The map shows that the species is sparsely distributed in the central cereal-growing areas northwards to the Waveney Valley, in north-west Suffolk, in low-laying areas around the Alde estuary and between the Deben and Orwell estuaries. Blackcaps nest in parks and large gardens in Ipswich town centre. Well-monitored sites show a steady increase in breeding pairs which conforms well with the national trend (Marchant *et al.* 1990). A study at a mixed farm at Reydon Grove from 1964-1971 revealed a range of 6-7 breeding pairs (Benson & Williamson 1972), compared with 13 in 1997 (Pearson 1998).

Blackcaps return to breeding areas during the first two weeks of April and, generally, only small numbers are noted at migration watch-points in spring passage. However, larger numbers are sometimes logged during autumn passage, especially when winds veer between north and east and accompany rain and overcast conditions. Blackcaps begin to move through in late August and migration peaks in late September and early October. The tail of Hurricane Hortense, on 4th October 1984, created freak conditions, which forced thousands of passerines to seek cover at Landguard Point, including 500 Blackcaps and the prevalence of easterly winds during the autumns of the early 1990s, together with the glow from the Port of Felixstowe, created conditions which attracted huge numbers to Fagbury Cliff. Counts of 100+ were logged there regularly and concentrations of c.200 were noted on 12th and 14th October 1991, 500 on 28th September 1992 and 150 on 3rd October 1993 and 11th September 1994. Autumn ringing totals for the site, were also very high for that period, with four-figure totals being achieved in each of 1992-1994. Suffolk-ringed Blackcaps have been recovered in Norway, France, Spain (3), Algeria (4) and Mauritania showing a more or less due south departure. Some of the Algerian birds were reared in Suffolk, but, as the Blackcap winters both to the north and south of the Sahara, it is possible that these birds were still migrating. Birds ringed in Belgium (7), the Netherlands (3) and Poland have been found in the county as part of a westerly drift into East Anglia during October.

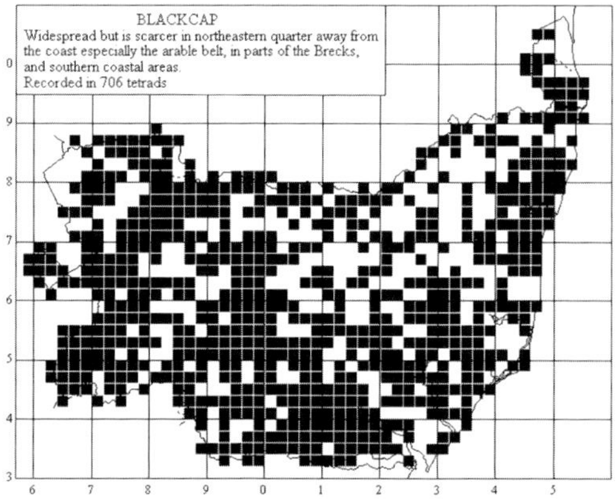

Overwintering is a comparatively recent phenomenon with birds increasingly frequenting well-established gardens in towns and villages, most regularly in Woodbridge, Ipswich and Felixstowe. Ticehurst listed no overwintering records and a female feeding on a Belton bird-table throughout the winter of 1950/1 is the first recorded occurrence. There were four further instances of wintering in the following ten years and few records for the 1960s. However, records for the period December to February are now annual, although estimating numbers present is difficult due to birds skulking in the shrubberies and showing only intermittently. Wintering Blackcaps are most often observed accompanying tit flocks and will regularly visit bird-tables. One at Landguard Point in January and February 1989 made daily visits to the feeding area and regularly fed from peanut-holders.

Greenish Warbler *Phylloscopus trochiloides*

Very rare passage migrant: seven records

1981	Minsmere: Sluice Bushes, male 1st September
1986	Lowestoft: Sparrow's Nest Gardens/Belle Vue Park, male 20th-22nd September
1990	Minsmere: Sluice Bushes, 27th-30th August
1992	Felixstowe: Landguard Point, male in song (trapped) 28th May
	Trimley St Mary: Fagbury Cliff, singing male 7th June
1993	Lowestoft: Flycatcher Lane, 9th May
1997	Felixstowe: Landguard Point, male in song (trapped) 8th July

Birds singing on spring migration is not unexpected, but proof of singing whilst on autumn migration was provided by the 1981 and 1986 individuals, the vocabulary of the latter being particularly well studied (Brown 1987).

The warbler's breeding range extends from north-east Germany and Finland through to east Siberia and south to the Himalayas. It winters in India and south-east Asia. It is a regular visitor to the British Isles, being noted on 358 occasions up to the end of 2000 (BBRC), with reports biased towards east-coast counties. The seven Suffolk records show equal numbers in spring and autumn, whereas nationally the trend leans towards autumn occurrences.

Arctic Warbler *Phylloscopus borealis*

Accidental: three records

1993 Trimley St Mary: Fagbury Cliff, 30th September-2nd October (trapped 30th September)
1996 Corton: 16th-18th September
2000 Dunwich: Greyfriars, trapped 25th September

The Trimley bird was one of several eastern vagrants which frequented sites adjacent to Felixstowe Docks during the autumn of 1993. Originally extracted from a mist-net (Crewe 1994), it became elusive on release, although it eventually delighted hundreds of visiting birdwatchers as it fed high in the canopy of old oak trees on the cliff. Suffolk's second Arctic Warbler was found in a railway cutting and was equally well watched but the third, trapped by a ringer in a Dunwich garden, was not subsequently seen after its release.

The species breeds in northern Scandinavia through arctic Siberia to Alaska. It has been positively identified in Britain and Ireland on 247 occasions up to the end of 2000 (BBRC).

Pallas's Warbler (Pallas's Leaf Warbler) *Phylloscopus proregulus*

A rare passage migrant: 84 records – all since 1963

When late autumn winds switch to the eastern quarter, appearances of this jewel from the Far East are almost inevitable. Suffolk's first occurrence involved one at Walberswick on 16th November 1963, followed by another at Minsmere on 4th November 1966. A third at Landguard Point on 22nd October 1977 was a prelude to things to come as, between 1981 and 1993, 25 Pallas's Leaf Warblers visited coastal Suffolk of which ten were in the Felixstowe area. Records have been exclusively coastal.

Strangely, Suffolk missed out in 1982, which brought 123 Pallas's Warblers to Britain, but in 1994 the county hosted 23 from a national influx of 180 (Rafe 1996). Again, sites around the Port of Felixstowe attracted the bulk of birds with Fagbury Cliff proving the most productive site with eight out of nine birds present being trapped by ringers.

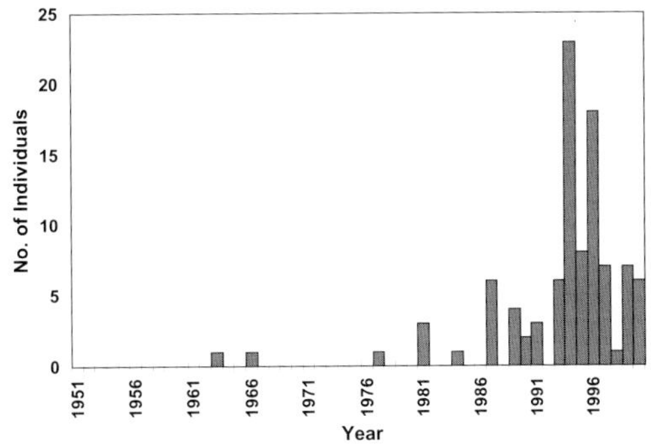

The annual totals of the Pallas's Warbler from 1951-2000

Most arrivals occur in late October and early November and one at Landguard Point on, 15th-16th October 1981, is the earliest occurrence. Arrivals in mid-November are not unusual, but singles at Landguard Point on 24th December 1987 and at Long Covert, Benacre from 1st-2nd December 1990 are the only records for that month.

Pallas's Warblers breed in central Siberia and east to the Sea of Okhotsk and also the Himalayas. It winters in southern China and northern south-east Asia.

Yellow-browed Warbler *Phylloscopus inornatus*

An uncommon autumn passage migrant: c.100 individuals

This tiny warbler occurs solely as a migrant on autumn passage, usually seen feeding actively in treetops or high scrub and often difficult to locate as it flicks quickly from leaf to leaf. It shows a distinct liking for broad-leaved trees such as sycamores and white poplars.

The Yellow-browed Warbler was formerly an extreme county rarity, being recorded on only five occasions up to 1983. There has since been a remarkable transformation with the species occurring in every year from 1984-1997, occasionally in numbers. One at Southwold on 3rd September 1910 is the first for the county and the next was shot at Aldringham, on 12th October 1915. The first occurrence was unusually early in the season as, nowadays, birds rarely show before the last week of September and October records predominate. The only November records are one at Landguard on 13th November 1986, two at Fagbury

Cliff till 13th November 1994, with one of these remaining till 16th November, and another at Easton Bavents on 17th November 2000.

The species' change in status is reflected nationally, which has seen a steady increase since the mid-1960s. There were exceptional influxes in 1985, 1988 and 1994.

One feeding with a tit-flock at Martlesham on 29th October 1984 and singles at the Nunnery, Thetford and one trapped at Lackford both during the autumn of 1993 are the only records away from the immediate coastline.

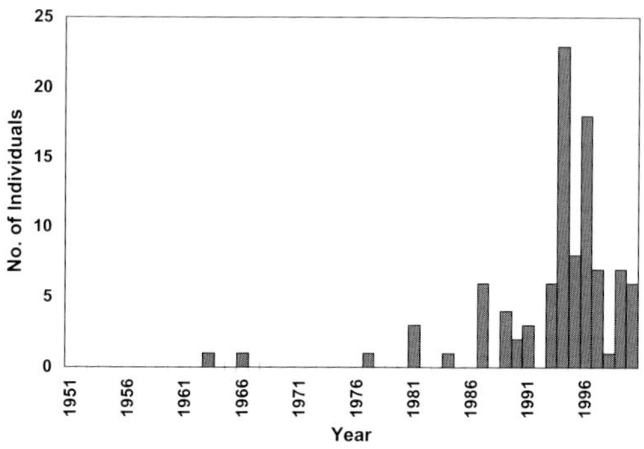

The annual totals of the Yellow-browed Warbler from 1951-2000

The breeding range extends from the eastern slopes of the northern Urals, eastwards through Siberia to the Sea of Okhotsk and south to the Sayan mountains (Cramp *et al.* 1974-1994).

As yet there has been no confirmed sighting of Hume's Leaf Warbler *P. humei*, which is now considered a separate species and occurs in Britain as a rare autumn migrant.

Radde's Warbler *Phylloscopus schwarzi*

A very rare passage migrant: 12 records

1964	Walberswick: Hoist Covert, trapped 4th October
1966	Minsmere: singles trapped 15th and 20th October
1991	Felixstowe: Landguard Point, 8th-9th October (trapped and photographed)
	Hollesley: trapped 12th October
1994	Kessingland: 2nd November
1995	Felixstowe: Landguard Point, trapped 15th October
1996	Lowestoft: Sparrow's Nest Gardens, 12th-13th October
2000	Aldringham-cum-Thorpe: Thorpe Common, at least 1st October
2001	Leiston-cum-Sizewell: Sizewell Nuclear Power Station, 13th October
2002	Orfordness: trapped and photographed 12th-13th October, another 30th

Ringing operations have undoubtedly boosted the number of records of this secretive warbler. Feeding low in coastal scrub, Radde's Warblers are often difficult to locate and probably occur more often than the records suggest.

Its breeding range extends from south-central Siberia eastwards to Sakhalin and it winters in south-east Asia. The species is an annual visitor to the Britain and Ireland having been noted on 228 occasions up to the end of 2000 (BBRC).

Dusky Warbler *Phylloscopus fuscatus*

A very rare passage migrant: nine records

1987	Felixstowe: Landguard Point, 27th October-1st November (trapped 27th)
1991	Dunwich: Greyfriars, trapped 25th October
1992	Westleton: 20th November
1997	Corton: Disused railway line, 23rd-24th October
1999	Corton: Stirrups Lane, 22nd-23rd October
2001	Southwold: Gun Hill, 14th October
	Felixstowe: Landguard Point, 23rd-29th October
2002	Aldringham-cum-Thorpe: 1st-3rd November
2002/3	Kessingland: 30th December-6th January

Dusky Warblers occur slightly later in the year than Radde's Warblers, but their habits of skulking low in vegetation are similar. There was only one British record prior to 1958, but a better understanding of the species' habitat requirements and plumage characteristics has led to an increase in sightings and, since 1978, the species has occurred annually. It is found predominantly in eastern counties, most often on the immediate coastline.

Suffolk's first was trapped and ringed at LBO. It then moved to the grounds of the Custom House where it was seen by hundreds of observers (Butterfield 1988). The second was trapped in a Dunwich garden, but the other seven were found and identified in the field.

The breeding range stretches from west-central to north-east Siberia and the species winter in north-east India and south-east Asia. It has been identified in Britain and Ireland on 224 occasions up to the end of 2000 (BBRC).

Western Bonelli's Warbler — *Phylloscopus bonelli*

Accidental: three records and two of Western/Eastern Bonelli's Warbler

1961	Walberswick: Dingle Hills, trapped 29th-30th April
1970	Minsmere*: 6th May
1981	Felixstowe*: Landguard Point, 13th September
1996	Felixstowe: Landguard Point, 2nd (trapped)-20th October
2000	Felixstowe: Landguard Point, singing male 27th (trapped)-29th May

*Insufficient plumage details and no notes on call means that these two birds cannot be assigned to either Eastern or Western Bonelli's Warbler with any certainty

The Western and Eastern Bonelli's Warblers *P. orientalis* have only recently been split into separate species (Anon. 1997), and only the trapped individuals (1961, 1996 and 2000) can be assigned to Western Bonelli's with certainty. However, the other two (marked with an asterisk) are likely to have been of this species.

Although the number of sightings is increasing, the Western Bonelli's Warbler is still a very rare visitor to the British Isles, being recorded on three occasions prior to 1958 compared with 55 records from then till the end of 2000 (BBRC). However, there are a further 145 records which have not been specifically assigned to either Western or Eastern Bonelli's Warbler and three that have been assigned to the latter species. The national trend is predominantly towards autumn occurrence.

The Western Bonelli's Warbler breeds in north-west Africa, through Iberia to central Europe east to Austria.

Wood Warbler — *Phylloscopus sibilatrix*

A scarce summer visitor and uncommon passage migrant

The distinctive descending trill of the Wood Warbler delivered from the high canopy is one of the delights of a birdwatcher's spring day. Singing males are noted in deciduous woodland from late April through to early June and occasionally one or two pairs breed. The species is most often recorded as a passage migrant and ringing operations have largely been responsible for a significant increase in records in recent years.

The Wood Warbler formerly bred regularly at a number of sites at both inland and coastal localities, but, during the past 50 years, nesting has become increasingly irregular. Breeding either definitely or probably took place during six years in the 1950s, three in the 1960s, four in the 1970s, three in the early 1980s, but only once from 1983-2000.

The species prefers oak, beech or chestnut woodlands with a closed canopy and little or no understorey (Gibbons *et al.* 1993). Suffolk woodlands have changed markedly since the 1950s, mainly due to lack of management and lack of grazing of the woodland floor by rabbits. Most woods are now infested with a tangle of bramble and bracken, ideal for Blackcaps and Garden Warblers, but not for Wood Warblers.

The first of the year is most often noted in the last few days of April or early May. One at Martlesham on 12th April 1972 is the earliest. Passage birds are regularly reported in Christchurch and Holywells Parks in Ipswich, and Wood Warblers are regularly noted amongst Willow Warbler flocks at coastal watch-points.

The high trees around Lowestoft, the poplars within the LBO compound and the plantations at Fagbury Cliff have been the most favoured sites in recent years. The Wood Warbler is one of the earliest birds of

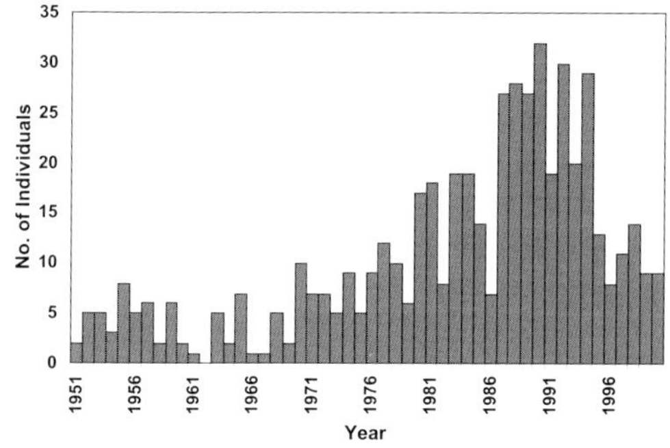

The annual totals of the Wood Warbler from 1951-2000

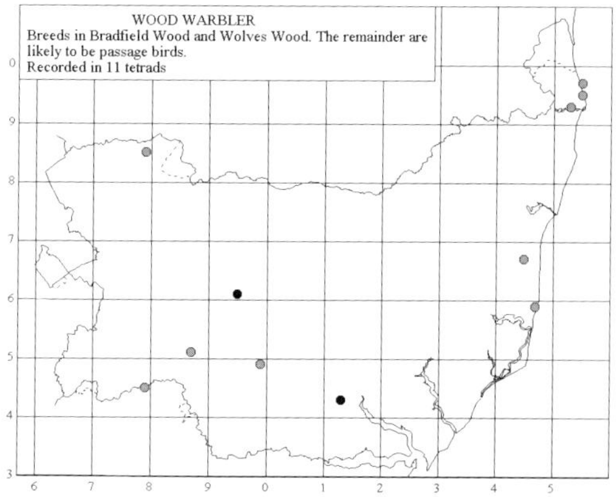

autumn passage with returning migrants noted from late July and usually peak numbers are present in early August. There are a few records up to mid-September and singles at Landguard Point on 1st October 1992, 3rd October 1993 and from 9th-11th October 1994 are the only records for that month.

Chiffchaff (Common Chiffchaff) *Phylloscopus collybita*

An abundant summer visitor and passage migrant. A few overwinter

This warbler favours mature deciduous woodland, with a good scrub layer, and, as its choice of habitat is less catholic than the Willow Warbler, it is somewhat less common.

The Chiffchaff is one of the earliest summer migrants to return to its breeding quarters with many singing birds back on territory by the end of March. The first migrants appear at migration watch-points during the first half of March and the main arrival takes place during the first two weeks of April. Passage birds continue to trickle through to early June. There are high breeding densities in coastal woodlands and the species is common in south and north-east Suffolk. The Chiffchaff is rare in open countryside and absent from much of cereal-dominated central areas, coastal marshes and heathland. It is also surprisingly scarce in many of the river valleys, e.g. by the Waveney between Beccles and Weybread and beside the Stour from Long Melford to Bures. Like the Blackcap, nesting occurs regularly in town centre parks and large gardens.

Although the Chiffchaff is regularly logged at migration watch-points, double-figure counts are rare and it rarely occurs in falls of other migrants. The 1965 'Great Fall' occurred too early in the autumn to affect the species' migration pattern, but the species failed to show well during significant falls on 4th October 1984 and 18th October 1988. The first of the autumn are normally noted at Landguard Point in early September and passage peaks at the end of that month. A few are still passing through in early November. Groups of 30 at Landguard Point on 21st September 1988, 50 at Fagbury Cliff on 13th October 1991 and 40 there on 25th September 1992 are the largest concentrations and all are associated with flood-light attraction around the Port of Felixstowe. There are relatively few ringing recoveries and most are within 500km of the ringing site. One ringed at Minsmere on 22nd August 1962 and recovered in Spain on 31st March 1966 was the only foreign recovery prior to 1978. From the 8,389 Chiffchaffs ringed in Suffolk during the period 1978-2001, only two have been found outside Britain – in the Channel Islands and the Netherlands. One each ringed in Spain and France have been found in Suffolk.

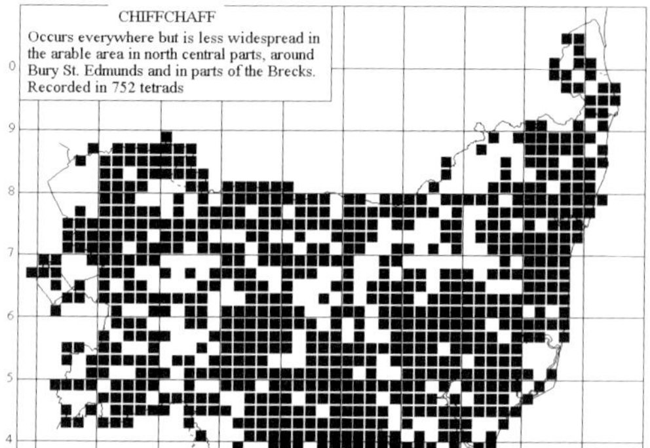

Wintering birds have been noted in Suffolk since 1873, but it has only been since 1974 that this has occurred on a regular basis. Such birds are greatly affected by periods of harsh weather, but this insectivorous species has learnt to exploit the warmer conditions at industrial sites, and particularly, sewage treatment works where groups congregate with Pied Wagtails to glean insects on the filter beds. Chiffchaffs also readily associate with tit-flocks, but reedbeds are generally avoided, unlike other southern counties where they are a favoured winter habitat (Lack 1986). In the early 1990s, the sewage works at Kessingland, Southwold, Holbrook, Stowmarket and Long Melford became a regular attraction where site-totals of up to six birds were reached annually. Smaller numbers have also been regularly noted at Beccles Marshes and Minsmere.

Scandinavian Chiffchaff *P. c. abietinus*

A common passage migrant

Ticehurst was of little doubt that the more greyish-olive Scandinavian Chiffchaff occurred in Suffolk, although he thought that specimens needed to be obtained to be certain. Birds showing characteristics of this race undoubtedly pass through migration watch-points, particularly in late October, but the presence of intergrades causes identification difficulties.

Siberian Chiffchaff *P. c. tristis*

A scarce passage migrant

Reports of the greyish-brown Siberian Chiffchaff have increased markedly in recent years, mostly at migration watch-points, although it occurs less often than the Scandinavian Chiffchaff. A corresponding increase in the frequency of Yellow-browed Warblers, a species sympatric with *tristis*, suggests a genuine increase in vagrancy of this race.

Neither Ticehurst nor Payn made reference to this race and, although the SBR for 1980 referred to the occurrence of 'northern races', the first fully-documented record was one trapped at Landguard Point on 27th October 1987. Thereafter, birds trapped at Landguard Point and Fagbury Cliff for the period 1987-2002 showed six spring occurrences, from 24th April to 8th May. Up to the end of 2000, SBRs have noted 29 autumn arrivals between 22nd October and 29th December, and many have stayed to overwinter. Sewage treatment works are favoured wintering sites.

Willow Warbler *Phylloscopus trochilus*

An abundant summer visitor and passage migrant

As the sallows burst into flower, the cascading notes of the Willow Warbler begin to dominate the spring dawn chorus. The species is Britain's commonest summer visitor, nesting along woodland edges, and in rides and clearings. It particularly favours young coppice and conifer plantations, but is also numerous on heathland with birch regeneration as well as along overgrown, railway embankments and hedgerows.

The map shows that the Willow Warbler is widespread throughout the county, although there are a few gaps. Densities appear to be particularly low in Lothingland, in the central cereal-growing areas, in parts of the west around Bury St Edmunds and south-east of Sudbury. Nationally, there has been little long-term change in population levels (Marchant *et al.* 1990), although the Reydon Grove Farm study from 1964-1971 revealed a range of 3-7 breeding pairs (Benson & Williamson 1972), compared with only two in 1997 (Pearson 1998).

The first migrants are often noted in late March, with one at Worlington on 16th March 1985 being the earliest. Males arrive in force during the second week of April and immediately begin singing. The females follow soon after and nesting occurs in early May. In spring, the species is most often seen in pairs or in small feeding groups, although falls are not uncommon with three-figure totals being noted on a number of occasions. Spring passage continues to early June.

Return migration gets underway in late July and

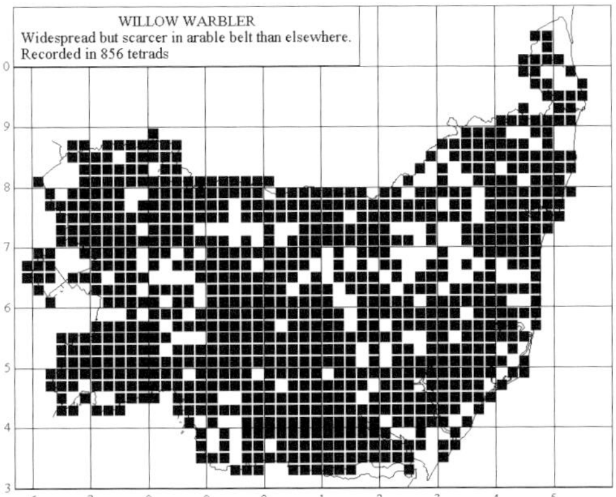

WILLOW WARBLER
Widespread but scarcer in arable belt than elsewhere.
Recorded in 856 tetrads

usually peaks in mid- to late August. Birds continue to pass through until mid-September, but the number of October records each year is small. One at Fagbury Cliff on 16th November 1994 is the latest of three records for that month. The species is often involved in large falls and, on such occasions, coastal bushes become alive with Willow Warblers flicking to and fro in search of insects. For example, during the 1965 'Great Fall', 500 were at both Lowestoft and Minsmere on 4th and 5th September. A similar number was present at Landguard Point on 23rd August 1987 and maxima at Fagbury Cliff were 300 on 26th August 1992 and 28th August 1993. Ringing recoveries link Suffolk with Denmark, the Netherlands, the Channel Islands, France, Spain and Morocco, showing a south-westerly migration route to its wintering grounds south of the Sahara.

The warbler is extremely rare between November and mid-March, being reported on only six occasions up to 1996. Two of these were found feeding with Chiffchaffs at a sewage treatment works.

There are only six records of the paler and greyer Scandinavian and Russian race *P. t. acredula*, but it probably occurs annually along the coast during passage periods. Ticehurst listed two early September specimens which were collected from offshore fishing boats, but modern-day records have been restricted to spring passage.

Goldcrest *Regulus regulus*

An abundant resident and passage migrant

This tiny and delicate species has benefited greatly from the transformation of heathland and Breckland landscapes to conifer plantations. Nesting also takes place in large gardens and churchyards containing yews and cypresses. In winter, the species readily associates with roving tit flocks and can be found in both coniferous and deciduous woodland. The Goldcrest moves vast distances on migration and coastal bushes occasionally play host to huge influxes in late autumn.

The map depicts not only the breeding distribution of the Goldcrest, but also the distribution of conifers. The highest densities occur in the large conifer plantations of Thetford and the King's Forest in Breckland and Dunwich, Tunstall and Rendlesham on the coast. The remaining dots are almost all designating smaller plantations and ornamental conifers in parks and gardens.

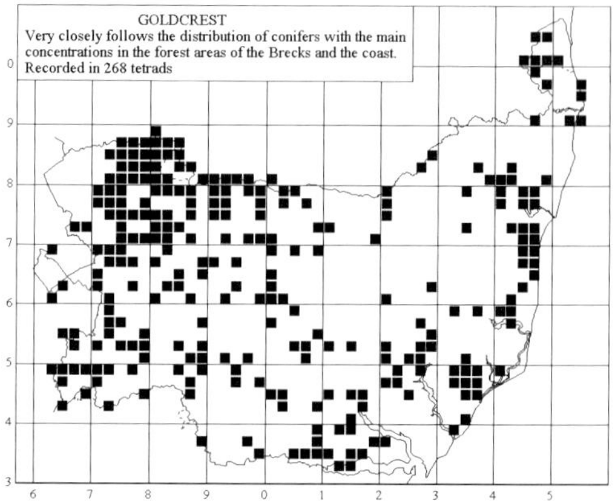

GOLDCREST
Very closely follows the distribution of conifers with the main concentrations in the forest areas of the Brecks and the coast.
Recorded in 268 tetrads

Fir plantations also offer a sustainable food supply throughout the winter and during a study in the King's Forest in 1975, the Goldcrest was found to be the most abundant species representing 18.5% of the total bird population (Last 1977). It is well known that the Goldcrest is susceptible to the effects of cold winters and the species was "brought close to extermination by cold winter of 1916-17", although some breeding birds were reported during the following summer (Jourdain & Witherby 1919). The population fell again, following consecutive cold winters in 1961/2 and 1962/3, and it took several years to regain its former abundance. There was a similar decline during prolonged frosts in 1985.

Goldcrests are comparatively scarce at migration watch-points during spring passage, although small numbers normally pass Landguard Point from early March to early May, with peak migration occurring during the first two weeks of April.

The first migrants normally appear in mid-September, but the main immigration takes place during the second half of October and early November and occasionally in such numbers that coastal gardens are alive with Goldcrests. Such birds often arrive in an exhausted state, weighing less than five grams and their survival rate is probably low. During a massive fall on 17th October 1988, c.1,000 were present at Benacre and 100 at Lowestoft. The species is readily trapped by coastal ringers and autumn Goldcrests found bearing rings from the Czech Republic, Poland, Norway, Sweden, Finland and the Low Countries demonstrate the substantial westerly drift during that season. Suffolk-ringed birds have been recovered in Wales, the Netherlands and Sweden.

Firecrest *Regulus ignicapillus*

An uncommon passage migrant and rare resident

The stunning colour combination of bronzy shoulders contrasting against a vivid green mantle and a striking black and white head pattern, makes this species one of our most attractive passerines. The Firecrest occurs principally as a passage migrant, with peak numbers occurring in both spring and autumn during south-easterly winds. A few overwinter and nesting pairs are noted in most years.

Ticehurst described the species as "amongst the rarest birds in Suffolk", although he thought it commoner than it would appear and overlooked during autumn passage. Five were found in a batch of 70 Goldcrests which had been collected on the Galloper light-vessel stationed 28 miles (48km) south-south-east of Orfordness, sometime prior to 1888, but there were few other records. There was formerly much confusion over identification between the Firecrest and the Goldcrest. For example, Payn listed single-observer, winter records involving flocks of Firecrests frequenting Wangford Warren, during the early 1950s and *British Birds* published a record of 20 there on 20th November 1952 from the same recorder, numbers which were unprecedented for that period. These records were omitted from Payn's second edition of his book and never appeared in SBRs, so were presumably considered erroneous.

Singing males have oversummered at Breckland localities since 1975 and it is likely that breeding regularly occurs there. The first confirmed instance of nesting occurred at Walberswick in 1974, when a male Firecrest apparently paired with a female Goldcrest. Nesting has since been noted regularly, most often in high yews or in holly and in both urban and rural localities. The number of breeding pairs peaked during the early 1980s, when up to 11 singing males held territories at six sites. Nesting pairs frequented

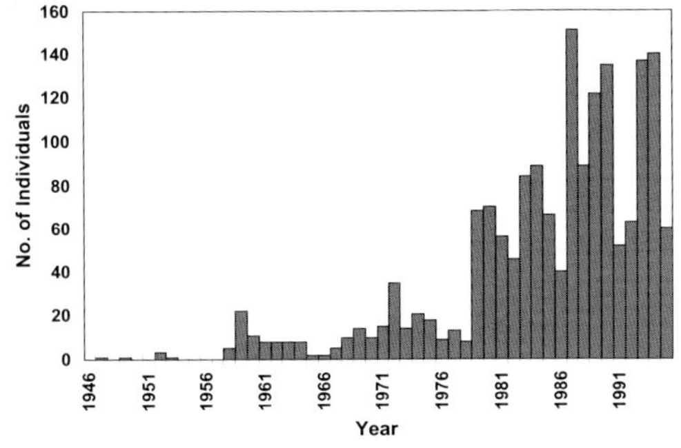

The annual totals of the Firecrest from 1946-1995

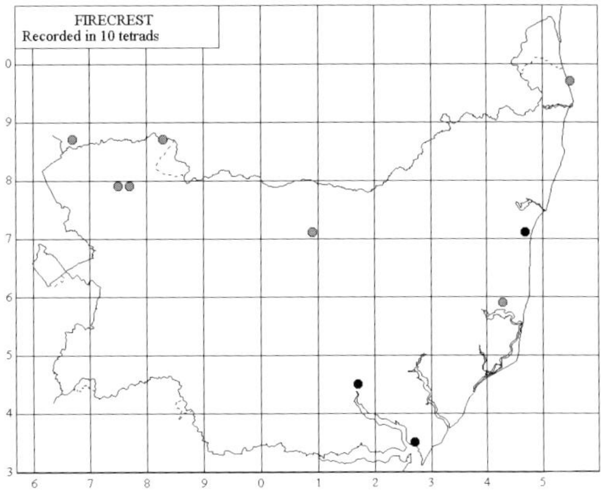

large gardens close to Christchurch Park, Ipswich and in small copses in and around Minsmere, but the species was most regular at Staverton Thicks, Wantisden, where the majestic hollies hosted up to nine singing males. There has been a dearth of records there in recent years. Nationally, numbers have fluctuated from 19-131 pairs between 1989-1999 (Ogilvie *et al.* 2000) with most confined to broadleaf forests of southern England. Contrary to statements in both the *New Atlas* and *Winter Atlas*, Suffolk's breeding Firecrests appear to be resident. Firecrests which bred at Staverton and Dunwich were also present during the winter months. The tit-like piping call can be heard in all months, although it is heard less often and is more difficult to detect in winter. Wintering Firecrests often associate with roving tit flocks.

Migration watch-points such as those at Lowestoft, Southwold, Minsmere, Landguard Point and Fagbury Cliff host the bulk of passage birds, but the species is undoubtedly more common at the southern sites. There is a protracted spring passage from early March to early June, normally peaking at the end of April. Firecrests most often occur in ones and twos, although groups of up to six are not uncommon. Return migration commences in early September, peaks in mid-October and continues through to mid-November. A report of 12 at Lowestoft in a small seafront park in October 1972 is the largest concentration. One at Minsmere on 26th November 1968 was ringed in Belgium the previous November, one trapped in the Bristol Channel on October 3rd 1986 was controlled at Landguard Point two springs later and another ringed at Landguard Point was recovered at Portland, Dorset, the same autumn. There has been a spectacular increase in occurrences since the 1950s, from less than ten per annum in the 1960s to about 100 each year from the late 1980s to the mid-1990s.

Spotted Flycatcher *Muscicapa striata*

A fairly common summer visitor and passage migrant

The Spotted Flycatcher is a familiar feature of parks and large gardens during summer and a common passage migrant. As can be seen from the map, the species is widely scattered throughout the county with no concentrations. This reflects its catholic habitat choice although it is nowhere common. Churchyards are often favourite sites.

The species is one of the last summer migrants to reach our shores and there are few April records. Singles at Badingham on 18th April 1976, Lound on the same date 1980 and Nacton on 9th April 1983 are the only pre-20th April arrivals. The breeding population has been in gradual decline since the early 1960s (Marchant *et al.* 1990) and the recent succession of cold springs in northern Europe has not helped its cause. The Reydon Grove study from 1964-1971 revealed a range of 1-4 breeding pairs (Benson & Williamson 1972), compared with a lone pair in 1997 (Pearson 1998). The species depends solely on a substantial supply of flying insects on its arrival, and, although the decline could be attributed to climate change, the use of insecticides seems to be a major factor in agricultural areas. The flycatcher often nests close to human habitation, such as on ivy-clad walls and trees, in old nests of Blackbirds or Swallows, in tree stumps and even on bird-tables and plant pots. Open-fronted nest-boxes are readily occupied. In 1978, a pair nested in a hanging basket at Mutford. The owner had not noticed until the birds were feeding young. He had been watering the basket and unknowingly the nest and eggs, without detrimental effect. So he carried on watering and the young fledged.

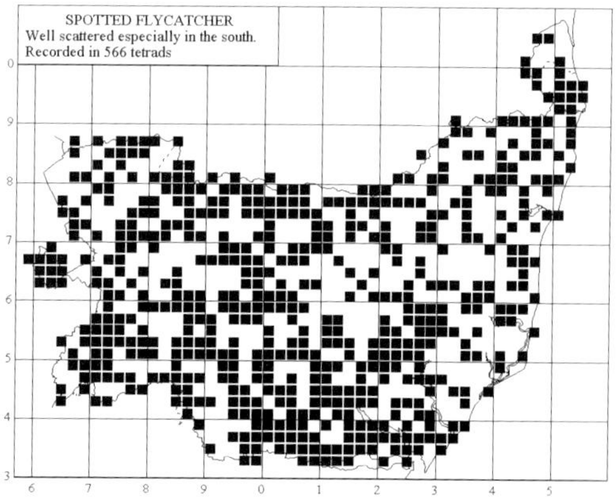

The species is a regular visitor to migration watch-points, usually in singles or groups of up to ten, but occasionally occurs in large numbers. The largest concentration was noted during the 1965 'Great Fall' when 300 were at Minsmere on 3rd September. However, a fall of 150 occurred at Landguard Point on 9th May 1988. Autumn migration gets underway from late August and peaks in mid-September. October records are rare with one at Landguard Point on 26th October 1977 and another at Shotley from 27th-29th October 1990 being the latest. Suffolk-ringed Spotted Flycatchers have been recovered in Germany, Spain, Italy, Morocco and Algeria.

Red-breasted Flycatcher *Ficedula parva*

A rare passage migrant (35 records – mostly autumn)

This tiny flycatcher, often first seen flicking from branch to branch in pursuit of insects high in the canopy, is a real birdwatchers' prize. The species is seen annually, mostly on autumn passage, occurring singly and exclusively at coastal localities. Occurrences have generally increased, perhaps reflecting the growth in the number of observers. The breeding range extends from southern Sweden, south to Austria and Bulgaria and east across Siberia. It winters in India, Pakistan and south-east Asia. It occurs in Britain as a regular passage migrant, with 2,141 records for the period 1958-85 (Dymond *et al.* 1989).

The first for the county was at Pakefield on 2nd September 1956 and was followed by another on the Shipwash Lightship on 22nd May 1959. Five were noted between 24th September and 13th October in 1964, Suffolk's best ever year, and there were a further five autumn occurrences that decade. There were six records during the 1970s and the species has occurred annually between 1982 and 1995, except for 1985.

The tall trees around north Lowestoft, have been favoured by the species and nearly a third of all occurrences have been around the towns, coastal parks and woods. Since 1977, Landguard Point has dominated the records with over half occurring there. There appears to have been a shift in seasonal movements. Up to 1990, all bar three of the 27 occurrences were confined to the period 2nd September-21st October, with most being noted during early October. Thereafter, five out of nine occurrences have been in the period of late May or early June. One at Lowestoft on 9th July 1975 was on an unusual date and probably relates to a late spring passage bird.

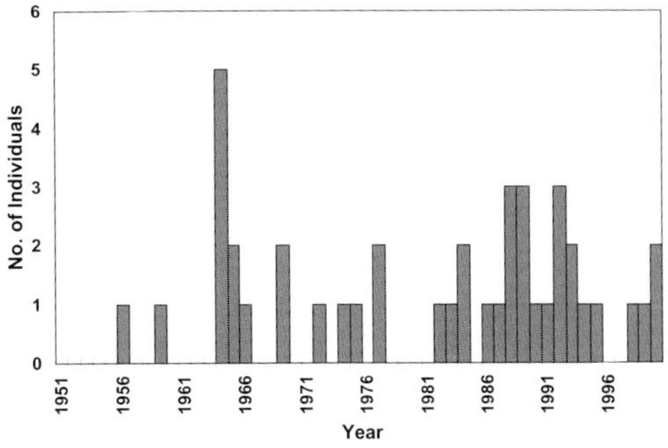

The annual totals of the Red-breasted Flycatcher from 1951-2000

One was noted onboard a ferry as it sailed past the Shipwash Buoy off Orfordness on 9th October 1991. It was seen to fly some distance from the ship in pursuit of a moth and then return to consume its prey, proving that insectivorous species are able to feed whilst hitching a ride!

Collared Flycatcher *Ficedula albicollis*

Accidental: one record

1985 Lowestoft: Sparrow's Nest Gardens/Lighthouse Score, male 13th-14th May

Suffolk's only record involved one found on the bowling green at the Sparrow's Nest Gardens. Despite the presence of many tall trees, the bird seemed to favour feeding on the ground and only perched on bushes occasionally (Brown 1987).

The Collared Flycatcher breeds in eastern France and Italy, through central Europe to Russia and winters south of the Sahara. It is an extremely rare visitor to Britain and Ireland, being noted on only 23 occasions up to the end of 2000 (BBRC).

Pied Flycatcher *Ficedula hypoleuca*

A fairly common passage migrant

The Pied Flycatcher occurs principally as a passage migrant, with spring migrants very occasionally lingering into the summer months.

The species occurs on spring passage in relatively small numbers, mostly at coastal localities, although a larger proportion of inland records occur in this season. Conspicuous black and white males are noted in most springs. The first of the year are often recorded in late April or early May, although there are a few records in early April including singles at Tostock on 1st April 1883 and on Havergate Island on 4th April 1958. Spring passage continues until early June.

Pied Flycatcher (*Stuart Ling*)

There are occasional nesting records for Norfolk and although pairs were said to have bred at Fritton and Ickworth in the 19th century, Ticehurst was sceptical of the records. Two singing males were discovered at a Breckland site in 1992, one held territory from 6th May into June and a second was heard on 29th May, but there was no sign of any females.

Autumn passage begins in late July and continues through to early October, with the species usually being noted singly or in groups of up to ten. Larger numbers usually accompany easterly winds. Ringing evidence suggests that a significant proportion of east coast migrants are of Scandinavian origin. Pied Flycatchers ringed in Norway and the Netherlands have been controlled at Landguard Point, the latter within six days of being originally ringed. Suffolk-ringed birds, *en route* to their West African wintering grounds, have been recovered in France and Iberia and a spring bird at Landguard Point was controlled at Heligoland the following spring. Ringed birds controlled at LBO show that British-bred birds also pass through the site during spring passage. This flycatcher figured highly in the 1965 'Great Fall', when "some tens of thousands" were located along the coast between Lowestoft and Minsmere (Axell & Pearson 1966), including an estimated 3,000 at the former and 5,000 at the latter locality on 5th September. These totals dwarf all other counts, although 100 were logged at the Dingle Hills on 2nd September 1956, 50 at Minsmere on 3rd September 1961 and 35 at Landguard Point on 4th-5th September 1986. Small numbers are noted annually at inland localities during autumn passage when it is a regular visitor to the Ipswich parks. There are a number of October records, but one at Landguard Point on 7th November 1982 is the only record for that month.

Bearded Tit *Panurus biarmicus*

An uncommon resident

The extensive reedbeds at Walberswick and Minsmere host the bulk of the breeding population, although

Bearded Tits
(*Adam Kennedy*)

there are a few pairs at other coastal resorts. The Bearded Tit is one of the more threatened breeding birds in Britain and Ireland and in 1992 an estimated 339-408 pairs were present (Campbell *et al.* 1996). The species is extremely susceptible to harsh winters, although recovery is normally swift. Regular autumn eruptions follow good breeding seasons, when flocks tower from reedbeds to considerable heights, before dispersing noisily southwards (Axell 1966). Although overwintering occurs at the main breeding sites, small flocks regularly occupy smaller reedbeds and reedy borrow-dykes. Autumn gatherings can be found at non-breeding localities, but it is surprisingly scarce at migration watch-points.

The characteristic 'pinging' has echoed through Suffolk's reedbeds since at least 1830, when it was described as common between Kessingland and Beccles (Ticehurst 1932). The Bearded Tit became scarce by the 1850s, although it remained at several sites in the Waveney Valley and also bred at Benacre and Easton Broads, Dunwich and three sites beside the Deben estuary. Breeding was noted in the Mildenhall Fens from about 1879-1883 and also on the River Lark up to 1900. Young taken from a nest at Sudbury in 1868 were hand-reared and exhibited in Crystal Palace Cage Bird Show the following year and the species continued to breed beside the Stour until at least 1923. Shooting, trapping and egg-collecting accounted for the loss of many pairs, but habitat destruction through drainage and reclamation schemes was the greatest threat. Ticehurst was convinced that the species owed its survival to the decline in reed-cutting for thatching. Bearded Tits were extremely scarce around 1900, although breeding pairs remained at Aldeburgh, Thorpeness and on the Deben. It became common at Oulton Broad once again in 1919 and three pairs bred on the Orwell in 1925. During the 1930s, Bearded Tits continued to increase, breeding along the Waveney, as far inland as Redgrave Fen and it began to colonise modern-day strongholds at Minsmere and Walberswick. This was accelerated by the flooding of coastal grazing marshes as a war-time anti-invasion measure, dramatically increasing the availability of suitable habitat, but the effect was nullified, in the pioneering years, as the species was brought to the verge of extinction by the effects of heavy snow cover in successive winters of 1939/40 to 1941/2 and again in 1946/7. The county's 2-4 pairs and a solitary male in Norfolk were the surviving remnants of East Anglia's once thriving population (Sharrock 1976). Recovery was sluggish with only 40 pairs nesting in Suffolk in 1958, but it rose quickly to around 140 by the early 1960s (Axell 1966). This sudden increase was largely due to a particularly fruitful breeding season in 1959, when reedbeds held remarkably large numbers of juveniles. At Walberswick, 800-1,000 were present, in flocks of up to 100, from mid-September and Minsmere held c.300 birds at the end of the breeding season. Eruptive behaviour was witnessed from July to early November and birds returned to their breeding sites the following March and April. The successive harsh winters of 1961/2 and 1962/3 had a less dramatic effect on survival and breeding continued, albeit in fluctuating numbers, throughout the next two decades. Breeding was confined to Minsmere and Walberswick, with a few pairs at Benacre and Easton Broads. However, isolated breeding attempts took place at two sites on the Alde in 1969 and 1970, at Oulton Broad and Belton in 1971 and in a small reedy dyke at Burgh Castle in 1973. An intensive study to provide estimates of the populations and survival rates from one year to the next was carried at Walberswick in 1989 and 1990 (O'Brien & Eaton 1991). An estimated 400 juveniles were said to be present in late July 1989, increasing to 1,089 in early August. The county population is currently at a low ebb with numbers plummeting to an estimated 43-52 pairs, perhaps as a result of four harsh winters between 1984 and 1992 (Campbell 1996).

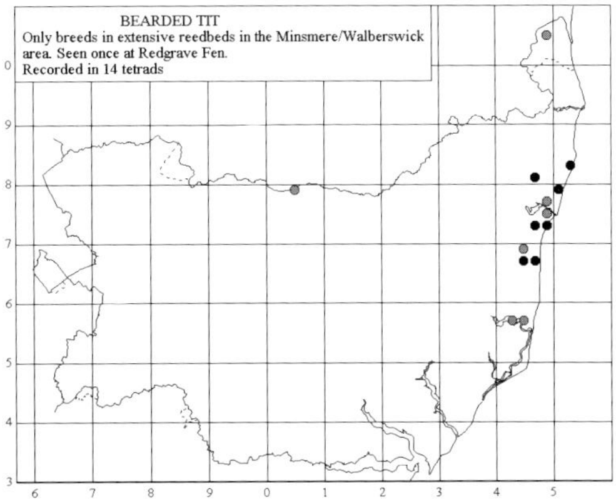

Ringing has shown that there is considerable movement away from the breeding areas during winter. This behaviour was once thought to be spasmodic, with a few birds dispersing each autumn following eruptions from the reedbeds. However, an established pattern of breeding and wintering was determined at two separate sites (O'Sullivan 1976). A pair, trapped at Farlington Marsh, Hampshire, on 18th December 1966, was found together at Minsmere the following summer, but were back at Farlington, on 25th November 1967. One of the pair returned to Minsmere the next summer, but was again back at Farlington in winter. The bulk of the birds leave the breeding sites in October, although this can occur as early as July, and into November. There has been some interchange between birds breeding in the Dutch polders and British sites (Mead and Pearson 1974), but of over 5,500 Bearded Tits ringed at Walberswick between 1959-1989, only one has been found in the Netherlands and no foreign-ringed birds have been discovered in Suffolk. Ringing recoveries link the county with south coast resorts and Walberswick birds were also located at Brandon Marsh, Warwickshire, and Wheldrake Ings in Yorkshire on 12th November 1987 and 23rd November 1992 respectively. Studies of plumage and iris-colour variation and moult in relation to eruptive behaviour have been conducted in the county's reedbeds and have featured in national journals (Pearson 1966, Pearson 1975).

Although coastal movements have been witnessed close to the breeding areas, elsewhere these are relatively rare. Landguard Point's two records are more than a century apart, with singles on 16th February 1887 and 12th October 1988. A flock of 13 at nearby Peewit Hill, Felixstowe, on 9th October 1994, is also worthy of note.

The Bearded Tit's contact call can be heard throughout the year and birds are invariably heard well before they are seen. Numbers vary considerably at non-breeding wintering sites, but flock sizes are normally in single figures. However, large concentrations were noted at Oulton Broad in the late 1960s, including 150-200 in November 1967. High counts elsewhere include 15 at Redgrave from 30th October until early December 1981 and 25 at Martlesham Creek on 14th February 1991. Away from the breeding sites, wintering flocks have also been noted at: Flatford Mill; Bourne Park; Alton Water; King's Fleet; Shotley; Chillesford and Snape.

Bearded Tits are scarce in West Suffolk, although in recent years ones and twos have increasingly been noted beside reed-fringed rivers and gravel workings in the Lark and Blackbourne valleys as well as at Livermere and Cornard Mere. Five at Lackford on 10th November 1983 is the largest recent inland gathering.

Long-tailed Tit *Aegithalos caudatus*

An abundant resident

Family parties, noisily making their way along hedgerows and through copses and gardens, are a common feature in both rural and urban localities. These delicate little birds wander far from their breeding areas and are regular visitors to migration watch-points.

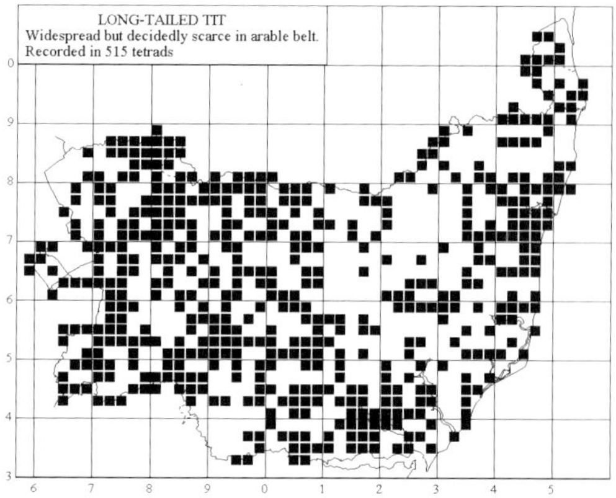

Populations fluctuate greatly from year to year, depending mostly on the severity of the preceding winter. Harsh weather in 1928/9, 1939/40 and 1946/7 caused massive declines and extinctions in some areas of West Suffolk. However, the species survived remarkably well during the successive arctic winters of 1961/2 and 1962/3. The population is more dense in west and south Suffolk and in the vicinity of the nature reserves in the central coastal zone. The species is all but absent in cereal-dominated, central Suffolk and is surprisingly scarce on the sandling belt between Sizewell and the Orwell.

Roving flocks of normally 8-20 are noted throughout the winter and consist mainly of family parties. Such flocking is thought to be the key to the species' survival, with birds huddling close together to keep each other warm during cold winter nights (Gibbons *et al.* 1993). Payn's largest was 32 at North Warren in 1977, but, since then, this figure has been regularly exceeded and flock sizes of 40 or more are now reasonably common. A mixed tit flock of nearly 200 at Sutton Heath on 31st July 1990 held about 90 Long-tailed Tits and other flocks of 50-80 were noted at: Minsmere on 17th December 1986, 17th September 1988 and 13th March 1994; Boney Wood, Barking, 27th May 1993; King's Forest, 28th May 1993; Levington, 12th June 1993; Staverton Park, 16th January 1994; Combs Lane, Stowmarket, 25th September 1994; Lackford, 8th August 1994 and Trimley, 21st August 1994. It would appear that there has recently been a genuine increase in flock sizes, rather than observers being more vigilant with their recording.

Flocks occasionally move many miles from their nuptial areas and ringing has shown that family parties stay together. For example, a flock of seven ringed at Landguard Point on 23rd October 1993 turned up at Happisburgh, Norfolk, seven days later. Other instances of multiple recoveries of parties include two that moved from Walberswick to Wanstead, London, two from Landguard Point to Wicken Fen, Cambridgeshire and five from Lackford to Sheringham, Norfolk. From 1909-1995, there were 52 recoveries of Suffolk-ringed birds of which 18 had moved less than 10km, 23 between 10-100km and 11 more than

100km. The species was prominent in an usually large movement of tits that passed through Landguard Point in autumn 1993. A total of 112 was ringed in October and early November of that year. The bulk of the Landguard Point records fall in these months with smaller numbers noted in March.

The beautiful bottle-shaped nest is normally found in blackthorn thickets, gorse bushes or dense hedgerows. Long-tailed Tits are one of the first birds to start nesting activities, with females breaking away from the family group to mate with males from another. One nest-building at Potter's Wood, Woodbridge, on 11th February 1993, was particularly early.

Although the species is not a regular visitor to bird-tables, birds are occasionally attracted to garden peanut-feeders and there are a few reports of Long-tailed Tits feeding on fat.

Ticehurst stated that the northern race *A. c. caudatus* "may very occasionally occur", although he made no reference to any particular Suffolk individual. Therefore, it would appear that a white-headed bird trapped at Rendlesham on 13th March 1983 is the county's one and only record, although it would be virtually impossible to rule out a mutant from a local brood.

Marsh Tit *Parus palustris*

A fairly common resident

The Marsh Tit is a resident of mature, broad-leaved woodland, parklands, old orchards and rural gardens. The species tends to avoid conifer plantations, favouring mixed woodland such as those on the Blackheath Estate at Snape, Minsmere and Walberswick. It is extremely sedentary and is exceedingly rare at migration watch-points.

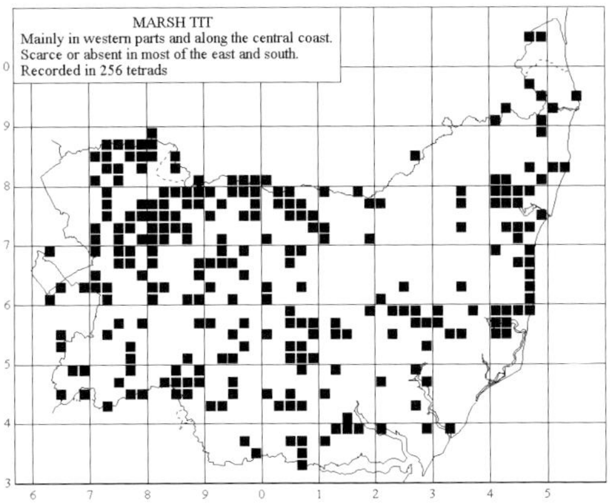

MARSH TIT
Mainly in western parts and along the central coast.
Scarce or absent in most of the east and south.
Recorded in 256 tetrads

Breckland woodlands host several pairs and there are good concentrations on the coastal strip between the Alde and the Blyth and in north-west and north-central Suffolk. The latter areas are also favoured by the Willow Tit. There are isolated pockets in central and south-west Suffolk, but, due to the lack of suitable woodlands, there are also large areas where the species is absent. Its almost total absence along the length of the Waveney Valley and in the Lothingland area is mysterious as there would appear to be many woods which are suitable. It is also scarce in south-east Suffolk. Urban areas are largely avoided and the species is mainly absent from larger towns.

The national population has been steadily declining since 1964 and this was particularly evident in eastern England during the 1970s (Marchant *et al.* 1990). The sharpest declines have followed cold periods, but, as winters were generally mild during the 1970s, there must be another reason for this long-term decline. The species shows a preference for open woodland with a rich understory and the neglect of traditional coppice may be a significant factor. Marsh Tits nest in natural holes, often low down, and do not take to nest-boxes as readily as other tits. Many managed woodlands show a distinct lack of nest sites.

Marsh Tits apparently pair for life and rarely wander away from their territories (Perrins 1979) and site fidelity and longevity were confirmed by one ringed as a nestling at Gt Glemham and still present there five years later. Birds will join roving tit flocks as they pass through their woods, but will leave once the flock crosses the territory boundary (Perrins 1979). For example, a mixed tit flock containing 80 birds at Minsmere on 28th December 1987, held only two Marsh Tits. Similarly, a flock of at least 200 tits at Knettishall Heath on 29th August 1988, comprising mostly Blue, Great and Coal Tits, contained only five Marsh Tits. Unpaired individuals may stay with the flock throughout the winter.

One trapped at Landguard Point on 20th June 1987 is the sole record at this site in 20 years (1983-2002) of intensive studies.

Willow Tit *Parus montanus*

An uncommon resident and scarce passage migrant

The Willow Tit is the rarest of the county's breeding tits, frequenting marshland carrs and damp woods, but also conifer plantations. The species is extremely scarce on the coast and its stronghold skirts the southern and eastern fringes of the brecks. There are one or two small concentrations in south Suffolk. The plumage characteristics closely resemble those of Marsh Tit and the species is most easily identified by its nasal call.

It was not until 1897 that the Willow Tit was first recognised as a British breeding species after being well known on the continent. Suffolk's first record involved a probable migrant which was shot in a hedge near Lowestoft on 17th October 1910 (Ticehurst 1932). The occurrence of this individual coincided with an incursion of continental Great Tits. Willow Tits were subsequently found nesting along the Waveney Valley and then at a number of inland and coastal sites. The species was undoubtedly overlooked previously and there are retrospective claims of nesting pairs in West Suffolk as early as 1891 (Jourdain 1914).

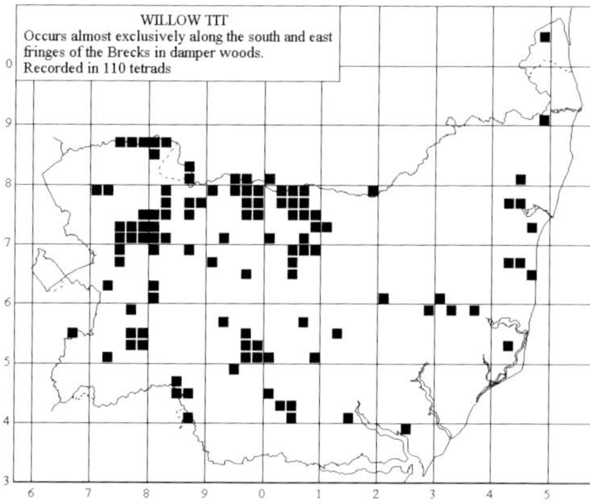

The species frequents more open country than Marsh Tit and formerly regularly nested in pollarded willows beside rivers and streams. The map shows concentrations in north-central and north-west Suffolk and small pockets around Hitcham, Hadleigh, and in the Hawkeden-Wickhambrook area. The northern sites are also favoured by the Marsh Tits and largely consist of damp woodlands that lie at the source of some of the county's main river systems: the Waveney; Little Ouse; Dove and Gipping. Likewise, the southern sites lie at the extremities of the rivers Glem and Brett. There are also a few pairs along the River Lark from where breeding pairs have expanded northwards to hold territories in the conifer plantations of the King's Forest. Breeding pairs downstream of Thetford, on the Little Ouse, also lie in the heart of an extensive conifer forest. Unlike its close relatives, Willow Tits excavate their own nest-holes and, although the occupation of nest-boxes is unknown in Suffolk, there are rare occasions when a lack of dead wood in young pine plantations elsewhere has resulted in their use (Perrins 1979).

The winter distribution is more or less the same as the breeding range. The Willow Tit is largely sedentary, remaining on territory throughout the year and rarely joining mixed tit-flocks, hence individuals seen in any season are probably indicative of nesting taking place. Insects form the bulk of the species' diet although bird-tables are occasionally frequented during winter. The populations of Fennoscandia are gregarious outside the breeding season and social groups are established in late summer and autumn and remain together throughout the winter (Cramp *et al.* 1974-1994). A group of six at West Stow on 12th April 1985 and two family parties totalling 12 at Santon Downham on 6th June 1995 demonstrate that such behaviour takes place at least occasionally in Suffolk.

British breeding birds are of the endemic race *P. m. kleinschmidti*, although individuals showing characteristics of the migrant northern race *P. m. borealis* occur as vagrants in some years. There are three claims for Suffolk: Minsmere's Sluice Bushes from 15th-16th September 1974; Landguard Point on 25th September 1983 and Worlingworth, 10th November 1990. Although none have been submitted to BBRC for consideration, the racial identity of the Minsmere individual seems certain (Limbert 1984) and an excellent description of the Worlingworth bird was published in *Suffolk Birds 1991* (Small 1991). Few details were taken to substantiate the more doubtful Landguard Point record.

In addition to the above, Willow Tits have been noted at Landguard Point on 9th September 1980 and on 26th June 1988.

Crested Tit *Parus cristatus*

Accidental: three 19th century records

c.1840	nr Bury St Edmunds: n.d.
1861	Aldeburgh: summer
1873	Melton: Melton Grange, shot

The species has been reported in southern England on about ten occasions, and the specimens examined have belonged to races from Scandinavia *P. c. cristatus* and central Europe *P. c. mitratus*. Two of the Suffolk birds were said to be of the former race (Snow 1971) and, although the racial identity of the third was not determined, its origins are likely to also lie on the continent.

The Crested Tit inhabits the forests of Europe, from Iberia through to the Balkans in the south of its range and from Fennoscandia east through Russia to the northern Urals in the north (Cramp *et al.* 1974-1994). The British population is confined to the Scottish Highlands and has become less widespread since the destruction of the Caledonian pine forests. This population is normally sedentary with young birds rarely dispersing more than two kilometres from their nest site (Thom 1986).

Coal Tit *Parus ater*

A common resident and scarce passage migrant

The Coal Tit shows a clear preference for coniferous forest and consequently is more plentiful in the north-west corner of the county. It is also common in forestry areas at Tunstall, Rendlesham and Dunwich, with small concentrations around Ipswich and Lowestoft, but is absent in the fens and many areas in central Suffolk. The beech-fringed coniferous plantations of Thetford and the King's Forest are ideal for Coal Tits and beech-mast forms a staple part of the species' diet. It mixes with other tits during winter and often forms substantial flocks. Small numbers are regular at garden feeding stations.

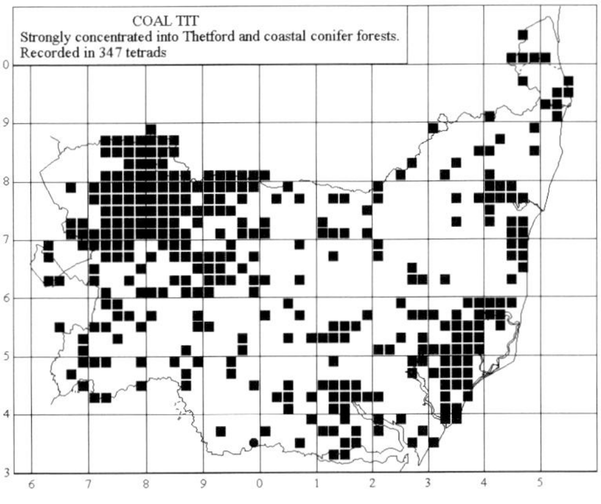

A survey of breeding densities at Breckland pine plantations from 1949-1957 (Lack 1966) shows fluctuations between 0.1-0.5 pairs (average 0.3) per hectare in Scots pine, but slightly lower for Corsican pine. The species will also breed in broad-leaved woodland, but at far lower densities. A count of 100 at Brandon, in January 1991, demonstrates the density of the resident population in that area and a transect study in the King's Forest, during the winter of 1975, revealed that Coal Tits formed 16.5% of the total bird population (Last 1977).

The species is relatively scarce at migration watch-points, with Landguard Point's year total normally in single figures. However, an exceptional tit movement occurred during the autumn of 1983, when at least 30 passed through the site, including a record 11 on 29th October, of which four flew in from the sea. Immigration is often difficult to prove, although Coal Tits showing characteristics of the nominate continental race *P. a. ater* are occasionally recorded. Suffolk's first two examples were both at Minsmere on 8th October 1962 and 1st October 1972, and the third was trapped at Landguard Point, 4th April 1994. A huge influx to south-eastern counties from 19th-24th September 1996 produced about 20 Suffolk records all confined to the stretch of coast between Shingle Street and Landguard Point. Several were trapped at Landguard Point including a Dutch-ringed bird, so giving an indication of their direction of travel. Up to three present at Landguard Point from 20th-26th March 1997 probably relate to birds on return migration. A further six individuals were noted at Landguard Point between 21st October and 10th November 1997.

An analysis of ringing data shows that from 1909-1995 there have been 20 recoveries of Suffolk-ringed Coal Tits, of which 17 moved less than 10km, two between 10-100km and only one over 100km. The latter individual was ringed at Snape on 1st February 1984 and controlled at Sheringham, Norfolk, on 3rd April 1986.

Blue Tit *Parus caeruleus*

An abundant resident

The Blue Tit is one of the most common and familiar of our birds, being a frequent visitor to garden feeding stations. It is principally a bird of broad-leafed woodland, but is common on farmland, along hedgerows and in parks, town gardens and even industrial areas. It is normally the dominant species in roving tit flocks and a common visitor to migration watch-points, where it occasionally passes through in considerable numbers.

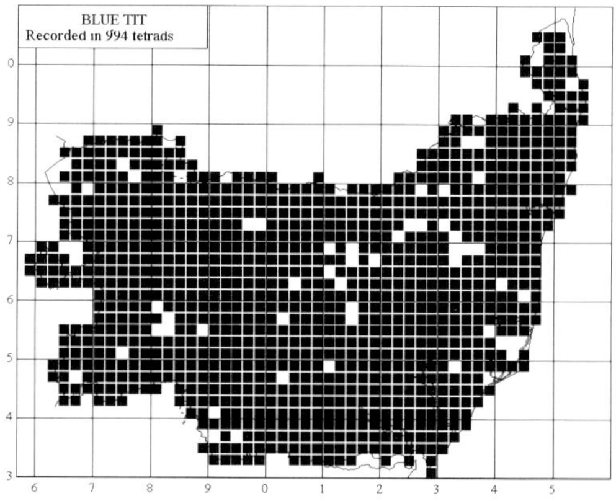

The species is the most common British tit, being widely distributed throughout the county, breeding in every 10-km square and almost every tetrad. It will forage for food in all habitats, will readily take to nest-boxes and raise young in the busiest suburban garden. Nationally, the population was relatively stable from 1964-1970, but increased until the mid-1970s and has since fluctuated around this level (Marchant *et al.* 1990). The Reydon Grove Farm study from 1964-1971 revealed a range of 24-35 pairs (Benson & Williamson 1972) compared with 26 pairs in 1997 (Pearson 1998).

The Blue Tit is largely sedentary, although it wanders in winter and, during some autumns, large coastal movements are reported. Ticehurst referred to passage birds being noted in bushes on Orford beach and there was a substantial movement in October-November 1949. From the 1,295 Blue Tits that were ringed at LBO, from 1983-1996, 308 (nearly 25%) were in the tit year of 1983. Most of the latter were noted during an exceptional autumn passage which included an influx of 100 on 24th September. There has always been some suspicion that the origins of passage migrants lie in Scandinavia or the near continent. Indeed, Payn referred to a great influx of tits during the autumn of 1957 when ten out of 70 trapped at Walberswick were said to be of the continental form *P. c. caeruleus*. However, the separation of the two races rests solely on brightness of plumage, a character which is no longer considered reliable. Any doubts of birds from overseas reaching Suffolk were dispelled by an individual trapped at Fagbury Cliff, on 17th October 1994, bearing a Norwegian ring. This was a remarkable find and, with the exception of one found on a North Sea oil platform in 1988, is Britain's first recovery from that region.

Of the 287 recoveries of Suffolk-ringed Blue Tits from 1909-1995, 232 moved less than 10km, 54 between 10-100km and only one over 100km. The latter individual was ringed at Rendlesham Forest in autumn 1969 and was found in Staplehurst, Kent, the following winter. One ringed in Wiltshire on 24th September 1966 travelled 256km to be found in Suffolk 14 months later.

Parties of 50 or more are regularly reported, principally during the winter months, but a flock of 150-200, in reedbeds at Easton Broad on 16th January 1964, is exceptional. When natural winter food is exhausted, Blue Tits will regularly leave woodland by day to feed in gardens. The species suffers greatly during severe winters, but mortality depends more on food availability rather than temperatures (Marchant *et al.* 1990).

Great Tit *Parus major*

An abundant resident

The Great Tit is widely distributed throughout the county, being found in all 10-km squares and scarce only on the fenland ridge and in a few parts of the arable belt. It is plentiful in wooded areas and is common in gardens where it regularly visit bird-tables. Large movements are occasionally logged at migration watch-points, particularly during late February and March.

Like other resident species, the Great Tit suffers from the effects of harsh winters, although recovery is usually swift. Nationally, population levels have been gradually increasing since the early 1960s – a trend which has been more marked on farmland (Marchant *et al.* 1990). The Reydon Grove Farm study from 1964-1971 revealed a range of 8-16 pairs (Benson & Williamson 1972) compared with 17 pairs in 1997 (Pearson 1998).

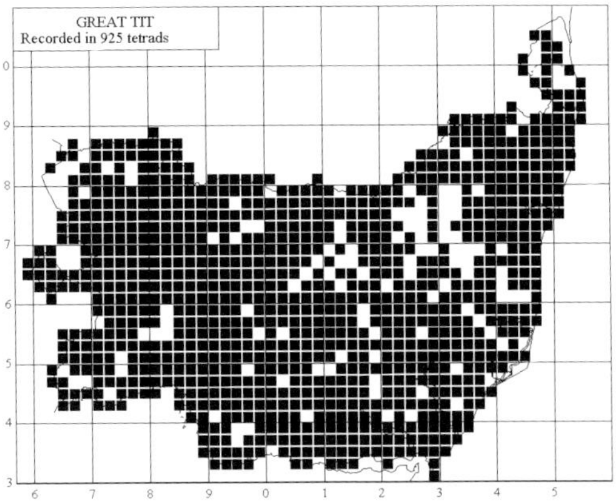

The Great Tit is much scarcer in the swathe of countryside east of Halesworth and north-west towards the Waveney Valley and it is sparsely distributed in central Suffolk and in the fenland edge.

Although largely sedentary, ringing recoveries show that Great Tits move further than other British tits. Suffolk-ringed birds have been recovered as far north as Cumbria and Yorkshire and there are two foreign recoveries: one from Sudbourne to Lille, France and another from Felixstowe to the Netherlands. Great Tits ringed in Yorkshire, Cheshire and Dorset have been controlled in Suffolk. The species was involved in a most remarkable movement in March 1994, when large numbers were noted at Benacre and Bawdsey and no fewer than 244 were trapped, from the total of 400 that passed through Landguard Point during that month. The highest numbers were between 6th and 11th March with 100 present (64 ringed) on 10th.

Both Ticehurst and Payn referred to immigrations of the continental form *P. m. major*, identified by a smaller and narrower bill (Payn 1978). Examples of this race occurred during the exceptional autumn passage in 1910 and others were noted in the big tit years of 1949 and 1957. There has been no attempt to determine the race of passage birds in recent years. Return migration was witnessed on 31st March 1960, when two were seen flying west-north-west from the Shipwash Lightship and four west-south-west the following day (Cramp 1964).

Nuthatch (Wood Nuthatch) *Sitta europaea*

A locally common resident

The Nuthatch frequents mature, deciduous woodlands and parklands throughout the county, especially those with a predominance of beech and oak. It is common in parks in Ipswich town centre and regularly visits bird-tables, particularly in rural areas. The species will often loosely associate with tit flocks during winter.

The Nuthatch has rather a patchy distribution, with concentrations around Breckland fringes, around Blythburgh and on the Shotley peninsula. It is absent from much of cereal-dominated central Suffolk.

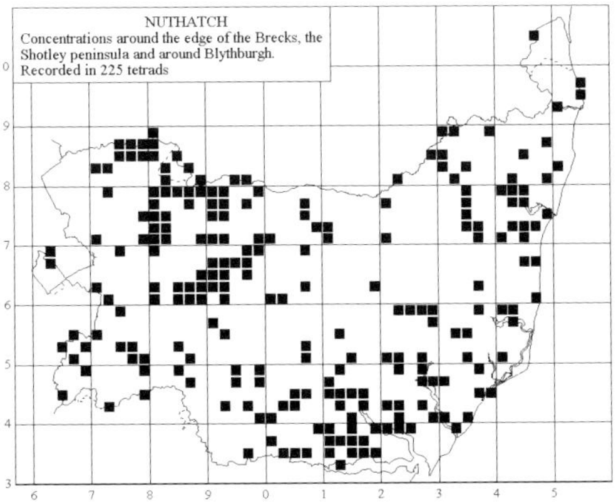

Holes in trees are the most favoured nest sites and the species will occasionally occupy nest-boxes, the entrances being cemented in a similar way to natural holes. One pair nested in a hole in the masonry of Martlesham Church in 1993, but perhaps the most unusual nesting site involved a pair which bred in a woodland Sand Martin colony at Ramsholt in 1980. The site was a sandy bank and the birds had coated the edges of the hole with mud. Nuthatches were found in over 200 of the county's tetrads during fieldwork for the *New Atlas* and, as the species is largely sedentary, it is likely that breeding occurred in all of them. Generally, the county's woodlands are not particularly suitable for Nuthatches and densities are relatively low. Optimistically, there could be as many as six pairs per tetrad, indicating a county population of around 1,200 pairs. This compares with an estimated 130,000 territories in Britain where numbers are increasing (Gibbons *et al.* 1993).

Movements exceeding 10km area are rare, so one ringed at Bawdsey and found dead 15km away at Melton is worthy of note. The species does not associate with passage migrants and one at Landguard Point on 2nd April 1999 is the sole record for the site. One on Minsmere dunes on 27th September 1973 was described in the SBR as "an apparent immigrant".

Treecreeper (Eurasian Treecreeper) *Certhia familiaris*

A common resident

Almost all areas of woodland hold a few pairs, from the smallest copse to extensive forest, although the weak, high-pitched call of the Treecreeper is often hard to detect or not recognised which could result in some being overlooked by fieldworkers. The species lives in both broad-leafed and coniferous woodland. During passage periods, Treecreepers occasionally frequent migration watch-points. The characteristic habit of communal roosting has been witnessed in Suffolk on several occasions.

The distribution is similar to that of the Nuthatch, although Treecreepers are widely scattered with small concentrations around the River Blyth, along the Deben and Alde, on the Shotley peninsula and south of the Little Ouse. It is rare or absent from many of the central cereal-growing areas.

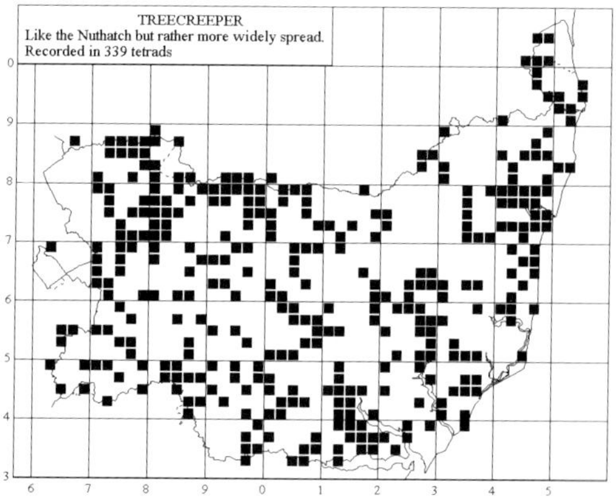

Treecreepers are vulnerable to effects of harsh weather and declines were particularly evident following the severe winters of 1961/2 and 1962/3. These are not solely due to low temperatures, but also to the effects of freezing fog, which often result in a coating of ice being formed on tree trunks, branches and twigs restricting feeding opportunities (Marchant *et al.* 1990). However, the species recovers quickly and there was little change in its status between the two national Atlas periods.

One showing characteristics of the northern form *C. f. familiaris* was collected at Martlesham during a rush of migrants on 18th March 1941 (Payn 1978).

Penduline Tit (Eurasian Penduline Tit) *Remiz pendulinus*

A very rare visitor: nine records of 11 birds

1989	Minsmere: 13th-25th April, presumed same 23rd-24th June; adult and two juvs 25th-29th October
1990	Minsmere: 4th April
1993	Minsmere: 25th July
1994	Minsmere: 11th-23rd September
1996/97	Trimley St Martin/Mary: Trimley Marshes, two intermittently 20th November-26th March
1999	Minsmere: 29th September
2000	Minsmere: 1st November

Coastal reedbeds provide an ideal feeding habitat for this species, although Minsmere's monopoly of the records was finally broken when a long-staying pair frequented Trimley Marshes during the winter of 1996/7. The county's first record involved an extremely elusive male which tugged at reed-mace heads at Minsmere, during two protracted spring periods in 1989 (Macklin 1990). The presence of an adult and two juveniles from 25th-29th October of that year caused some speculation that breeding had taken place. However, as no female was seen and an exhaustive search during the winter months failed to yield a nest, it was assumed that there was no connection between the two sets of records.

The Penduline Tit is a summer visitor in the northern part of its range where it breeds sporadically in the Netherlands and then from Germany eastwards through Asia to Manchuria. It is a resident and winter visitor in Iberia around the northern Mediterranean through to south-west Asia. The species is occasionally eruptive and visitations to Britain and Ireland have increased rapidly since the early 1980s. For example, there were a mere three records up to 1980 compared with a further 148 up the end of 2000 (BBRC). The increase coincides with range expansion in northern Europe and colonisation of east coast reedbeds appears more than a possibility during the next decade, if it has not happened already.

Golden Oriole (Eurasian Golden Oriole) *Oriolus oriolus*

A scarce summer visitor and passage migrant

Golden Oriole
(*Adam Kennedy*)

The striking yellow and black plumage of the male Golden Oriole, together with its diagnostic fluting song, makes the species one of the most attractive birds on the British list. However, Golden Orioles normally stay high in the canopy, where they are well camouflaged amongst the leaves, making detection difficult and many records relate to birds that are heard but never seen. A small colony became established in the north-west corner of the county during the mid-1960s, but the trees were felled in the 1980s and now only 1-2 pairs breed annually. The records suggest that it is scarce on passage.

The Golden Oriole nested only occasionally during the 19th century and would have done so more frequently had new arrivals not been the target of gunners. A female, shot at Campsea Ashe, sometime prior to 1824, was the first for the county and there were a further 30 occurrences up to 1932 of which 18 were collected. Nesting attempts were noted irregularly during the 19th century. A male with a young bird was present at Scotts Hall, Minsmere, in 1852 and a nest from Suffolk was used by Meyer (1853) in his *Illustrations of British Birds and their Eggs*. One was heard singing in East Suffolk in July 1936.

In 1965, Golden Orioles were found nesting in maturing plantations of hybrid black poplar in north-west Suffolk. The bulk of the population was located at the May and Baker Estate at Lakenheath, where numbers increased as the trees matured. The population was monitored annually, but estimating numbers was difficult and the colony peaked at 12-14 pairs in 1981. The location of the colony was one of Suffolk's worst-kept secrets, with thousands of birdwatchers making the annual pilgrimage to this fascinating site to observe these stunning birds. There was much disturbance and, as expected, the birds drew the attention of egg-collectors, although it was the harvesting of the poplars which led to the final demise. Conservation bodies managed to safeguard around 40 hectares (Dagley 1994), which have regularly hosted 2-3 pairs, but there has been little replanting. However, the site has recently been purchased by the RSPB which bodes well for the future.

The species normally arrives during the first or second week of May, although there are a few April records with one on the 19th (1987) being the earliest. The Golden Oriole is a scarce passage migrant mostly in late May or early June, but occasionally in July to late August. One at Hadleigh, on 3rd October 1920, was exceptionally late. Records from south-east Suffolk are relatively regular in spring which suggests that East Anglian breeding birds arrive by this route. It is likely that this population originated from the Low Countries (hence the use of poplars) which is contra to the Sussex/Kent population which prefers oak and chestnut and probably originate from French stock.

Two nestlings ringed at Norfolk breeding sites in June 1993 were recovered in August of the same year at Dunwich and Burstall. The former bird was controlled by another ringer, whereas the latter died after colliding with a window.

Isabelline Shrike *Lanius isabellinus*

Accidental: two records

1976 Benacre: Benacre Pits, imm. 30th August
1997 Boyton: Boyton Marshes, first-winter 23rd November

The Isabelline Shrike has only recently been considered as a separate species, having been formerly treated as a subspecies of Red-backed Shrike. The species' breeding range extends from Iran through to Mongolia. There were 57 records for Britain and Ireland up to the end of 2000 (BBRC).

The 1976 individual was not identified by its finders until they had consulted text books that evening and consequently it was seen by only a handful of observers. A more efficient communication system in 1997 created better viewing opportunities for local birdwatchers at least. Both individuals showed characters of the race *L. i. phoenicuroides.*

Red-backed Shrike *Lanius collurio*

A rare summer visitor and uncommon passage migrant

Red-backed Shrike
(*Adam Kennedy*)

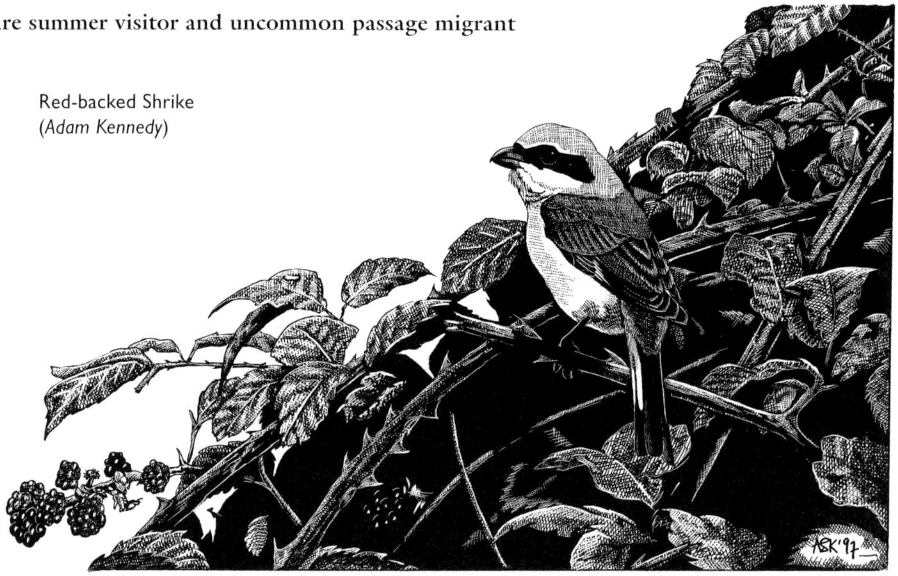

The Red-backed Shrike was common and widespread as a breeding species in the 19th century, but it has now ceased to breed in the county. Suffolk was one of its last strongholds, but nowadays, migration watch-points are the best localities to observe the species.

This was one of the last summer visitors to reach Britain, with birds rarely back at their breeding territories before the end of May. One noted on 17th April is exceptionally early.

The Red-backed Shrike was described as "common or tolerably common" in all districts towards the end of the 19th century (Babington 1884-1886), although it was already in national decline (Holloway 1996). By the 1930s, the shrike was sparsely distributed throughout Suffolk and local decreases were attributed to the grubbing-up or close trimming of hedgerows (Ticehurst 1932). However, from 1930-1955, populations remained relatively high, so much so that there are no estimates of numbers. Breeding took place on heaths and commons and the shrike was a familiar feature of Breckland. It also bred on farmland, in overgrown orchards and gardens, on bushy pastures, railway cuttings and embankments and in tall hedgerows and, as the nests were easy to find, they were frequently robbed by egg-collectors. A marked decline became noticeable by 1950, although in 1955-1956, no less than 30 pairs nested in the Walberswick area alone (Pearson 1973) and it is reasonable to assume that the county population was then well into three figures. From 1962-1971, the county population stood at around 40-60 pairs, but by the late 1970s these numbers had halved and the few remaining pairs were restricted to bushy heaths on the coast and Breckland. The decline was reflected nationally and continued unabated through to its ultimate extinction. By 1989, the Red-backed Shrike was lost as a regular breeding species, although a pair did successfully rear young at a coastal site in 1992. The latter occurrence was considered to be a one-off event resulting from a chance meeting of two migrants.

Loss of habitat, climatic conditions, use of pesticides and high mortality on the wintering grounds have been blamed for its demise. Following very low egg-fertility in the early 1960s, tests on unhatched eggs revealed traces of DDT and chlordane (Payn 1978). However, the Red-backed Shrike further declined at a time when other affected species were recovering from the poisoning. It is probably no coincidence that the 1950s decline coincided with the myxomatosis epidemic which decimated the rabbit population. A combination of changing habitat, resulting from the lack of grazing, together with a reduction in larger insects seems to be the principal reason for its demise as a Suffolk breeding bird.

The shrike has long been widely known as the Butcher-bird due to its curious habit of storing food items by impaling them on thorns or barbed wire. Suffolk larders have contained beetles, bees, wasps, butterflies, moths, caterpillars, lizards and a variety of small passerines. More unusual items include shrews, field mice and pheasant chicks and one was seen to kill a young Sand Martin in flight (Ticehurst 1932).

The Red-backed Shrike is now rarely seen on spring passage and usually occurs along with other typical over-shooting migrants. Autumnal easterly winds often produce a few juveniles which occasionally linger at coastal sites for several weeks. Late August to mid-September is the most productive period and laggards are occasional noted in October. Singles at Somerleyton and Oulton on 8th and 12th November 1883 respectively and at Gunton on 5th November 1994 are the only records for that month and Suffolk's latest involved one which lingered at Lake Lothing from 25th November to 1st December 2001.

Lesser Grey Shrike — *Lanius minor*

Accidental: five records

1970	Hollesley: trapped 22nd-23rd May
1973	Blythburgh-Walberswick: 10th June
1977	Lakenheath: 4th June
1989	Lound/Ashby: 10th-12th September
1996	Walberswick: Walberswick Common, 25th May

The Lesser Grey Shrike breeds from France and Germany eastwards to Afghanistan and has been recorded in Britain and Ireland on 161 occasions up to the end of 2000 (BBRC).

The dominance of spring occurrences conforms to the national trend (Dymond *et al.* 1989).

Great Grey Shrike (Northern Grey Shrike) — *Lanius excubitor*

An uncommon passage migrant and winter visitor

The Great Grey Shrike generally favours open countryside with a predominance of exposed perches. It requires large winter territories and therefore can be elusive. Heath and Breckland are the most favoured habitats during winter and it is occasionally noted at migration watch-points. The species has become quite scarce in recent years.

In the early 1900s, the shrike wintered in small numbers in most years (Ticehurst 1932) and, by the 1950s, it was described as a familiar visitor to suitable localities (Payn 1978). A series of influxes during the early 1970s led to an increase in the wintering population and SBRs show that 30-40 individuals occurred annually. Wintering numbers have since declined markedly to about 9-10 per annum during the 1980s to 7-8 per annum for 1990-1995. Great Grey Shrikes have been heard singing and observed carrying nesting material on coastal heaths during three springs: 1954, 1993 and 1994.

Most leave their wintering quarters in late March, although laggards are frequently noted up to mid-April. The species has been reported in May on eight occasions: Akenham, 19th 1950; Minsmere, 26th-27th 1952; Kessingland, 24th 1953; Nacton, 31st 1956; Westleton Heath, until 11th 1959; Tuddenham Heath, from 8th (to 6th June) 1960, Breckland, 11th 1968 and Havergate Island, 2nd 1980. One at Carlton Colville from May 18th to July 8th 1991 was probably attempting to oversummer and there are two ancient July records: Baylham 9th 1816 and Cockfield 26th 1877.

Great Grey Shrike (*Brian Small*)

A few arrive in mid-October, although these are normally passage birds at coastal localities and quickly pass through. Overwintering individuals normally set up territories in late November and remain until March or early April. Individuals noted in Suffolk on 3rd September 1964 and 29th September 1970 are particularly early returning birds and the only records for that month.

It was presumably the same individual which overwintered in seven consecutive years at Mayday Farm, Brandon, from 1986-1993. It was occasionally joined by a second bird and the site became a popular venue for visiting birdwatchers, who were able to observe the species at close quarters. It was seen to capture a Goldcrest which it jammed by the head into a cleft between two branches, presumably being stored for later consumption. It was also seen to catch and eat a common lizard and impale a dragonfly to a twig in early November. One was seen to catch a vole and impale it on a gorse bush at Southwold in 1974. An analysis of 30 pellets collected at Benacre in 1954 showed that 80% were of bird remains, 16% insects and 3% mammal. Linnets constituted 70% of the avian diet.

The shrike is a scarce visitor at migration watch-points and has been known to occur during falls of smaller passerines. For example, up to four were thought to have been in the Landguard Point area during a large fall of warblers in October 1984 and the species was present at five sites between 9th and 20th October 1988, which coincided with one of the county's largest ever fall of Robins and Goldcrests.

During the 1960s, Great Grey Shrikes were frequently caught in Bullfinch traps in inland fruit orchards (SBRs 1966 and 1967).

Southern Grey Shrike *Lanius meridionalis*

Accidental: two records

1986 Felixstowe: Landguard Point, 6th December
1992 Easton Bavents: Southend Warren, 4th-7th October

The BOURC has only recently split the northern and southern forms of the Great Grey Shrike into separate species and there is some discussion as to whether the migratory, eastern form *L. m. pallidirostris*, colloquially known as the Steppe Shrike, should also be split. The above occurrences both involved Steppe Shrikes and constitute the third and sixth records for Britain and Ireland. The species has been noted in Britain and Ireland on 16 occasions up to the end of 2000. It is sedentary over much of its range which extends from Iberia through southern France, northern Africa across the Middle East and Arabia to India and southern Asia.

The above individuals were most confiding, allowing birdwatchers to study the plumage characteristics in the field. The Landguard Point bird was found in the Observatory compound and was trapped and measured (Marsh 1987a). It was initially wrongly identified by visiting birdwatchers, being described as a juvenile Great Grey Shrike moulting into first-winter plumage. It was watched for some time as it fed on the remains of a dead rabbit. The 1992 individual frequented a bushy sheep paddock where it showed a preference for ground feeding, chasing prey across the sheep-grazed turf (Cawston 1994).

Woodchat Shrike *Lanius senator*

A very rare passage migrant: 26 records

The Woodchat Shrike occurs almost annually and almost exclusively at coastal localities during the months of April or May with the vast majority frequenting sandling heaths. The clear bias towards spring occurrences conforms to the national trend (Dymond *et al.* 1989), although to a much lesser extent. The shrike breeds from France and north-west Africa eastwards to Iran and the Ukraine.

One shot at Bradwell in April 1829 is the first for the county and there were three further spring reports up to 1860. There then followed almost a 90 year gap before one visited Waldringfield in April 1947, but there were three more during the early 1950s, including one at Mellis which was the first away from the coastal region. One at Minsmere on 8th June 1963 is the only record for that decade and a long-stayer at Walberswick, from 18th July-30th August 1971, is the first of only four autumn records. There were three further records during that decade, including one at Walberswick on 20th-21st June 1976 which had previously been ringed on Skokholm, Wales, the same month and a juvenile at Landguard Point, from 17th-21st August 1977. There were seven records for the 1980s including a male at Little Heath, Thetford, from 8th-16th June 1980, which constitutes the sole record for West Suffolk. This individual allegedly hybridised with a female Red-backed Shrike, although it failed to rear young (Sharrock *et al.* 1982). There were six records for the period 1994-2000, including a second record for Landguard Point in the autumn of 1994.

Jay (Eurasian Jay) *Garrulus glandarius*

A common resident and scarce passage migrant. Subject to autumn influxes

Woodlands, farmland, hedgerows and even large suburban gardens are favoured habitats of this most arboreal of corvids. The Jay is generally secretive during the breeding season, but becomes more obvious in autumn when they gather acorns from more open ground. Groups of six to ten are fairly common, but 20 or more are rare. The Jay is frequently logged at migration watch-points and is occasionally noted crossing the North Sea.

The species was common throughout the county during the 19th century, although populations were suppressed on well-keepered estates. Jays are undoubtedly prolific nest-robbers and were persecuted mostly for the preservation of game. However, they were also killed for their plumage, the blue wing-coverts being sought after by both Victorian fashion gurus and fly-fishermen. Coinciding with the decline in the number of gamekeepers, the population has increased steadily throughout the 20th century. The species has also benefited by the afforestation of the heath and Breckland which began in earnest during the 1930s. The population has remained relatively stable in recent years and, if anything, has increased further.

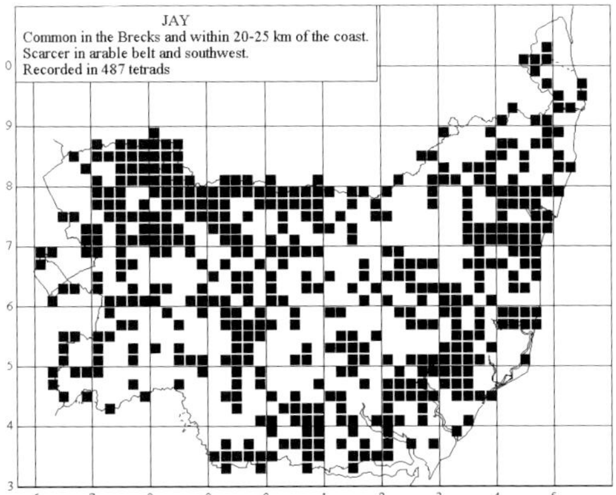

The species is widely distributed throughout the county, although very much scarcer in the arable belt and in the south-west than elsewhere. It is quite numerous in Breckland, eastwards along the Little Ouse valley and around the conifer forests of Dunwich, Rendlesham and Tunstall. The Jay also breeds in suburban areas and one or two pairs nest in Christchurch Park in Ipswich town centre, but its scarcity in Lothingland and around Sudbury suggests intensive game preservation in those areas.

Deciduous woodland offers the Jay a breeding and feeding habitat throughout the year, although they are also commonly seen in pinewoods. The Jay's association with acorns is well known and large amounts are stored to be collected during the winter when food becomes scarce. It is widely believed that failure of the acorn crop elsewhere in northern Europe causes eruptive movements of Jays into Britain. However, incursions are often associated with large movements of tits (e.g. 1910, 1957 and 1983), and therefore, beech-mast availability may also be a significant factor.

There is little difference between the summer and winter distributions, although birds are more likely to wander during winter once their food stores become depleted. From the 30 recoveries from 1909-1995 involving Suffolk-ringed Jays, only two travelled more than 10km and none have been found outside the county.

In the early 19th century, "some thousands" were noted flying inland at Tunstall and in the winter of 1846-1847 unusually high numbers were in the Thetford district (Ticehurst 1932). A large influx during the autumn of 1910 was witnessed along the coast from Norfolk through to Sussex, a large flock flew over Lowestoft in May 1924 and there was an influx into Southwold in the second week of October 1925. One shot by Ticehurst near Lowestoft on 29th September 1915 was considered to be of the nominate race *G.g. glandarius*, although modern-day opinion suggests that most are indistinguishable from the British race *G.g. rufitergum*. The arrival of so many Jays from offshore during influx years suggests that many originate from the continent. An invasion between 23rd September and 23rd October 1957 saw large numbers at coastal localities and the influx coincided with a massive irruption of tits (Cramp *et al.* 1960). The biggest invasion of recent times occurred from late September 1983, when Jays were reported flying in from offshore at several sites and numbers increased dramatically throughout the county. Concentrations included 40 at Benacre on 8th October, 20 flying south at Hollesley the next day and 24, including 12 arriving from offshore, at Gunton on 15th October. Small parties totalling 120 were seen heading inland from the sea, between Southwold and Kessingland, on 18th October, "extraordinary" numbers were at Sotterley on 30th October and the Lound/Somerleyton/Fritton area was said to be "saturated with Jays" (SBR/John & Roskell 1985). The incursion was less noticeable in West Suffolk, although a group of 11 at Exning on 2nd October is exceptional for that area. One ringed at Hollesley on 26th September 1983 and recovered at Boxted, near Bury St Edmunds, exactly two months later, indicates that some immigrants soon moved further inland.

The Jay has been seen to take small passerines from the ground and one at Sutton Heath on 10th June 1989 was seen carrying a live toad.

Magpie (Black-billed Magpie) *Pica pica*

A common resident

The Magpie is widely distributed throughout the county and in recent years has increased rapidly. Although the species nests in a wide range of habitats and is more abundant in rural areas, it is also common in towns and regularly nests in gardens. The conspicuous black and white plumage makes the Magpie one of our most familiar birds, but it is often portrayed as a villain. It is common in most areas, but is noticeably rarer in north-west and north-central parts probably due to the high density of gamekeepers.

The Magpie has been one of the county's most persecuted birds, shot, trapped and poisoned remorselessly, at times almost to extinction. Its confiding and inquisitive nature makes it an easy target and even today several hundred fall victim annually to the gun and to Lassen decoy-traps. A price was on its head as early as 1568 as shown by an entry in the Bedingfield Parish accounts which reads: "item pd for one mole and fower pyes heds [four Magpie's heads] and 10 myse [mice] .... 8d" (Ticehurst 1932). In the late 19th century, the Magpie was considered to be a rare bird and extinct in some districts (Babington 1884-1886) and after two were seen at Corton in 1909 it was absent for 30 years (B. J. Brown citing F. Cook). Numbers increased whilst gamekeepers were away during the Great War and by the early 1920s a recovery was noticed in many parts of Suffolk, which continued through to the 1950s. There was a temporary blip during the 1960s when the species once again became scarce as a result of the use of organochlorine pesticides.

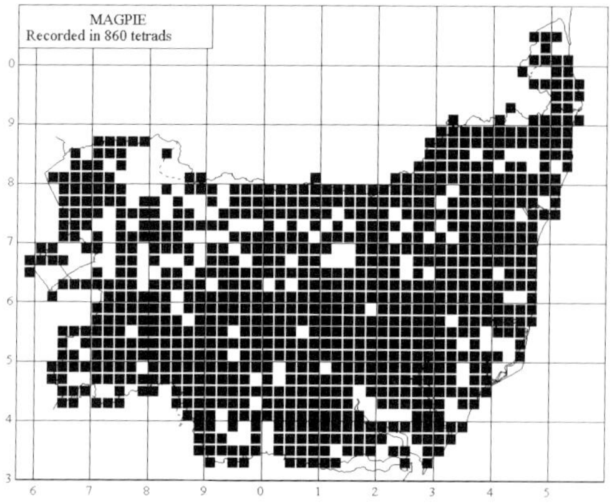

The Magpie spread into towns and larger villages during the 1940s and there has been much concern about the species predating urban songbirds. Despite its bad reputation, the Magpie has been vigorously defended by conservation bodies.

Although the species is more gregarious in winter, its summer and winter distribution is almost identical and an increase in flock sizes has coincided with an upward trend in the breeding population. Gatherings of 30-40 were rare up to the early 1980s, but, since 1990, groups of 50 or more have been recorded annually. The RSPB reserve at North Warren regularly hosts concentrations of 70 or more, but c.100 at Potter's Bridge, Reydon, on 10th February 1999, is the highest count of recent times. However, all counts are eclipsed by a huge winter roost of 600-700, which gathered in blackthorns at Sotterley in 1947.

Nutcracker (Spotted Nutcracker) *Nucifraga caryocatactes*

A very rare visitor – prone to irruptions: 93 records (75 in 1968)

The Nutcracker visits Britain every few years, including the occasional national influx, which coincides with failures in the arolla pine cones and hazelnuts in their native Siberian forests. Two races have been recorded in Britain: the thick-billed race *N. c. caryocatactes* which breeds in the mountains of central and south-eastern Europe, central Scandinavia and south-east Finland east to the Urals and the eastern slender-billed race *N. c. macrorhynchos* which breeds from north-east Russia, Siberia, northern Mongolia and northern Manchuria. All Suffolk records racially assigned belong to the latter race. From the 93 records, 75 occurred in the large national influx of 1968.

Ticehurst listed seven 19th century records including one which was shot by a fisherman off Yarmouth. There were only three reports for the first half of the 20th century, one of which involved a surprise visitor to a Southwold house during the rough and stormy night of 19th October 1922. This bird scratched at a window and, when the window was opened, the bird flew in and perched on a cupboard where it remained until early morning.

There was an unprecedented influx into Britain from 6th August to October 1968 involving 315 birds (Dymond *et al.* 1989). Nutcrackers were seen on the shore at Minsmere, Covehithe and Felixstowe on 24th August, 5th September and 12th September respectively, which probably indicate arrival dates from the continent. There was a fair scattering of records along the coastal strip, but the species was largely concentrated in pine forests between the Blyth and the Deben estuaries. Five or six at Theberton and six at Eyke were the largest concentrations, although a confiding individual, which frequented Covehithe churchyard, from 22nd August-15th September, was well-watched. There were only three inland records: Hemingstone; Tuddenham St Martin and Leavenheath. Spotted Nutcrackers by their nature are highly mobile and determining numbers involved was a complex operation. However, allowing for duplication it was estimated that at least 75 passed through the county.

Records since 1968 include: two (one later found dead) at Hinton on 29th July 1969; one on Lowestoft's seafront on 27th October 1971; another at Minsmere on 4th November 1973 and lastly one at Westleton from 2nd November-7th December 1985. The appearance of the Westleton bird caused quite a stir, being the first 'twitchable' bird for the new wave of birdwatchers. This confiding individual delighted thousands of admirers as it made frequent visits to some small apple trees in a cottage garden. Sadly, this bird was found dead in a cabbage patch on 7th December.

Chough (Red-billed Chough) *Pyrrhocorax pyrrhocorax*

Accidental: one record

1888 Felixstowe: Landguard Point, two NW 2nd April

The above individuals were, quite feasibly, wild birds prospecting the coastline and the record was originally published in the *Brit. Assoc. Report on Migration* for 1888. They were reported by the Landguard Point lighthouse keeper (Mr Owen Boyle) who stated: "two crows put in an appearance, 7.30 a.m.; larger than Jackdaws; they had red beaks and legs, and went north-west" (Christy 1890). The record's authenticity was doubted by Ticehurst on the grounds that vagrancy into Suffolk was unlikely. The Chough was lost as a breeding species to Kent and Northumberland some 40 years previously, but was still nesting in Dorset at that time (Holloway 1996).

The British and Irish populations are mainly sedentary (Cramp *et al.* 1974-1994), although one ringed as a nestling at Strathclyde on 31st May 1986 and recovered at Beaconsfield, Buckinghamshire, on 12th

December 1991 (Mead & Clark 1993) shows that substantial movements can happen, but it is of course possible that this unprecedented movement was aided by man. The identification of the Landguard Point birds was, apparently, not in question and, as the birds occurred as a pair and at a coastal locality, escapees from captivity was considered unlikely.

A Chough was shot at Hawstead on 19th September 1882, although this bird was a known escapee from a nearby collection.

Jackdaw (Eurasian Jackdaw) *Corvus monedula*

A common resident, winter visitor and passage migrant

The species breeds widely throughout the county and the resident population is reinforced by immigrants from the continent in autumn and winter. Jackdaws nest in colonies most often in cavities in mature hedgerow trees, woods and parks and, occasionally, derelict buildings. Jackdaws join other corvids and fly high overhead to woodland roosts just before dusk. The corvid's beady blue eyes and mischievous habits made it a very popular pet amongst schoolboys during the 1950s and 1960s and many nestlings were taken for home rearing.

Although the Jackdaw suffered at the hands of keepers in a similar way as did other corvids, the populations did not decline to the same extent. Jackdaws became a target following an Act issued by Queen Elizabeth I which called for the destruction of 'vermin'. This is typified by an entry in the Cratfield parish accounts, for the year 1580, which reads in old English: "cadowes hedes I pye iiiid," and translates to "heads of Jackdaws plus one Magpie paid fourpence" (Ticehurst 1932). The Jackdaw generally increased in Britain during the early 1900s (Marchant *et al.* 1990) and a general upward trend has followed to present day. However, the Reydon Grove Farm study from 1964-1971 revealed an estimated 20 pairs (Benson & Williamson 1972) compared with only three pairs in 1997 (Pearson 1998).

The map shows that the Jackdaw is widespread throughout the county and the largest densities appear around Newmarket and Bury St Edmunds. It is scarce or absent from the conifer plantations around Thetford and in Tunstall and Rendlesham and over much of the central cereal growing areas.

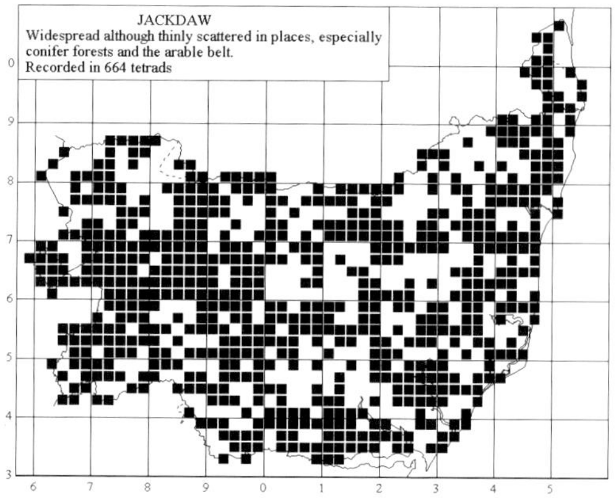

The species gathers in large flocks during the winter and feeds on pastures, stubbles, freshly ploughed fields, pig fields and rubbish tips, often in association with Rooks. Groups of 50 or more are commonplace and larger gatherings are occasionally reported. Non-roost counts of 500 or more have been logged on only eight occasions, with 820 at Eastbridge on 22nd December 1985 and 1,100 on the pig fields at Blythburgh on 16th July 1999, being the largest reported.

Immigrants are frequently observed crossing the North Sea each October, most often in the company of Rooks. Cold weather movements are occasionally reported with 300 arriving at Thorpeness on 27th January 1983 being the largest immigration of recent years. Direct emigration is occasionally noted as flocks fly high eastwards out to sea and this was typified at Kessingland and Landguard Point on 26th March 1994, when 100 and 49 flew north respectively.

Individuals showing characters of the Scandinavian race *C. m. monedula* have been claimed in recent winters and it was a result of the identification of two birds, shot at Corton in March 1911, that this race was added to the British list (Payn 1978). Ticehurst identified birds of this race hung up as scarecrows, in fields near Lowestoft presumably during the 1920s, but the plumage of British-reared Eurasian Jackdaws is highly variable and, in consequence, field records should be viewed with suspicion. Immigration is confirmed by two Danish-ringed birds, recovered at Benacre and Yoxford in April 1957 and April 1981 respectively, and another from Germany found in Eye in March 1967. One ringed at Minsmere in December 1961 was found in June eight years later in Belgium.

Unusual nesting sites include: rabbit burrows on the open breck (Ticehurst 1932) and a colony of 12-15 pairs which built open nests in the branches of Scots pines at Lakenheath (Payn 1978).

Rook *Corvus frugilegus*

A common resident, winter visitor and passage migrant

The Rook is widely distributed throughout the county, although is at much lower densities on the sandlings and in the breck, probably due to the presence of dense conifer plantations. The resident population is boosted by immigrants from the continent during winter and arrivals become obvious at coastal watch-points in October and early November. Rooks make regular evening flights to woodland roost sites.

The Rook has been persecuted for centuries. An Act to destroy Choughs (Jackdaws), Crows and Rooks came into force in 1533, to counter alleged damage to grain crops. Each parish had to provide nets to capture corvids or pay a fine of ten shillings a day. An entry in the Cratfield parish accounts of 1583 reads: "item pd for the Roocke neete ..... IXd", which translates to "item paid for Rook meat equals ninepence" and in the Bedingfield accounts for 1568, one shilling paid "for threscore and syxt crowes and roks heds and one bozzards hede" (36 crows and rooks heads and one buzzard's head). By the end of the 18th century, people began to realise that Rooks were of some benefit to farmers because they fed on wireworms, leatherjackets and grubs.

A nationwide survey, sponsored by the Agricultural Research Council, was organised in 1945, but, due to wartime restrictions, coverage was only achieved in the southern half of Suffolk. Nevertheless, 3,183 nests were found in 56 rookeries. From 1952-1955, a census of rookeries around Newmarket found that numbers fluctuated between 402-525 pairs. A county-wide survey carried out by the SOG in 1975 found 929 rookeries containing some 15,850 nests (Jeanes & Snook 1975). Comparable figures for exactly the same area which was covered in 1945 found 121 rookeries and 1,724 nests – i.e. roughly twice as many rookeries, but only half as many nests in 1995 – a population decline of 46%. The great majority of the rookeries surveyed in 1975 held less than 25 nests, 47 held between 50-100 nests and only seven more than 100 nests. The largest were at Ashmans Hall, Beccles with 170 nests, the Grange, Burgh Castle, 165 nests and Wattisfield, 157 nests. An incomplete survey, organised to monitor the effects of the 16th October 1987 gales (Piotrowski 1988c), revealed 130 rookeries of which at least 60 contained 12 nests or more. Generally, some rookeries had been deserted, but most were relocated closeby. The map clearly shows the distribution throughout the centre of the county and that it is nearly absent from the conifer forests of the Brecks and coastal areas.

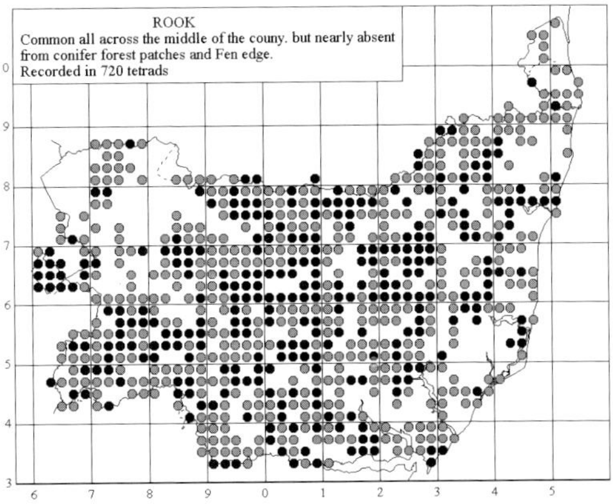

There has been a recent trend for Rooks to utilise man-made structures. Three nests were found on a floodlight tower in Felixstowe Docks in 1988 and electric pylons beside the A14 on the outskirts of Ipswich hosted between one and three nests from 1996-2001.

Ticehurst was fascinated with the immigration of the Rook – a subject that extended his account of this species to over seven pages. Immigration is most evident during late October and early November. Ticehurst describes how "masses" arrived with Jackdaws and Hooded Crows each autumn – the migration extending from Lowestoft throughout the whole of the Suffolk coast. Although immigration is still noted at migration watch-points, numbers are apparently significantly lower than they were in Ticehurst's day. Rooks normally arrive soon after day-break and sometimes continue throughout the day. Ringing recoveries show movements from Sweden (2), Denmark, Germany (4), the Netherlands (4), Latvia and Lithuania.

Woodland roost sites often hold several thousand corvids and Rooks travel with other crows along well-defined flight lines to reach them. A mixed gathering of Rooks and Jackdaws totalled 20,000 at Wordwell during the winter of 1950 and there were still 10,000-12,000 present in April. A corvid roost at Culpho has been well-monitored since the 1970s and often hosts up to 5,000 and another at Gipping has hosted up to 7,000 since 1997.

Carrion Crow *Corvus corone*

A common resident, winter visitor and passage migrant

The Carrion Crow is widely distributed throughout the county, although there are some surprising gaps between Bungay and Halesworth and around Bury St Edmunds which may well be connected to game preservation. Nesting occurs in both rural and urban areas with the species being a common feature in town centre parks. Pre-roost gatherings are regularly noted and the crow occasionally occurs as an immigrant.

In the late 19th century, the Carrion Crow was rare throughout the county (Babington 1884-1886), having already suffered the effects of intense persecution for over 300 years. It was virtually extinct by 1914, although a few pairs managed to breed (Ticehurst 1932). The crow is responsible for widespread predation of birds' eggs and young and its attacks on livestock made it a target for gamekeepers and farmers alike. A decline in game-preservation during the inter-war years of 1918 and 1939 saw the species increase and it has since adapted well to changes in agricultural practices. Although the Carrion Crow usually nests in trees, one or two pairs regularly use the lighting towers at Felixstowe Docks, successfully rearing young in most years.

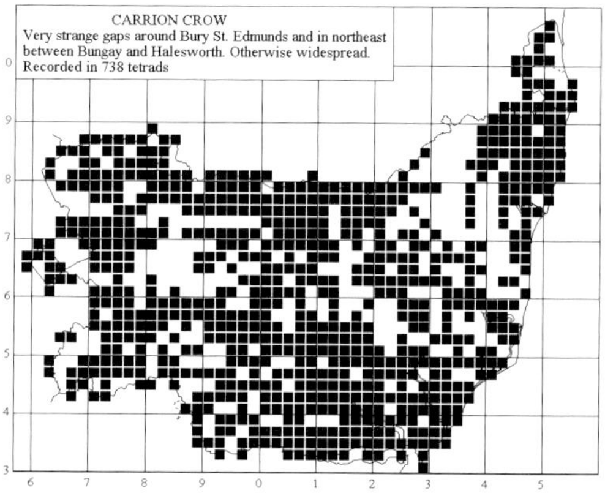

The Carrion Crow is highly sedentary with adults remaining near their breeding territories throughout their lives. There is some short-distance dispersal of offspring and these, along with non-breeding birds and migrants, congregate with flocks of other corvids to scavenge rubbish-tips, pig-fields and mudflats.

Flocks of 100 or more regularly congregate on the shore at Wherstead Strand before flying off to roost. Totals occasionally reach 200-250, but 400 there on 16th October 1986 is exceptional. Elsewhere, three-figure counts are rare, with roost counts yielding the highest numbers. Counts of 500 at Lakenheath on 22nd November 1998 and 400 at Gipping Great Wood on 17th November 1999 are the largest gatherings to date.

One found long dead at Freckenham in May 1993 had been ringed near Budby South Forest, Nottinghamshire, the previous spring. This represents the second most distant recovery of a British-ringed Carrion Crow (Mead *et al.* 1995).

Hooded Crow *Cornix cornix*

An uncommon winter visitor and passage migrant

The Hooded Crow was formerly a common winter visitor, being noted throughout the county, particularly favouring more open areas. During the early part of the 20th century, immigrants crossing the North Sea were a common sight from early October, sometimes in late September and Ticehurst described this arrival as "an almost daily event ... and on some days, after the stream has been held up by gales, they continue the whole day long". He went on to say that Hooded Crows travelled in "pure flocks unmixed with other species" and they would "crowd" on a fishing boat or lightship during blustery conditions or when held up at sea at nightfall. Hooded Crows were regular visitors to Breckland warrens and on agricultural land around Bury St Edmunds, where they were highly persecuted. About 100 were shot during a single winter at Gt Ashfield (Babington 1884-1886) and it was not uncommon at Rougham, Ickworth, Sicklesmere and Whepstead.

The Hooded Crow decreased markedly in the late 1940s, initially becoming scarce at inland districts. Concentrations of 50 or more were regularly attracted to the West Stow sewage farm during the early 1950s, but, thereafter, the population declined. Single-figure flocks were still noted in Breckland up to the early 1970s, but, nowadays, it is a very scarce bird in this district. Large numbers lingered at Walberswick, following the 1953 east-coast floods, increasing from 20 on 21st February to 42 on 15th May and a concentration of 40, noted at Kessingland on the latter date, was still present on 22nd May. A flock of 62 flew north-north-west over Reydon on 22nd February 1974 and 45-50 were counted, amongst a considerable movement of corvids, off Benacre-Covehithe on 30th March of that year. About 40 went to roost at Benacre on 10th January 1976 and 70 at Walberswick in January and February 1977, constitutes the county's largest gathering of recent times. The species still visited the coast in good numbers up to the early 1980s, but it has become progressively less common in recent times and, by the 1990s, only a handful of records were received each year.

Climatic change is thought to be the principal reason for the north-westerly shift in the zone of hybridisation between Carrion and Hooded Crows in Scotland during the 20th century (Cook 1975). A similar retreat elsewhere in north-west Europe may be responsible for the decline in the numbers wintering on Britain's east coast (Williamson 1975).

Hooded Crows were recorded nesting on more than ten occasions from 1843-1924, but undoubtedly did so more frequently. Post-breeding adults and their protégés, shot in August, were at that time considered as early return migrants or over-summering birds too old to leave the previous spring. A small breeding population was largely confined to the Lothingland area and along the Waveney Valley as far as Bungay, although nesting also occurred as far south as Hazelwood Marshes, beside the Alde.

There are two old ringing recoveries which demonstrate the origins of the wintering population. One recovered in Suffolk on 10th November 1921 had been ringed in South Lapland and another at Somerleyton on 12th December 1935 was ringed in East Prussia the previous April.

Raven (Common Raven) *Corvus corax*

Accidental: eight individuals since 19th century. Previously quite common

1954	Walberswick: 14th September
1979/80	Walberswick-Sutton area: 8th November-7th March
1988	West Stow: found dead under wires 25th January
	Minsmere: 15th-20th May
1991	Minsmere: Scottshall Covert, 27th April and 27th May
1993	Felixstowe: Landguard Point, feeding on dead rabbit, 28th October
1996	Felixstowe: Landguard Point, 5th March
2002	Ipswich: 2nd June

During the early part of the 19th century, the Raven appears to have been fairly common in many parts of Suffolk. However, persecution by farmers and gamekeepers, egg-collectors and young being taken from the nest for pets, eventually saw its demise. The last nest on the coast was at Stutton in 1869 and, in West Suffolk, at Robbinghouse spinney in Euston Park, the following year. A few unpaired birds lingered on for a few years with records from Brandon in 1879, Needham Market in 1884, two at Landguard Point 1886 and Tuddenham St Mary in 1888 and 1889.

There were no reports at all for the first half of the 20th century and one, being pursued by a pair of Kestrels at Walberswick on 14th September 1954, was the first record for 65 years. This was followed by a long-staying and wide-ranging individual which wintered principally in the Walberswick/Minsmere area from 8th November 1979 to 7th March 1980, but was also seen at Boyton and Methersgate Hall, Sutton. A remarkable ringing recovery involved one which was found dead under wires at West Stow in 25th January 1988, having been ringed as a pullus at Altiffinan Glen, Antrim, Northern Ireland in May of the previous year. Three years later an elusive individual was sighted twice during a protracted stay at Scottshall Covert, Minsmere, and there are two records for Landguard Point – the first involved a well-watched bird which fed on a rabbit carcass on 28th October 1993 and the second came in off the sea and then flew north on 5th March 1996.

Starling (Common Starling) *Sturnus vulgaris*

An abundant resident, winter visitor and passage migrant

The Starling is one of our most familiar birds, being found in all habitats and often in vast numbers. Nesting takes place in every farm and village and a town the size of Ipswich is likely to hold many thousands of breeding pairs. The resident population is boosted by thousands of immigrants during winter and Starlings crossing the North Sea are a common sight during late autumn. The Starling is extremely social, gathering to feed on grassland, stubbles and recently-ploughed fields and swooping in to dominate garden feeding stations. Thousands exploit livestock feeding areas, such as pig units and chicken farms.

There was a national decline in the 18th century, but a recovery ensued from 1830 and expansion has continued through to this century (Marchant *et al.* 1990). The CBC index shows that the breeding population again declined during the early 1980s, as part of a general decline over much of northern Europe. The Reydon Grove Farm study from 1964-1971 revealed an estimated 15 pairs (Benson & Williamson 1972), but there were none in 1997 (Pearson 1998).

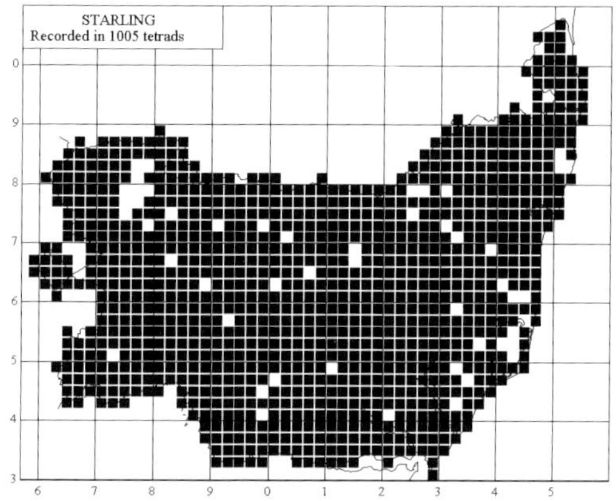

Constant streams of Starlings flying to woodland and reedbed roosts, often numbering many thousands, are observed towards dusk throughout autumn and winter. Birds often gather into pre-roost assemblies, where feeding and bathing take place prior to moving on to the roost site. A Haverhill roost numbered about 120,000 in 1933 and a half a million birds were said to have roosted at Combs Wood, Stowmarket (Payn 1978). The reedbeds at Easton Bavents, Walberswick and Minsmere regularly host wheeling flocks often reaching five and sometimes six-figures. Excessive disturbance at dusk will sometimes cause the relocation of a roost and there are often concerted attempts to discourage the birds. A roost in the holm oaks at Landguard Point steadily built from 2,000 birds in June 1994 to 10,000 on 21st October, before there was a rapid decline. The presence of six Long-eared Owls, which were seen hunting in the vicinity of the roost, no doubt persuaded these Starlings to sleep elsewhere.

Large-scale, diurnal immigration is reported annually at coastal watch-points from mid-October to mid-November. Starlings normally arrive in flocks of 10-30, from mid-morning onwards, sometimes continuing until dusk. Day-counts regularly reach three figures and occasionally several thousand come ashore. An arrival involving 4,718, logged at Landguard Point on 26th October 1992, is the largest of recent times. Although immigration peaks from mid-October onwards, some birds arrive much earlier as shown by one which was ringed as a nestling in Denmark on 25th May 1991 and controlled at Landguard Point six weeks later. There are numerous ringing recoveries involving birds moving to and from Scandinavia, northern Europe, the Baltic States and Russia and one which moved from Ipswich to Azerbaijan in 1968 is exceptional.

Rose-coloured Starling *Sturnus roseus*

Accidental: 26 records (16 from the 19th century)

1938	Melton: n.d.
1956	Leiston: 23rd November
1960	Lowestoft: Lowestoft Hospital, ad. 13th-20th May
1993	Felixstowe: Landguard Point, juv. 4th-9th September
1995	Lowestoft: Ness Point/North Denes, ad. 17th-27th June
1999	Hollesley: ad. 20th June
	Trimley St Mary: ad. 21st June
2001	Felixstowe: Landguard Point, ad. 12th June and juv. 16th-17th October
	Carlton Colville: 30th-31st July

Visitations have been far less frequent during the 20th century than in the early 19th century. There were 16 records between 1815 and 1871 (Babington 1884-1886), with only eight further records up to the end of 2001.

Rose-coloured Starlings breed from Hungary through to Kazakhstan and southern Iran, but are extremely nomadic often invading Asia Minor and through the Balkans as far as Italy. Eruptions are often influenced by locust swarms that penetrate southern Europe (Ticehurst 1932) and the decline in occurrences of Rose-coloured Starlings may well reflect a retraction in the insect's range. There are 581 records for Britain and Ireland up to the end of 2000 (BBRC).

House Sparrow *Passer domesticus*

An abundant resident

The House Sparrow is not as common as is generally thought, being largely restricted to areas dominated by man. It is scarcer on heaths, Breckland and open marshes and is almost absent in forestry areas. The sparrow is remarkably social, nesting and roosting communally and feeding in flocks during winter. It is a regular visitor to garden feeding stations where it will take peanuts and kitchen scraps. Coastal movements are witnessed annually at migration watch-points. The population has declined rapidly since the 1970s – probably as a result of changes in farming practices.

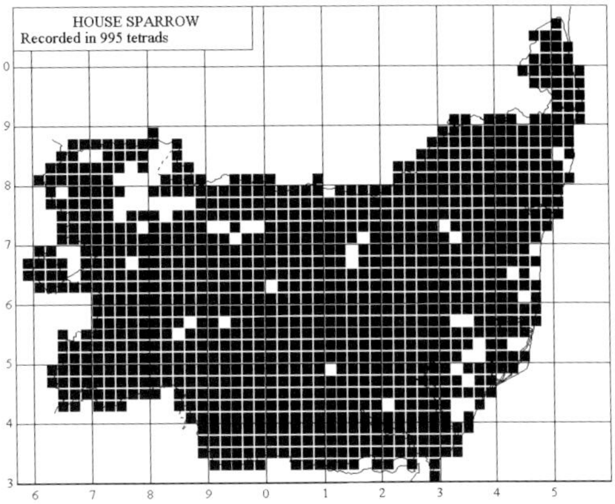

The species has always been an abundant resident of towns and villages, but, urban areas are largely deserted in late summer, when the species gathers into large flocks to invade ripening corn fields in the vicinity. The liking for grain resulted in the sparrow being considered as vermin and a bounty of 3d (about one penny in modern currency) per dozen were paid for 38 dozen by St Margaret's South Elmham parish in 1772. Similarly, various sums were paid for 2,587 sparrows and 34 dozen sparrow's eggs between 1819-1835 at Rattlesden (Ticehurst 1932).

The map shows that the House Sparrow nests almost everywhere, although it breeds at far lower densities in open areas of much of Breckland and the coastal marshes. It is also scarce in the conifer plantations of Tunstall, Rendlesham and Thetford.

House Sparrows are scarcely mentioned in SBRs between 1950 and 1980, probably because there were no significant population fluctuations during this period. Gatherings of up to 100 were then commonplace, but surprisingly, there were no four-figure flocks reported. Significant gatherings were still reported during the 1980s and a flock of 400 around the Sproughton B.F. ponds on 10th December 1986 is the largest of recent times. The CBC index shows a decline in all habitats and the BTO's Garden Bird Feeding Survey shows a fall in visitations to suburban gardens of between 15-20% during the period 1978-1988 (Marchant *et al.* 1990). The Reydon Grove Farm study from 1964-1971 revealed an estimated 75 pairs (Benson & Williamson 1972) compared with only one pair in 1997 (Pearson 1998). It has been suggested that the Sparrowhawk's penetration into urban areas has been responsible for a reduction in the House Sparrow population (Gibbons *et al.* 1993).

The House Sparrow is particularly gregarious during winter and their chirping call is a familiar sound as they form pre-roost gatherings as evening approaches. Roost sites include hedgerows, ivy-clad walls, ornamental fir trees, thatched roofs and farmyard buildings.

Ticehurst referred to coastal movements and the *British Association Reports on Migration* detailed autumn immigration based on records from offshore light-vessels, which included a flock flying west by the Corton light-vessel on 28th September 1879 and numbers flying north-west by the Shipwash on 14th October 1881 and again 22nd September 1885. There has long been much speculation regarding the origins and intended destinations of flocks passing south over Landguard Point each autumn, which has yet to be confirmed conclusively by ringing returns. The sparrows are usually in the company of Linnets and Greenfinches and are logged from late September to early November, although numbers have dropped dramatically since the early 1980s. For example, an October total of 1,710 in 1983 included a peak day-count of 350 on 6th, 100 flying south on 21st October 1984, 138 on 27th September 1986, 169 on 1st November 1989 and 131 on 10th October 1990. This compares with autumn totals of no more than 300 and peak day-counts of no more than 45 in the period 1991-1996.

House Sparrows are extremely sedentary and from the 58 recorded movements of Suffolk-ringed birds only one bird has travelled over 10km. Birds recovered in Suffolk from outside the county include one ringed in Kent on 16th January 1959 and found dead at Felixstowe, on 12th December 1960, and another ringed in Lincolnshire in 28th April 1966 and found at Lakenheath, 19th May 1967.

Tree Sparrow (Eurasian Tree Sparrow) *Passer montanus*

An uncommon resident and passage migrant

The Tree Sparrow is now thinly distributed through the county with the highest densities in north-eastern, north central and south-western parishes. The sparrow has decreased rapidly since the mid-1980s and is now absent from many parts of the county. Large flocks formerly gathered at stubble and weed fields during winter and large movements were logged at coastal watch-points.

Tree Sparrow (*Brian Small*)

The sparrow was never plentiful, but bred locally in small colonies. It mostly nests in holes in trees, thatched buildings and old orchards and readily takes to nest boxes. Ticehurst located a colony in holes in a cliff-face, formerly used by Sand Martins, and the author found Tree Sparrows nesting in Grey Herons' nests at Methersgate during the early 1970s. The Reydon Grove Farm study from 1964-1971 showed that the Tree Sparrow was one of the most numerous breeding species with numbers ranging from 10-38 pairs (Benson & Williamson 1972). By 1997, the species was lost completely from the farm (Pearson 1998).

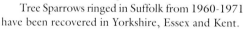

The map shows that Tree Sparrows are widely scattered throughout the county with small concentrations in north-central and south-west Suffolk and in the vicinity of the towns of Framlingham, Halesworth and Beccles. There are now few nesting pairs along the coastal strip and it is absent from most of north-west Suffolk. However, it is likely that the population has declined still further.

Wintering flocks of 100-150 were regularly recorded up to the mid-1980s and, occasionally, four-figure gatherings were reported. Around 800-1,000 were noted going to roost by the River Kennett, at Dalham, on 25th October 1953 and flocks totalling 2,000-3,000 were at Benacre 7th November 1967, 1,000 at Aldeburgh in January and February 1981 and 1,500 at Walberswick, on 15th January 1982. Nowadays, flock sizes are far smaller with three-figure concentrations extremely rare. Since 1991, flocks of 50 at Sudbourne and Badley in February 1992 and up to 81 at Timworth and 40 at Lakenheath during the winter of 1994/5 are large by modern-day standards and, although a few flocks have been reported elsewhere, these have contained less than 30 birds.

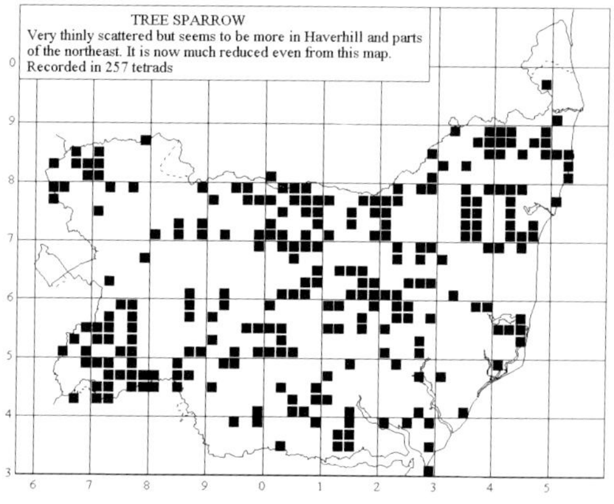

TREE SPARROW
Very thinly scattered but seems to be more in Haverhill and parts of the northeast. It is now much reduced even from this map.
Recorded in 257 tetrads

Southerly movements were formerly significant with three-figure counts regularly being reached in October and November. The largest involved 8,000 at Minsmere, between 3rd October and 17th November 1961, including 2,350, in three hours, on 11th; c.1,000 in two hours at Landguard Point on 12th October 1980 and 4,675 at Landguard Point from 6th October-13th November 1983, which included impressive peaks of 2,000 on 17th and 20th October. The decline in passage birds coincided with the demise of the breeding population and, nowadays, Landguard Point's annual totals rarely reach three figures.

Tree Sparrows ringed in Suffolk from 1960-1971 have been recovered in Yorkshire, Essex and Kent.

Rare examples of hybridisation between Tree and House Sparrows were noted at Bury St Edmunds on 13th January 1894 and at nearby Timworth on 28th December 1995.

Red-eyed Vireo *Vireo olivaceus*

Accidental: four records

1988	Lowestoft: Warrenhouse Wood, North Denes, 29th September
1991	Lowestoft: Sparrow's Nest Gardens, 6th October
1995	Southwold: St Edmund's Churchyard, 12th-14th October
	Aldringham-cum-Thorpe: 12th-15th October

The Red-eyed Vireo is a rare visitor to the British Isles, although it is the commonest American land bird to occur here, being recorded on 127 occasions up to the end of 2000 (BBRC). The above records are Suffolk's only live examples of Nearctic insectivorous passerines.

The two Lowestoft birds were found within a mile of each other and the 1995 records were part of a remarkable influx into Britain which involved at least 14 individuals (BBRC). It is particularly noteworthy that two were found on the same date in Suffolk in 1995 only a few miles apart.

Chaffinch *Fringilla coelebs*

An abundant resident, winter visitor and passage migrant

The Chaffinch is the county's most ubiquitous species, breeding widely in all types of habitat. It nests freely wherever there are trees and bushes, including parks and large gardens in town centres. The wintering population is boosted by the autumn arrival of birds from Scandinavia and the near continent and there are occasional cold-weather movements.

It was Suffolk's most common finch in the 1930s (Ticehurst 1932) but, due to agrochemical poisoning, it declined on farmland in the 1950s and reached an all-time low around 1960-1962 (Marchant *et al.* 1990). The population then began to recover and has since increased steadily. The Reydon Grove Farm study from 1964-1971 revealed a range of 23-28 pairs (Benson & Williamson 1972) compared with 41 pairs in 1997 (Pearson 1998). A ten-year ringing summary, from 1986-1995 (Marsh 1997), shows a significant increase in the numbers ringed, probably reflecting increases in passage and wintering birds.

Wintering flocks feed on a variety of seeds and generally frequent woodland and hedgerows. Groups of 30-50 are regularly reported and three-figure flocks are not unusual. Gatherings of 500 were noted at Aldeburgh in January and February 1981 and in the King's Forest on 30th January 1991 and 650 were at Minsmere on 30th January 1994. A cold-weather, southerly movement involving 1,000 birds was noted at the latter site on 1st January 1962.

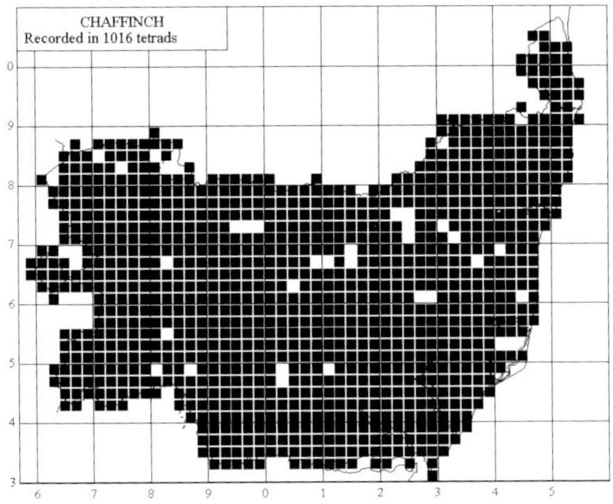

Locally bred Chaffinches are largely sedentary, with few moving far from their natal areas. There is normally a considerable immigration between late September and mid-November and, in favourable conditions, small flocks can be seen arriving from offshore throughout the day. Such arrivals are noted annually at Landguard Point and autumn day totals often reach three-figures. Few birds coast southwards with other finches and therefore totals are normally much lower. However, during the 1960s, substantial totals were logged at Minsmere of flocks arriving from offshore – the largest being 800 on 19th October 1963 and 500 on 23rd and 3,000 on 23rd October 1967. Return passage occurs from late March and until May, but this often goes unnoticed. However, 7,000 moving north with Starlings, at Minsmere on 26th March 1964, is the county's largest recorded movement.

Movements between Suffolk and Scandinavia and to and from the continent have been confirmed by Chaffinches ringed in Belgium, the Netherlands (3), Germany and Denmark being recovered in Suffolk and Suffolk-ringed birds being found in France, Belgium (2), the Netherlands, Germany, Denmark (2), Norway (2), Finland and Sweden (8). Interchange between Suffolk and the Welsh coast is confirmed by one ringed at Benacre on 2nd October 1960 and found dead in Fishguard, Pembrokeshire, on 5th January 1962 and another ringed Bardsey Island, on 10th October 1993 and controlled at West Stow Country Park, on 8th October 1994. It should be noted that the Benacre bird was found during a severe weather period.

Brambling *Fringilla montifringilla*

A common winter visitor and passage migrant

Bramblings are noted annually throughout the county usually in single-species flocks, but ones and twos often mix with Chaffinches. The species is most often seen feeding on beech-mast although it is also attracted to winter stubbles, weed fields and linseed crops. The nasal cry is regularly heard at migration watch-points where, in some years, several hundred pass through.

Wintering numbers vary greatly from one winter to the next, although flocks of 20-50 are reported in most years. Groups of 100-200 are not uncommon where there is an abundance of food and, during 'Brambling-years', the birds gather in single-species flocks, sometimes in very large numbers. Ticehurst stated that "great numbers" wintered during 1879/80, 1884/5, and 1894/5 and that Bramblings were "unusually abundant" in 1910. "Thousands" were seen going to roost in rhododendrons at Watling Wood, Butley, in February 1966 and 2,000 were at North Warren during that period. Counts of c.1,000 were logged at Lakenheath in January 1967 and March 1973 and at Honington in 1976. By far the largest gatherings, however, were in the Eriswell/Lakenheath area in January 1994, where huge feeding flocks, totalling at least 4,000 birds, were attracted to a number of linseed fields which had been left unharvested over the winter.

Brambling
(Brian Small)

Bramblings begin to arrive at coastal localities in early October with immigration normally peaking towards the end of the month. There are three August records with one flying south at Minsmere on the 14th being the earliest autumn return.

Superb males amongst pre-emigrating flocks enlighten a birdwatcher's spring day. Feeding flocks are frequently reported until early May, particularly at Breckland localities and there are four records for June and July: a pair in Euston Park, on 13th June 1895; one at Iken, 16th June 1974; a male, with House Sparrows at Orford, 22nd July 1978 and a male at West Stow Country Park from 25th June to 3rd July 1994.

There were only 11 recoveries of Suffolk-ringed Bramblings during the period 1909-1995 and five of these were from overseas. A catch at Minsmere on 3rd-4th February 1963 included one recovered in the Netherlands the following autumn and two controlled within three days of each other in Belgium and Germany in April 1964. Bramblings ringed at Butley in March and April 1967 were found in Germany and Finland. Bramblings from Russian, Norway, the Netherlands and Belgium have been found in Suffolk.

Serin (European Serin) *Serinus serinus*

A very rare passage migrant: 32 records

Occurrences of this tiny finch are comparatively rare considering that it is a common breeding bird over much of Europe. It is predominantly a spring visitor with most records referring to brief sightings of birds passing through migration watch-points. Since the late 1980s, there has been the occasional long-staying individual, including some singing males that have held territories.

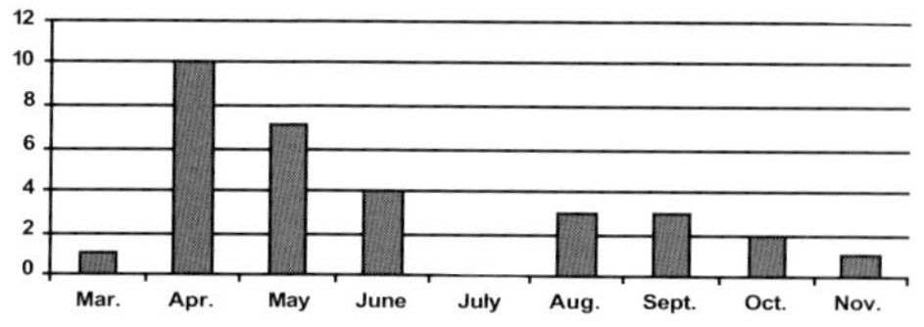

The seasonal occurrences of the Serin from 1922-2000

A female trapped at Saxmundham during the spring of 1893 was the first for the county. This individual was taken to Yarmouth and lived in captivity until July of that year (Ticehurst 1932). The next was also a female and was captured in Cobholm gardens on the Suffolk side of Breydon Water on 1st May 1922 and another was watched at Ness Point, Lowestoft on 16th August 1936. There then followed a 34-year gap before one visited Walberswick on 19th September 1970. This was the first of five records for that decade. One at Landguard Point on 2nd November 1980 was the first record away from north-east Suffolk and is the only occurrence for that month. There were four further records for the 1980s including a pair frequenting suitable breeding habitat at Mildenhall from 14th-20th June 1987. There has since been a significant increase in occurrences with 18 records from 1992-2000. This includes singing males at Southwold in 1992, 1994 and 1995, indicating perhaps that breeding will soon take place – if it hasn't already.

Most recent records have involved birds seen during spring passage coinciding with the arrival of Linnet flocks.

Extreme dates are 24th March 2002 and 14th June 1987 for spring passage and 13th August 1993 and 2nd November 1980 for autumn.

Greenfinch (European Greenfinch) *Carduelis chloris*

An abundant resident, winter visitor and passage migrant

The Greenfinch breeds widely throughout the county and is common both on passage and during winter. Flocks feed on weeds in cultivated fields, on stubbles, shingle beaches, saltings and tidelines, at garden feeding stations and in both deciduous and coniferous woodland. It is a regular visitor to migration watch-points, where it occasionally passes through in considerable numbers.

In the late 19th century, it was described as being "very common everywhere" (Babington 1884-1886) and in the 1930s as "generally distributed throughout the county, especially in the agricultural districts, and is common enough" (Ticehurst 1932). Nationally, there was an apparent increase during the 1950s, particularly in urban and suburban areas (Marchant *et al.* 1990), although there is no documented evidence for Suffolk. The population was at a low ebb during the early 1960s probably as a result of poisoning due to the application of organochlorine pesticides and seed dressings, but also the effects of the severe winters of 1961/2 and 1962/3. Recovery was fairly swift and the number of birds trapped for ringing suggest that an all time high was reached in Suffolk during the mid-1980s. The Reydon Grove Farm study from 1964-1971 revealed a range of 3-8 (Benson & Williamson 1972) compared with four pairs in 1997 (Pearson 1998).

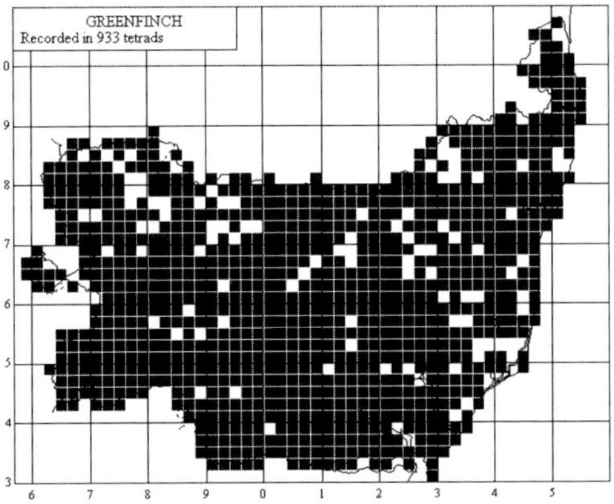

The map shows that the Greenfinch is widespread throughout the county, although the population is less dense in Breckland and coastal forest areas and in some parts of central Suffolk.

Wintering flocks of 20-30 birds are commonplace, but, occasionally, much larger gatherings concentrate in areas of food-rich fields. The largest of these include: 1,000 at Wantisden, in February 1967; c.2,000 in the breck on 6th January 1980; 1,000 at Herringswell on 11th December 1988, 1,000 at Lackford in February 1994 and 1,000 at Stallode Wash, Lakenheath, on 28th December 1995. A flock of 1,100 in the Long Melford/Cavendish area on 13th September 1989 probably contained a high proportion of passage birds.

Garden feeding stations offer the species an important food source in winter and spring and the species has become extremely adept at balancing on peanut holders. A few begin to arrive into gardens in November, but reach their greatest numbers in late winter and early spring. Small flocks constantly come and go throughout the day and the total numbers of birds involved can sometimes be staggering. A ringing study in the author's Ipswich garden in March 1985 revealed that over 300 had visited the feeding station in a three-week period. As natural seed stocks become depleted in spring, Greenfinches become increasingly reliant on artificial food supplies and replenished peanut holders will continue to attract birds until early June.

Greenfinches are partial migrants in Britain and substantial southerly movements occur each October. Ticehurst noted that its migration pattern was similar to that of the Tree Sparrow and Chaffinch and he referred to a "migratory stream" at Lowestoft, during the early morning of 11th October 1911, when 4,000 passed over in the space of one hour. Extraordinary southerly movements were logged at Landguard Point in the autumns of the early 1980s, the highest being 10,500, between 27th September and 26th November 1981, peaking at 3,500 on 10th October and c.14,625 in October 1983 peaking at c.4,750 on 20th October. Spring passage occurs mainly from March to early May and traditionally more are trapped at Landguard Point during this season than in autumn as a greater proportion stop off to feed. A continual decline in the numbers ringed at this site was noted from 1986-1993, from a high of 1,429 for the period March to May and 443 for September to November 1986, to respective totals of 286 and 104 for 1993.

During the 1980s, flocks of 200-300 were a regular feature at Landguard Point from September to November, where birds collected seeds of sea kale and other plants from the shingle ridge. Maritime habitats are frequented throughout the winter with flocks of 20-30 regularly noted on saltmarshes and, occasionally, with Snow Buntings, on open shingle.

A total of 1,010 Suffolk-ringed birds was recovered in Britain and Ireland, during the period 1909-1995, which show a predominantly east to west movement to and from the county. Of these, 482 have been found within a 10km radius of the ringing site, 399 between 10-99km and 129 of 100km or over. Passage to and from Norway, the Low Countries, the Channel Islands and France, has also been confirmed.

Goldfinch (European Goldfinch) *Carduelis carduelis*

An abundant summer visitor and passage migrant. Small numbers overwinter

The Goldfinch breeds widely throughout the county, particularly favouring open country. It frequents farmland, parkland, areas of scrub and woodland edges, but will also venture into suburban gardens where it nests in shrubs and trees. Charms are widely reported on passage, but only small numbers overwinter.

A marked decrease was noted towards the end of the 19th century mainly due to the cultivation of weed fields, but also to the widespread commercial trapping for cage-bird enthusiasts. So many were netted that it became virtually unknown in some districts, particularly around Sudbury and Bury St Edmunds. Nationally, the Goldfinch was at its lowest ebb in the 1870s (Holloway 1996), but benefited from protective legislation in 1880, 1881, 1894, 1933 and 1954. It remained scarce in the early years of the 20th century to such an extent that one eminent naturalist of that time failed to see the species in Suffolk prior to 1914 (Hervey 1952). The keeping of finches in parlours soon became unfashionable and, as poorer land was taken out of cultivation, weeds thrived once again. By the 1930s, it was "not uncommon throughout the County" (Ticehurst 1932). Its "remarkable adaptation to suburban life... e.g. Felixstowe" (Hervey 1952) was thought to have aided its recovery and, by the 1950s, it was widespread and comparatively common everywhere. The national CBC index showed this upward trend continuing throughout the 1960s, but it fell away sharply during the 1980s after peaking in 1977 (Marchant *et al.* 1990). Although the long-term trend shows a decline of 28% over the past 25 years (Gregory *et al.* 1996), there are encouraging signs that a recovery is underway this decade (Marchant & Wilson 1996). The Reydon Grove Farm study from 1964-1971 revealed a range of 3-11 pairs (Benson & Williamson 1972) compared with two pairs in 1997 (Pearson 1998).

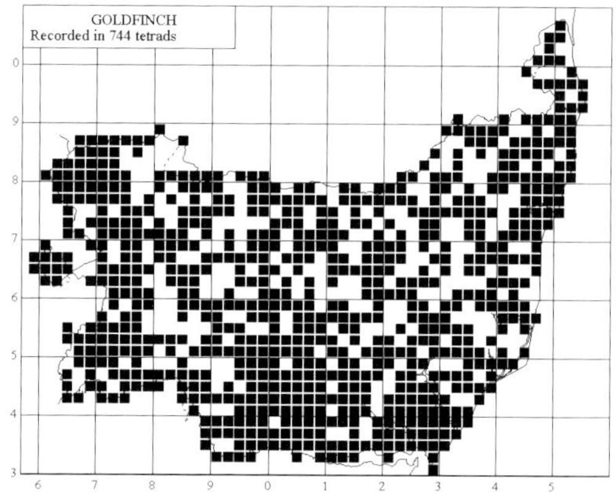

The greatest densities occur around Dunwich and in South Suffolk and its presence in urban areas such as Felixstowe and Ipswich town centre is confirmed. However, it is scarce in the conifer forests of Thetford, Tunstall and Rendlesham and is only sparsely distributed in the cereal-dominated areas of West and north-central Suffolk.

Although small numbers remain throughout the year, around 80% migrate south to winter in Belgium, France and Spain (Newton 1972). A number of Suffolk-ringed birds have been found in these regions between late October and March. A female ringed at Hollesley in May 1985 and shot in Malta in December of that year occurred much further south and east than usual. Coastal movements are most obvious in autumn from mid-September until early November and on some days the twittering flight call, of small parties overhead, can be heard throughout the morning. Southerly movements were logged at Minsmere during the 1960s and the highest day-total of that period was 2,000 on 8th October 1964. The largest recorded movements were logged at Landguard Point during the early 1980s. For example, in 1981, 21,100 Goldfinches passed through in late September and October, including 7,500 on 10th October, and in 1983, 24,275 moved south between 17th September and 29th November, including 4,250 on 20th October. Spring passage is less pronounced, although returning birds are regularly noted from late

April to mid-May. Northerly movements at Minsmere include: 600 on 15th May 1962; 400 on 10th May 1965; 400 on 28th April 1967 and 500 on 10th May 1968.

Newton (1972) stated that like other cardueline finches, Goldfinches tend to nest in loose colonies. However, there is no evidence to suggest that communal nesting takes place in Suffolk, which may explain the relatively lower densities at larger sites such as Minsmere and North Warren.

The species will often congregate in a particular weed field where the flocks periodically rise in unison to explore a new area. Charms of up to 10-20 birds are regularly attracted to fields containing patches of thistles, burdocks, grounsel, dandelion, ragwort, knapweed, charlock and teasels. The birds normally feed low to the ground, but in winter and early spring will join other finches to take seeds from the tops of alders, birches and even conifers. Goldfinches are often attracted to estuarine saltings where they feed on sea aster. Large pre- or post-migration gatherings include: 500 at Hitcham from October-early November 1956 and a peak of 700 on 16th September the following year: c.500 at Leiston on 20th October 1957; 1,000 along the Orford-Tunstall road on 22nd April 1969 and c.400 at Minsmere on 1st October 1980. A roost of c.150 at Watling Wood, Butley, in January 1970, is exceptional for midwinter, although there was a phenomenal series of counts in late January and February 1994 which included: 120 at Westleton on 27th January increasing to 700 on 13th February; 1,000 at Mildenhall on 9th February and flocks of 100-200 at seven other sites.

Siskin (European Siskin) — *Carduelis spinus*

A common winter visitor, passage migrant and uncommon resident

Flocks busily feeding high in alders are a common sight during most winters and, towards the end of the season, the species regularly visits garden feeding stations, being particularly attracted to red peanut bags. The wintering population varies considerably, being influenced greatly by food supplies both here and elsewhere. It is eruptive in some years. The species is commonly seen on passage, sometimes in considerable numbers, and visible immigration is regularly noted. Since the early 1960s, a small breeding population has become established in forestry areas in Breckland and on the coastal strip.

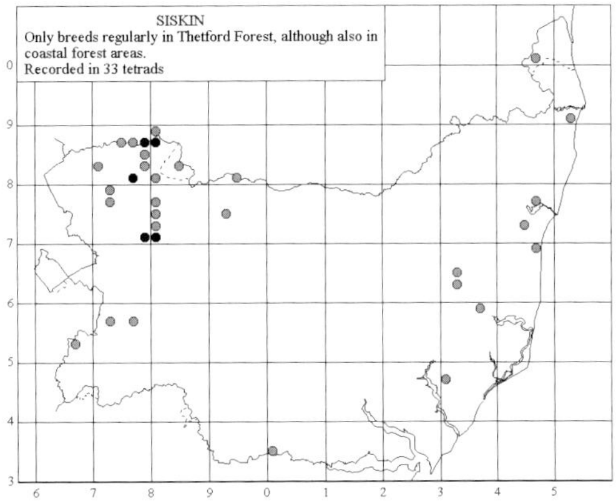

Large-scale afforestation of the breck and sandlings has created an ideal breeding habitat and colonisation began soon after the plantations matured. Nesting was suspected in forested areas, on both sides of the county, as early as 1962, although a pair seen carrying nesting material at Santon Downham in 1964 was the first signs of breeding behaviour. This was a prelude to regular nesting and two years later a pair was watched feeding young at Herringfleet. A pair bred at Dunwich and a brood of four recently-fledged young was seen in Tunstall Forest in 1967. Thereafter, breeding numbers increased steadily and, by the late 1980s, it was considered to be a common breeder in Thetford Forest (Hoblyn 1991), although it only nests sporadically on the coast.

Although alder carr is the most favoured winter feeding habitat, Siskins will also frequent stands of birch and larch and will readily associate with Lesser Redpolls. Flocks will often feed in a particular group of trees for several weeks. Wintering flocks normally number around 50 although these sometimes increase considerably in late winter and parties of up to 200 are not uncommon. Counts of 5,000 at Lakenheath in March 1973 and 1,000 at Brandon in January-February 1981 show that numbers occasionally build up considerably. Three records of Siskins feeding on peanuts in 1970 (Spencer & Gush 1974) were the county's first instances of behaviour which is now commonplace. Garden visitors arrive in variable numbers and are more common in late winter as their natural food becomes depleted.

The distinctive flight call from passing Siskins is a familiar sound at migration watch-points and substantial southerly movements are not uncommon. The first of the autumn are occasionally noted at Landguard

Point as early as late June, but immigration normally gets underway in mid-September and usually peaks later in that month. Siskins usually pass through in small single-species flocks of around 10-20 birds during the autumn, but more often singly in spring. The county's highest passage totals were 600 south over Minsmere on 22nd September 1960 and 1,070 the following day, with similar numbers noted at Walberswick over the same period. Prolonged passage at Landguard Point, during the autumn 1993, included 2,208 moving through the site between 14th September to 27th December with a peak of 240 south on 2nd November.

Ringing data show that Scottish-bred birds make up a significant proportion of the wintering population. Suffolk-ringed birds have been found in Norway (2), Sweden, Germany, Belgium (7), the Netherlands (5) and France (2).

Linnet (Common Linnet) *Carduelis cannabina*

A common resident, summer visitor and passage migrant. Smaller numbers overwinter

The Linnet breeds widely throughout the county, with the greatest densities around the River Blyth, around Stowmarket and in much of south Suffolk. Nesting takes place in small colonies on open farmland, young plantations, heathland and other scrub areas and, in recent years, suburban gardens in Felixstowe have been colonised. Large post-breeding gatherings are noted, mostly at coastal localities, and wintering flocks are not uncommon. Extensive movements are logged at migration watch-points.

A reduction in arable weeds which coincided with agricultural improvements in the late 19th century, caused a decline in the national population (Marchant *et al.* 1990). However, the finch remained common everywhere in Suffolk (Babington 1884-1886) and hundreds nested on furze-clad heaths around Thetford (Clarke 1897). Large-scale trapping also took its toll, but following restrictions on this activity, together with an agricultural recession which saw poor land left fallow, the finch increased once again. Up to 1940, it was considered to be common throughout the county and "great clouds of Linnets" were seen to rise from winter stubbles (Payn 1978), but by 1952 the destruction of gorse reduced breeding numbers (Hervey 1952). The grubbing of hedgerows and the loss of extensive tracts of heath and commons, resulted in a further and more-marked decline and the species is now lost from much of what is now 'prairie-land' of north-central and western Suffolk. There are also some gaps just in from the coast. The Linnet commanded little interest amongst the county's ornithologists between 1951-1981, indeed it did not get a single mention in SBRs for that period. However, national statistics show that the species is on a downward trend having declined by 53% from 1970-1995 (Gregory *et al.* 1996). As a result, the Linnet is now of high conservation concern and has been placed on the red data list of endangered species.

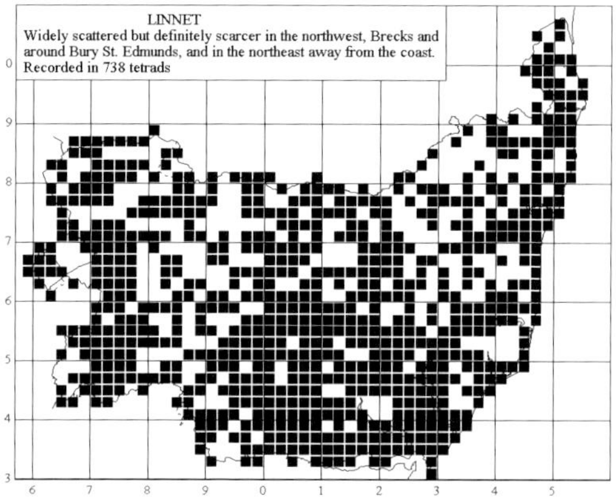
LINNET
Widely scattered but definitely scarcer in the northwest, Brecks and around Bury St. Edmunds, and in the northeast away from the coast.
Recorded in 738 tetrads
0
9
8
7
6
5
4
3
6
7
8
9
0
1
2
3
4
5

Linnets gather into huge flocks in spring and late summer. Around 2,000 in two flocks were noted at Butley in early May 1965, 500 were on Felixstowe Ferry Golf Course, on 27th April 1981, 400 at Lowestoft's Oval on 20th-21st April 1983, 600 at Landguard Point on 26th April 1984 and 410 at Minsmere, on 31st March 1994. There has been a massive increase in the cultivation of oil-seed rape since the 1970s, and the Linnet has been quick to exploit this new food source. Some of the largest flocks of the 1990s have been seen foraging on rape stubble on Trimley Marshes, the highest counts being: 1,200 on 31st August, 500 on 21st September 1990 and c.3,000 throughout July and August 1991.

Winter flocks are found on open fields, stubbles and saltings. Linnets feed on seeds, often with other finches in flocks of 50-100, although the larger concentrations sometimes occur including 1,000 at Walberswick, on 22nd December 1981 and 600 on Chantry Estate, Ipswich on 2nd January 1983. Winter roosts have been noted in gorse or other scrub, the largest involving over 1,000 near Staverton Park in December 1966. A flock of 100, at Butley in October 1965, roosted with Skylarks amongst stubbles.

Passage birds are noted in numbers in late September and October and several thousand pass though coastal watch-points in most years. Movements normally peak during early October. Southerly movements were monitored at Minsmere during the 1960s and early 1970s and peak day-totals ranged from 750-1,500 for the period 1962-1967. Landguard Point logged 11,530 in October 1983, including 2,750 on 20th and 4,560 in October 1984, peaking at 1,250 on 7th. However, 1983 was exceptional for finch movements and numbers at Landguard Point have since been well below this figure. In 1994, the autumn total was 4,928 birds with maxima of 562 on 27th September, 730 on 28th and 423 on 8th October.

Spring movements are noted from early April to mid-May, although these are normally less spectacular than those in autumn. The county's largest ever movement, however, was logged at Minsmere on 20th April 1962, when 12,000 flew south, approximately one mile inland from the shore. Flocks coast both north and south in spring and additional four-figure totals were logged at Minsmere in 1964, 1965, 1967, 1968 and 1982. These huge spring movements correspond well with peak breeding numbers as shown by the CBC index (Marchant *et al.* 1990). Suffolk-ringed Linnets have been found in Denmark (first from Britain), Belgium (2), France (3) and Spain (10). A significant proportion of the latter were caught by cage bird enthusiasts near Madrid. Linnets bearing Belgian and Spanish rings have been found in Suffolk.

Twite *Carduelis flavirostris*

A locally common winter visitor and passage migrant

The Twite feeds almost exclusively on salt-marshes and around vegetated coastal lagoons on the seeds of marsh samphire and sea starwort. The sight of the flock suddenly rising and then 'dancing' together before alighting on to a new feeding area, enlivens a cold winter's day. Its diagnostic nasal call betrays its presence amongst other finches and although it will associate with Linnets, it is most often noted in single-species flocks. Small numbers regularly pass through migration watch-points, particularly during autumn passage. It is rare away from the estuaries or immediate coastline.

Twite (*Brian Small*)

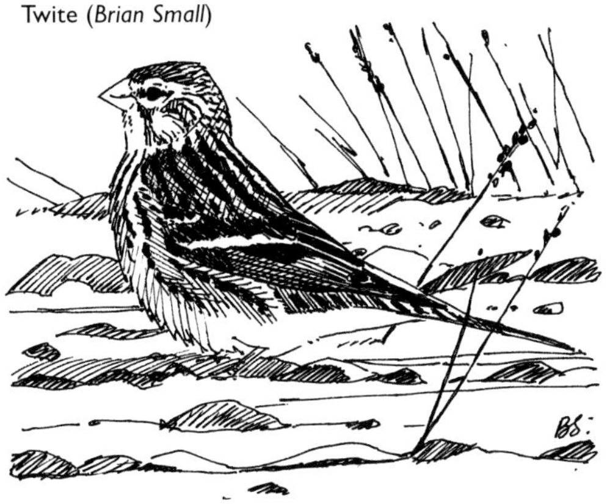

Feeding flocks of 40-80 or more are regularly reported, but occasionally these reach three figures. Walberswick shore pools and the saltings on the Alde, Deben and Orwell estuaries are the most favoured localities. Gatherings of 150-200 were regularly reported up to the mid-1980s, although larger counts were noted during the 1970s. For example, 300 were at Minsmere and Walberswick in 1972 and 1976 respectively and 400 were on Havergate Island on October 1975. Wintering numbers have declined markedly in recent years and flock-sizes are now generally much smaller. Since 1988, there has been only two flocks exceeding 100 birds.

Suffolk's two ringing recoveries involved birds in the Walberswick flock: one ringed there on 15th October 1961 was controlled at Foulness Island, Essex, almost exactly one year later and another ringed as a nestling on Withens Clough Moor, Yorkshire, on 8th June 1995 was recognised by colour-rings at the shore pools in November of that year. The latter recovery indicates the likely origins of the county's wintering population and ties in well with recoveries elsewhere in East Anglia which also confirm the presence of birds from the Pennine breeding population.

Passage birds are noted annually at migration watch-points from mid-October onwards, although there are normally a few reports in September and two at East Lane on 17th August 1952 is the only record for that month. Monthly figures at Landguard Point seldom reach three figures, although 1982 proved to be an exceptional year with no less than 530 passing through in October including high counts of 250 on 11th and 150 on 15th.

The Twite's preference for saline localities is well documented, although very occasionally, small numbers are reported at sites just inland from the coast, such as at Alton Water reservoir. It is a rare visitor to West

Suffolk, being noted on 11 occasions. The vast majority of these records fall between the dates of 10th-27th October, the exceptions being December occurrences at Tuddenham Fen in 1947 and at West Stow in 1975, and one at Cavenham on 22nd April 1995.

Common Redpoll *Carduelis flammea*

Uncommon winter visitor and passage migrant

The taxonomy of redpolls is a complex matter, with the species formerly split into two species: Common Redpoll and Arctic Redpoll, and then into five races for the former and two for the latter. British breeding birds were one of the five races and, in 1999, the BOURC decided that it should be treated at a separate species *C. cabaret*. Fluctuating numbers of Common Redpoll occur during winter and in passage periods. Two or three are noted in most years, but the largest gatherings include: 20-30 at Walberswick during October and November 1964 and 20 on the beach at Minsmere on 21st February 1965. A massive irruption of redpolls occurred in November and December 1995, when flocks of 300-400 at coastal and Breckland localities consisted almost entirely of Common Redpolls. Flocks comprising 200 or more Common Redpolls were noted at the King's Forest, Cavenham, Sutton and Hollesley Commons, Thorpeness, Minsmere and Martlesham. Most were centred around heathland birch patches and alder woods.

A female, controlled at Landguard Point, on 7th May 1989, had been ringed at Rheinland-Pfalz & Hessen, Germany, on 18th January 1989.

Lesser Redpoll *Carduelis cabaret*

A locally common but declining resident, winter visitor and passage migrant

Birchwoods and scrub on heathland edges are the species' most favoured breeding habitats, although their populations have been subject to long-term fluctuations during the 20th century. Lesser Redpolls become more obvious during winter when the finch flocks take seeds from alder and birch trees, often in the company of Siskins. When the preferred food becomes scarce, the Lesser Redpoll will gather, with other finches, to feed in weed fields. It is occasionally subject to eruptions.

During the early part of the 20th century, Lessser Redpolls bred locally throughout the county (Ticehurst 1932), with the highest densities on the coast and Breckland. Although always elusive in summer, the species was lost altogether from the cereal-growing areas of central Suffolk between 1930 and 1950 and it also became scarce in other districts. In the 1930s and 1940s, a few pairs remained around Ipswich and along the sandling belt to Lowestoft. Occasional pairs bred during most years at Walberswick in the 1950s, but increased rapidly to become abundant by 1963 (Pearson 1973). There were similar increases at many sites up to the mid-1970s, particularly on the coastal heaths, but Lesser Redpolls also frequented gardens around Ipswich. A small colony was established in a cluster of sallows in the heart of the Benacre reedbed and 35 pairs bred at Minsmere in 1977. Thereafter, the population declined almost everywhere and it is becoming scarce during the summer months. These fluctuations conform with the national CBC Index, which shows a peak in 1977 followed by a widespread decline (Marchant *et al.* 1990). Minsmere's population averaged around five pairs from 1990-1993. The map shows that the largest densities are in urban areas especially in Ipswich and in woodland edges around Hadleigh. There are also pockets along the Alde and between Lowestoft and Bungay along the Waveney Valley. It is sparsely distributed in the breck and is absent from most central areas.

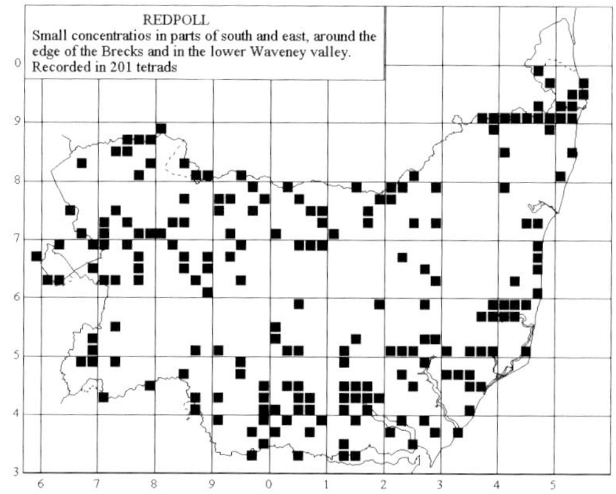
REDPOLL
Small concentratios in parts of south and east, around the edge of the Brecks and in the lower Waveney valley.
Recorded in 201 tetrads
0
9
8
7
6
5
4
3
6 7 8 9 0 1 2 3 4 5

Winter flocks normally number around 30-50 birds, although they occasionally reach three figures. The largest concentrations include: 250 at Stanton on 27th December 1950; 800 at Tuddenham St Mary in January and February 1976 and 200 at Kesgrave during the same period; 250 at Minsmere on 13th

April 1987 and 300 at West Stow in January 1988. Its distinctive call is frequently heard at migration watch-points, although total passage numbers are normally low. An autumn movement of 500 birds at Landguard Point in 1981 included an exceptional 250 south on 12th October.

Suffolk-ringed birds have been recovered in Belgium and France and birds from Belgium have been found in Suffolk.

Arctic Redpoll *Carduelis hornemanni*

A very rare winter visitor: 11 records involving 18 individuals

Records of Arctic Redpolls in Britain have increased greatly in recent years, undoubtedly due to better observer awareness of the species' plumage characteristics. It is most often located amongst mixed-redpoll flocks and visits usually coincide with eruptions of Common Redpolls. The species is often difficult to locate amongst roving flocks, and identification is tricky. Consequently, many of those claimed have never been submitted for consideration by the BBRC.

Nevertheless, the county is well placed to receive immigrants from northern Eurasian breeding grounds and the ten individuals reported since 1953 represent a significant proportion of numbers noted nationally. Two on Lowestoft Denes, on 19th October 1953, were the first for the county, and followed by another there with Bramblings, two days later. The next was trapped at Oulton Broad on 5th November 1972 and another was located in a redpoll flock at Martlesham from 11th-28th January 1989. One landed briefly in front of seawatchers at Southwold on 5th November 1990 and four visited Suffolk in early 1991, including two in the King's Forest, West Stow, constituting the first record for west Suffolk. A huge eruption of redpolls was noted during the winter of 1995/6, when as many as 16 Arctic Redpolls could have been present at three coastal and two Breckland sites. To date nine of these have been accepted by BBRC.

A pair at Landguard Point from 18th February to 17th March 1982 caused much discussion (Piotrowski 1988b), but although these birds were well-described, and photographed, the identification remained indeterminate. Claims of a flock of six on Bungay Common on 9th March 1962 and one at Lowestoft on 20th October 1965 were not submitted for consideration by BBRC.

Two-barred Crossbill *Loxia leucoptera*

Accidental: three records involving 10-11 individuals

pre-1839	nr Ipswich: 5-6 (one obtained) n.d.
1846	Drinkstone: flock (three obtained) May
1889	Burgh Castle: two 1st September

The above records all occurred over a century ago and another visitation is now long overdue. Up to the end of 2000, there were 124 records for Britain and Ireland with 84 of these being post 1957 (BBRC).

The Two-barred Crossbill has a circumpolar breeding range, although visitors to Britain are likely to originate from Fennoscandia and Siberian populations.

Crossbill (Common Crossbill) *Loxia curvirostra*

A locally common resident and irruptive visitor

Conifer forests on the coast and in Breckland offer this species a suitable habitat throughout the year, although in recent years coastal sites have been largely deserted. Breeding pairs are noted from December and family parties from March through to May. Eruptions normally become apparent in midsummer when flocks can be seen flying over open countryside. Numbers fluctuate markedly from year to year and the breeding population appears to be sustained by regular reinforcements from the continent.

The first reference to the Crossbill in Suffolk was in 1810, when it was said to be plentiful at Offton (Payn 1978). Nesting occurred sporadically, during the 19th century, being reported at Often, Aldeburgh, Orwell Park, Nacton, Livermere, Thetford, Wangford, Brandon, Elveden, Ipswich, Stoke-by-Nayland and Normanston Park, Lowestoft. The questionable status of the Crossbill as a British breeding bird prompted considerable discussion during early editions of *British Birds* (Vols. 1, 3, 4, 6, 7 and 9), with many contributors citing breeding records from Suffolk as evidence. Ticehurst had little doubt that the species bred annually, although numbers increased substantially following invasion years. This became particularly noticeable following a massive eruption in 1909/10, when numerous nests were found and it is widely believed that the resident Breckland population was founded on the strength of this invasion (Payn 1978, Lack 1986).

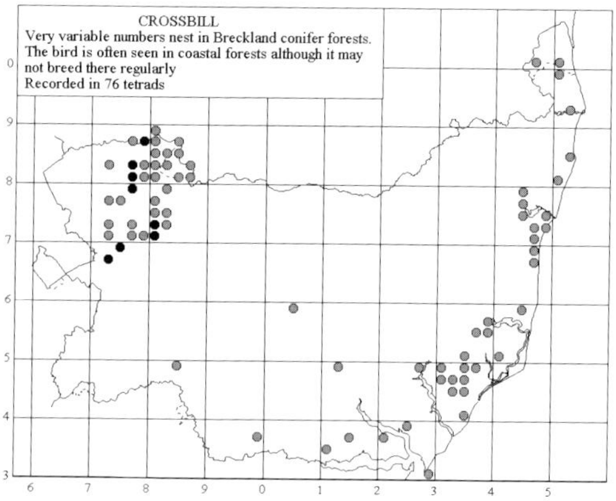
CROSSBILL
Very variable numbers nest in Breckland conifer forests.
The bird is often seen in coastal forests although it may not breed there regularly
Recorded in 76 tetrads

Eruptive behaviour is noted every year or so, and occasionally the species occurs in substantial numbers. The most notable invasions occurred in 1821, 1838-1839, 1909, 1927, 1953, 1962, 1966, 1977, 1990 and 1997. Crossbills feed almost exclusively on pine seeds, although during influx years, starving birds are forced to exploit other food sources. They were blamed for orchards being ravaged in southern England as early as 1251 (Mead 1983) and, in 1930, the species was seen to take sunflower seeds (Payn 1978). During an exceptional influx in 1990, well-watched flocks frequented gardens in Lowestoft and Southwold and were seen to consume a variety of berries, woolly aphids and apple leaves.

The Crossbill is one of the earliest species to begin nesting activities, with eggs sometimes being laid as early as December. In 1952, a recently-fledged juvenile was found at a Breckland site on the early date of 14th January, indicating nest-building activity as early as the first week of December and possibly before (Robertson 1954). Generally, however, incubation begins in late February or March.

Flocks of 20-80 are common in forestry areas on the coast and breck and occasionally similar sized flocks fly over open heaths during the summer months. During invasion years, numbers increase substantially and three-figure gatherings are not uncommon from mid-June onwards. Flocks of around 200 were noted in Breckland on 3rd July 1953, 15th October and 19th-24th November 1990 and 1st July-30th August 1991. Flocks totalling 204 passed over Minsmere on 30th May 1994, but the largest movement involved 330 birds which flew south over Landguard Point on 28th June 1997. The latter birds passed by in groups of 20-30 with the largest flock numbering 57.

Interchange between the coastal and Breckland populations is confirmed by one ringed at Tangham on 29th April 1984 and found dead at Flempton in West Suffolk, on 12th September 1986.

Parrot Crossbill *Loxia pytyopsittacus*

A very rare winter visitor: c.30 individuals. Has bred

The normal breeding range extends from Scandinavia through to West Russia but it periodically spreads westwards to reach Britain. Parrot Crossbills occur in Suffolk from time to time, most often coinciding with national influxes. Breeding behaviour was noted in both Tunstall and Thetford Forests between 1984 and 1991 and juveniles were fledged at both sites. Parrot Crossbills are most often found associating with Crossbills and splitting the two species requires a good understanding of the birds' structures and plumage characteristics.

One obtained at Blythburgh in 1818 is the first record for Britain and the next was at Saxham in November 1850. Over a century passed before an adult was found amongst Crossbills at Tunstall, on 20th February 1984. In the same year, the presence of two adults and three juveniles there from 29th April to late summer indicated that breeding had taken place. A pair with two juveniles was noted at the same site the following year and individuals were reported in the area until at least 17th March 1986. The largest influx was noted in 1990-1991 when up to 12 frequented the Mayday Farm area, near Brandon from 19th November-2nd February. A pair from this group was seen displaying and nesting in that area was suspected.

The BBRC has accepted 491 records up to the end of 2000, with 208 occurring in 1990 alone.

Trumpeter Finch *Bucanetes githagineus*

Accidental: one record

1971 Minsmere: 30th May-15th June

This long-staying individual was found on Minsmere's beach and constituted Britain's first record. The occurrence failed to attract the attention of local birdwatchers as it was widely believed that the individual was an escape from captivity. However, it has since been established that the species has expanded its range in North Africa, reflected by increasing records in southern Spain (Cramp *et al.* 1974-1994), which indicate that genuine vagrancy was more than a possibility. This theory is further reinforced by the occurrence of a second individual which visited Handa Island, Sutherland, on 8th-9th June 1971, coinciding with the Suffolk bird, and there have been four subsequent records for Britain (BBRC).

This small finch breeds in North Africa, eastwards to India and has recently spread into southern Spain.

Common Rosefinch *Carpodacus erythrinus*

A very rare summer visitor and passage migrant: 22 records

Small numbers of Common Rosefinches are now reported annually, principally at coastal localities, with areas of heathland and marshland being the most favoured habitats. Most birds have occurred during June and breeding was confirmed at two sites in 1992 and a pair probably bred in 1999.

A massive increase in records since the late 1980s, is an indication that this finch is attempting to colonise Britain. Its breeding range covers much of northern Europe, through Scandinavia to eastern Siberia, and a marked westward and northward expansion is in progress (Cramp *et al.* 1974-1994). Reports show that at least 20 individuals have visited Suffolk and all bar two have been noted since 1989. The Common Rosefinch is an extremely rare breeding bird in Britain, with maxima of 2-20 pairs for the period 1989-1999 (Ogilvie *et al.* 2001). It is particularly noisy during spring and its presence is often detected by its distinctive song. The vast majority of records relate to pioneering males, in first-year plumage, often singing from groups of trees and bushes. Bright-red mature males have also been reported, although it is likely that many non-singing birds are overlooked.

Suffolk's first was trapped at Benacre Pits on 2nd September 1959 and the next involving a male in song in the 'Oriole' woods at Lakenheath, on 11th June 1982, constituting the only inland record. Another singing male was noted at Minsmere on the same date in 1989 and, during the following year, an immature was noted at Easton Bavents, on the extremely late date of 15th November. One glimpsed at Southwold on 2nd June 1991, was followed by a remarkable influx into Britain during the spring of 1992. At least eight individuals were noted in Suffolk and breeding was confirmed at Bawdsey Manor and Minsmere Cliffs. Two young fledged at the former site (Beecroft 1993), but, although a bird was seen carrying a faecal sac at the latter, which confirmed that eggs had hatched, no young were subsequently seen. A breeding pair frequented gardens in Felixstowe during June 1999.

Extreme dates are 27th May (1993) and 15th November (1990).

Bullfinch (Common Bullfinch) *Pyrrhula pyrrhula*

A common resident

The Bullfinch is found widely throughout the county. It is a shy bird which, despite its striking plumage, hides well in overgrown hedgerows and blackthorn thickets. It will also frequent old gardens and woodland edge and is most often noted in pairs or family groups. There has been a marked decrease in recent years. The species is an occasional visitor to migration watch-points and is subject to cold-weather movements.

The Bullfinch has been blamed for causing considerable damage to fruit buds and, in consequence, has been persecuted since at least the 16th century. An entry in the Bedingfield parish accounts for March 1568 reads: "item paid to Thomas Revet for iiii young bulfynches and two old bulfynches and iii moules viid" (Ticehurst 1932), which translates to seven old pence (about 3p in modern currency) paid for six

Bullfinches (two adults and four young) and three moles. During the 19th century, the finch was a very popular cage bird, being kept for both its startling plumage and, more surprisingly, its song (Holloway 1996). Ticehurst described it as fairly common and widely distributed throughout the county. The Bullfinch was still considered a pest in 1964 and, in consequence, East Suffolk gained an exemption from the Wild Bird Protection Acts. There is evidence to suggest that there was a national increase during the 1940s and 1950s which was still in progress at the start of CBC monitoring in 1962 (Marchant *et al.* 1990). However, after maintaining high levels during the 1970s, the population then went into decline, a trend which has continued through to the present day. The Reydon Grove Farm study from 1964-1971 revealed a range of 4-6 pairs (Benson & Williamson 1972) compared with a single pair in 1997 (Pearson 1998).

Bullfinch
(*Brian Small*)

The Bullfinch has a rather patchy distribution with the densest populations around Framlingham and to the south and west of Ipswich. There are also good concentrations around Lowestoft and Dunwich and in north-central Suffolk. The Bullfinch prefers dense cover and avoids open areas such as heathland, coastal marshes and expansive arable farmland. The decline of the Sparrowhawk in the 1950s could well have allowed the Bullfinch to exploit more open areas – a trend which has been reversed since the raptor's recovery (Newton 1993).

The seeds from ash and elm form an important part of the species' diet, but blackberries are also taken. Alternative food sources such as fruit buds are exploited when seed supplies become scarce. During a period of severe weather in January-February 1979, Bullfinches were observed feeding on a chicken carcass and a ham bone at Hartest (Payn 1982).

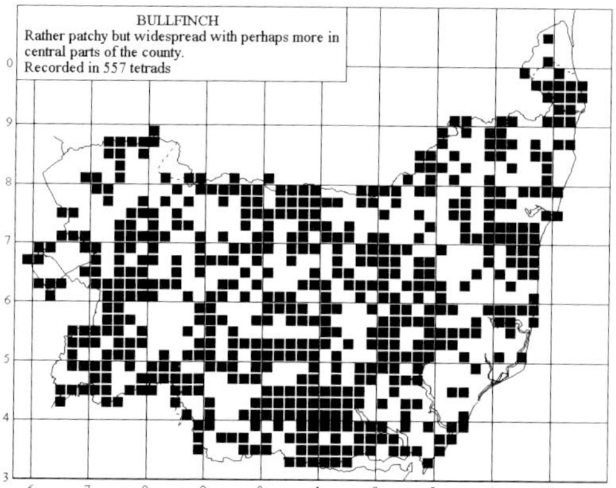

The Bullfinch is hardly renowned for coastal passage and is generally rare at migration watch-points. However, four were noted arriving from offshore at Benacre on 30th October 1971 and southerly movements at Minsmere included 74, in a two hour period, on 21st October 1952 and 50 on 21st October 1961. The largest numbers occurred at the onset of harsh weather on 1st January 1962, when 200 were logged flying south at Minsmere. The species is normally sedentary and from the 97 recoveries of Suffolk-ringed birds from 1909-1995 only 12 have moved more than ten km. A male ringed at Ingatestone, Essex, in January 1978 and found dead at Aldeburgh three winters later constituted the furthest recorded movement.

Examples of the larger and brighter race *P. p. pyrrhula*, from northern Eurasia, have been recognised on only seven occasions. Four were noted on Lowestoft's Denes on 9th December 1910 and another on 14th February 1911. Two were at Lowestoft, from 19th November until December 1937, two were at Herringfleet on 24th November 1946 and singles were trapped at Fagbury Cliff on 19th May and 26th October and at Bawdsey on 1st November 1994. The largest ever recorded influx of this race into Britain was noted during the latter year, most of which occurred in Shetland and Orkney.

Hawfinch *Coccothraustes coccothraustes*

An uncommon resident and rare passage migrant

This unobtrusive species often goes undetected as it feeds high in the treetops and the recognition of its explosive 'tik' call often confirms its presence. Hawfinches usually nest colonially in mature deciduous woodlands and parkland, although single pairs also occur. Flocks of up to 40 are noted during autumn and winter when birds gather to collect seeds, particularly those of hornbeam and cherry, but also of field maple and sloe. In spring, it feeds on buds of beech and oak and frequently take the larvae of the oak-leaf roller moth from bursting buds (Robertson 1954). It is a scarce visitor to migration watch-points.

It has probably always been thinly distributed throughout the county. The first breeding record dates back to 1830, when a nest was found at Bury St Edmunds. Eighteenth century naturalists believed that the Hawfinch occurred only as a winter visitor as they were unable to locate the species during the summer months (Holloway 1996). Early in the 20th century, however, it had become quite common and Ticehurst considered that there was "hardly a parish where a pair or so do not breed more or less regularly". During the 1940s-1950s, the Hawfinch was probably more numerous in Suffolk than in any other English county and was most common in Breckland woods (Mountfort 1957). A well-watched colony near Bury St Edmunds, bred in a mixed wood, consisting of oak, birch, sycamore and wych-elm, with hawthorn scattered round the edges and along the rides (Robertson 1954). Nesting occurred in nearby orchards, dense hawthorns and in the top leaders of sycamores. A colony, discovered in north-west Suffolk in 1948, peaked at 15-20 pairs in the mid-1950s and ten pairs remained in 1977 (Payn 1978). Perhaps this was the same colony listed by Mountfort which contained 25 nests in 1953. Breeding numbers appeared to increase further to reach a peak in the early 1970s. Dense stands of tall sycamore saplings is the most favoured breeding habitat on the coast, with the nest site often 10-15 metres from the ground. Nests have also been found in oak, holm oak and holly. The ancient oaks and hollies at Staverton Thicks have hosted a viable population for many years, but numbers have decreased there since the 1980s and sightings were rare in the late 1990s. Around Woodbridge, Hawfinches favour sycamore and lime in spring and a pair were seen to feed on London plane tree seeds at Nacton (SBR.). Regular sightings in the poplar plantations – a habitat which is favoured in the Netherlands – at Lakenheath during the 1980s raised speculation that the site would be colonised. However, the potential of the site was never realised due to the felling of the woodland. Breeding is now restricted to three sites on the coast – one in south Suffolk and three in Breckland.

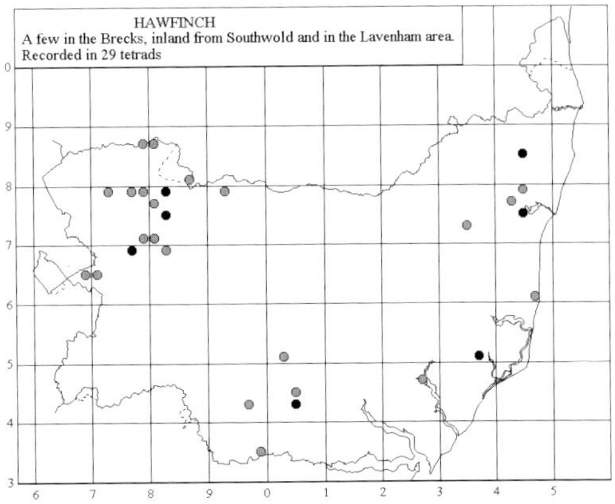

Winter flocks are normally found close to the breeding areas and the highest counts have coincided with the peak in the breeding population. For example, 40 were at Sibton during early autumn 1972, 40 at Staverton during the winter of 1974 and c.30 at Redgrave and Burgate during January 1975. Hawfinches have become extremely scarce since the late 1980s and the 'Great Storm' of 16th October 1987 has been cited as a contributory factor (Gibbons *et al.* 1993). Peak winter counts of between 30 and 40 at Barnhamcross Common in 1993 and 1997 are the highest of recent times and is perhaps a sign of a recovery in Breckland at least. Pre-breeding assemblies were a feature of Staverton Thicks during the period 1967-1981, the largest being 30-40 in spring 1973 and 33 in April 1975. There has been no reports of double-figure gatherings in East Suffolk since 1990 and the decrease in wintering numbers is perhaps indicative of the fall in the coastal breeding population.

The resident population is largely sedentary and a juvenile ringed at Kesgrave and recovered 15km away at Tunstall is the only recovery of a Suffolk-ringed Hawfinch. However, birds from outside the British Isles are highly migratory (Cramp *et al.* 1974-1994) and it is suspected that immigrants from the continent regularly arrive to supplement the winter population. Ticehurst was convinced that large flights of immigrants occurred under the stress of severe weather and he considered that such birds, noted during the winters of 1823, 1855, 1859 and 1872, helped populate the county by remaining to breed. In more recent times, coastal migrants have been chiefly noted in April and October-November. For example, in autumn 1988, Hawfinches were noted at Landguard Point on 16th October, at Southwold's St Edmund's churchyard on 28th October and one was seen flying in from the sea at Benacre on 11th November. This coincided with Suffolk's largest-ever fall of Robins. Similar numbers were present during an influx of eastern vagrants in October-November 1994.

White-throated Sparrow *Zonotrichia iliaca*

Accidental: two records

1968/69 St Olaves/Herringfleet: The Wilderness, 16th November-1st January
1992 Trimley St Mary: Fagbury Cliff area, 31st May-8th June

The above records refer to birds found close to the county's principal ports and therefore ship-assistance appears to be likely. The St Olaves individual regularly visited a bird table, in the observer's garden, before it was found dead on New Year's Day. The Fagbury bird frequented a derelict garden and young plantations and was observed by thousands of birdwatchers.

The sparrow breeds mainly in Canada and winters in the USA and northern Mexico and is an extremely rare visitor to Britain and Ireland, being recorded on 22 occasions up to the end of 2000 (BBRC).

Lark Sparrow *Chondestes grammacus*

Accidental: one record

1981 Felixstowe: Landguard Point, 30th June-8th July

There are few birds which have prompted so much discussion over status than the Lark Sparrow at Landguard Point. This Nearctic sparrow was found in midsummer and most agree that it almost certainly crossed the Atlantic on board ship, although this alone should have not have been a reason for its exclusion from the British list. The record was the first for Britain, but placed in the 'pending tray' (Category D) for several years before the BOURC, somewhat begrudgingly, changed its rules following the occurrence of a second bird at Winterton, Norfolk, on 15th May 1991.

The Landguard Point bird was very confiding spending much of its time feeding in the open on the short-cropped grassland or on sandy-shingle ground (Charlton 1995). The occurrence was Landguard Point's first and, as yet, only American passerine which drew large crowds of admirers.

Lapland Bunting (Lapland Longspur) *Calcarius lapponicus*

An uncommon passage migrant and winter visitor

The Lapland Bunting is one of the most difficult buntings to view on the ground, being easily flushed from short vegetation. Small numbers are noted annually at migration watch-points and are usually recognised by their distinctive, rattling, contact call. Britain's winter population is confined almost entirely to the English east coast (Lack 1986) and occurs in Suffolk in variable numbers, exclusively at coastal localities and usually on saltmarshes, rough grazing marshes or stubbles. The species will often mix with Skylarks or Snow Buntings.

The species was extremely rare during the 19th century and Babington could trace only one record. However, an easterly gale on 14th October 1882 heralded the arrival of many birds with 56 being captured in the Yarmouth area alone (Ticehurst 1932). Thereafter, the Lapland Bunting occurred in small numbers more or less annually, although there were years when none were reported. Lapland Buntings wintering in Britain are thought to have originated from both Scandinavia and Greenland, but one taken at Aldringham on 9th November 1915 was possibly an eastern bird judging by the paleness of its plumage (Williamson and Davis 1956). There were several blank years during the 1940s and 1950s and a flock of 11 at Walberswick, on 19th October 1953, was significant for that period, forming part of an autumn invasion into eastern counties. A stubble field at Minsmere attracted a group of 15 during November and December 1961, but the species remained relatively scarce until 1985 when a regular but small wintering population was discovered on coastal marshes. A flock of 20 was at Easton Bavents on 5th January 1986 and significant gatherings were also noted at Minsmere and Sudbourne. From 1987-1992, wet stubbles at Sudbourne Marshes hosted gatherings of between 15 and 50 per year, although early 1991 proved exceptional when numbers rose from 50 on 3rd January to 70 on 5th and 100 on 13th. The latter were loosely associated with a flock of 200 Snow Buntings. In recent years, Lapland Buntings have once again become scarce.

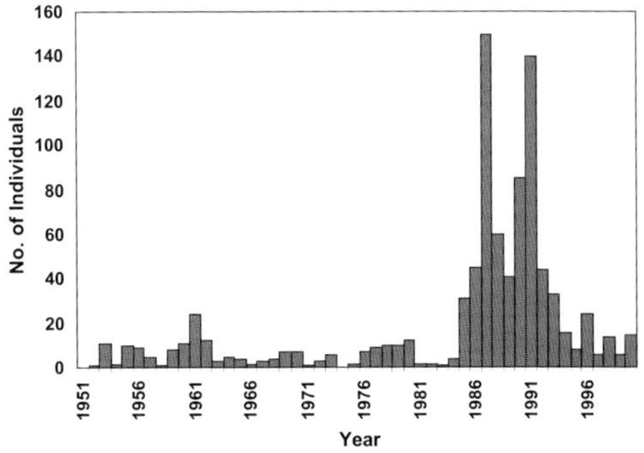

The annual totals of the Lapland Buntings from 1951-2000

Most birds leave in March although a few linger into April and there are four May records, with a singing male at Minsmere on 26th-27th May 1984 being the latest. The first returning birds are normally noted from late September, although the earliest autumn birds were at Minsmere on 9th September 1968 and 1986.

There has yet to be a record from West Suffolk and one at Alton Water, on 30th October 1977 and another at Campsea Ashe, on 22nd November 1990, are the furthest records away from the coast and estuaries.

Snow Bunting *Plectrophenax nivalis*

A locally common winter visitor and passage migrant

The sparsely vegetated shingle banks and denes along the length of the Suffolk coast are the most favoured wintering haunts. Snow Bunting flocks are regularly reported on the flooded grass on Lowestoft Denes and the species will occasionally flock to winter stubbles. Small numbers regularly occur at migration watch-points.

Snow Buntings (*Brian Small*)

Flock sizes vary enormously from single-figure groups to 200 or more. Gatherings of this magnitude have been noted at Lowestoft, Benacre and Orfordness, with the largest count being 326 near Slaughden Quay on 11th December 1988. These birds regularly commuted to Sudbourne Marshes to feed with Skylarks and Lapland Buntings on water-logged stubble fields.

Two at Sizewell, on 30th August 1952, are the earliest returning birds, although large wintering gatherings do not appear until November. Snow Buntings depart in early March, and April records are rare. A lone male oversummered at Aldeburgh in 1968.

Snow Buntings were formerly regular at inland localities. Small flocks frequented Newmarket Heath, although during a great snowstorm in January 1881, many starved to death (Ticehurst 1932). The bunting was also seen on other Breckland heaths and there were records from Gt Barton, Westley and Bacton during the 19th century. Nowadays, Snow Buntings are rarely seen away from the coast and estuaries, being reported inland on only five occasions from 1950-2000: two at Ellough on November 1950; followed by singles at Brome, 7th December 1964; Rodbridge, 10th December 1973; Brandon, 27th January 1984 and Moulton, 9th October.

An amazing ringing recovery involved one trapped at Walberswick on 4th November 1962 and shot 14 days later near the mouth of the River Po, in Italy. The bird was shot well south of its normal wintering range, but the ring was returned and the shooter described his trophy as being sparrow-like and not familiar to him. A colour-ringed bird seen at Kessingland, on 5th March 1992, was back at its Cairngorm breeding site, where it was originally trapped, only 13 days later and another, ringed at Landguard Point on 4th March 1987, was controlled at Sandwich Bay, Kent, the following winter. Interchange between North Norfolk and Suffolk coastal sites has been confirmed on at least three occasions.

From a total of 114 trapped in three sessions at Felixstowe Ferry in February 1997, 90 were of the Icelandic race *P. n. insulae*, 12 were of the nominate race *P. n. nivalus* and 12 were indeterminate (Odin 1997b). The low retrap rate on the last of the three sessions, suggests that the numbers using the site was much higher than the maximum day count of 120.

Pine Bunting *Emberiza leucocephalos*

Accidental: one record

1995 Corton: male 28th October

Suffolk's sole record involved a male which frequented arable fields in the company of Linnets and Yellowhammers. For the most of the day views were very distant, but at dusk it was seen well as it went to roost in a hawthorn hedge.

The Pine Bunting breeds in Siberia and winters in Pakistan, north-west India and northern China. The bunting is a rare visitor to the British Isles, being noted on only 37 occasions up to the end of 2000 (BBRC).

A male bunting in aberrant plumage was present at Sizewell from 21st-23rd April 1982. It superficially resembled a Rock Bunting *E. cia*, although following much discussion it was identified as a hybrid Yellowhammer x Pine Bunting (Charlton 1985).

Yellowhammer *Emberiza citrinella*

A common resident and passage migrant

The Yellowhammer is a typical bird of open farmland, but it is also common on gorse-clad heaths, commons and woodland edge. Yellowhammers have decreased drastically during the past three decades. The bunting is widely spread throughout the county, breeding on open heaths, in areas of scrub, corners of rough meadows, hedgerows, roadside verges and gardens. The populations are less dense in Breckland.

Yellowhammer populations have declined rapidly in recent years and are giving some cause for concern. There is little doubt that the uprooting of hedgerows and the ploughing of marginal land contributed greatly to the species' decline, although the widespread use of chemical sprays and seed-dressings would also have had a significant effect. Nationally, food shortages have resulted in a fall in numbers in cereal-growing areas (Marchant *et al.* 1990) and the CBC farmland index reached a record low in 1995 (Marchant & Wilson 1996). The Reydon Grove Farm study from 1964-1971 revealed a range of 16-24 pairs (Benson & Williamson 1972) compared with only three pairs in 1997 (Pearson 1998).

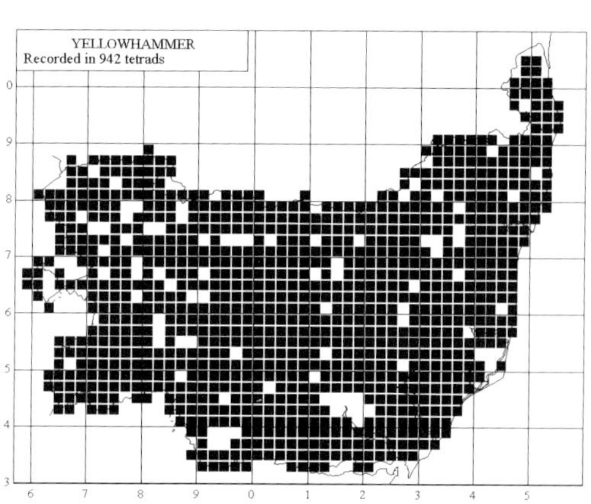

Yellowhammers gather in large flocks during winter and are affected greatly during periods of harsh weather. A southerly movement involving 800 birds was noted at Minsmere at the onset of harsh weather on 1st January 1962. Grain spills, livestock feeding areas and stockyards attract large feeding flocks. A spillage of wheat, salvaged from a wreck off Landguard

Point, during February and March 1986, attracted several hundred Yellowhammers to the Observatory compound, of which no fewer than 71 were trapped. Normally, the Yellowhammer is a scarce visitor to Landguard Point, being reported irregularly during passage periods. Gatherings of 500-700 were also noted at Minsmere in January 1960, at Livermere on 13th February 1983, by the Alde on 9th February 1986 and at Onehouse, 25th December 1999.

Ticehurst said the species was not recognised as a distinct migrant, but he referred to "newly arrived flocks" on the coast at the end of September and during October and small numbers passing south. Although he had no direct evidence of immigration, he listed a number of reports of birds found on light-ships in autumn and spring. A few are logged at Landguard Point each autumn and, on 29th October 1995, one came aboard a ferry sailing towards Felixstowe when the ship was 20-25 miles off Sizewell.

There are very few ringing recoveries, although an adult male trapped at Minsmere on 16th February 1960 was found at Oise, France five years later and another male ringed at Boyton in February 1969 was controlled at Blakeney Point, Norfolk in May of that year.

Cirl Bunting *Emberiza cirlus*

Accidental: four records involving five individuals

1888	Breydon Water: Cobholm, two males netted and killed 29th January
1955	Minsmere: female 28th April and 11th June
1959	Westleton: male 20th February

Suffolk's first records involved two males, which were trapped close to the Suffolk bank of Breydon Water, during a severe frost. The specimens are now on display in the Birmingham City Museum (Taylor *et al.* 2000). The Cirl Bunting was then breeding sporadically in Cambridgeshire and Essex and it is likely that the species visited far more regularly than the records suggest. There were a number of sightings in the Westleton area during the late 1950s, which perhaps indicate an attempted colonisation of the area, although most reports were unsubstantiated. The species' range has since contracted significantly and it is now restricted to south-western counties (Gibbons *et al.* 1993).

Ortolan Bunting *Emberiza hortulana*

A rare passage migrant: 52 records

Ortolan Bunting
(*Brian Small*)

The breeding range extends from continental Europe, through Scandinavia and eastwards to northern Iran. It is an annual visitor to the British Isles, being a scarce but regular passage migrant at coastal localities. It is normally most confiding, being found feeding with finches and pipits on rabbit-grazed grassland such as Lowestoft Denes and Landguard Point. There are no inland records.

The bunting was a rare visitor prior to the 1980s, being noted in only seven years since the first was

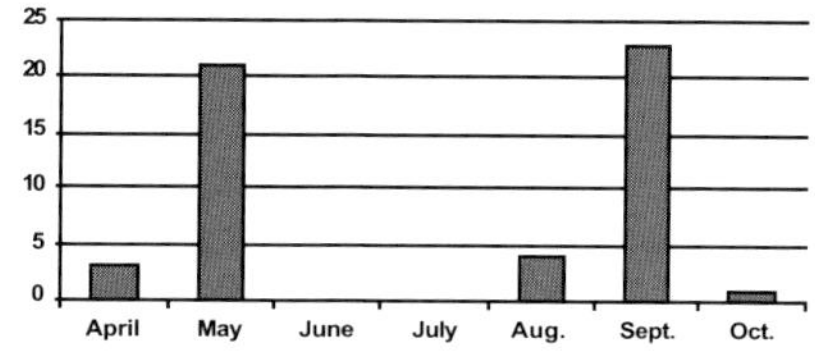

Seasonal distribution of Ortolan Buntings

killed on Lowestoft Denes on 5th May 1859. However, an increase in the number of observers has resulted in a massive increase in records and, between 1981 and 1996, there were only two blank years: 1982 and 1989. The principal months are May and September, although an obvious spring bias is masked by 14 of the 21 autumn individuals being noted in two years: ten during the 'Great Fall' of September 1965 and a flock of four (possibly six) at Landguard Point in 1990. This is contrary to the national trend which shows a 30%-70% split in favour of autumn records (Dymond *et al.* 1989). Only four, from the flock of six, which alighted on Landguard Point on 23rd September 1990, could be relocated for positive identification.

Extreme dates are 22nd April 1994 and 29th October 1967.

Rustic Bunting *Emberiza rustica*

Accidental: three records

1962	Minsmere: female, trapped 24th October
1992	Felixstowe: Landguard Point, first-winter, trapped 3rd October
1996	Corton: age/sex uncertain, 14th September

The Rustic Bunting is reported annually on Britain's east coast, principally during May and October. Suffolk's records are exclusively autumnal and all have involved relatively short stayers. Two of the three individuals were trapped.

The bunting breeds in Scandinavia eastwards through Siberia and winters from Turkestan to Manchuria and China. No fewer than 441 individuals had been found in the British Isles up to the end of 2000 (BBRC), so Suffolk's total is rather meagre.

Little Bunting *Emberiza pusilla*

Accidental: eight records involving 11 individuals

1948	Aldeburgh: 20th November.
1949	Corton: two, 11th February
	Reydon: two, 13th February
1952	Lowestoft: The Denes, 16th October
1954	Walberswick: two, 11th October
1976	Walberswick: 31st October
1986	Felixstowe: Landguard Point, trapped, 10th October
1987	Felixstowe: Landguard Point, trapped, 19th October

Small numbers visit Britain annually, principally during autumn passage. Suffolk's occurrences, all occurring on the immediate coastline, are typically dated, except the 1949 records, which probably relate to overwintering birds. One trapped at Landguard Point in 1986 (Marsh 1987b) is one of the few rarities to be discovered just after first light. Most are found from late morning onwards.

The Little Bunting breeds from Scandinavia through northern Siberia to the Pacific Ocean and it winters from Turkestan to south-east Asia.

Yellow-breasted Bunting *Emberiza aureola*

Accidental: two records, presumably involving the same individual

1993	Felixstowe: Landguard Point, imm., 4th September
	Trimley St Mary: Fagbury Cliff, presumably the same, 6th September

The above record involved an immature which stopped briefly at two sites adjacent to the Port of Felixstowe. At Landguard Point, the bird was quite approachable as it fed on the short turf in the company of Linnets (Kitchener 1994) but, eventually, increasing crowds proved too much and it disappeared from the site. It was relocated in an arable field close to Fagbury Cliff two days later, although on this occasion it was more elusive.

A second record involved an adult which was trapped at Landguard Point on August 12th 1999. It was thought unlikely that a genuine migrant would reach us so early in the season, so the this individual was considered to be an escape.

The Yellow-breasted Bunting's breeding range extends from north-east Europe through Siberia and it winters in India and south-east Asia. The species is an annual visitor to Britain, the vast majority of records coming from Shetland (Dymond *et al.* 1989). The bunting had been noted in the British Isles on 211 occasions up to the end of 2000 (BBRC).

Reed Bunting *Emberiza schoeniclus*

A common resident and passage migrant

The Reed Bunting is a widespread resident breeding in coastal marshes, river valleys and rough pastures. It occurs in flocks with other buntings and finches during winter and will occasionally venture into urban gardens, particularly during severe weather when it suffers greatly. Small numbers pass through migration watch-points during passage periods.

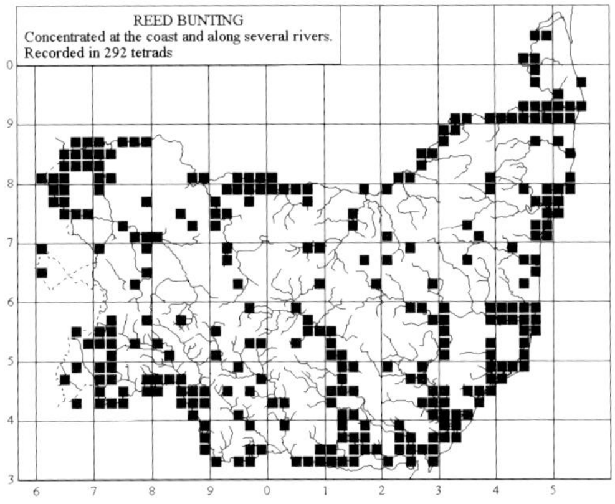

The Reed Bunting is thinly scattered throughout the county and its affinity with water can be clearly seen from the distribution map. Concentrations occur along most riverbanks, gravel-pits, reservoirs, large ponds and borrow-dykes, especially those that are open and surrounded by rough grassland or *Phragmites*. It is absent from the upper reaches of the River Orwell and Blyth, as well as much of the Little Ouse, Lark, Linnet, and Dove – presumably due to the lack of such conditions.

Reed Buntings become more widespread during winter, with feeding flocks moving onto farmland, waste ground and often gardens during the day, but returning to their marshland roosts each evening. Winter flocks rarely number 20 or more, although flocks of 100 were noted at Aldeburgh in January and February 1981, Haverhill, 31st March 1984 and Fagbury, December 1988. Severe weather in consecutive winters of 1961-1962 and 1962-1963, resulted in a widespread decline and, although a recovery was maintained throughout the 1970s, a further decline followed harsh winters in 1979 and 1981, from which there has yet to be a recovery.

Reed Buntings are noted annually at Landguard Point and were particularly obvious in the early 1980s, when October counts of 50-70 were regularly reported. A total of 29, on 6th October 1981, is the highest day-count for the site. An analysis of data from LBO logs for the period 1983-1995, showed that few birds pass through in spring, and that autumn migration begins in mid-September, peaks in the third and fourth week of October and is over by mid-November (Odin 1997a). Ringing returns have shown that the British breeding population is mainly sedentary, with less than 1% of birds moving abroad in winter (Lack 1986). Suffolk-ringed birds have been recovered in Norfolk, Essex and Devon and Reed Buntings ringed in Essex and Kent have been controlled in the county. One trapped in an Ipswich garden on 7th March 1965, was recovered in Sweden four years later, which constituted the first British recovery from that country, and another ringed at Fagbury Cliff on 1st October 1992 was found in Garonne, France, on 1st November 1993. The Scandinavian bird was presumably on passage through Suffolk.

The 1906 individual occurred during a heat-wave which also brought other southern European species, including flocks of Glossy Ibises and Red-crested Pochards, and a White Pelican, to our shores. There has been considerable speculation over the origins of more recent occurrences, the 1995 bird reported as coinciding with a northerly movement of flamingos from the drought-stricken south of Spain (SBR).

The Greater Flamingo breeds in southern Europe, southwest Asia and Africa and, although there are many records, its status is clouded by the presence of known escapees from ornamental collections. The species is migratory and will often disperse in numbers when feeding areas dry out, although influxes into new areas are erratic. Although vagrancy into Britain is likely, the Greater Flamingo has yet to be accepted onto the British list.

Wood Duck *Aix sponsa*

A scarce visitor

Babington listed four 19th century records including a pair shot at Livermere on 24th October 1848. Nowadays, Wood Ducks are noted annually with an average of three records per annum.

The Wood Duck is widespread in North America being found largely in two separate populations: on the west coast from British Columbia, Washington, Oregon and California and on the east coast north of Manitoba and New Brunswick and south to southern Texas and Cuba.

Marbled Teal *Marmaronetta angustirostris*

Two records involving three individuals

1982 Reydon: shot 13th November
2001 Minsmere: two 13th-14th October

The 1982 individual was shot and found to be close-ringed. Although the origins of the Minsmere individuals remain uncertain, the occurrence coincided with a spell of southerly gales, raising speculation that they could be genuine vagrants from southern Europe.

The species has a patchy distribution around the western Mediterranean and from Turkey east to central Asia.

Falcated Duck

Two records probably referring to the same individual

1981 Ixworth: male 27th May
1984 Ixworth: male n.d.

The status of the Falcated Duck was reviewed by the BOURC in 1993 and it was concluded that: "whilst the possibility of escape cannot be excluded, neither can a natural origin, although the latter seems unlikely" (*Ibis* 135: 493-499). In consequence, the species was added to category D1 of the list of birds for Britain and Ireland. The above individual was not amongst the eight records reviewed and in all probability it was an escapee from a nearby wildfowl collection.

The breeding range extends from eastern Siberia to India and through to northern Indochina.

Baikal Teal *Anas formosa*

Accidental: two records

1951 Nacton: Nacton Decoy, female trapped 10th November
2001 Minsmere: male 18th November-1st December

Suffolk's first record involved one trapped at Nacton decoy and transferred to aviaries at Ipswich and Hartest where it was incarcerated for three years, before being loaned to the Severn Wildfowl Trust (now the WWT). The possibility of an escapee from captivity in this country was ruled out at the time, but the SBR reported that Continental collections, particularly in the Netherlands, held very wild birds from where some full-winged individuals had escaped. It was concluded that, while the bird may have been a genuine vagrant, there was insufficient evidence for it to be treated as such.

The second appeared on Minsmere's Scrape and was watched by hundreds of birdwatchers as it fed with a group of Teal.

The Baikal Teal breeds in the forests of north to northeast Siberia and migrates to wintering areas in Japan and east and southeast China. There have been ten records for Britain and Ireland up to the end of 1995, although there has been much debate over its status. It was formerly listed under Category D of the British and Irish list of species, promoted to Category A for a short period and then relegated back to D.

Saker *Falco cherrug*

Four records involving falconers' escapees

There are Suffolk records from Minsmere in 1988, Felixstowe and Trimley St Martin in 1993 and Orfordness in 2002. The Saker is most favoured by falconers and has recently been employed to scare gulls and other birds from rubbish tips and airfields. Although the Minsmere individual did not appear to be carrying jesses, there were rumours of it being in the area during the previous three weeks and it was believed to be a falconer's escape. The 1993 and the 2002 individuals were wearing a combination of bells and transmitters, the latter bird captured and returned to its owner at Hollesley Prison after being identified by tags.

Chukar *Alectoris chukar*

Formerly a common resident, but declined since releases have been curtailed

The Chukar and Chukar x Red-legged Partridge hybrids became so common that it became difficult to locate a pure-bred Red-legged Partridge. The BOURC added the species to Category D4 of the British list to encourage monitoring.

Red-headed Bunting *Emberiza bruniceps*

A very rare passage migrant – 14 records

1957	Orford: Havergate Island, 30th June
1961	Breydon: ad. male 13th and 20th May
1962	Lakenheath: 13th April
	Walberswick: 29th May
1963	Minsmere: trapped 12th September
1966	Minsmere: male 7th-8th May, another 28th August
	Walberswick: East Hill, male paired with probable Yellowhammer 4th-29th July
1965	Sudbourne: 28th September
1977	Sproughton: 18th May
1989	Lowestoft: Warrenhouse Wood, 14th September
1990	Felixstowe: Gulpher Rd, singing male 15th June
1993	Ipswich: Sandringham Close, singing male 6th-10th May

Although genuine vagrancy is a good possibility, the likelihood of escape is considered greater. As a consequence, the Red-headed Bunting has yet to be accepted onto the British list. It is interesting to note that all occurrences have been between April and September. The species is a commonly kept cage-bird, although why escapees fail to appear during the winter months, when damage to aviaries is far more likely, is puzzling indeed!

A mixed-species breeding pair was located at Walberswick in July 1966. A male was seen singing and displaying to a female bunting, probably a Yellowhammer, on 4th July and the latter was flushed from a nest with three eggs, on the 8th, with one egg hatching on 10th (Benson 1968). The finder originally claimed hybridisation between a male Red-headed Bunting and a female Yellowhammer, although the female was inadequately described. The 'pair' was last seen on 29th July when they flew off together.

The bunting breeds from Iran and Kazakhstan eastwards to northwest China and winters in India.

INTRODUCED SPECIES THAT HAVE NOT BECOME ESTABLISHED

Red Grouse *Lagopus lagopus*

An introduced resident which became established for a brief period, but soon died out

Four birds were liberated at Butley Abbey in 1866, but one was shot the same year and the rest soon disappeared. A series of introduction attempts to Breckland heaths, during the mid-1800s, led to a viable population being established at the turn of that century. The Elveden population was estimated to be about 350 in 1908, but numbers declined during the Great War and the species was extinct by the 1930s. Ticehurst was convinced that the lack of a suitable water supply was the root cause of the failures. Lord Iveagh of Elveden paid special attention to this problem and a small population of Red Grouse would have been sustainable had the Great War not intervened.

Black Grouse *Tetrao tetrix*

An introduced resident which became established for a brief period, but soon died out

Although indigenous to Norfolk, there is no proof that it ever was so in Suffolk. As with the previous species, many attempts to establish this grouse were made between 1865-1900, both on coastal and Breckland heaths. Although a few pairs bred and broods were seen, few, if any, survived to fledge with many falling prey to foxes. Suffolk's dry climate was considered to be the principal factor in the species' failure to colonise (Ticehurst 1932).

Capercaillie *Tetrao urogallus*

Two unsuccessful introduction attempts

Unsuccessful attempts to introduce this species to the Elveden estate were made in 1865 and 1878. Eggs were brought from Scotland, but there are no records of fledged young.

Bobwhite *Colinus virginianus*

An introduced resident which became established for a brief period, but soon died out

There have been some 20 attempts to establish this gamebird in Britain and Ireland for shooting purposes, but none have been successful (Cramp *et al.* 1974-1994). Introductions in the late 1800s resulted in several being noted at Breckland localities, but there is little information on success. A male killed at Elveden c.1882 was preserved and another was trapped, probably at the same locality, on 1st August 1871 (Babington 1884-1886).

About 60 were released at Sizewell in 1956 and the species became fairly common around Dunwich. This species was a regular feature of Minsmere's Reports from 1963-1973 and the 1963 Annual Report reads: "Birds have been heard and occasionally seen on the Reserve in 1961 and 1962. In 1963 they were more often seen and a pair were seen with young in Grimston's Belt". Bobwhites nested at Minsmere throughout the 1960s and coveys of up to 15 were reported annually. Two to eight pairs bred successfully between 1968-1972, when up to 40 were present during winter (Sharrock 1976), although the species was already declining rapidly in this period. The final reference to breeding was in June 1971, when 16 newly-hatched chicks were seen at Minsmere, where, after being apparently absent for about a year, the quail was last recorded on 27th May 1973.

The species was largely ignored by SBRs except for the occasional reference to their presence complicating records of Quail.

The Bobwhite is native to North America, south to Mexico and inhabits cultivated areas and open woodland.

Barbary Partridge *Alectoris barbara*

More than one unsuccessful introduction attempt

Ticehurst reported that the Barbary Partridge had been introduced at Elveden "on more than one occasion" during the 1800s and that it was said to have hybridised with Red-legged Partridge. One shot at Sudbourne about 1840 was believed to have derived from eggs introduced with those of the Red-legged Partridge c.1770 (Babington 1884-1886). Others shot at Freston and near Ipswich about the same time were likely to be of similar origin.

Lady Amherst's Pheasant *Chrysolophus amherstiae*

One or two 'escapees' were formerly noted annually

The mountains of south-west China, south-east Tibet and northern Burma host the native population. This species was brought to Britain in the early 1800s, but the only documented introduction attempt in Suffolk was made at Elveden in 1950. Initially, the birds adapted well to the Breckland habitat, but any success was short-lived and they disappeared after a few years (Sharrock 1976). Modern-day records may relate to relics of the Elveden experiment, although more recent escapees, or deliberate releases, are a more likely explanation.

It was once recognised as a Suffolk bird mainly on the strength of a male, present in the Herringswell area from 1976-1991, together with other reports from nearby sites. As these records hardly constituted a viable population, the species has since been withdrawn from the county list.

Lady Amherst's Pheasants readily hybridise with Golden Peasants both on their native eastern Palearctic breeding grounds and amongst feral populations in Britain. In consequence, releases of Lady Amherst's in Breckland could seriously threaten the Golden Pheasant population and therefore should be discouraged. The males from the mixed blood population in the Sandringham/Wolferton areas of north Norfolk are noticeably different to the Suffolk birds.

Black Woodpecker *Dryocopus martius*

A few records from failed introduction attempt

Populations have increased in lowland areas of north-west Europe since the 1950s, and it has spread to woodland backing onto sand dunes on the Dutch coast – this represents the nearest breeding sites. Although there has yet to be a genuine vagrant to be proved to reach Britain, colonisation of East Anglia in future years seems more than a remote possibility.

Sightings of up to three birds at Euston Park, Ixworth and Brandon in 1897, and then at Santon Downham and Fakenham to at least 24th October 1902, were initially considered to be of wild origin. However, it later transpired that young birds were brought from Sweden in 1897 and, after being kept in an aviary at Brandon for two months, 7-8 were liberated. Southwell, writing in 1909, said "it is most reprehensible that birds.... should be thus secretly introduced to the disturbance of the British fauna". Sentiments that echo the thoughts of many ornithologists today.

In recent years, there have been a number of sightings of probable Black Woodpeckers, all on the immediate coastline, although there has yet to be a record that has been fully substantiated.

SPECIES OCCURRING IN SUFFOLK AS ESCAPEES, SHIP-ASSISTED BIRDS OR TIDELINE CORPSES

Up to the late 1970s, birdwatchers showed little interest in birds that had escaped from zoos, wildfowl collections or aviaries. Birds deemed to be escapees were readily dismissed as 'some escaped cage-bird' and there was little effort to determine its identity. In fact, it was not until 1977 that SBR documented the presence of such birds in the appendices of the report. Love them or hate them escapees are an integral part of our avifauna and it is important that they are properly recorded. Some species have been added to the British List after forming feral breeding populations - e.g. Egyptian Goose, Ruddy Duck and Ring-necked Parakeet. Others deemed to be escapees have later been accepted onto the British and Irish List once a pattern of European vagrancy had been established – e.g. Allen's Gallenule.

Suffolk has accrued an impressive list of escaped birds and the liberation of some would have undoubtedly caused a few tears.

Suspected escapees involving species listed on Categories A to C on the British and Irish list are dealt with under the species heading in the main text or for Category D species in Appendix 1. The records of species that have occurred on less than four occasions are listed otherwise they are summarised. Further details of many records can be found in the Bird Report of that particular year.

Red-billed Tropicbird — *Phaethon aethereus*

Tropical, subtropical Atlantic, Pacific and Indian Oceans

1993 Felixstowe: Landguard Point, probable imm. dead on tideline, 17th February

The above individual was found on the tideline and there was some initial speculation that it may have arrived unaided. The bird was in good condition and apparently uninjured. It belonged to the race *indicus* that is normally found in the Red Sea, Persian Gulf and Arabian Sea. The bird's plumage was slightly oiled and it was suspected that the bird came aboard a container ship in the Red Sea area where it died. Its body was probably tossed overboard once the ship reached Felixstowe (Knox *et al.* 1994).

Dalmatian Pelican — *Pelecanus crispus*

South-east Europe to south-west Siberia

Listed by Payn, but no details given.

Pink-backed Pelican — *Pelecanus rufescens*

Locally in Africa (south of the Sahara) and Madagascar

1999 Lowestoft: Harbour, 30th-31st March

Sacred Ibis — *Threskiornis aethiopicus*

Africa to west Asia and south-west Pacific islands

A long-staying individual frequented the stretch of coast between Minsmere and Aldeburgh from the late 1970s to at least 1981 and was noted on many occasions. Another visited Weybread on two occasions in 2000.

Straw-necked Ibis — *Threskiornis spinicollis*

Australia and Tasmania

1992 Tuddenham St Mary-Mildenhall: June to September

African Spoonbill *Platalea alba*

Africa: south of the Sahara and Madagascar

A wandering individual was noted at Martlesham on 12th September 1988 and at Lowestoft and Ramsholt on 14th and 25th March 1989 respectively.

Chilean Flamingo *Phoenicopterus chilensis*

Southern South America

Up to four Chilean Flamingos have been noted annually on the coast and estuaries, occasionally in the company of a Greater Flamingo.

Fulvous Tree-Duck *Dendrocygna bicolor*

Southern United States to Argentina; Asia and Africa

Long-staying individuals were noted at Minsmere in 1986 and 1992.

Black Swan *Cygnus atratus*

Australia and an introduction to New Zealand

There have been 5-6 records annually since the late 1980s. A pair bred in Essex in 1988 and 1996.

Black-necked Swan *Cygnus melanocorypha*

Southern Brazil to Argentina; Falkland Islands

1982 Brantham: Seafield Bay, 21st January

Trumpeter Swan *Cygnus buccinator*

Probable accidental from North America

1886 Aldeburgh: five (four shot) in from sea 27th October

Ticehurst referred to a flock of five that was first seen out at sea, on 27th October 1866, before circling Thorpe Meare and finally settling at Slaughden. The birds were tired and allowed an easy approach that resulted in four being shot. Although Whooper Swans were sometimes referred to as Trumpeters, there is no doubt over identification, which is confirmed from photographs by Babington and by a mounted specimen for many years displayed at the Ipswich Museum. The date of arrival is ideal for North American migrants and five together points to genuine vagrancy from that region. However, the record was never formally submitted to the BOURC for consideration as a new species to Britain and Ireland and escapees are the only other possibility.

The Trumpeter Swan is an endangered species in North America, formerly breeding from arctic Canada westwards to coastal Alaska and southwards through to the Grand Prairie region of north-west Alberta to Minnesota and Indiana. Its range is now restricted to western Canada and Alaska with isolated pockets in north-western parts of the United States, where it has been reintroduced to some former breeding areas.

Swan Goose *Anser cygnoides*

Eastern Palearctic region

This species is often noted amongst flocks of Greylag or Canada flocks, but individuals have always shown characters of the domesticated variety known as Chinese Goose.

Bar-headed Goose *Anser indicus*

An uncommon resident

One or two are occasionally noted amongst large flocks of Greylag and Canada Geese at coastal and inland localities.

A national survey of introduced and escaped geese in summer 1991 revealed 85 individuals, including a flock of six at the Otter Trust's H.Q. near Bungay (Delaney 1993). Elsewhere in Suffolk, the species has been most often noted singly with the occasional pair.

The Bar-headed Goose breeds on Alpine lakes in central Asia and transverses the Himalayas to winter in India and Burma

Ross's Goose *Chen rossii*

Canada to southern United States

A Ross's Goose frequented Lackford in three successive years from 1991-1993 and up to three were in the Trimley/Levington area from spring 2001 with one remaining to the end of January 2002.

Emperor Goose *Chen canagica*

Tundra of north-east Siberia to coastal western Alaska

The species is occasionally found amongst large flocks of Canada or Greylag Geese, with c.15 records from mostly at West Suffolk sites.

Hawaiian Goose *Branta sandvicensis*

Endemic to the Island of Hawaii

One was noted at sites in and around Lowestoft from 1989-1992 and was last seen at Wickham Market in 1993.

Blue-winged Goose *Cyanochen cyanopterus*

Highlands of Ethiopia

1985 Ixworth: n.d.

Upland Goose *Chloephaga picta*

Resident in Argentina, Chile and the Falkland Islands – two county records

Noted at Ixworth in 1983 and 1991.

South African Shelduck *Tadorna cana*

Southern Africa

There are four records involving five individuals: one at Livermere on 19th November 1983, two at Benacre from 12th September to 6th October 1984 and singles at Levington and Trimley on 27th October 1990 and 11th September 1997 respectively.

Australian Shelduck *Tadorna tadornoides*

South-west and south-east Australia

1981 Benacre: 27th September
1982 Ixworth: pair 31st January
2000 Benacre: 22nd July and 17th September

Paradise Shelduck *Tadorna variegata*

Widespread in mountains of the North, South and Stewart Islands of New Zealand

1988 Wrentham: female 3rd April

Muscovy Duck *Cairina moschata*

A locally common resident

One or two pairs breed in town centre parks and on a few scattered farm ponds. A feral population has become established in Lothingland, where four pairs raised at least 24 young in 1995 and up to 95 were present during the following autumn.

The Muscovy Duck was originally brought from its native South America to Europe in the 16th century and is said to have been imported into England in 1550 (Kear 1990). It was principally reared as a food source for both its eggs and its meat, but it also found its way into ornamental wildfowl collections and readily associated with other domestic waterfowl with which it hybridised. It has a protracted breeding season and populations can grow quite quickly. A feral population became established in Stonelodge Park in south-west Ipswich during the late 1960s from where the duck spread into gardens of the nearby housing estates. Birds frequently grazed on roadside verges and garden lawns to such an extent that the Ipswich Council was forced to instigate control measures and the ducks were subsequently exterminated.

Maned Duck *Chenonetta jubata*

Widespread and common throughout Australia

1981 Ixworth: 27th May
1998 Boyton: Boyton Marshes, 20th November

Ringed Teal *Callonetta leucophrys*

Southern Brazil to northern Argentina

1986 Gt/Lt Livermere: 30th May
1995 Needham Mkt: male 18th February

Chiloe Wigeon *Anas sibilatrix*

Central Chile, Argentina to Tierra del Fuego; Falkland Islands; winters in south-east Brazil

The Chiloe Wigeon is reported annually in Suffolk amongst other wildfowl species, mainly at coastal localities. The species regularly congregate with Wigeon and have on occasions been misidentified as American Wigeon.

Speckled Teal *Anas flavirostris*

Widespread in South America

Noted at Lackford in 1989 and 1990, Benacre in 1992, Stanstead in 1996 and Minsmere in 1998.

Cape Teal *Anas capensis*

Africa north to Ethiopia and eastern Sudan

1986 Minsmere: 24th May to 16th June

Grey Teal *Anas gracillis*

Andamans; Java to Australia and New Zealand

One was captured at Kesgrave and released Alton Water in 1980, one was at Minsmere in May 1984 and another was at Hadleigh in August 1998.

Yellow-billed Duck *Anas undulata*

Widespread and abundant in Africa south of the Sahara

1985 Ixworth: n.d.

Yellow-billed Pintail *Anas georgica*

Resident in Columbia, Ecuador to Chile and Argentina

1898 Suffolk: three shot 1st October (Ticehurst)
1991 Minsmere: 26th April

White-cheeked (Bahama) Pintail *Anas bahamensis*

Widespread in South America and the West Indies

The White-cheeked Pintail is a fairly common escapee being noted almost annually since the mid-1980s, most often on the coast and usually in association with other wildfowl species.

Red-billed Duck *Anas erythrorhyncha*

East and southern Africa and Madagascar

1997 Minsmere: male 8th February and 8th, 15th and 25th March
Aldringham-cum-Thorpe: North Warren, male 5th May
1998 Aldringham-cum-Thorpe: North Warren, male 25th January

Puna Teal *Anas puna*

Puna of Peru to Chile and Argentina

Probably the same individual was noted at Ixworth in 1987 and Lackford and Ixworth in 1988.

Cinnamon Teal *Anas cyanoptera*

Canada to Argentina and the Falkland Islands

1988 Ixworth: n.d.

Hooded Merganser *Mergus cucullatus*

Breeds sporadically from Alaska to Mexico

1829 Breydon: killed "winter" (Babington 1884-1886)
pre 1886 Orford: ad. male shot, n.d. (Babington 1884-1886)
1988 Ixworth: n.d.

White-headed Duck *Oxyura leucocephala*

Mediterranean basin to central Asia

1996 Minsmere: Island Mere, male 18th April

The origins of all White-headed Ducks in Britain are open to question as, although the duck is migratory, they are popular with wildfowl enthusiasts and there is no evidence of true vagrancy to this country. The Minsmere bird is probably the same as the long-staying individual that frequented Abberton Reservoir, Essex, from 2nd January 1995 to 12th May 1996 and later at Dungeness and Stodmarsh, Kent, till 23rd May 1996. Although there are no doubts over identification, the species has yet to be accepted onto any category of the British list (BBRC).

The breeding range is fragmented and extends from the Mediterranean basin through to Kazakhstan and central Asia. The species has declined considerably during the late 20th century, although conservation measures in Spain have led to a partial recovery.

Lake Duck *Oxyura vittata*

South-east Brazil to Argentina and Chile

This South American stiff-tail has been noted amongst the Livermere Lake Ruddy Duck population in 1993/4, 1999 and 2000.

Lammergeier *Gypaetus barbatus*

Mountains of southern Europe to India, Tibet and eastern Africa

1890 Sutton: Methersgate, shot, n.d. (before May)

There has been some speculation that the above individual occurred as a vagrant from wild stock (Mendel 1989). This was largely fuelled by the number of visiting raptors that were logged during the late 19th century that included four Spotted Eagles to East Anglia in 1881. However, the record has yet to be submitted to the BOURC for consideration and therefore must languish in the escapee files.

Red-tailed Hawk *Buteo jamaicensis*

Widespread in North and Central America and the West Indies

A wide-ranging individual was seen at a number of sites as far apart as Lowestoft and Lackford from 7th-22nd March 1998. The bird was wearing jesses and was thought to have escaped from a falconer employed to scare gulls from landfill sites.

Ferruginous Hawk *Buteo regalis*

Praries and plains of southern Canada to northern Mexico

2000 Cavenham: Cavenham Heath, September to 8th October

The above was known escapee from Stonham Barns Bird of Prey Centre. It proved well able to survive in the wild as it plundered the local rabbit population.

Lanner *Falco biarmicus*

Africa to Arabia, Armenia and Iraq

1997 Minsmere: 6th and 27th April
2002 Levington: 2nd April
Orfordness: presumably same June to October

Identification of larger falcons is becoming increasingly difficult due to widespread inter-breeding by falconers. One oversummered on Orfordness in 2002 in the company of a male Peregrine and was presumably the same as that seen at Levington earlier in the year.

Prairie Falcon *Falco mexicanus*

Arid interior of North America

1992 Trimley St Martin/Mary: Trimley Marshes, 8th September

Japanese Quail *Coturnix japonica*

Widespread in eastern Palearctic region

1992 Felixstowe: Landguard Point, male trapped 25th August

This individual was initially identified as a European Quail, with its true identity determined after close, in-hand examination. If the bird had not been trapped, it would have almost certainly been recorded as a European Quail. LBO ringers may well have struggled to assign a female to either species.

Blue-breasted Quail *Coturnix chinensis*

Sri Lanka, India to Burma and Thailand

1992 Ipswich: St Edmund's Rd, male captured 25th September

Silver Pheasant *Lophura nycthemera*

Mountains of southern China to Indochina; Hainan

1991 Levington: Research Centre, 27th March

Reeves' Pheasant *Syrmaticus reevesii*

Hills of north and central China north of Yangtze River

Noted at Holton St Mary in 1987, Cavenham in 1988 and 1989, Mildenhall in 1989, Great Bealings in 1998 and Covehithe and Wantisden in 1999. Two adult males noted at the last site on 31st December 1999 were calling continuously.

Indian Peafowl *Pavo cristatus*

Sri Lanka and lowlands of Indian Subcontinent

Free-flying birds are occasionally noted away from the gardens of stately homes where they are commonly kept.

Black-crowned Crane *Grus pavonina*

Sub-Saharan Africa – Senegal to Nigeria, Ethiopia

1977 Suffolk Coast: reports from various sites throughout the year

Demoiselle Crane *Anthropoides virgo*

Widespread Palearctic region, Oriental mainland – one county record

1900 Lavenham: three shot n.d.

Sarus Crane *Grus antigone*

India to South-east Asia and the Philippines

1981 Benacre: 12th June
1984 Kessingland: 7th May to 16th June

White-breasted Waterhen *Amaurornis phoenicurus*

Native of Southeast Asia, Malay Archipelago and the Philippine Islands

1999 Felixstowe: Port of Felixstowe, mid-October

The above individual was seen by dockworkers as it scampered amongst the containers on Felixstowe Docks. Subsequently, it was found dead and taken to LBO where it was photographed.

Purple Swamphen *Porphyrio porphyrio*

Widespread in Africa, Eurasia to Australasia

1965 Minsmere: imm. 7th November

The above individual was considered to be of the Indian race *P. p. poliocephalus*. Four additional British records have been documented up to early 1990s (Evans 1994) and two or three thereafter.

Blacksmith Plover *Vanellus armatus*

Native to eastern and southern Africa

2002 Stoke-by-Nayland: 4th-28th August
Redlingfield: 29th September

The two records undoubtedly refer to the same bird and represents Suffolk's only escaped wader.

Laughing Dove *Streptopelia senegalensis*

Widespread from Africa to India – two county records

One was seen regularly as it fed on a Felixstowe bird table from 1993-1995 and another visited Landguard on 26th May 2001. Laughing Doves are widely kept in captivity and records almost certainly refer to escapees.

Barbary Dove *Streptopelia risoria*

Domesticated – wide distribution worldwide

One or two have been noted almost annually since 1985, most often in the company of Collared Doves.

Diamond Dove *Geopelia cuneata*

Widespread savannahs of Australia

There are four records: one caught by a cat in Felixstowe on 27th June 1988, another at Landguard on 29th-30th May 1989, one at Lowestoft on 1st October 1990 and an injured bird at Gunton on 18th August 1999.

Sulphur-crested Cockatoo *Cacatua galerita*

New Guinea and adjacent islands to Australia and Tasmania

This large white parrot has only been noted on four occasions since 1984, although five were present at Great Finborough during 1984 where a pair was reported nesting in a hole in a black poplar.

Cockatiel *Nymphicus hollandicus*

Widespread and abundant in interior of Australia – fairly common escapee

The popularity of the Cockatiel as a household pet is demonstrated by the up to ten escapees noted annually. It is likely that many more go unreported.

Red-fronted Parakeet *Cyanoramphus novaezelandiae*

New Zealand and Norfolk and Caledonia islands

1980 Sproughton: 24th September

Eastern Rosella *Platycercus eximius*

Australia: Queensland to Victoria and Tasmania

1992 Felixstowe: Landguard Point, 26th June

Red-rumped Parrot *Psephotus haematonotus*

Interior of south-east Australia

1982 Ipswich: 9th September

Budgerigar *Melopsittacus undulatus*

Interior of Australia

The Budgerigar is perhaps not surprisingly Suffolk's most commonly reported escapee, with four to five being noted annually.

Superb Parrot *Polytelis swainsonii*

Interior and south-east Australia

1997 Felixstowe: Landguard Point, 22nd March

Alexandrine Parakeet *Psittacula eupatria*

Indian subcontinent to Southeast Asia

This large parakeet was seen in Lowestoft on 26th February and 9th November 1982 and again on 29th April the following year and at Aldeburgh on 21st March 1996.

Peach-faced Lovebird *Agapornis roseicollis*

Subdeserts of south-western Angola to north Cape Province

The Peach-faced Lovebird is commonly kept in captivity and most escapees are noted in the vicinity of larger towns. All records are from the period 1982-2000.

Black-cheeked Lovebird *Agapornis nigrigenis*

Mopane woodlands of south-west Zambia, north-east Namibia and north-west Zimbabwe

1998 Stowmarket: Combs Lane Water Meadows, 11th July

Grey Parrot *Psittacus erithacus*

Gulf of Guinea islands to Kenya and Tanzania

The Grey Parrot is popular household pet, usually caged in parlours rather than in outside aviaries. Escapees are noted more or less annually.

Blue-and-yellow Macaw *Ara ararauna*

Eastern Panama to Paraguay, Brazil

1985 Bury St Edmunds: two 14th June
2000 Stowmarket: pair 17th November and 6th December

Scarlet Macaw *Ara macao*

Southern Mexico to Bolivia, Brazil

Singles at Oulton on 9th July 1978 and Fritton on 4th April 1979 could well relate to the same individual. Another was at Ufford on 5th December 1985.

Burrowing Parrot *Cyanoliseus patagonus*

Central Chile and northern and central Argentina

1992/3 Cavenham-Icklingham: Temple Bridge, 31st December to 1st January

Nanday Parrot *Nandayus nenday*

Pantanal of north Argentina, Paraguay and south-west Brazil

1996 Icklingham: five 24th November
1997 Icklingham: four 26th-28th January, three 27th May and 7th September

Blue-headed Parrot *Pionus menstruus*

Tropical Central and northern South America

1998 Felixstowe: Langer Park, 15th April

Eagle Owl *Bubo bubo*

Widespread Palearctic region to India and southern China

1843 Suffolk: "one taken"
1990 Felixstowe: 22nd November
1996 Melton: Bury Hill Close, 18th April

Ticehurst doubted whether the 1843 individual occurred in the wild state. The Felixstowe bird was found exhausted in a garden during heavy rain and fresh north-easterly winds (Martin 1993), but nevertheless was considered to be an escapee.

Northern Carmine Bee-eater *Merops nubicus*

Savanna and grasslands of sub-Saharan Africa

2002 Hadleigh: 19th May

The above individual was photographed as it perched on a linen-line and was also seen in Essex on the same day and subsequently in Norfolk.

Desert Lark *Ammomanes deserti*

Deserts of southern Palearctic region

1997 Minsmere: tideline corpse 2nd April

Sooty-headed Bulbul *Pycnonotus aurigaster*

Southern China to Indochina and Java

1989 Felixstowe: Landguard Point, trapped 3rd-4th September

Verditer Flycatcher *Eumyias thalassina*

Nepal, India to Yunnan, Malaysia, Sumatra and Borneo

1994 Felixstowe: Landguard Point, 12th May

The above was a heavily abraded bird that frequented trees in the caravan park, Adastral Close and on the nature reserve at Landguard Point, Felixstowe and is one of two records for Britain. It was the last of four British records of Far Eastern flycatchers for the period 1991-1994. A Mugimaki Flycatcher *Ficedula mugimaki* occurred in 1991, a Brown Flycatcher *Muscicapa latirostris* in 1992 and another Verditer Flycatcher in 1993. There were rumours that a number of Far Eastern birds, part of an illegal assignment, were liberated at Felixstowe Docks, but these were not substantiated.

White-throated Laughing Thrush *Garrulax albogularis*

Himalayas of Kashmir to western Java

1981 Lowestoft: 31st May to mid-August

Red-billed Leiothrix *Leiothrix lutea*

Himalayas of Pakistan to Szechwan, Burma, Tonkin

The species has been noted in Suffolk on at least seven occasions with most records referring to singing males. Reports were from Lowestoft (1990), Landguard (1994, 1998, 2000 and 2001), West Stow (1997) and Lavenham (1997).

Purple/Palestine Sunbird *Cinnyris asiaticus/oseus*

1987 Felixstowe: Landguard Point, 26th-27th May
Orford: Havergate Is., 31st May

Silver-eye *Zosterops lateralis*

Fiji Islands to Australia, New Zealand

1991 Lowestoft: Flycatcher Lane, 8th-12th November

Blue Magpie *Urocissa erythrorhyncha*

Himalayas to Malaysia, Indochina; Hainan

1988 Lakenheath: May

Rufous Treepie *Dendrocitta vagabunda*

Widespread in India to Indochina; Hainan; Taiwan

1982 Tuddenham-Rushmere St Andrew: 30th June to 8th July

Common Hill Myna *Gracula religiosa*

Widespread in Oriental region mainland and islands

1987 Southwold: late March
1990 Dunwich: Greyfriars, 8th August

Red-billed (Silky) Starling *Sturnus sericeus*

Lowlands of south Central China

1997 Felixstowe: Langer Park, 12th April

Purple Glossy Starling *Lamprotornis purpureus*

Senegal to the Sudan, Uganda, Kenya

The same individual was noted intermittently at Landguard Point and Coronation Drive, Felixstowe, from 12th to 19th August 1990 and another was at Minsmere on 16th September 1997.

Sudan Golden Sparrow *Passer luteus*

Widespread and common in Somalia to Ethiopia, Kenya

There are eight records of this species all between 25th April and 14th August and six of these were noted at Landguard Point. The exceptions were at Lowestoft in 1996 and Covehithe in 2002.

White-winged Snowfinch *Montifringilla nivalis*

Restricted to the mountain ranges of the Alps, Carpathians, Caucusus and Himalayas

1969/70 Lakenheath: late July until February

This long-staying individual was noted feeding on the grassy swards of the airfield.

African Masked Weaver *Ploceus velatus*

Widespread mostly in East and South Africa, but also from Senegal east to Ethiopia

There are four records falling in the period of 1990-1993 and include one which made daily visits to a bird-table at Bottesdale. All Suffolk records have been assigned to the West African race *P. v. vitellinus* (Vitelline Masked Weaver).

Village Weaver *Ploceus cucullatus*

Widespread in Africa south of Sahara

The Black-headed Weaver is the most frequently recorded weaver species in Suffolk, being noted at coastal migration sites on more than ten occasions between 1983 and 1992.

Red-headed Quelea *Quelea erythrops*

Widespread in grasslands of Africa south of the Sahara

2002 Felixstowe: Landguard Point, trapped 8th June

The above was feeding with House Sparrows in LBO's Heligoland Trap and was found to be in pristine condition.

Red-billed Quelea *Quelea quelea*

Widespread in grasslands of Africa south of the Sahara

1980 Felixstowe: Landguard Point, 28th September
1983 Felixstowe: Landguard Point, trapped 12th August

Yellow-crowned Bishop *Euplectes afer*

Tropical swampy grasslands of Ethiopian region

1980 Minsmere: 4th September
1981 Bawdsey: 9th September

Also known as the Napoleon Weaver.

Black-winged Bishop *Euplectes hordeaceus*

Sub-Saharan Africa from Uganda south to Zambia and Zimbabwe

2000 Bury St Edmunds: male November

Red Bishop *Euplectes orix*

Grasslands of Africa south of the Sahara

1978 Walberswick: 16th September

Golden-backed Bishop *Euplectes aureus*

Coastal Gabon to Angola; SaoThome Island

1991 Benacre: Beach Fm, 21st-25th November

Black-rumped Waxbill *Estrilda troglodytes*

Semiarid Senegal to Ethiopia, the Sudan, Uganda

1988 Minsmere: 25th-26th August and 2nd October
Felixstowe: Landguard Point, two 17th September

Common Waxbill *Estrilda astrild*

Widespread in Africa south of the Sahara

The species has been noted on three occasions: at Haverhill (1987), Benacre (1997) and Landguard Point (2000). A small population has become established in southern Portugal presumably from feral stock.

Red Avadavat *Amandava amandava*

Widespread in the Oriental region mainland and islands

1993 Trimley St Mary: Fagbury Cliff, 17th October

Zebra Finch *Taeniopygia guttata*

Dry open woodlands throughout Australia

The Zebra Finch is commonly kept in aviaries and free-flying birds were noted on seven occasions between 1981 and 1994.

Pin-tailed Whydah *Vidua macroura*

Widespread in Africa south of the Sahara

There are four records that probably relate to two individuals: a female/immature that passed through Landguard in 1988 and a male that frequented several sites between Benacre and Minsmere during the autumn of 1989.

Eastern Paradise Whydah *Vidua paradisae*

Angola to south-east Sudan, Ethiopia and Kenya south to north-east South Africa

1864 Little Waldingfield: shot August

The above was noted by Babington as a "Whidah Bird... a West African genus... doubtless an escaped bird".

House Finch *Carpodacus mexicanus*

British Columbia to southern Mexico; introduced in Hawaii

1988 Gazeley: March

Black-headed Greenfinch *Carduelis ambigua*

Mountains of south-east Tibet to northern Vietnam

2000 Brent Eleigh: 29th January to 6th February

The above was a surprise visitor to a garden feeding station.

Fire-fronted Serin *Serinus pusillus*

Mountains of southern Asia to western China

1992 Felixstowe: Landguard Point, ad. male 6th June

Another was noted amongst Linnets in Rotterdam Harbour, the Netherlands, on 29th April 1993 and perhaps the same was at Joss Bay, Kent, two weeks later (Evans 1994).

Island Canary *Serinus canaria*

Canary islands, Azores and Madeira Island

There are few reports of this species that is surprising bearing in mind the number kept in captivity. The plumage of one at Landguard Point on 12th April 1998 was identical to that of a wild bird.

Yellow-fronted Canary *Serinus mozambicus*

Widespread Africa south of the Sahara

One was at Gunton, Lowestoft, on 12th-16th September 1982, a pair took up residence in the Landguard-Fagbury Cliff area from 4th August to 14th September 1990 and probably one of the same was at Peewit Hill, Felixstowe on 28th March the following spring. Another was at the latter site on 9th September 1997.

Grey-headed Bullfinch *Pyrrhula erythaca*

Himilayas and north-east China

2000 Felixstowe: Landguard Point, 15th-16th May

Desert Finch *Rhodopechys obsoleta*

Palestine to Russia and Chinese Turkestan

1994 Felixstowe: Landguard Point, female 4th November

The above individual flew in from the north, stayed for about ten minutes and then departed south. There has been one previous British record of this species that involved a female, considered to be an escapee, which frequented a farm at Deeping St Nicholas, Lincolnshire, during the winter of 1990-1991 (Evans 1994). A Blyth's Pipit arriving at Landguard on the same day as the Desert Finch caused some speculation as to whether the Suffolk individual was of wild origin.

Long-tailed Rosefinch *Uragus sibiricus*

Eastern Palearctic, Japan

1991 Walberswick: East Hill, male 26th September
1994 Minsmere: male 21st April

There were four additional records for Britain from 1989-1994 and several others for other countries in north-west Europe and Scandinavia during the same period (Evans 1994).

Yellow-billed Grosbeak *Eophona migratoria*

Forests and bamboo of east-central Asia

1998 Felixstowe: Landguard Point, 18th June

Northern Cardinal *Cardinalis cardinalis*

Widespread from Canada to Honduras

1984 Bury St Edmunds: 16th February

The above occurrence, omitted by Evans (1994), is one of three for Britain, all in the period 1966-1984.

Red-winged Blackbird *Agelaius phoeniceus*

Widespread from Canada to Costa Rica and West Indies

1824 Holton: June
1882 Hadleigh: two 17th May

Large numbers were imported into Britain and deliberately released during the 1800s in an attempt to establish a viable feral population. During the period 1824-1885 there were 18 British records including a male captured at 3 am, at Nash Lighthouse, in South Wales, on 27th October 1866 that was perhaps a genuine migrant (Evans 1994).

Eastern Meadowlark *Sturnella magna*

South-east Canada to northern Brazil and Cuba

1860 Thrandeston: shot March

There were three subsequent British records, but none after 1876 (Evans 1994).

GAZETTEER

Acton	TL8944
Acton Airfield	TL8944
Acton Hall	TL8945
Akenham	TM1448
Alde Estuary	TM3957-4450
Alde Marshes	TM4455
Aldeburgh	TM4656
Aldeburgh, Halfway House	TM4658
Aldeburgh Town Marshes	TM4556
Alderton	TM3441
Aldham Church	TM0344
Aldringham	TM4560
Aldringham-cum-Thorpe	TM4461
Aldringham Walks	TM4661
Alton Water Res	TM1436
Ampton	TL8671
Ampton Water	TL8770
Angel Hill, Bury St. Edmunds	TL8564
Ashbocking	TM1654
Ashby	TM4899
Ashby Warren	TG4800
Ashmans Hall, Beccles	TM4189
Bacton	TM0567
Badingham	TM3068
Badley	TM0655
Bardwell	TL9475
Barham	TM1451
Barnby	TM4789
Barnby Broad	TM4890
Barnham	TL8779
Barnhamcross Common	TL8681
Barrow	TL7663
Barsham	TM4090
Barton Mere	TL9166
Barton Mills	TL7173
Bawdsey	TM3337
Bawdsey Cliffs	TM3438
Bawdsey Manor	TM3337
Bawdsey Marshes	TM3338
Baylham	TM1051
Beach Fm, Benacre	TM5383
Beccles	TM4290
Beccles Marshes	TM4391
Beck Row	TL6967
Bedingfield	TM1768
Belle Vue Gardens, Lowestoft	TM5594
Belstead	TM1341
Belstead Brook	TM1541
Belton	TG4702
Belton Heath	TG4702
Benacre	TM5184
Benacre Broad	TM5382
Benacre Denes	TM5384
Benacre Marshes	TM5283
Benacre Ness	TM5383
Benacre Pits	TM5384
Benacre Sluice	TM5384
Berner's Heath	TL7976
Bildeston	TL9949
Bixley Heath, Ipswich	TM1943
Black Ditches, nr. Icklingham	TL7672
Blackheath Estate, Friston	TM4259
Black Heath, Ipswich	TM1943
Blaxhall	TM3856
Blundeston	TM5197
Blundeston Lake	TM5196
Blythburgh	TM4575
Blythburgh Fen	TM4674
Bonny Wood, Barking	TM0751
Bosmere	TM0954
Bourne Pk, Ipswich	TM1542
Bourne Pk Water Meadows	TM1541
Boxford	TL9640
Boxted	TL8250
Botany Bay	TL6785
Boyton	TM3747
Boyton Marshes	TM3946
Bradfield Combust	TL8957
Bradfield St Clare	TL9057
Bradfield St George	TL9357
Bradfield Woods	TL9357
Bradwell	TG5003
Bramford	TM1246
Bramford Water Pk	TM1248
Brampton	TM4381
Brampton Hall	TM4381
Brandon	TL7886
Brandon Country Pk	TL7885
Brandon Heath	TL7185
Brantham	TM1034
Brent Eleigh	TL9447
Brettenham	TL9653
Bredfield	TM2652
Breydon Water	TM4575-TM4776 [TM4907]
Bright's Fm, Lavenham	TL9049
Brightwell	TM2543
Brockley	TL8354
Brome	TM1376
Bromeswell	TM3050
Bungay	TM3489
Bungay Common	TM3290
Bungay G.P.	TM3290
Bures	TL9034
Bures Mill	TL9034
Burgate	TM0875
Burgh Castle	TG4704
Burnt Fen, Mildenhall	TL6581
Burstall	TM0934
Bury St Edmunds B. F Ponds	TL8665
Bury St. Edmunds	TL8464
Buss Creek, Reydon	TM5077
Butley	TM3651
Butley Abbey	TM3749
Butley Creek	TM3949
Butley River	TM3851-TM3947
Campsea Ash	TM3355
Capel St. Andrew	TM3748
Capel St. Mary	TM0938
Carlton Colville	TM5090
Carlton Marshes	TM5092
Castle Marsh	TM4791
Cattawade	TM1033
Cavendish	TL8046
Cavenham	TL7669
Cavenham G. P.	TL7671
Cavenham Heath	TL7672
Chantry Estate, Ipswich	TM1443
Chantry Pk, Ipswich	TM1343

Charsfield	TM2556
Chelmondiston	TM2037
Chevington	TL7859
Chillesford	TM3852
Christchurch Pk, Ipswich	TM1645
Church Fm Marshes, Aldeburgh	TM4656
Clamphouse Marshes, R. Orwell	TM2237
Clare	TL7645
Claydon	TM1349
Cliff Quay, Ipswich	TM1642
Cobholm gardens, Breydon Water	TG5107
Cockfield	TL9054
Coddenham	TM1354
Combs Lane, Stowmarket	TM0457
Combs Lane Water Meadows	TM0458
Combs Wood, Stowmarket	TM0556
Commercial Road, Lowestoft	TM5492
Coney Weston	TL9578
Constitution Hill, Southwold	TM5075
Copdock (Tesco's car park)	TM1242
Cornard	TL8940
Cornard Mere	TL8838
Cornhill, Ipswich	TM1644
Corporation Marshes, Dunwich	TM4973
Corton	TM5497
Corton Church	TM5398
Corton Disused Railway Line	TM5398
Corton, Stirrups Lane	TM5398
Cosford	TM0144
Cove Bottom	TM4979
Covehithe	TM5281
Covehithe Broad	TM5280
Cransford	TM3164
Cratfield	TM3175
Creeting St Mary	TM0956
Cretingham	TM2260
Culford	TL8270
Culpho	TL8370
Dales Wasteland, Ipswich	TM1546
Dalham	TL7261
Dallinghoo	TM2654
Darmsden	TM0953
Darsham	TM4269
Deadman's Grave	TL7874
Decoy Fen, Lakenheath	TL6685
Delft Marsh, Lakenheath	TL7082
Denes Oval, Lowestoft	TM5594
Denston	TL7652
Depden	TL7756
Dingle Hills	TM4873
Dingle Marshes	TM4771
Drinkstone	TL9561
Dunwich	TM4770
Dunwich Forest	TM4671
Dunwich Greyfriars	TM4770
Dunwich Heath	TM4768
Dunwich Shore Pools	TM4873
East Bergholt	TM0735
Eastbridge	TM4566
East Hill, Walberswick	TM4873
East Lane, Bawdsey	TM3540
Easton Bavents	TM5178
Easton Broad	TM5179
Ellingham Lock	TM3691
Ellough	TM4487
Elmswell	TL9863
Elveden	TL8279
Eriswell	TL7278
Euston	TL8979
Euston Pk	TL9078
Exning	TL6165
Eye	TM1473
Eyke	TM3151
Fagbury Cliff	TM2734
Fagbury Flats	TM2634
Fagbury Pt	TM2535
Fagbury Rd, Felixstowe	TM2734
Fakenham	TL8876
Fakenham Magna	TL9176
Falkenham	TM2938
Falkenham Marshes	TM3138
Felixstowe	TM3034
Felixstowe Docks	TM2832
Felixstowe Ferry	TM3237
Felixstowe Golf Course	TM3236
Felixstowe, Cobbold's Pt	TM3134
Felixstowe, Landguard Pt	TM2831
Felixstowe Sewage Works	TM2833
Felsham, Monk's Wood	TL9457
Flatford	TM0733
Flatford Mill	TM0733
Flempton	TL8169
Flempton Golf Course	TL8169
Flixton	TM3187
Flixton Lake	TM5195
Flycatcher Lane, Lowestoft	TM5594
Fornham	TL8367
Fornham St Martin	TL8537
Forward Green	TM0959
Fox's Heath	TM2041
Foxhall	TM2244
Foxhall Heath	TM2244
Foxhall Refuse Tip	TM2343
Framlingham	TM2863
Framlingham Mere	TM2863
Framsden	TM1959
Freckenham	TL6672
Freston	TM1639
Friston	TM4160
Fritton	TG4600
Fritton Decoy	TM4799-TG4800
Fritton Lake	TG4800
Fritton Warren	TG4600
Gallow's Hill G. P., Barking	TM1054
Gazeley	TL7163
Gedding	TL9557
Gedgrave	TM4048
Gipping	TM0763
Gipping Gt Wood	TM0762
Gipping Valley G. Ps	TM0954-TM1248
Gisleham	TM5188
Glemham	TM3461
Glemsford	TL8248
Glevering Hall	TM2957
Gorleston-on-Sea	TG5203
Gorleston Cliffs	TG5302
Gorleston Harbour	TG5303
Gorleston South Pier	TG5303
Gt Ashfield	TL9967
Gt Barton	TL8967
Gt Bealings	TM2348
Gt Blakenham	TM1150
Gt Bricett	TM0350
Gt Fakenham	TL9176

Gt Finborough	TM0157
Gt Glemham	TM3361
Gt Livermere	TL8871
Gt Waldingfield	TL8943
Gt Welnetham	TL8759
Greyfriars, East Bergholt	TM0735
Grimston's Belt, Sizewell	TM4667
Groton	TL9541
Groton Woods	TL9743
Grove Fm, Reydon	TM4879
Grundisburgh	TM2250
Gun Hill, Southwold	TM5075
Gunton	TM5396
Gunton Cliffs	TM5496
Hacheston	TM3059
Hadleigh	TM0242
Halesworth	TM3877
Hall Heath Refuse Tip, Lackford	TL7963
Hardwick	TL8562
Harkstead	TM1834
Harkstead Hall	TM1935
Harleston	TM0160
Hartest	TL8352
Hasketon	TM2450
Haughley	TM0262
Havergate Island	TM4147
Haverhill	TL6745
Hawkedon	TL7953
Hawstead	TL8559
Hazelwood Marshes	TM4357
Helmingham	TM1857
Hemingstone	TM1552
Hemley	TM2843
Hengrave	TL8268
Henham	TM4577
Herringfleet	TM4797
Herringswell	TL7169
Hessett	TL9361
Heveningham Hall	TM3573
Higham	TL7465
Higham Pool	TM0335
Hintlesham	TM0843
Hinton	TM4473
Hitcham	TL9851
Hoist Covert	TM4874
Holbrook	TM1636
Holbrook Bay	TM1733
Holbrook Gardens	TM1736
Holbrook Creek	TM1735
Holbrook Marshes	TM1733
Holbrook Sewage Fm	TM1735
Hollesley	TM3544
Hollesley Heath	TM3546
Holton St Mary	TM0536
Holywells Pk, Ipswich	TM1743
Homersfield	TM2885
Homersfield G. P.	TM2885
Honington	TL9174
Hopton	TL9979
Hopton-on-Sea	TG5200
Hopton Cliffs	TG5300
Horham	TM2172
Horn Heath	TL7877
Hoxne	TM1877
Hunston	TL9768
Huntingfield	TM3473
Icklingham	TL7772
Icklingham Mill	TL7773
Ickworth	TL8161
Ickworth Pk	TL8161
Iken	TM4155
Iken Decoy	TM4155
Iken Marshes	TM4256
Ilketshall St Andrew	TM3886
Ilketshall St Lawrence	TM3883
Ipswich	TM1644
Ipswich Docks	TM1643
Ipswich Wet Dock	TM1643
Island Mere, Minsmere	TM4666
Ixworth	TL9370
Ixworth Thorpe	TL9172
Joist Fen	TL6885
Kedington	TL7046
Kesale	TM3865
Kenny Hill, Mildenhall	TL6679
Kesgrave	TM2145
Kessingland	TM5286
Kessingland Levels	TM5285-TM5384
Kessingland Wildlife Pk	TM5286
King's Forest	TL8173
Kingsfleet	TM3037-TM3137
Kirkley Cliff, Lowestoft	TM5391
Kirton	TM2739
Knettishall	TL9780
Knettishall Heath	TL9580
Lackford	TL7970
Lackford G. P.	TL7971
Lackford Wildfowl Reserve	TL7971
Lackford Quarry	TL7971
Landguard Pt	TM2831
Lake Lothing	TM5292
Lakenheath	TL7183
Lakenheath Fen	TL7082
Lakenheath Warren	TL7481
Lakenheath Washes	TL7083
Lantern Marshes, Orfordness	TM4552
Lavenham	TL9149
Lavenham Railway Line	TL9049
Laxfield	TM2972
Leathes Ham	TM5393
Leavenheath	TL9536
Leiston	TM4462
Leiston-cum-Sizewell	TM4462
Leiston Marshes	TM4563
Levington	TM2339
Levington Creek	TM2338
Levington Lagoon	TM2338
Levington Heath	TM2440
Lighthouse Score, Lowestoft	TM5594
Little Cornard	TL9039
Little Heath, Thetford	TL8577
Little Livermere	TL8872
Livermere Lake	TL8871
Livermere Pk	TL8771
Little Waldingfield	TL9245
Long Covert, Frostenden	TM4980
Long Melford	TL8645
Loompit Lake, Trimley St. Martin	TM2537
Lothingland	TM5199
Lound	TM5099
Lound Waterworks	TG5000
Lower Holbrook	TM1834
Lowestoft	TM5493
Lowerstoft Amusement Arcade	TM5492

BIBLIOGRAPHY

Alerstam, T. 1990. *Bird Migration*. Cambridge University Press. Cambridge.

Alexander, W. B. & Lack, D. 1944. Change in status of British breeding birds. *Brit. Birds*, 38: 62-69.

Allard, P. R. 1990. *The birds of Great Yarmouth*. Norfolk & Norwich Naturalists' Society. Hunstanton.

Anon., 1974. Nest box project. *Suffolk Ornithologists' Group Bulletin*, 10: 2-3.

Anon., 1986. River Warbler in Suffolk approx. 13th July to 2nd August 1984. *Suffolk Birds 1984*. pp. 72-73.

Anon., 1996. Western Palearctic news. *Birding World*, 9: 49.

Anon., 1997. Four new British birds and some name changes. *Brit. Birds*, 90: 70.

Appleton, G. F., Adams, S. Y., Clark, J. A., Simons, J. R. & Peach, W. J. 1997. Bird ringing in Britain and Ireland in 1995. *Ring. & Migr.*, 18: 113-158.

Askins, J. R. 1989. Paddyfield Warbler - first for Suffolk. *Suffolk Birds*, 38: 122-123.

Askins, J., Clarke, R. & Piotrowski, S. 1995. *Orfordness gull report 1994*. Landguard Bird Observatory. Felixstowe.

Askins, J., Clarke, R. & Piotrowski, S. 1997. *Orfordness gull report 1996*. Landguard Bird Observatory. Felixstowe.

Axell, H. E. 1960. R. S. P. B. Minsmere Bird Reserve, 1959. *Trans. Suffolk Nat. Soc.*, 11: 441-450.

Axell, H. E. 1964. Huboura Bustard in Suffolk. *Brit. Birds*, 57: 247-249.

Axell, H. E. 1966. Eruptions of Bearded Tit during 1959-65. *Brit. Birds*, 59: 513-543.

Axell, H. 1977. *Minsmere - Portrait of a bird reserve*. Hutchinson, Tiptree.

Axell, H. E. & Pearson, D. J. 1966. The great fall of migrants - a special report. *Trans. Suffolk Nat. Soc.*, 13: 250-266.

Axell, H. E. 1969. *Selected list for December 1969*. Unpublished m.s.

Babington, C. 1884-1886. *Catalogue of the birds of Suffolk*. John Van Voorst. London.

Babbs, S. 1998. *Suffolk River Valleys and Coast Breeding Wader and Wildfowl Survey 1997*. Suffolk Wildlife Report Part 2.

Bamber, T. B. 1985. Observations of wintering Canada Geese in north-west Suffolk (1981-85). *Suffolk Ornithologists' Group Bulletin*, 67: 6-10.

Banks, P. A. 1971. Unpublished MS Diary.

Banwell, A. 1993. Black-headed Bunting - first for Suffolk. *Suffolk Birds*, 42: 151-152.

Barnes, J. A. G. 1953. The migrations of the Lesser Black-backed Gull. *Brit. Birds*, 46: 238-252.

Batten, L. A., Bibby, C. J., Clement, P., Elliott, G. D. & Porter, R. F. 1990. *Red data birds in Britain*. Poyser, London.

Beardall, C. H., Dryden, R. C. & Holzer, T. J. 1988 *The Suffolk Estuaries*. Suffolk Wildlife Trust, Saxmundham.

Beardall, C. 1989. Suffolk estuaries breeding wader and wildfowl survey 1988. *Suffolk Birds*, 38: 18-20.

Beardall, C. & Casey, D. 1995. *Suffolk's changing countryside - wildlife habitats and their conservation in Suffolk*. Suffolk Wildlife Trust. Ashbocking.

Beecroft, R.C. 1985. Black Redstarts in Suffolk. *Suffolk Ornithologists' Group Bulletin*, 68: 7-12.

Beecroft, R.C. 1987. The Suffolk Black Redstart breeding survey 1986. *Suffolk Ornithologists' Group Bulletin*, 75: 16-19.

Benson, G. B. G. 1968. Red-headed Bunting breeding in Suffolk. *Brit. Birds*, 60: 343-344.

Benson, G. B. G. & Williamson, K. 1972. Breeding birds of a mixed farm in Suffolk. *Bird Study*, 19: 34-50.

Berry, R. 1978. Breeding Bitterns at Minsmere 1977. *Trans. Suffolk Nat. Soc.*, 17: 319-322.

Berry, R. & Bibby, C. J. 1981. A breeding study of Nightjars. *Brit. Birds*, 74: 161-169.

Bibby, C. J. 1981. Wintering Bitterns in Britain. *Brit. Birds*, 74: 1-10.

Bimpson, A. 1994. Winter gull roosts in Suffolk. *Suffolk Birds*, 42: 7-13.

Bircham, P. M. M. 1989. *The birds of Cambridgeshire*. Cambridge University Press, Cambridge.

Bowden, C. G. R. 1990. Nightjars in Suffolk. *Suffolk Birds*, 39: 14-16.

Bowden, C. & Hoblyn, R. 1990. The increasing importance of restocked conifer plantations for Woodlarks in Britain: implications and consequences. *RSPB Conserv. Rev.*, 4: 26-31.

Boyd, H. 1954. The wreck of Leach's Petrels. *Brit. Birds*, 47: 137-163.

Brown, B. J. 1979. Franklin's Gull in Suffolk. *Brit. Birds*, 72: 479-482.

Brown, B. J. 1980. A review of the winter period January to early April 1979. *Suffolk Birds 1979*, pp 30-39. Suffolk Naturalists' Society, Ipswich.

Brown, B. J. 1981. The Nightingale in Suffolk - 1980. *Suffolk Birds 1980*. Suffolk Naturalists' Society, Ipswich.

Brown, B. J. 1982. BTO Nightjar Survey 1981. *Suffolk Birds 1981*. Suffolk Naturalists' Society, Ipswich.

Brown, B. J. 1986. White-crowned Black Wheatear: new to Britain and Ireland. *Brit. Birds*, 79: 221-227.

Brown, B. J. 1986. A history of the Kittiwake in Suffolk. *Suffolk Birds 1984*. pp 66-71.

Brown, B. J. 1987. Collared Flycatcher at Lowestoft 13th and 14th May. *Suffolk Birds 1985*. pp. 81-82.

Brown, B. J. 1987. Greenish Warbler - 'second' for Suffolk. *Suffolk Birds*, 36: 65-66.

Brown, B. J. 1987. Claud Buchanan Ticehurst. *The Harrier*, 77: 17-23.

Brown, B. J. 1990. Further notes on the Kittiwake in Suffolk. *Suffolk Birds*, 39: 21-23.

Bunn. D. S., Warburton, A. B. & Wilson, D. S. 1982. *The Barn Owl*. Poyser, Calton.

Burgess, N., Evans, C. & Sorenson, J. 1990. Heathland management for Nightjars. *RSPB Conserv. Rev.*, 4: 32-35.

Burn, D. M. & Mather, J. R. 1974. The White-billed Diver in Britain. *Brit. Birds*, 67: 257-296.

Burton, J. F. 1979. Continuous nocturnal singing by Cetti's Warbler. *Brit. Birds*, 72: 184-185.

Burton, J. F. 1995. *Birds and climate change*. Christopher Helm, London.

Butt, D. V. & Vine, A. E. 1948. Unusual nest-site of Stock Doves. *Brit. Birds*, 41: 89.

Butterfield, D. 1988. Dusky Warbler - first for Suffolk. *Suffolk Birds*, 37: 112.

Cadbury, C. J., Hill, D., Partridge, J. & Sorensen, J. 1989. The history of the Avocet population and its management in England since recolonisation. *RSPB Conserv. Rev.*, 3: 9-13.

Cage, A. 1975. Kingfisher Survey. *Suffolk Ornithologists' Group Bulletin*, 17: 2-6.

Campbell, L., Cayford, J. & Pearson, D. 1996. Bearded Tits in Britain and Ireland. *Brit. Birds*, 89: 335-346.

Camphuysen, C. J. 1989. *Beached bird survey in the Netherlands, 1915-1988*. Techn. Rapport Vogelbescherming 1, Amsterdam.

Candler, C. 1888. *Observations on the birds of the district.* In: Galpin, F. W. 1888. *An account of the flowering plants, ferns and allies of Harleston.* Bartlett & Co., London.

Carter, I. 1998. The changing fortunes of the Red Kite in Suffolk. *Suffolk Birds,* 46: 6-15.

Carter, I. 2000. Suffolk Red Kites. *The Harrier,* 120: 5-6.

Caton, R. B. 1931. An annotated list of Vertebrata occurring about Euston beside the Suffolk breckland. *Trans. Suffolk. Nat. Soc.,* 1: 162-177.

Cawston, J. M. 1993. The Long-tailed Skua in Suffolk. *Suffolk Birds,* 41: 15-18.

Cawston, J. 1993. Franklin's Gull - second for Suffolk. *Suffolk Birds,* 41: 143-144.

Cawston, J. 1994. "Steppe" Shrike - second for Suffolk. *Suffolk Birds,* 42: 150-151.

Chandler, R. J. 1981. Influxes into Britain and Ireland of Red-necked Grebes and other waterbirds during winter 1978/79. *Brit. Birds,* 74: 55-81.

Charlton, T. D. 1985. First for Britain? *Suffolk Birds 1983.* pp 56-57.

Charlton, T. D. 1995. Lark Sparrow in Suffolk: new to the Western Palearctic. *Brit. Birds,* 88: 395-400.

Clarke, R. E. 1991. Mallard. *Suffolk Estuaries Report 1991,* 4: 30-35.

Clarke, R. 1988. Winter status of the Hen Harrier in Suffolk 1984-88. *Suffolk Birds,* 37: 16-18.

Clarke, R. & Palmer, D. 1987. The diet of Hen Harriers roosting on a Breckland heath. *Suffolk Birds,* 36: 71-75.

Clarke, W. G. 1925. *In Breckland Wilds.* Robert Scott, London.

Clarke, W. G. 1897. A list of the vertebrate animals found in the neighbourhood of Thetford. *Trans. Norfolk & Norwich Nat. Soc.,* 6: 300-327.

Clements, J. F. 2000. *Birds of the World: a checklist (fifth edition).* Ibis Publishing Company, Vista.

Collings, D. W. 1948. Pall and a Buzzard. *Trans. Suffolk. Nat. Soc.,* 6: 260-261.

Cook, A. 1975. Changes in the Carrion/Hooded Crow hybrid zone and the possible importance of climate. *Bird Study,* 22: 165-168.

Cook, F. C. 1944. Some birds of the Suffolk coast. *Trans. Suffolk. Nat. Soc.,* 5: 135-136.

Cox, S. 1984. *A new guide to the birds of Essex.* The Essex Bird Watching and Preservation Society. Ancient House Press, Ipswich.

Cramp, S. 1963. Movements of tits in Europe in 1959 and after. *Brit. Birds,* 56: 237-263.

Cramp, S., Bourne, W. R. P. & Saunders, D. 1974. *The Seabirds of Britain and Ireland.* Readers Union.

Cramp, S., Pettet, A. & Sharrock, J. T. R. 1960. The irruption of tits in autumn 1957. *Brit. Birds,* 53: 49–77, 99–117, 176–192.

Cramp, S. *et al.* (eds.) 1977-1994. *Handbook of the birds of Europe, the Middle East and North Africa (The Birds of the Western Palearctic)*: vols I to IX, Oxford University Press, Oxford.

Cranswick, P. A., Kirby, J. S. & Waters, R. J. 1992. *Wildfowl and wader counts 1991-92.* Wildfowl & Wetlands Trust, Slimbridge.

Cranswick, P. A., Waters, R. J., Evans, J. & Pollitt. M. S. 1995. *The Wetland Bird Survey 1993-94: Wildfowl and Wader Counts.* BTO/WWT/RSPB/JNCC, Slimbridge.

Crewe, M. D. 1987. Waxwings eating snow. *Suffolk Birds,* 36: 80.

Crewe, M. D. 1994. Arctic Warbler - first for Suffolk. *Suffolk Birds,* 43: 157-158.

Crewe, M. 1996. Field identification of Goshawk. *The Harrier,* 109: 9-12.

Dagley, J. R. 1994. Golden Orioles in East Anglia and their conservation. *Brit. Birds,* 87: 205-219.

Davenport, D. L., 1982. Influxes into Britain of Hen Harriers, Long-eared Owls and Short-eared Owls. *Brit. Birds,* 75: 309-316.

Davis, P. G. 1980. Nightingales in Britain in 1980. *Bird Study,* 29: 73-79.

Day, J. C. U. 1981. Status of Bitterns in Europe since 1976. *Brit. Birds,* 74: 10-16.

Day, J. C. U. & Wilson, J. 1978. Breeding Bitterns in Britain. *Brit. Birds,* 71: 285-300.

Delaney, S. 1993. Introduced and escaped geese in summer 1991. *Brit. Birds,* 86: 591-599.

Donald, P. F., Wilson, J.D. & Shepherd, M. 1994. The decline of the Corn Bunting. *Brit. Birds,* 87: 106-132.

Dunn, J. 1983. Sabine's Gulls in Britain in winter. *Brit. Birds,* 76: 91.

Dymond, J. N., Fraser, P. A. & Gantlett, S. J. M. 1989. *Rare birds in Britain and Ireland.* Poyser, Calton.

Easton, A. C. 1994. Roof nesting by Common Terns in Lowestoft. *Suffolk Birds,* 43: 18-19.

Ekins, G. 1994. The Abberton Reservoir tree-nesting Cormorant Colony. *The Essex Bird Report 1994,* pp. 153-167.

Elkins, N. 1983. *Weather and bird behaviour.* Calton, Poyser.

Elliston, W. R. 1940. An effect of the severe winter. *Trans. Suffolk Nat. Soc.,* 4: 218.

Evans, L. G. R. 1994. *Rare birds in Britain 1800-1990.* LGRE Publications, Amersham.

Fox, A. D. 1988. Breeding status of the Gadwall in Britain and Ireland. *Brit. Birds,* 81: 51-66.

Fox, A. D. 1991. History of the Pochard breeding in Britain. *Brit. Birds,* 84: 83-98.

Fraser, A. P. & Rogers, M. J. 1999. Report on scarce migrant birds in Britain in 1999. *Brit. Birds,* 94: 560-589.

Fuller, R. J. 1982. *Bird Habitats in Britain.* T. & A.D. Poyser, Calton.

Fuller, R. J. & Youngman, R. E. 1979. The utilisation of farmland by Golden Plovers wintering in southern England. *Bird Study,* 26: 37-46.

Furness, R. W. 1987. *The skuas.* Poyser, Calton.

Garrod, J. D. 1989. Kingfisher impaling its catch. *Brit. Birds,* 82: 29.

Gibbons, D. W., Reid, J. B. & Chapman, R. A. 1993. *The new atlas of breeding birds in Britain and Ireland: 1988-1991* British Trust for Ornithology, Scottish Ornithologists' Club and Irish Wildbird Conservancy. Poyser, London.

Gibbons, D. W., Avery, M. I. and Brown, A. F. 1996. Population trends of breeding birds of the United Kingdom since 1800. *Brit. Birds,* 89: 291-305.

Giles, C. C. T. 1949. A new goose to Suffolk. *Trans. Suffolk Nat. Soc.,* 7: 38.

Glue, D. E. 1977. Breeding biology of Long-eared Owls. *Brit. Birds,* 70: 318-331.

Goode, D. 1981. Report of the Nature Conservancy Council's Working Group on lead poisoning in swans. NCC, London.

Graham, Tree perching Egyptian Geese. *The Harrier,* 99: 16-17.

Grant, J. H. 1988. Weather trends and their effect on the county's avifuana 1987. *Suffolk Birds,* 37: 19-23.

Grant, P. 1986. Four problem stints. *Brit. Birds,* 79: 609-621.

Green, R. 1988. Stone-curlew conservation. *RSPB Conserv. Rev.,* 2: 30-33.

Green, R. 1989. Conservation of Stone Curlews. *Trans. Norwich and Norfolk Nat. Soc.,* 28: 254-258.

Gregory, R. Crick, H. & Baillie, S. 1996. Birds of conservation concern - the new list of priority species. *BTO News,* 207: 8-9.

Hagemeijer, W. J. M. & Blair, M. J. 1997. *The EBCC Atlas of European breeding birds, their distribution and abundance.* European Bird Census Council. Poyser, London.

Halls, J. 1994. Black-headed Bunting – second for Suffolk. *Suffolk Birds,* 43: 158.

Harrison, C. J. O. 1978. A Long-tailed Duck *Clangula hyemalis* from the Norwich crag of Suffolk. *Trans. Suffolk Nat. Soc.,* 17: 358-359.

Harrison, T. H. & Hollom, P. A. D. 1932. The Great Crested Grebe Enquiry – 1931. *Brit. Birds,* 26: 62-92.

Heathcote, G. D. 1988. The gale of October, 1987. *Trans. Suffolk Nat. Soc.,* 24: 95-96.

Hele, N. F. 1870. *Notes or jottings about Aldeburgh, Suffolk.* Russell Smith, London.

Hele, N. F. 1890. *Notes or jottings about Aldeburgh, Suffolk* 2nd Edn. S. & W. J. King, Ipswich.

Hervey, A. C. C. 1952. Changes in the bird population of Suffolk 1900-1950. *Trans. Suffolk Nat. Soc.,* 8: 5-11.

Hervey, A. C. C. 1954. Changes in the bird population of Suffolk 1900-1950 II. *Trans. Suffolk Nat. Soc.,* 9: 44-48.

Hoblyn, R. 1991. Siskins breeding in Breckland. *Suffolk Birds,* 40: 164.

Hoblyn, R. 1997. RSPB/FE Woodlark Research 1996. Unpublished MS. RSPB/Forest Enterprise.

Hollom, P. A. D. 1941. Shelduck "Increase in Suffolk". *Brit. Birds,* 34: 85.

Holloway, S. 1996. *The Historical Atlas of breeding birds in Britain and Ireland: 1875-1900.* Poyser, Calton.

Holzer, T. J. 1991. 1989/90 Suffolk River Valley ESA Winter Bird Survey. *Suffolk Birds,* 40: 35-39.

Holzer, T. C., Beardall, C. H., Dryden, R. C. and West, R. B. 1993. Breeding waders and other waterfowl on the coastal marshes and saltings of Suffolk in 1988 and 1989. *Suffolk Birds,* 41: 19-28.

Hudson, R. 1972. Collared Doves in Britain and Ireland during 1965-70. *Brit. Birds,* 65: 139-155.

Hudson, R. 1974. Allen's Gallinule in Britain and the Palearctic. *Brit. Birds,* 67: 405-413.

Hudson, R. 1977. Nightingales in Britain in 1976. *Bird Study,* 26: 204-212

Hutchinson, C. D. & Neath, B. 1978. Little Gulls in Britain and Ireland. *Brit. Birds,* 71: 563-582.

Hughes, S. W. M., Bacon, P. & Flegg, J. J. M. 1979. The census of the Great Crested Grebe in Britain. *Bird Study,* 26: 213- 226

Jeanes, M. J. F. 1973. *The Cuckoo Survey 1973.* The Suffolk Ornithologists' Group. Ipswich.

Jeanes, M. J. F. & Snook, R. 1976. *The Rook in Suffolk.* The Suffolk Ornithologists' Group. Ipswich.

John, A. W. G. & Roskell, J. 1983. Jay movements in autumn 1983. *Brit. Birds,* 78: 611-637.

Jonsson, L. 1998. Baltic Lesser Black-backed Gull *Larus fuscus fuscus* - moult, ageing and identification. *Birding World,* 11: 295-317.

Jourdain, F. C. R. 1913. Breeding habits of the Marsh- and Willow-tits. *Brit. Birds,* 7: 141-144.

Jourdain, F. C. R. 1930. Green Woodpecker attacking hives. *Brit. Birds,* 23 (10): 273-274.

Jourdain, F. C. R. & Witherby, H. F. 1918. The effect on the winter of 1916-1917 our resident birds. *Brit. Birds,* 12 (2): 26-35.

Kear, J. 1990. *Man and wildfowl.* Poyser, Calton.

Kelly, G. 1986. *The Norfolk bird atlas.* Norfolk and Norwich Naturalists' Society.

Keynes, G. 1931. The works of Sir T. Browne. Vol. 5. Faber & Faber Ltd. London.

Killeen, I. J. 1992. *The land and freshwater molluscs of Suffolk.* Suffolk Naturalists Society. Ipswich.

King, W. D. 1838. List of the birds of the Sudbury district in Foulcher's *Sudbury Journal.*

Kirby, J. S., Ferns, J. R., Waters, R. J. & Prys-Jones, R. P. 1992. *Wildfowl and wader counts 1990-91.* The Wildfowl & Wetlands Trust, Slimbridge.

Kirby, J. S., Evans, R. J. & Fox, A. D. 1993. Wintering seaducks in Britain and Ireland: populations, threats, conservation and research priorities. *Aquatic Conservation: Marine and Freshwater Ecosystems,* 3: 105-137.

Kitchener, P. 1994. Yellow-breasted Bunting - first for Suffolk. *Suffolk Birds,* 43: 155-156.

Knox, A. G. 2001. The Bufflehead in Britain. A review. *Brit. Birds,* 94: 61-73.

Knox, A. G., Mendel, H. & Odin, N. 1994. Red-billed Tropicbird in Suffolk. *Brit. Birds,* 87: 488-491.

Lack, D. 1966. *Population studies of birds.* Clarendon Press, Oxford.

Lack, P. (ed.) 1986. *The Atlas of wintering birds in Britain and Ireland.* British Trust for Ornithology. Poyser, Calton.

Limbert, M. 1984. Vagrant races of Willow Tit in Britain. *Brit. Birds,* 77: 123.

Lamb, H. H. 1987. Some aspects of climate and life in East Anglia down the ages. *Trans. Norf. & Norwich Nat. Soc.,* 27 (5): 385-397.

Lancaster, A. A. K. 1987. Marsh Warbler - 'first' for Suffolk. *Suffolk Birds,* 36: 64.

Last, A. J., 1975. House Martin survey of Bury St Edmunds 1975. *Suffolk Ornithologists Group Bulletin,* 15: 1-2.

Last, A. J. 1976. The passage of waders and terns through West Suffolk. *Trans. Suffolk Nat. Soc.,* 17: 109-115.

Last, A. J. 1977. The winter bird population of the King's Forest. *Trans. Suffolk Nat. Soc.,* 17: 197-202.

Lever, C. 1977. *The naturalised animals of the British Isles.* Hutchinson, London.

Lloyd, C., Tasker, M. L. & Partridge, K. 1991 *The status of seabirds in Britain and Ireland.* Poyser, London.

Longhurst, J. 1985. A parish Rook survey - East Bergholt. *Suffolk Ornithologists' Group Bulletin,* 70: 6-14.

Lowe, F. A., 1954. *The Heron.* Collins, London.

Lubbock, R. 1845. *Observations on the Fauna of Norfolk.* Longmans, London.

Macklin, R. 1990. Penduline Tit - first record for Suffolk. *Suffolk Birds,* 39: 124-125.

Marchant, J. 1997. Rooks rally. *BTO News,* 209: 6.

Marchant, J. H., Hudson, R, Carter, S. P. & Whittington, P. 1990. *Population trends in British breeding birds.* British Trust for Ornithology. Tring.

Marchant, J. & Wilson, A. 1996. Common Bird Census: 1994-95 index report. *BTO News,* 204: 9-13.

Marquiss, M. & Newton, I. 1982. The Goshawk in Britain. *Brit. Birds,* 75: 243-260.

Marsh, M. 1979. 1977 Mute Swan Survey. *Suffolk Ornithologists' Group Bulletin,* 36: 9-11.

Marsh, M. 1987*a*. Great Grey Shrike - showing characteristics of the race *pallidirostris* colloquially known as the Steppe Shrike. Race new to Suffolk and only the third for Britain. *Suffolk Birds,* 36: 66-67.

Marsh, M. 1987*b*. Little Bunting -seventh record for Suffolk and the first since 1976. *Suffolk Birds,* 36: 68.

Marsh, M. 1993. Suffolk Ringing Report. *Suffolk Birds,* 41: 162-174.

Marsh, M. 1994. Suffolk Ringing Report. *Suffolk Birds,* 43: 166-175.

Marsh, M. 1996. Sardinian Warbler -first for Suffolk. *Suffolk Birds,* 44: 154-155.

Marsh, M. 1997. 1995 Suffolk Ringing Report. *Suffolk Birds,* 45: 178-195.

Martin, A. 1988. Lark Valley Canada Goose study. *Suffolk Birds,* 37: 16.

Martin, J. R. 1988. Barn Owl mortality during the winter of 1986/87 *Suffolk Birds,* 37: 12-15.

Martin, J. R. 1993. A brief summary of the Eagle Owl's status in Europe and its possible implications for Suffolk and Britain *Suffolk Birds,* 41: 11-14.
Matthews, G. V. T. 1969. Nacton Decoy and its catches. *Wildfowl,* 20: 131-137.
Mead, C. 1983. *Bird Migration.* Country Life Books, Feltham.
Mead, C. J. & Clark, J. A. 1993. Report on bird ringing in Britain and Ireland for 1991. *Ring. & Migr.,* 14: 1-72.
Mead, C. J., Clark, J. A. & Peach, W. J. 1995. Report on bird ringing in Britain and Ireland for 1993. *Ring. & Migr.,* 16: 16-64.
Mead, C. J. & Pearson, D. J. 1974. Bearded Tit populations in England and Holland. *Bird Study,* 21: 205-227.
Mendel, H. 1984. A tour round the Vice-Counties of Suffolk. *Trans. Suffolk. Nat. Soc.,* 20: 1-9.
Mendel, H. 1989. The Suffolk Lammergeier. *Suffolk Birds,* 38: 125-126.
Mendel, H. 1992. *Suffolk Dragonflies.* Suffolk Naturalists' Society. Ipswich.
Mendel, H. & Piotrowski, S. H. 1986. *The butterflies of Suffolk.* Suffolk Naturalists' Society. Ipswich.
Meyer, H. L. 1842-50. *Coloured illustrations of British birds and their eggs.* G. W. Nickisson, London.
Mikkola, H. 1983. *Owls of Europe.* Poyser. Calton.
Miller, A. 1993. Twenty years of the Common Birds Census on Hollesley Heath. *Suffolk Birds,* 41: 7-11.
Millington, R. & Vinicombe, K. 1992. The new approach in action: Felixstowe '82 revisited. *Birding World,* 5: 433-437.
Montagu, G. 1813. *Ornithological Dictionary, and Supplement.* White, London.
Moore, A. 1985. Wren swimming. *Brit. Birds,* 78: 456.
Moore, D. R. & Piotrowski, S. H. 1983. Hybrid Coot x Moorhen resembling American Coot in Suffolk. *Brit. Birds,* 76: 407-409.
Moore, D. R. 1987. A brief history of the breeding of the Marsh Harrier in Suffolk. *Suffolk Birds,* 36: 76-79.
Moore, D. R. 1990. The Hobby as a breeding bird in Suffolk. *Suffolk Birds,* 39: 16-18.
Moore, N. W. & Walker C. H. 1964. Organic chlorine insecticide residues in wild birds. *Nature,* 201: 1072-1073.
Moore, N. W. 1975. Status and habitats of the Dartford Warbler, Whitethroat and Stonechat in Dorset in 1959-60. *Brit. Birds,* 68: 196-202.
Morley, C. 1949. Kittiwakes in Suffolk before 1333. *Trans. Suffolk. Nat. Soc.,* 7: 41.
Morgan, R. A. & Glue, D. E. 1981. Breeding Survey of Black Redstarts in Britain, 1977. *Bird Study,* 28: 163-168.
Moser, M. E. 1987. A revision of population estimates for waders *Charadrii* wintering on the coastline of Britain. *Biol. Cons.,* 39: 153-164.
Moser, M. E. & Summers, R. W. 1987. Wader populations on the non-estuarine coasts of Britain and Northern Ireland: results of the 1984-85 Winter Shorebird Count. *Bird Study,* 34: 71-81.
Mountford, G. 1957. *The Hawfinch.* Collins, London.
Murphy, P. W. & Piotrowski, S. H. 1981. Suffolk Tufted Duck Survey 1980. *Suffolk Ornithologists' Group Bulletin,* 52: 3-12.
Musgrove, A. J. 2002. The non-breeding status of the Little Egret in Britain. *Brit. Birds,* 95: 62-80.
Murton, R. K., 1966. A statistical investigation of the effects of Woodpigeon shooting as evidenced by the recoveries of ringed birds. *Statistician,* 16: 183-202.
Nethersole-Thompson, D. & M. 1986. *Waders their breeding, haunts and watchers.* Calton. Poyser.
Newton, I. 1972. *Finches.* Collins, London.
Newton, I. 1986. *The Sparrowhawk.* Poyser. Calton.
Newton, I. 1993. Studies of West Palearctic birds. 192. Bullfinch. *Brit. Birds,* 86: 638-648.
Newton, I. & Haas, M. B. 1984. The return of the Sparrowhawk. *Brit. Birds,* 77: 47-70.
Nisbet, I. C. T., 1957. Records of Wood Sandpipers in Britain in the autumn of 1952. *Brit. Birds,* 49: 49-62.
Norman, D. 1994. *The Fieldfare.* Hamlyn, London.
Norman, R. K. & Saunders, D. R. 1969. Status of Little Terns in Great Britain and Ireland in 1967. *Brit. Birds,* 62: 4-13.
Norris, K. & Buisson, R. 1994. Sea-level rise and its impact upon coastal birds in the UK. *RSPB Conserv. Rev.,* 8: 63-71.
O'Brien, M. & Eaton, D. 1991. Further studies on Bearded Tits at Walberswick. *Suffolk Birds,* 40: 12-14.
O'Conner, R. J. & Mead, C. J. 1984. The Stock Dove in Britain 1930-80. *Brit. Birds,* 77: 181-201.
O'Sullivan, J. M. 1976. Bearded Tits in Britain and Ireland 1966-74. *Brit. Birds,* 69: 473-489.
Odin, N. 1991. The Blackbird *Turdus merula* at Landguard Point. *Landguard Bird Observatory Annual Report 1991.* Landguard Bird Observatory.
Odin, N. 1993. Migrant Northern Wheatears at Landguard Point. *Suffolk Birds,* 41: 153-154.
Odin, N. 1996. The Sparrowhawk at Landguard Point, Felixstowe. *White Admiral,* 33: 33-34.
Odin, N. 1997a. An analysis of the occurrences of Wren, Dunnock and Reed Bunting at Landguard Point, Suffolk. *Suffolk Birds,* 45: 16-21.
Odin, N. 1997b. Snow Buntings at Felixstowe Ferry - early 1997. *The Harrier,* 111: 7-9.
Odin, N. & Marsh, M. 1996. Blyth's Pipit - first for Suffolk. *Suffolk Birds,* 44: 151-152.
Ogilvie, M. A. 1969. The status of the Canada Goose in Britain 1967-69. *Wildfowl,* 20: 79-85.
Ogilvie, M. A. 1975. *Ducks of Britain and Europe.* Poyser. Berkhamsted.
Ogilvie, M. A. 1978. *Wild geese.* Poyser. Berkhamsted.
Ogilvie, M. A. 1981. The Mute Swan in Britain, 1978. *Bird Study,* 28: 87-106.
Ogilvie, M. A. and the Rare Breeding Birds Panel. 1996. Rare breeding birds in the United Kingdom in 1994. *Brit. Birds,* 89: 387-417.
Ogilvie, M. A. and the Rare Breeding Birds Panel. 1998. Rare breeding birds in the United Kingdom in 1995. *Brit. Birds,* 91: 417-447.
Ogilvie, M. A. and the Rare Breeding Birds Panel. 2000. Rare breeding birds in the United Kingdom in 1998. *Brit. Birds,* 93: 358-393.
Ogilvie, M. A. and the Rare Breeding Birds Panel. 2001. Rare breeding birds in the United Kingdom in 1999. *Brit. Birds,* 94: 344-381.
Owen, M. 1980. *Wild Geese of the world.* Batsford, London.
Paget, C. J. & Paget J. 1834. *Sketch of the Natural History of Great Yarmouth and its Neighbourhood.* Yarmouth.
Parslow, J. L. F. 1967. Changes in status among breeding birds in Britain and Ireland. *Brit. Birds,* 60: 2-47, 97-123, 177-200, 261-285, 396-404, 493-508.
Parslow-Ostu, M. 1991. Bean Geese in the Yare Valley, Norfolk. *Brit. Birds,* 84: 161-170.
Parslow-Outo, M. & Elliott, G. D. 1991. Red-necked Grebe breeding in England. *Brit. Birds,* 84: 188-191.
Pashby, B. S. & Cudworth, J. 1969. The Fulmar 'wreck' of 1962. *Brit. Birds,* 62: 97-109.
Paine, A. J. R. 1978. Cuckoo Survey Report - May 27th 1978. *Suffolk Ornithologists' Group Bulletin,*34: 3-5.
Paine, A. R. J. 1980. *Birds of Prey in Suffolk 1973-1978.* The Suffolk Ornithologists' Group. Ipswich.

Paine, A. R. J. 1983. Roving tit flocks - winter 1980/81. *Suffolk Ornithologists' Group Bulletin,* 59: 6-10.
Payn, W. H. 1962. *The birds of Suffolk.* Barrie and Rockliff, London.
Payn, W. H. 1973. The numbers and distribution of the Canada Goose in Suffolk, 1972. *Trans. Suffolk Nat. Soc.,* 16: 158-161.
Payn, W. H. 1978. *The birds of Suffolk* 2nd Edn. Ancient House Press, Ipswich.
Pearson, D. J. 1963. The Dingle Bird Club - Walberswick. *Trans. Suffolk Nat. Soc.,* 7: 293-301.
Pearson, D. J. 1966. Observations on the iris colour of the Bearded Tit. *Bird Study,* 13: 328-330.
Pearson, D. J. 1973. Changes in the status of heath and marshland breeding birds in the Walberswick area, 1953-72. *Trans. Suffolk Nat. Soc.,* 16: 152-157.
Pearson, D. J. 1975. Moult and its relation to eruptive activity of the Bearded Reedling. *Bird Study,* 22: 205-227.
Pearson, D. J. 1998. *Breeding Birds of Reydon Grove Farm Suffolk.* Report to Suffolk Wildlife Trust and English Nature.
Perrins, C. M. 1979. *British Tits.* Collins, Glasgow.
Piotrowski, S. H. 1980. Suffolk Ringed Plover Survey 1979. *Suffolk Ornithologists' Group Bulletin,* 43: 1-9.
Piotrowski, S. H. 1982. The travels of a Hoopoe. *Suffolk Birds 1981.* pp.58-59.
Piotrowski, S. H. 1983a. Seabird movement - September 5th 1982. *Suffolk Birds 1982,* pp 53-54.
Piotrowski, S. H. 1983b. Seabird movement - November 5th-7th 1982. *Suffolk Birds 1982,* pp 54-57.
Piotrowski, S. H., 1986. The ornithological recording boundaries of Suffolk. *Suffolk Ornithologists' Group Bulletin,* 73: 7-13.
Piotrowski, S. H. 1988. Hobby taking Migrant Hawker Dragonflies. *Suffolk Natural History,* 24: 7-8.
Piotrowski, S. H. 1988b. The criteria used for the identification of two 'Arctic' Redpolls *Carduelis hornemanni exilipes* at Landguard Point, Felixstowe, February 18th to March 17th 1982. *Suffolk Ornithologists' Group Bulletin,* 80: 6-11.
Piotrowski, S. H. 1988c. Suffolk rookeries - 1988. *Suffolk Ornithologists' Group Bulletin,* 79: 14-16.
Piotrowski, S. H. 1990a. Breeding Cormorants in East Anglia. *Suffolk Birds,* 39: 19-21.
Piotrowski, S. H. 1990b. A fishy story. *The Harrier,* 87: 12-13.
Piotrowski, S. H. 1994. Red-footed Falcon stealing from Kestrel. *Suffolk Birds,* 42: 142.
Piotrowski, S. H. 1994. Blyth's Reed Warbler - first for Suffolk. *Suffolk Birds,* 43: 156-157.
Piotrowski, S. H. 1996. Why so many ducks on Alton Water? *The Harrier,* 107: 8-11.
Pollitt, M. S., Cranswick, P. A., Musgrove, A. J., Hall, C., Hearn, R. D., Robinson, J. A. & Holloway, S. J. 2000. *The Wetland Bird Survey 1998-99: Wildfowl and Wader Counts.* BTO/WWT/RSPB/JNCC, Slimbridge.
Porter, R. F. 1987. Wintering cormorant survey 1985/86. *BTO News,* 150: 11.
Potts, G. R. 1986. *The Partridge: Pesticides, Predation and Conservation.* Collins, London.
Prater, A. J. 1976. Breeding populations of Ringed Plovers in Britain. *Bird Study,* 23: 155-161.
Prater, A. J. 1981. *Estuary birds of Britain and Ireland.* Poyser, Calton.
Prestt, I. & Mills, D. H. 1966. A census of the Great Crested Grebe in Britain 1965. *Bird Study,* 13: 163-203.
Prince, P. & Clarke, R. 1993. The Hobby's breeding range in Britain. *British Wildlife,* 4: 341-346.
Rafe, R. 1996. The 1994 influx of Pallas's Warblers in Suffolk. *Suffolk Birds,* 44: 21-22.
Rafe, R. & Carter, I. 2000. The Red Kite re-introduction project in England. *The Harrier,* 120: 2-4.
Ravenscroft, N. O. M. 1989. The distribution and status of the Nightjar on the Suffolk Sandlings, 1981 to 1988. *Suffolk Birds,* 38: 26-32.
Ray, J. 1678. *The ornithology of Francis Willughby.*
Reyce, R. 1618. *Suffolk in the 17th Century: The breviary of Suffolk.* MS. British Museum.
Robertson, A. W. P. 1954. *Bird Pageant.* Batchworth Press Ltd., London and Dorking.
Robertson, I. R., 1994. The exceptional passage of raptors at Minsmere in September 1993. *Suffolk Birds,* 43: 20-22.
Rogers, M. J. 1982. Ruddy Shelducks in Britain in 1965-79. *Brit. Birds,* 75: 446-455.
Rogers, M. J. and the Rarities Committee, 1993. Report on rare birds in Great Britain in 1992. *Brit. Birds,* 86: 447-540.
Rogers, M. J. and the Rarities Committee, 1994. Report on rare birds in Great Britain in 1993. *Brit. Birds,* 87: 503-571.
Rogers, M. J. and the Rarities Committee, 1995. Report on rare birds in Great Britain in 1994. *Brit. Birds,* 88: 493-558.
Rogers, M. J. and the Rarities Committee, 1996. Report on rare birds in Great Britain in 1995. *Brit. Birds,* 89: 481-531.
Roselaer, C. S. & Gerritsen, G. J. 1991. Recognition of Icelandic Black-tailed Godwit and its occurrence in The Netherlands. *Dutch Birding,* 13: 128-135.
Sage B. L. & Whittington, P. A. 1985. The 1980 sample survey of rookeries. *Bird Study,* 32: 77-81.
Salmon, D. G. 1988. The numbers and distribution of Scaup *Aythya marila* in Britain and Ireland. *Biological Conservation,* 43: 267-278.
Salmon, J. D. 1836. MS Diary (in Norwich Museum).
Sangster, G., Collinson, M., Helbig, A. J., Knox. A. G. Parkin, D. T. and Prater, A. 2001. The taxonomic status of the Green-winged Teal *Anas carolinensis. Brit. Birds* 94: 218-226.
Scott, R. E. 1978. Rough-legged Buzzards in Britain in 1973/74 and 1974/75. *Brit. Birds,* 71: 325-338.
Seago, M. J. 1967. *Birds of Norfolk.* Jarrold & Sons, Norwich.
Sharrock, J. T. R. 1974. *Scarce migrant birds in Britain and Ireland.* Poyser, Berkhamsted.
Sharrock, J. T. R. 1976. *The Atlas of breeding birds in Britain and Ireland.* British Trust for Ornithology, Poyser, Berkhamsted.
Sharrock, J. T. R. 1993. European News. *Brit. Birds,* 86: 36-47.
Sharrock, J. T. R. and the Rare Breeding Birds Panel. 1982. Rare breeding birds in the United Kingdom in 1980. *Brit. Birds,* 75: 154-178.
Sharrock, J. T. R. & Davies, C., 2000. The European Bird Report. *Brit. Birds,* 93: 114-128.
Sharrock, J. T. R. & Hilden, O. 1983. Survey of some of Europe's breeding birds. *Brit. Birds,* 76: 118-123.
Shawyer, C. R. 1987. *The Barn Owl in the British Isles: its past, present and future.* The Hawk Trust, London.
Sheppard, R. & Whitear, W. 1824-25. A catalogue of Norfolk and Suffolk birds, with remarks. *Trans. Linn. Soc.,* 15: 1-62.
Simpson, F. W. 1982. *Simpson's Flora of Suffolk.* Suffolk Naturalists' Society. Ipswich.
Sitters, H. P. 1986. Woodlarks in Britain, 1968-83. *Brit. Birds,* 79: 105-116.
Sitters, H. P., Fuller, R. J., Hoblyn, R. A., Wright, M. T., Cowie, N. and Bowden, C. G. R. 1996. The Woodlark *Lullula arborea* in Britain: population trends, distribution and habitat occupancy. *Bird Study,* 43: 172-187.

Small, B. 1991. Willow Tit showing characters of the race *Parus montanus borealis. Suffolk Birds,* 40: 145-146.

Snow, D. W. 1971. *The status of birds in Britain and Ireland.* Blackwell Scientific Publications, Oxford and Edinburgh.

Snow, D.W. & Perrins, C.M. 1998. *The birds of the Western Palearctic - Concise Edition:* vols I to II Oxford University Press. Oxford and New York.

Spencer, R. 1990. Rare breeding birds in 1988. *Brit. Birds,* 83: 353-390.

Spencer, R. & Gush, G.H. 1973. Siskins feeding in gardens. *Brit. Birds,* 66: 91-99.

Stevenson, H. 1866. *The birds of Norfolk.* Van Voorst. London.

Spalding, T. M. 1846. *List of birds rarely and occasionally met with in the County of Suffolk.* In: Suckling, A. 1846. The *History and Antiquties of The Countyof Suffolk* (xxxv-xxxix). John Weale, London.

Taylor, M., Seago, M., Allard, P. & Dorling, D. 1999, 2000. *The birds of Norfolk.* Pica Press. East Sussex.

Thom, V. M. 1986. *Birds in Scotland.* Poyser, Calton.

Thompson, A. L. 1926. Early bird-marking records. *Brit. Birds,* 20: 181.

Ticehurst, C. B. 1932. *A history of the birds of Suffolk.* Gurney and Jackson, London.

Ticehurst, N. F. & Witherby, H. F. 1940. Report on the effect of the severe winter of 1939-40 on bird-life in the British Isles. *Brit. Birds,* 34: 118-132, 142-155.

Tomlinson, R. F. 1994. Egyptian Geese and trees. *The Harrier,* 100: 30-31.

Tuck, J. G. 1891. *Ornithology of Suffolk.* in White's History, Gazetteer and Directory of the County Suffolk.

Turnbull, S. 1986. Osprey catching two fish in one dive. *Brit. Birds,* 79: 502-503.

Tyler, G., 1994. Management of reedbeds for Bitterns and opportunities for reedbed creation. *RSPB Conserv. Rev.,* 8: 57-62.

Vine, A. E. 1951. The status of gulls in Breckland. *Brit. Birds,* 44: 34-36.

Vinicombe, K., Marchant, J & Knox, A. 1993. Review of status and categorisation of feral birds on the British List. *Brit. Birds,* 86: 605-614.

Vinicombe, K., & Harrop, A. H. J. 1999. Ruddy Shelducks in Britain and Ireland 1986-94. *Brit. Birds,* 92: 225-255.

Voisin, C. 1991. *The Herons of Europe.* Poyser, London.

Vulliamy, L. H. 1943. Great increase of our terns. *Trans. Suffolk Nat. Soc.,* 5: 131.

Wallace, D. I. M. 1979. Review of British records of Semipalmated Sandpipers and claimed Red-necked Stints. *Brit. Birds,* 72: 264-274.

Waller, C. S. 1991. Water Rail catching and killing Water Shrew. *Suffolk Birds,* 40: 144-145.

Warren, R. B. 1981. The overland movements of Cormorants in Suffolk. *Suffolk Ornithologists' Group Bulletin,* 49: 10-11.

Waters, R. 1987 Survey of Woodlark *Lullula arborea* Coastal Suffolk 1986.*Suffolk Ornithologists' Group Bulletin,* 76: 11–22.

Waters, R. 1990. Common Gull catching and eating Yellowhammer. *Brit. Birds,* 83: 122.

Waters, R. J. 1985. BTO Breeding Ringed Plover survey. *Suffolk Ornithologists' Group Bulletin,* 68: 12-18.

Waters, R. J. 1986a. Wintering Cormorants in Suffolk. *Suffolk Ornithologists' Group Bulletin,* 73: 14-21.

Waters, R. J. 1986b. Wintering Cormorants in Suffolk and other BTO news. *Suffolk Ornithologists' Group Bulletin,* 74: 21.

Waters, R. 1987 Survey of Woodlark *Lullula arborea* Coastal Suffolk 1986. *Suffolk Ornithologists' Group Bulletin,* 76: 11-22.

Waters, R. J. 1994. Wintering Gulls 1953-1993 *BTO News,* 190: 9–10.

Waters, R. J. & Cranswick, P.A. 1993. *The wetland bird survey 1992/93: Wildfowl and wader counts.* BTO/WWT/RSPB/JNCC, Slimbridge.

Wernham, C.V., Toms, M.P., Marchant, J.H., Clark, J.A., Siriwardena, G.M. & Baillie, S.R. (eds). 2002. *The Migration Atlas: movements of birds of Britain and Ireland.* T. & A.D. Poyser, London.

Williamson, K. & Davis, P. 1956. The autumn 1953 invasion of Lapland Buntings and its source. *Brit. Birds,* 49: 6-25.

Williamson, K. 1975. Birds and climatic change. *Bird Study,* 22: 143-164.

Wilson, A, & Marchant, J. 1997. Common birds census and waterways bird survey: 1995-96 index report. *BTO News,* 210-211: 16-21.

Wilson, A. & Wright, M. T. 2000. Nightingale Survey in Suffolk 1999. *Suffolk Birds,* 49: 26-28.

Witherby, H. F., Jourdain, F. C. R., Ticehurst, N. F. & Tucker, B. W. 1938-1940. *The handbook of British Birds.* Witherby, London.

Wotton, S. R. & Gillings, S. 2000. The status of breeding Woodlarks *Lullula arborea* in Britain in 1997. *Bird Study,* 47: 212-224.

Wright, M. T. 1985. Winter Shorebird Count. *Suffolk Ornithologists' Group Bulletin,* 66: 14-15.

Wright, M. T. 1986a. The Grey Heron. *Suffolk Ornithologists' Group Bulletin,* 71: 6-10.

Wright, M. T. 1986b. Concise history of Suffolk Heronries. *Suffolk Ornithologists' Group Bulletin,* 72: 6-14.

Wright, M. T. 1988. 1987 survey of nesting Lapwings in Suffolk. *Suffolk Ornithologists' Group Bulletin,*79: 24-25.

Wright, M. T. 1989. Birds of Estuaries Enquiry – the first twenty years. *Suffolk Birds,* 38: 6-14.

Wright, M. T. 1990a. Suffolk Heronries 1985-89 and the October '87 'hurricane'. *Suffolk Birds,* 39: 6-11.

Wright, M. T. 1990b. Census of breeding Woodlarks in coastal Suffolk 1989. *Suffolk Birds,* 39: 11-14.

Wright, M. T. 1991. Mute Swans in Suffolk 1990. *Suffolk Birds,* 40: 14-18.

Wright, M. T. 1994. Survey of breeding Shelduck in Suffolk 1992. *Suffolk Birds,* 42: 14-17.

Wright, M. T. 1996. 1996 Sandling Woodlark Census. Unpublished MS. Suffolk Wildlife Trust.

Wright, M. T. 2000. Survey of Breeding Lapwings in Suffolk 1998. *The Harrier,* 122: 2-7.

Wright, M. T. 2001. *Survey of Breeding Raptors and Owls in Suffolk 1995-1998.* Suffolk Ornithologists' Group. Ipswich.

Wright, M. T. & Waters, R. J. 1991. Breeding seabirds in Suffolk. *Suffolk Birds,* 40: 19-34.

Wyllie, I. 1981. *The Cuckoo.* Batsford, London.

INDEX

NORF
SUFF
CAMBS
ESSEX
Great Ouse
Little Ouse
BRANDON
LAKENHEATH
Ouse
RED
LOPH
MILDENHALL
Lark
CAVENHAM
HEATH
LACKFORD
LAKES
NEWMARKET
Kennett
BURY ST EDMUNDS
STOWMA
Glem
HAVERHILL
Brett
WOLV
HADL
SUDBURY
Stour